CARSWELL

2018
Pocket Ontario
OH&S Act &
Regulations

(R.S.O. 1990, c. O.1)
Consolidated Edition
Plus Regulations including:
Confined Spaces (O. Reg. 632/05)
Construction Projects (O. Reg. 213/91)
Control of Exposure to Biological or Chemical Agents (Reg. 833)
Designated Substances (O. Reg. 490/09)
Farming Operations (O. Reg. 414/05)
Health Care and Residential Facilities (O. Reg. 67/93)
Industrial Establishments (Reg. 851)
Mines and Mining Plants (R.R.O. 854)
WHMIS (Reg. 860)
Plus:
Summary conviction offences under the Occupational Health and
Safety Act
Fully Indexed

 THOMSON REUTERS

©2018 Thomson Reuters Canada Limited

NOTICE AND DISCLAIMER: All rights reserved. No part of this publication may be reproduced, stored in a retrieval system, or transmitted, in any form or by any means, electronic, mechanical, photocopying, recording, or otherwise, without the prior written permission of the publisher (Thomson Reuters Canada, a division of Thomson Reuters Canada Limited).

Thomson Reuters Canada and all persons involved in the preparation and sale of this publication disclaim any warranty as to accuracy or currency of the publication. This publication is provided on the understanding and basis that none of Thomson Reuters Canada, the author/s or other persons involved in the creation of this publication shall be responsible for the accuracy or currency of the contents, or for the results of any action taken on the basis of the information contained in this publication, or for any errors or omissions contained herein.

No one involved in this publication is attempting herein to render legal, accounting, or other professional advice. If legal advice or other expert assistance is required, the services of a competent professional should be sought. The analysis contained herein should in no way be construed as being either official or unofficial policy of any governmental body.

A cataloguing record for this publication is available from Library and Archives Canada.

ISBN 978-0-7798-8573-2

Printed in Canada.

TELL US HOW WE'RE DOING

Scan the QR code to the right with your smartphone to send your comments regarding our products and services.
Free QR Code Readers are available from your mobile device app store.
You can also email us at feedback.legaltaxcanada@tr.com

 THOMSON REUTERS

THOMSON REUTERS CANADA, A DIVISION OF THOMSON REUTERS CANADA LIMITED

One Corporate Plaza	Customer Support
2075 Kennedy Road	1-416-609-3800 (Toronto & International)
Toronto, Ontario, M1T 3V4	1-800-387-5164 (Toll Free Canada & U.S.)
	Fax 1-416-298-5082 (Toronto)
	Fax 1-877-750-9041 (Toll Free Canada & U.S.)
	Email CustomerSupport.LegalTaxCanada@TR.com

PREFACE

The most significant change to the Ontario *Occupational Health and Safety Act* (OHSA) over the past year was the dramatic increase to maximum fines as a result of Bill 177, the *Stronger, Fairer Ontario Act* (Budget Measures) 2017. Bill 177, which came into force on December 14, 2017, quadrupled the maximum fines that may be imposed for an offence under the Act from $25,000 to $100,000 for an individual, and tripled the fines from $500,000 to $1,500,000 for a corporation. Individuals may also be subject to imprisonment for up to one year for contravention of the OHSA. There is a surcharge of 25per cent to be added to the fines under the *Provincial Offences Act*.

Bill 177 also amends the limitation period for bringing a prosecution under the Act or regulations from one year from the date of the alleged offence to one year from the later of the last act or default upon which the prosecution is based, or the date an inspector becomes aware of the alleged offence. This could potentially result in charges being laid for an offence that happened several years previously if an inspector becomes aware of the offence after the fact.

The Bill 177 amendments add a new reportable incident for structural inadequacies. In particular, the changes impose an obligation on employers to notify a Director if a joint health and safety committee (JHSC) or health and safety representative identifies potential structural inadequacies of a building, structure, or any other part of a workplace as a source of danger or hazard to workers. Additional reportable incidents may also be added through regulations. Bill 177 provides for regulations to specify additional notice requirements that must be met in the event of a death, injury, accident, explosion or fire, including who is required to provide the notice, the timeframe within which it must be provided and the information it must contain.

Finally, Bill 177 introduces potential future changes to obligations regarding reportable injury notices with respect to content and timing. The Act now allows for future regulations that specify who must give notice if an accident, explosion, fire or other incident occurs at a project site or mine. These changes enhance the requirements placed on employers and dramatically increase fines and penalties under the Act for both corporations and individuals.

The Occupational Health and Safety Awareness and Training Regulation under the *Occupational Health and Safety Act* has been amended as of April 1, 2017. Section 7 of the Regulation sets out the employer requirements relating to working at heights training for workers on construction sites who are required to use a fall protection system, including a travel restraint system, fall restricting system, fall arrest system, safety net, work belt or a safety belt (pursuant to the Construction Projects Regulation).

Employers must ensure that the workers in question have successfully completed a working at heights training program that meets specified requirements. Workers who had completed training pursuant to the Construction Projects Regulation before April 1, 2015, were given until April 1, 2017, to complete the working at heights training under the Occupational Health and Safety Awareness and Training Regulation. The amendments extended that date to October 1, 2017, as long as the worker was enrolled in a working at heights training program that meets the requirements set out in the Regulation, the training program was scheduled to be completed before October 1, 2017, and the employer has written proof of the worker's enrolment in the training program. Written proof must include the name of the worker, the name of the approved training program, the name of the approved training provider and the date on which the approved training was scheduled to be completed. The employer must provide the written proof of enrolment to an inspector upon request.

On January 16, 2017, the Ontario Ministry of Labour clarified the meaning of "critical injury" in Regulation 834, Critical Injury – Defined, under the *Occupational Health and Safety Act*. Section 1 provides that: For the purposes of the Act and the Regulations, "critically injured" means an injury of a serious nature that:

(a) places life in jeopardy,

(b) produces unconsciousness,

(c) results in substantial loss of blood,

(d) involves the fracture of a leg or arm but not a finger or toe,

(e) involves the amputation of a leg, arm, hand or foot but not a finger or toe,

(f) consists of burns to a major portion of the body, or

(g) causes the loss of sight in an eye.

The Ministry interprets clause 1(d) to include the fracture of a wrist, hand, ankle or foot, noting that any such fracture would constitute a critical injury if it is of a serious nature. Although the fracture of a single finger or toe is not a critical injury, the fracture of more than one finger or toe does constitute a critical injury if it is an injury of a serious nature. Regarding clause 1(e), although the amputation of a single finger or toe does not constitute a critical injury, the amputation of more than one finger or toe does constitute a critical injury if it is an injury of a serious nature. The Ministry also notes that a critical injury must be reported under section 51 of the *Occupational Health and Safety Act* if there is a connection between the hazard that gave rise to the injury and worker health and safety. Employers in Ontario should review the clarification of the meaning of "critical injury" and ensure that they meet their reporting requirements under section 51 of the Act.

While primarily about changes to the *Employment Standards Act*, 2000 and the *Labour Relations Act*, Bill 148, the *Fair Workplaces, Better Jobs Act*, 2017, also amended the *Occupational Health and Safety Act*. This change, which came into force on November 27, 2017, prohibits employers from requiring a worker to wear footwear with an elevated heel unless such footwear is required to perform the work safely (this prohibition does not apply to performers in the entertainment or advertising industries). As a result, employers in Ontario should ensure that their employee dress codes and uniforms do not require employees to wear high heels unless necessary for the work being performed.

The Construction Projects Regulation under the *Occupational Health and Safety Act* was amended on January 1, 2017. The amendments address the use of suspended access equipment. The Ministry of Labour must be informed before suspended access equipment is used for the first time on a site. The requirements for roof plans, site specific work plans and employee training are now more stringent. The physical requirements for design, engineering, inspection, testing, and maintenance have also been strengthened and enhanced. Employers in the construction sector in Ontario should review the amendments to familiarize themselves with the changes. They should ensure that any suspended access equipment in use is in compliance with the new standards, which came into effect on January 1, 2017.

The Control of Exposure to Biological or Chemical Agents Regulation under the *OOccupational Health and Safety Act* has been amended to update the definition of the ACGIH (American Conference of Governmental Industrial Hygienists) Table and to broaden an employer's obligation to take all measures reasonably necessary in the circumstances to protect workers from exposure to an atmospheric oxygen level that is less than 19.5 per cent by volume and related hazards such as fire and explosion where the agent is present in the air at the workplace to agents for which the listing in the ACGIH Table includes the reference "or see Appendix F: Minimal Oxygen Content" (in addition to the current reference to "simple asphyxiant"). Ontario employers whose workers may be exposed to biological or chemical agents should review the amendments to the Regulation and revise their policies, practices and training to ensure that they are compliant with the changed safety obligations, which was required by January 1, 2018.

The Designated Substances Regulation under the *Occupational Health and Safety Act* has been amended to add additional substances to the Isocyanates, organic compounds section, effective January 1, 2018. Ontario employers that manufacture, use, store or transport Isocyanate organic compounds should review the amendments and revise their policies, procedures and training practices to ensure that they were compliant regarding the newly added substances by January 1, 2018.

The Industrial Establishments Regulation under the *Occupational Health and Safety Act* has been amended to change the threshold atmospheric pressure oxygen content level below which a worker must be protected by mechanical ventilation from 18 per cent to 19.5 per cent, effective January 1, 2018. Ontario employers whose workers may be exposed to lower than normal atmospheric pressure oxygen content levels in the workplace should revise their policies, practices and training to ensure that workers are protected by mechanical ventilation in accordance with the amendments that came into force on January 1, 2018.

The Federal Government has delayed the final deadline for WHMIS 2015 compliance for manufacturers and importers. The extension from June 1, 2017, to June 1, 2018, will allow additional time to comply with the new requirements as a result of the implementation of the Globally Harmonized System of Classification and Labelling of Chemicals (GHS). The new system put into place as a result of Canada's implementation of the GHS is known as WHMIS 2015. Changes under WHMIS 2015 include new pictograms, labeling changes, revised safety data sheets (SDSs) (formerly material safety data sheets (MSDSs)), and revised classification requirements.

Prior to the revised deadline, suppliers must continue to comply with the requirements of the previous WHMIS program launched in 1988. However, suppliers may choose to comply with the WHMIS 2015 requirements prior to the deadline. By June 1, 2018, suppliers (manufacturers and importers) will need to comply with the requirements of the Federal Hazardous Products Regulations, and all distributors must comply with the Regulations by September 1, 2018. WHMIS 2015 was implemented in Ontario as a result of amendments to the Workplace Hazardous Materials Information System (WHMIS) Regulation, R.R.O. 1990, Reg. 860, in 2016. During the second transition period (between June 1, 2018 and November 30, 2018), employers may continue to use hazardous products already in the workplace with labels and safety data sheets that comply with the WHMIS 1988 regime and provide worker education under the old program.

For more information on these initiatives see online:
< www.labour.gov.on.ca > .

NEW THIS YEAR

- **Mines and Mining Plants** — O.Reg. 167/16, amending R.R.O. 1990, Reg. 854, with respect to risk assessments, underground mining occurrences, water and drainage, and written traffic management programs, in force January 1, 2017.
- **Industrial Establishments** — O.Reg. 289/17, amending R.R.O. 1990, Reg. 851, with respect to oxygen content of air, in force January 1, 2018.
- **Designated Substances** — O.Reg. 288/17, amending O.Reg. 490/09, with respect to Isocyanates, organic compounds, in force January 1, 2018.
- **Control of Exposure to Biological or Chemical Agents** — O.Reg. 287/17, amending R.R.O. 1990, Reg. 833, with respect to chemical substances, physical agents and biological exposure indices, in force January 1, 2018.
- **Construction Projects** — O.Reg. 142/17, amending O. Reg. 213/91 with respect to toilet, urinal and cleanup facilities, suspended work platforms and miscellaneous provisions, in force May 19, 2017; O.Reg. 471/16, amending O. Reg. 213/91

> with respect to suspended work platform systems and boat-
> swain's chairs, in force January 1, 2017; O.Reg. 242/16,
> amending O. Reg. 213/91 with respect to suspended work
> platforms, in force January 1, 2017.
>
> We have also updated the Accident Prevention, Investigation and Re-
> porting section, the list of OH&S Resources and the Index and have
> revised the Table of Contents.
>
> Should you find any errors or omissions in the current edition, or if you
> have any suggestions for improving the *Ontario OH&S Act and Reg-
> ulations — Consolidated*, please do not hesitate to call or e-mail us im-
> mediately.
>
> Brian Kreissl, LLM, CHRL
> Product Development Manager
> Thomson Reuters Legal, Canada
> brian.kreissl@tr.com

Other Initiatives and Activities

On January 1, 2018, Bill 127, the *Stronger, Healthier Ontario Act* (Budget Measures), 2017, received Royal Assent. Schedule 33 of Bill 127 amended the Ontario *Workplace Safety and Insurance Act*, 1997. The most significant amendment expands the entitlement to benefits for mental stress, to provide that a worker is entitled to benefits for chronic or mental stress arising out of and in the course of his or her employment. As a result of the amendment, the Act no longer restricts workers from entitlement to benefits for mental stress only in the case of an acute reaction to sudden and unexpected traumatic events.

These mental stress amendments are now in force without retroactive application. Additional amendments include new rules for determining the amount of benefits payable for full and partial loss of earnings, updates to the amounts used to calculate compensation for non-economic loss and death benefits when a worker dies, all of which came into force on December 3, 2017. Further amendments include the granting of power to the Workplace Safety and Insurance Board (WSIB) to establish policies concerning the interpretation and application of the Act, and evidentiary requirements and adjudicative principles for establishing entitlement to benefits.

The General Regulation under the Workplace Safety and Insurance Act, 1997 has been amended to change the date on which certain changes to the Regulation will come into force from January 1, 2019 to January 1, 2020. The changes that are affected are:

- revocation of the definition section;
- replacement of the Classes of Industry, Excluded Industry, Occupational Diseases schedules; and
- exclusion of foreign diplomats, competitors in individual or team sports, stunt performers and circus performers from benefits coverage under the Act.

Bill 174, the *Cannabis, Smoke-Free Ontario and Road Safety Statute Law Amendment Act*, 2017 has received Royal Assent on December 12, 2017. Schedule 3 of Bill 174 enacts the *Smoke-Free Ontario Act*, 2017 (and repeals the *Smoke-Free Ontario Act* and the *Electronic Cigarettes Act*, 2015), and will come into force on Proclamation. The new *Smoke-Free Ontario Act*, 2017 will apply to tobacco products, vapour products and medical cannabis, and will prohibit smoking or holding lighted tobacco, smoking or holding lighted medical cannabis, or using an electronic cigarette in specified locations, including an enclosed workplace. Employers will be under positive obligations to ensure compliance with this prohibition, including, for example, posting prescribed signs, and ensuring that anyone not in compliance does not remain in the workplace. In addition, employees who act in accordance with the Act or seek its enforcement are protected from reprisal.

The Government of Ontario has also announced that it will be developing resources to assist employers, labour groups, and others in managing workplace safety issues related to impairment at work as a result of the upcoming legalization of recreational cannabis use. The resources will focus on education and awareness issues.

The Ontario Government announced new initiatives on May 11, 2017 under its Construction Health and Safety Action Plan on how to help prevent workplace injuries, illnesses and fatalities for workers on construction sites. The new initiatives include:

- developing online tools, apps and web portals to provide easy access to construction health and safety information such as key hazards;

- conducting multi-media campaigns and targeted enforcement blitzes to raise awareness of construction health and safety and key hazards;
- exploring options for increasing fines for violations of the Occupational Health and Safety Act and Regulation for Construction Projects;
- considering roof anchors and other solutions for working at heights to prevent falls (the leading cause of construction deaths);
- including construction health and safety topics in existing school curricula and apprenticeship training programs;
- consulting with stakeholders on an accreditation program that would recognize employers who successfully implement occupational health and safety programs; and
- creating and distributing resources to fill gaps in existing health and safety information for employers and workers.

Employers in Ontario should follow the implementation of these new initiatives and may wish to consider participating in the stakeholder consultations regarding an accreditation program. They should consider using the online tools, apps and web portals once those have been developed, and should obtain the resources created to fill gaps in occupational health and safety information.

Inspection Blitzes and Initiatives

The MOL continued with its health and safety enforcement programs aimed at specific industry sectors and hazards. During the year, the following province-wide sector-specific blitzes and smaller scale provincial and regional initiatives have been conducted:

Province-Wide Workplace Inspection Blitzes (2017-2018)		
Focus	**Sector/Business Type**	**Date**
Processing – Safe Work Practices – Mine Plants	Mining	February 1, 2017 – March 31, 2017
New and young worker	Food services and drinking places; retail trade; amusement, gambling and recreation industries; services to buildings and dwellings; other sectors known to employ young and new workers	May 1, 2017 – August 31, 2017
New and young worker	Industrial	May 1, 2017 – August 31, 2017
Hours of work	Construction; transportation and	May 1, 2017 – August 31,

Province-Wide Workplace Inspection Blitzes (2017-2018)		
	warehousing; services to buildings and dwellings; retail trade; other sectors known to have a high number of hours worked	2017
Supervisor awareness and accountability	Construction	June 1, 2017 – July 31, 2017
Occupational disease in mines and mining plants	Mining	July 1, 2017 – August 31, 2017
Residential projects	Construction	September 1, 2017 – November 30, 2017
Falls – ladder safety	Construction	October 2, 2017 – November 24, 2017
Falls – in-	Health care	October 2,

Province-Wide Workplace Inspection Blitzes (2017-2018)		
cluding slips and trips		2017 – November 24, 2017
Falls – including slips and trips	Industrial	October 2, 2017 – November 24, 2017
Falls – including slips and trips and musculoskeletal disorders in mines and mining plants	Mining	October 2, 2017 – November 30, 2017
Machine guarding and electrical hazards	Industrial	January 15, 2018 – February 28, 2018
Compliance on personal protective equipment and high visi-	Mining	February 1, 2018 – March 31, 2018

Province-Wide Workplace Inspection Blitzes (2017-2018)		
bility clothing		

Regional Workplace Inspection Blitzes (2016-2017)		
Focus	**Sector/Business Type**	**Date**
Central East	**Industrial:** Heavy Raw Material Handling	December 1, 2016 – February 17, 2017
Central East	**Construction:** Toilets / Wash up Facilities	January 1, 2017 – February 28, 2017
Central West	**Industrial:** Landscapers / Snow Removal	November 1, 2016 – March 31, 2017
Western	**Industrial:** Elevating Work Plat- forms in the Farming Sector	October 1, 2016 – March 31, 2017

Provincial Initiatives (2017-2018)		
Focus	**Sector/Business Type**	**Date**
Preventing "struck by" injuries	Industrial	April 1, 2017 – March 31, 2018
Noise	Industrial	April 1, 2017 – March 31, 2018
Noise	Construction	April 1, 2017 – March 31, 2018
Noise	Health care	April 1, 2017 – March 31, 2018
Noise	Mining	April 1, 2017 – March 31, 2018
Noise	All sectors: Specialized Professional Services: occupational hygiene inspection and evaluation	April 1, 2017 – March 31, 2018

Provincial Initiatives (2017-2018)		
Joint health and safety committee (JHSC) compliance	Mining	April 1, 2017 – March 31, 2018
Ground control	Mining	April 1, 2017 – March 31, 2018
Workplace Hazardous Materials Information System (WHMIS)	All sectors: Specialized Professional Services: occupational hygiene inspection and evaluation	April 1, 2017 – March 31, 2018
Ergonomics: • Workplaces with a high rate of musculoskeletal disorders • Food processing / manufacturing	All sectors: Specialized Professional Services: ergonomics inspection and evaluation	April 1, 2017 – March 31, 2018

Provincial Initiatives (2017-2018)		
• Tire handling and storage • Ladder use and access for manual materials handling		
Outstanding rejected X-ray installation applications	All sectors: Specialized Professional Services: radiation protection services inspection and evaluation	April 1, 2017 – March 31, 2018
Open treatment dental X-ray sources at veterinary clinics	Veterinary clinics: Specialized Professional Services: radiation protection services inspection and evaluation	April 1, 2017 – March 31, 2018
Engineering: • Engineering reviews (ground control, water management and	Underground mines: Specialized Professional Services: engineering	April 1, 2017 – March 31, 2018

Provincial Initiatives (2017-2018)		
ventilation programs)		
"Struck by" hazards	Construction	May 1, 2017 – March 31, 2018
Fall protection	Construction	May 1, 2017 – March 31, 2018
Health care sector enforcement initiative: • Internal responsibility system – long-term care / retirement homes • Internal responsibility system, workplace violence, needle safety – primary care (family health teams,	Health care	September 1, 2017 – March 31, 2018

Provincial Initiatives (2017-2018)		
community health centres) • Workplace violence – hospitals		

Regional Initiatives (2017-2018)		
Focus	**Sector/Business Type**	**Date**
Central East	Grocery stores	October 1, 2017 – January 31, 2018
Central West	Construction: Road construction projects / what to look for in traffic control and traffic protection plans	May 1, 2017 – May 31, 2017
Central West	Industrial and construction: Temporary labour agencies – focus on worker training and hazard exposure	June 1, 2017 – March 31, 2018
Central West	Industrial: Food and beverage manufacturing – focus on sector hazards	October 1, 2017 – December 31, 2017
Central West	Grocery stores	

Regional Initiatives (2017-2018)		
		October 1, 2017 – January 31, 2018
Eastern	Mining: Quarry blasting operations	May 1, 2017 – October 2017
Eastern	Kiosks in shopping malls	November 1, 2017 – January 31, 2018
Northern	Professional services (dentists, law firms)	October 1, 2017 – December 31, 2017
Northern	Mining: Four point-in-time (PIT) inspections at mines and mining plants	April 1, 2017 – March 31, 2018
Western	Industrial: Golf courses – joint education and outreach with employment standards officers	April 1, 2017 – March 31, 2018
Western	Industrial: Temporary foreign workers on farms –	April 1, 2017 – March 31, 2018

Regional Initiatives (2017-2018)		
	joint with Workplace Safety and Insurance Board (WSIB)	
Western	Construction: Electrical contact	April 1, 2017 – March 31, 2018
Western	Seasonal businesses	November 1, 2017 – January 31, 2018

Updated and further information is available on enforcement plans by consulting the various Sector Plans on the MOL website at: www.labour.gov.on.ca/english/hs/sawo/sectorplans/index.php.
There are 2016-2017 Sector Plans for the following sectors:

- Industrial Sector
- Mining Sector
- Construction Sector
- Health Care Sector
- Specialized Professional Services Work Plan

SUMMARY CONVICTION OFFENCES UNDER THE OH&S ACT

Increased Enforcement

Since July 2004, Ministry of Labour inspectors have been authorized to issue on-the-spot summary conviction notices for a wide range of offences under the Ontario OH&S Act and associated Regulations. An updated list of the offences and the fines associated with them follows here.

Fines

Depending on the offence, summary conviction tickets carry fines, including court costs, of $200 or $300, as set by the Chief Justice of the Ontario Court of Justice. Money collected from the fines goes to the municipality in which the offence took place. In addition, there is a victim surcharge, which goes into the the provincial Victims Justice Fund Account.

Options if Issued a Ticket

An employer, supervisor or worker has three options if issued a ticket:

- Plead guilty by signing the guilty plea on the ticket and paying the set fine at the court office specified on the ticket.
- Give notice of intention to appear in court and request a trial. At trial, plead guilty and make submissions respecting the fine before a provincial judge or justice of the peace. The provincial judge or justice may impose a set fine or reduce it.
- Plead not guilty by giving notice of intention to appear in court and requesting a trial before a provincial judge.

ONTARIO COURT OF JUSTICE

Schedule 67.3

Occupational Health and Safety Act (as it relates to Regulation 851 of the Revised Regulations of Ontario, 1990)			
ITEM	**COLUMN 1**	**COLUMN 2 SECTION**	**SET FINE (INCL COSTS OF $5.00)**
1.	Employer failing to ensure a safe work surface for worker under s. 11 of Reg. 851	clause 25(1)(c)	$300.00
2.	Supervisor failing to ensure worker is working on a safe work surface under s.11 of Reg. 851	clause 27(1)(a)	$200.00
3.	Worker failing to work on a safe work surface under s.11 of Reg. 851	clause 28(1)(a)	$200.00
4.	Supervisor failing to ensure worker works with guarded opening under s. 13(1) of Reg. 851	clause 27(1)(a)	$300.00
5.	Worker failing to work with guarded opening under s.13(1) of Reg. 851	clause 28(1)(a)	$200.00
6.	Supervisor failing to ensure worker works with covered opening under s. 15 of Reg. 851	clause 27(1)(a)	$300.00

	Occupational Health and Safety Act **(as it relates to Regulation 851 of the Revised Regulations of** **Ontario, 1990)**		
ITEM	**COLUMN 1**	**COLUMN 2 SECTION**	**SET FINE (INCL COSTS OF $5.00)**
7.	Worker failing to work with covered opening under s. 15 of Reg. 851	clause 28 (1) (a)	$200.00
8.	Supervisor failing to ensure worker uses a machine with adequate guarding under s. 24 of Reg. 851	clause 27 (1) (a)	$300.00
9.	Worker failing to use a machine with adequate guarding under s. 24 of Reg. 851	clause 28 (1) (a)	$300.00
10.	Supervisor failing to ensure worker uses a machine with adequate guarding under s. 25 of Reg. 851	clause 27 (1) (a)	$300.00
11.	Worker failing to use a machine with adequate guarding under s. 25 of Reg. 851	clause 28 (1) (a)	$300.00
12.	Supervisor failing to ensure worker uses a machine with adequate guarding under s. 26 of Reg. 851	clause 27 (1) (a)	$300.00

	Occupational Health and Safety Act **(as it relates to Regulation 851 of the Revised Regulations of Ontario, 1990)**		
ITEM	COLUMN 1	COLUMN 2 SECTION	SET FINE (INCL COSTS OF $5.00)
13.	Worker failing to use a machine with adequate guarding under s. 26 of Reg. 851	clause 28 (1) (a)	$200.00
14.	Supervisor failing to ensure worker works with effective operating control that acts as a guard under s. 28 (o) of Reg. 851	clause 27 (1) (a)	$300.00
15.	Worker failing to work with effective operating control that acts as a guard under s. 28 (c) of Reg. 851	clause 28 (1) (a)	$300.00
16.	Employer failing to provide safe chain saw under s. 39 of Reg. 851	clause 25 (1) (a)	$300.00
17.	Employer failing to ensure that chain saw provided under s. 39 of Reg. 851 is used safely	clause 25 (1) (d)	$300.00
18.	Supervisor failing to ensure worker uses a chain saw safely under s. 39 of Reg. 851	clause 27 (1) (a)	$200.00
19.	Worker failing to use chain saw safely under s. 39 of Reg. 851	clause 28 (1) (a)	$200.00

	Occupational Health and Safety Act (as it relates to Regulation 851 of the Revised Regulations of Ontario, 1990)		
ITEM	**COLUMN 1**	**COLUMN 2 SECTION**	**SET FINE (INCL COSTS OF $5.00)**
20.	Supervisor failing to ensure no work is done on or near live exposed parts of electrical installations, equipment or conductors without the power supply being disconnected, locked out and tagged under s. 42 (1) of Reg. 851	clause 27 (1) (a)	$300.00
21.	Worker working on or near live exposed parts of electrical installations, equipment or conductors without the power supply being disconnected, locked out and tagged under s. 42 (1) of Reg. 851	clause 28 (1) (a)	$300.00
22.	Supervisor failing to ensure worker uses protective equipment and procedures while doing electrical work under s. 42.1 (2) of Reg. 851	clause 27 (1) (a)	$300.00
23.	Employer failing to provide portable electrical tool protected	clause 25 (1) (a)	$300.00

Occupational Health and Safety Act (as it relates to Regulation 851 of the Revised Regulations of Ontario, 1990)			
ITEM	COLUMN 1	COLUMN 2 SECTION	SET FINE (INCL COSTS OF $5.00)
	by a ground fault circuit interrupter under s. 44.1 of Reg. 851		
24.	Employer failing to ensure portable electrical tool protected by a ground fault circuit interrupter provided under s. 44.1 of Reg. 851 is used	clause 25 (1) (d)	$300.00
25.	Supervisor failing to ensure worker using a portable electrical tool protected by a ground fault circuit interrupter under s. 44.1 of Reg. 851	clause 27 (1) (a)	$200.00
26.	Worker failing to use a portable electrical tool protected by a ground fault circuit interrupter under s. 44.1 of Reg. 851	clause 28 (1) (a)	$200.00
27.	Employer failing to ensure that lifting device is operated safely under s. 51 (2) (b) of Reg. 851	clause 25 (1) (c)	$300.00
28.	Supervisor failing to ensure operator of a lifting device works safely under s. 51 (2) (b) of Reg.	clause 27 (1) (a)	$300.00

	Occupational Health and Safety Act (as it relates to Regulation 851 of the Revised Regulations of Ontario, 1990)		
ITEM	**COLUMN 1**	**COLUMN 2 SECTION**	**SET FINE (INCL COSTS OF $5.00)**
	851		
29.	Operator of lifting device failing to work safely under s. 51 (2) (b) of Reg. 851	clause 28 (1) (a)	$200.00
30.	Supervisor failing to ensure worker works on or near an immobilized and secure unattended vehicle under s. 57 of Reg. 851	clause 27 (1) (a)	$300.00
31.	Worker failing to immobilize and secure unattended vehicle under s. 57 of Reg. 851	clause 28 (1) (a)	$200.00
32.	Supervisor failing to ensure worker works around attended lifting equipment when forks, bucket, blades and similar parts are unsupported under s. 58 of Reg. 851	clause 27 (1) (a)	$300.00
33.	Worker working around unattended lifting equipment when forks, bucket, blades and similar parts are unsupported under s.	clause 28 (1) (a)	$200.00

Occupational Health and Safety Act (as it relates to Regulation 851 of the Revised Regulations of Ontario, 1990)			
ITEM	COLUMN 1	COLUMN 2 SECTION	SET FINE (INCL COSTS OF $5.00)
	58 of Reg. 851		
34.	Supervisor failing to ensure that worker does not bring object closer than specified distance to overhead electric supply line under s. 60 of Reg. 851	clause 27 (1) (a)	$300.00
35.	Worker bringing object closer than specified distance to overhead electric supply line under s. 60 of Reg. 851	clause 28 (1) (a)	$300.00
36.	Employer failing to provide safe portable ladder under s. 73 of Reg. 851	clause 25 (1) (a)	$300.00
37.	Employer failing to ensure that a portable ladder provided under s. 73 of Reg. 851 is used safely	clause 25 (1) (d)	$300.00
38.	Supervisor failing to ensure worker uses a portable ladder safely under s. 73 of Reg. 851	clause 27 (1) (a)	$200.00
39.	Worker failing to use portable ladder safely under s. 73 of Reg.	clause 28 (1) (a)	$200.00

Occupational Health and Safety Act (as it relates to Regulation 851 of the Revised Regulations of Ontario, 1990)			
ITEM	**COLUMN 1**	**COLUMN 2 SECTION**	**SET FINE (INCL COSTS OF $5.00)**
	851		
40.	Supervisor failing to ensure worker works around safely secured temporarily elevated machinery, equipment or material under s. 74 of Reg. 851	clause 27 (1) (a)	$300.00
41.	Worker failing to work around safely secured temporarily elevated machinery, equipment or material under s. 74 of Reg. 851	clause 28 (1) (a)	$200.00
42.	Supervisor failing to ensure worker works on a safely secured machine under s. 75 of Reg. 851	clause 27 (1) (a)	$300.00
43.	Worker failing to work on a safely secured machine under s. 75 of Reg. 851	clause 28 (1) (a)	$300.00
44.	Supervisor failing to ensure worker works on a machine with proper precautions where starting may endanger the safety of a worker under s. 76 of Reg. 851	clause 27 (1) (a)	$300.00

Occupational Health and Safety Act (as it relates to Regulation 851 of the Revised Regulations of Ontario, 1990)			
ITEM	COLUMN 1	COLUMN 2 SECTION	SET FINE (INCL COSTS OF $5.00)
45.	Worker failing to work on a machine with proper precautions where starting may endanger the safety of a worker under s. 76 of Reg. 851	clause 28 (1) (a)	$300.00
46.	Employer failing to ensure appropriate head protection provided under s. 80 of Reg. 851 is used	clause 25 (1) (d)	$300.00
47.	Supervisor failing to ensure worker wears appropriate head protection under s. 80 of Reg. 851	clause 27 (1) (a)	$200.00
48.	Employer failing to ensure appropriate eye protection provided under s. 81 of Reg. 851 is used	clause 25 (1) (d)	$300.00
49.	Supervisor failing to ensure worker wears appropriate eye protection under s. 81 of Reg. 851	clause 27 (1) (a)	$200.00
50.	Employer failing to ensure ap-	clause 25	$300.00

ITEM	COLUMN 1	COLUMN 2 SECTION	SET FINE (INCL COSTS OF $5.00)
	Occupational Health and Safety Act (as it relates to Regulation 851 of the Revised Regulations of Ontario, 1990)		
	propriate foot protection provided under s. 82 of Reg. 851 is used	(1) (d)	
51.	Supervisor failing to ensure worker wears appropriate foot protection under s. 82 of Reg. 851	clause 27 (1) (a)	$200.00
52.	Employer failing to ensure proper skin protection provided under s. 84 of Reg. 851 is used	clause 25 (1) (d)	$300.00
53.	Supervisor failing to ensure worker works with proper skin protection under s. 84 of Reg. 851	clause 27(1)(a)	$200.00
54.	Worker failing to work with proper skin protection under s. 84 of Reg. 851	clause 28 (1) (a)	$200.00
55.	Supervisor failing to ensure worker wears fall protection equipment under s. 85 of Reg. 851	clause 27 (1) (a)	$300.00

	Occupational Health and Safety Act **(as it relates to Regulation 851 of the Revised Regulations of Ontario, 1990)**		
ITEM	**COLUMN 1**	**COLUMN 2 SECTION**	**SET FINE (INCL COSTS OF $5.00)**
56.	Employer failing to ensure protective clothing provided is worn to protect from hazards caused by molten metal under s. 93 of Reg. 851	clause 25 (1) (d)	$300.00
57.	Supervisor failing to ensure worker wears protective clothing provided to protect from hazards caused by molten metal under s. 93 of Reg. 851	clause 27 (1) (a)	$200.00
58.	Worker failing to wear protective clothing provided to protect from hazards caused by molten metal under s. 93 of Reg. 851	clause 28 (1) (a)	$200.00
59.	Employer failing to ensure a tree is felled, limbed, bucked or topped safely under s. 109 of Reg. 851	clause 25 (1) (c)	$300.00
60.	Supervisor failing to ensure logger fells, limbs, bucks or tops a tree safely under s. 109 of Reg. 851	clause 27 (1) (a)	$300.00

	Occupational Health and Safety Act (as it relates to Regulation 851 of the Revised Regulations of Ontario, 1990)		
ITEM	**COLUMN 1**	**COLUMN 2 SECTION**	**SET FINE (INCL COSTS OF $5.00)**
61.	Logger failing to fell, limb, buck or top a tree in safely under s. 109 of Reg. 851	clause 28 (1) (a)	$300.00
62.	Employer failing to ensure a hang up is dealt with safely under s. 110 of Reg. 851	clause 25 (1) (c)	$300.00
63.	Supervisor failing to ensure worker deals with a hang up safely under s. 110 of Reg. 851	clause 27 (1) (a)	$300.00
64.	Worker failing to deal with a hang up safely under s. 110 of Reg. 851	clause 28 (1) (a) (v)	$200.00
65.	Employer failing to ensure a spring pole is cut safely under s. 111 of Reg. 851	clause 25 (1) (c)	$300.00
66.	Supervisor failing to ensure worker cuts a spring pole safely under s. 111 of Reg. 851	clause 27 (1) (a)	$300.00
67.	Worker failing to cut spring pole safely under s. 111 of Reg. 851	clause 28 (1) (a)	$200.00
68.	Employer failing to ensure that	clause 25	$300.00

	Occupational Health and Safety Act **(as it relates to Regulation 851 of the Revised Regulations of Ontario, 1990)**		
ITEM	**COLUMN 1**	**COLUMN 2 SECTION**	**SET FINE (INCL COSTS OF $5.00)**
	skidding is done under s. 112 of Reg. 851	(1) (c)	
69.	Supervisor failing to ensure logger skids under s. 112 of Reg. 851	clause 27 (1) (a)	$300.00
70.	Logger failing to skid under s. 112 of Reg. 851	clause 28 (1) (a)	$200.00
71.	Employer failing to provide a vehicle used for hauling logs that complies with s. 116 (1) of Reg. 851	clause 25 (1) (a)	$300.00
72.	Employer failing to ensure vehicle provided for hauling logs is used in compliance with s. 116 (1) of Reg. 851	clause 25 (1) (d)	$300.00
73.	Supervisor failing to ensure worker uses a vehicle used for hauling logs in compliance with s. 116 (1) of Reg. 851	clause 27 (1) (a)	$300.00
74.	Worker failing to use a vehicle used for hauling logs in compliance with s. 116 (1) of Reg. 851	clause 28 (1) (a)	$200.00

ITEM	COLUMN 1	COLUMN 2 SECTION	SET FINE (INCL COSTS OF $5.00)
Occupational Health and Safety Act **(as it relates to Regulation 851 of the Revised Regulations of Ontario, 1990)**			
75.	Employer failing to provide vehicle used to transport loggers in compliance with s. 119 of Reg. 851	clause 25 (1) (a)	$300.00
76.	Supervisor failing to ensure worker uses a vehicle used to transport loggers in compliance with s. 119 of Reg. 851	clause 27 (1) (a)	$200.00
01/05			

Schedule 67.4

ITEM	COLUMN 1	COLUMN 2 SECTION	SET FINE (INCL COSTS OF $5.00)
	Regulation 851 of the Revised Regulations of Ontario, 1990 under the Occupational Health and Safety Act		
1.	Worker failing to use protective equipment and procedures while doing electrical work	subsection 42.1 (2)	$300.00
2.	Worker failing to wear appropriate head protection	section 80	$200.00
3.	Worker failing to wear appropriate eye protection	section 81	$200.00
4.	Worker failing to wear appropriate foot protection	section 82	$200.00
5.	Worker failing to wear fall protection equipment	section 85	$300.00
01/05			

Schedule 67

ITEM	COLUMN 1	COLUMN 2 SECTION	SET FINE (INCL COSTS OF $5.00)
Occupational Health and Safety Act (as it relates to Ontario Regulation 213/91)			
1.	Worker failing to work in compliance with subsection 26.1(2) of Ontario Regulation 213/91 by not being adequately protected by fall protection	28 (1) (a)	$300.00
2.	Worker failing to work in compliance with section 115 of Ontario Regulation 213/91 by using loose object as workplace or as support for object	28 (l) (a)	$200.00
3.	Worker having or using stilts or leg extension devices contrary to section 116 of Ontario Regulation 213/91	28 (l) (a)	$200.00
4.	Employer failing to ensure compliance with stilts and leg extension devices requirements in section 116 of Ontario Regulation 213/91	25 (l) (c)	$300.00
5.	Supervisor failing to ensure worker working in compliance with stilts and leg extension	27 (l) (a)	$300.00

Occupational Health and Safety Act (as it relates to Ontario Regulation 213/91)			
ITEM	COLUMN 1	COLUMN 2 SECTION	SET FINE (INCL COSTS OF $5.00)
	devices requirements in section 116 of Ontario Regulation 213/91		
6.	Worker failing to work in compliance with subsection 195.1(1) of Ontario Regulation 213/91 by using inadequately grounded cord-connected equipment or tools	28 (l) (a)	$200.00

Schedule 67.1

ITEM	COLUMN 1	COLUMN 2 SECTION	SET FINE (INCL COSTS OF $5.00)
	Ontario Regulation 213/91-Construction Projects under the Occupational Health and Safety Act		
1.	Worker failing to wear protective headwear	22	$200.00
2.	Worker failing to wear protective footwear	23	$200.00
3.	Worker failing to wear eye protection	24	$200.00
4.	Worker failing to use provided protective respiratory equipment	46 (2)	$200.00
5.	Worker who may be endangered by vehicular traffic failing to wear prescribed garment	69.1	$200.00
6.	Operator leaving the controls of machine unattended	102	$200.00
7.	Signaller failing to wear prescribed garment	106 (1.1)-(1.4)	$200.00
8.	Worker failing to wear adequate personal protective equipment while using fastening tool	117 (3) (a)	$200.00
9.	Worker failing to wear adequate	117 (3) (b)	$200.00

	Ontario Regulation 213/91-Construction Projects under the Occupational Health and Safety Act		
ITEM	**COLUMN 1**	**COLUMN 2 SECTION**	**SET FINE (INCL COSTS OF $5.00)**
	eye protection while using fastening tool		
10.	Worker failing to wear full body harness connected to fall arrest system while on suspended equipment	141 (1)	$300.00

Schedule 67.2

ITEM	COLUMN 1	COLUMN 2 SECTION	SET FINE (INCL COSTS OF $5.00)
	Ontario Regulation 629/94-Diving Operations under the Occupational Health and Safety Act		
1.	Failing to ensure the Ministry of Labour is given adequate notice of a diving operation	5	$300.00
2.	Failing to have required documents available at the dive site	8	$300.00
3.	Diving supervisor failing to be at the dive site and in direct control of the diving operation	12 (2)	$300.00
4.	Diving supervisor failing to ensure that an adequate number of standby divers are present and properly positioned	12 (4) (a)	$300.00
5.	Diving supervisor failing to ensure that no standby diver dives except in an emergency	12 (4) (f)	$300.00
6.	Diver failing to have log book at dive site	13 (1) (c)	$200.00
7.	Diver failing to undergo medical examination	13 (1) (d)	$200.00
8.	Standby diver unlawfully diving where no emergency	13 (9) (a)	$200.00

ITEM	COLUMN 1	COLUMN 2 SECTION	SET FINE (INCL COSTS OF $5.00)
	Ontario Regulation 629/94-Diving Operations under the Occupational Health and Safety Act		
9.	Standby diver unlawfully performing other duties	13 (9) (b)	$200.00
10.	Standby diver being inadequately dressed or equipped	13 (9) (c)	$200.00
11.	Failing to ensure adequacy of diving equipment and related materials	15	$300.00
12.	Diving supervisor failing to ensure that an adequate lifeline or strength member is attached to each diver	18	$300.00
13.	Failing to ensure adequate crew for S.C.U.B.A.	37	$300.00
14.	Failing to ensure adequate crew for surface-supplied diving	39	$300.00
15.	Failing to ensure water flow hazards are identified and adequately controlled	54 (2)	$300.00
16.	Failing to ensure mechanisms hazardous to divers comply with applicable CSA Standard	55	$300.00

Schedule 68

ITEM	COLUMN 1	COLUMN 2 SECTION	SET FINE (INCL COSTS OF $5.00)
	Occupational Health and Safety Act (as it relates to Regulation 854 of the Revised Regulations of Ontario, 1990)		
1.	Worker failing to use a fall arrest system as required by subsection 14 (1) of Reg. 854	28 (1) (a)	$355.00
2.	Supervisor failing to ensure worker uses a fall arrest system as required by subsection 14 (1) of Reg. 854	27 (1) (a)	$455.00
3.	Supervisor failing to ensure hazardous opening on a surface is guarded or covered as required by subsection 54 (2) of Reg. 854	27 (1) (a)	$455.00
4.	Employer failing to ensure hazardous opening on a surface is guarded or covered as required by subsection 54 (2) of Reg. 854	25 (1) (c)	$555.00
5.	Worker failing to use a fall arrest system when working on top of bulk material as required by clause 60 (2) (a) of Reg. 854	28 (1) (a)	$355.00
6.	Supervisor failing to ensure worker uses a fall arrest system	27 (1) (a)	$455.00

Occupational Health and Safety Act (as it relates to Regulation 854 of the Revised Regulations of Ontario, 1990)			
ITEM	COLUMN 1	COLUMN 2 SECTION	SET FINE (INCL COSTS OF $5.00)
	when working on top of bulk material as required by clause 60 (2) (a) of Reg. 854		
7.	Worker failing to examine and make safe ground conditions in underground mine as required by subsection 66 (1) of Reg. 854	28 (1) (a)	$355.00
8.	Supervisor failing to ensure worker examines and makes safe ground conditions in underground mine as required by subsection 66 (1) of Reg. 854	27 (1) (a)	$455.00
9.	Worker failing to securely cover opening in an underground mine as required by section 74 of Reg. 854	28 (1) (a)	$355.00
10.	Supervisor failing to ensure opening in an underground mine securely covered as required by section 74 of Reg. 854	27 (1) (a)	$455.00
11.	Worker failing to work in accordance with subsection 88 (1) of Reg. 854 where powered	28 (1) (a)	$255.00

Occupational Health and Safety Act (as it relates to Regulation 854 of the Revised Regulations of Ontario, 1990)			
ITEM	**COLUMN 1**	**COLUMN 2 SECTION**	**SET FINE (INCL COSTS OF $5.00)**
	equipment used		
12.	Supervisor failing to ensure worker works in accordance with subsection 88 (1) of Reg. 854 where powered equipment used	27 (1) (a)	$455.00
13.	Worker failing to work in accordance with subsection 88 (2) of Reg. 854 where powered equipment not used	28 (1) (a)	$255.00
14.	Supervisor failing to ensure worker works in accordance with subsection 88 (2) of Reg. 854 where powered equipment not used	27 (1) (a)	$455.00
15.	Worker undercutting working face contrary to subsection 88 (3) of Reg. 854	28 (1) (a)	$355.00
16.	Failing to ensure mechanisms hazardous to divers comply with applicable CSA Standard	27 (1) (a)	$455.00
17.	Worker failing to remove mate-	28 (1) (a)	$255.00

ITEM	COLUMN 1	COLUMN 2 SECTION	SET FINE (INCL COSTS OF $5.00)
	Occupational Health and Safety Act (as it relates to Regulation 854 of the Revised Regulations of Ontario, 1990)		
	rials near rim of surface mine as required by subsection 91 (1) of Reg. 854		
18.	Supervisor failing to ensure removal of materials near rim of surface mine as required by subsection 91 (1) of Reg. 854	27 (1) (a)	$455.00
19.	Worker failing to sound warning of motor vehicle running on rails as required by clause 103 (1) (d) of Reg. 854	28 (1) (a)	$255.00
20.	Supervisor failing to ensure worker sounds warning of motor vehicle running on rails as required by clause 103 (1) (d) of Reg. 854	27 (1) (a)	$455.00
21.	Worker failing to wash or examine face before drilling or sampling in an underground mine as required by subsection 136 (1) of Reg. 854	28 (1) (a)	$355.00
22.	Supervisor failing to ensure worker washes or examines face	27 (1) (a)	$455.00

Occupational Health and Safety Act (as it relates to Regulation 854 of the Revised Regulations of Ontario, 1990)			
ITEM	**COLUMN 1**	**COLUMN 2 SECTION**	**SET FINE (INCL COSTS OF $5.00)**
	before drilling or sampling in an underground mine as required by subsection 136 (1) of Reg. 854		
23.	Worker drilling or sampling near a blasted hole contrary to subsection 136 (4) of Reg. 854	28 (1) (a)	$355.00
24.	Supervisor failing to ensure no drilling or sampling near a blasted hole contrary to subsection 136 (4) of Reg. 854	27 (1) (a)	$455.00
25.	Worker failing to work in accordance with subsection 158 (3) of Reg. 854 when working on electrical equipment or conductors	28 (1) (a)	$355.00
26.	Supervisor failing to ensure worker works in accordance with subsection 158 (3) of Reg. 854 when working on electrical equipment or conductors	27 (1) (a)	$455.00
27.	Employer failing to ensure flow of air where diesel-powered equipment is operating as re-	25 (1) (c)	$555.00

Occupational Health and Safety Act (as it relates to Regulation 854 of the Revised Regulations of Ontario, 1990)			
ITEM	COLUMN 1	COLUMN 2 SECTION	SET FINE (INCL COSTS OF $5.00)
	quired by section 183.1 of Reg. 854		
28.	Worker failing to guard moving part of machinery as required by subsection 185 (2) of Reg. 854	28 (1) (a)	$355.00
29.	Supervisor failing to ensure moving part of machinery is guarded as required by subsection 185 (2) of Reg. 854	27 (1) (a)	$455.00
30.	Worker failing to ensure machine has an automatic protection device as required by subsection 185 (3) of Reg. 854	28 (1) (a)	$355.00
31.	Supervisor failing to ensure a machine has an automatic protection device as required by subsection 185 (3) of Reg. 854	27 (1) (a)	$455.00
32.	Worker failing to ensure a conveyor is guarded as required by subsections 196 (3), (3.1) and (3.2) of Reg. 854	28 (1) (a)	$355.00
33.	Supervisor failing to ensure a	27 (1) (a)	$455.00

Occupational Health and Safety Act (as it relates to Regulation 854 of the Revised Regulations of Ontario, 1990)			
ITEM	COLUMN 1	COLUMN 2 SECTION	SET FINE (INCL COSTS OF $5.00)
	conveyor is guarded as required by subsections 196 (3), (3.1) and (3.2) of Reg. 854		

TABLE OF CONTENTS

Note: The number appearing after each entry refers to the page number where that entry begins.

Table of Contents

Table of Contents

Table of Contents

Table of Contents

Table of Contents

Table of Contents

Regulations Under the Occupational Health and Safety Act

This brief list of the Regulations under the *Occupational Health and Safety Act* included in this book will help to ensure your information is as up to date as possible.

Confined Spaces
    Ontario Regulation 632/05
    as am. O. Reg. 23/09 [ss. 1-3, 4 (French version)]; 492/09; 95/11; 346/15

Construction Projects
    Ontario Regulation 213/91
    as am. O. Reg. 631/94; 143/99; 571/99; 145/00; 527/00; 85/04; 627/05; 628/05; 443/09; 96/11; 88/13; 252/14; 345/15; 242/16; 471/16; 142/17, ss. 1-42, 43 (Fr.)

Control of Exposure to Biological or Chemical Agents
    Regulation 833
    as am. O. Reg. 513/92; 597/94; 388/00; 100/04; 16/05; 77/05; 177/05; 607/05; 83/07; 248/08; 491/09; 419/10; 149/12; CTR 16 MA 14 - 2; 274/14; 347/15; 287/17

Criteria to be Used and Other Matters to be Considered by Adjudicators under Subsection 46(6) of Act
    Ontario Regulation 243/95
    as am. O. Reg. 22/09 [ss. 1-3, 4 (French version)]

Critical Injury—Defined
    Regulation 834
    as am. O. Reg. 351/91 (French version)

Designated Substances
    Ontario Regulation 490/09
    as am. O. Reg. 259/10 [ss. 1, 2 (French version)]; 148/12; 288/17

Designated Substance—Asbestos on Construction Projects and in Buildings and Repair Operations
Ontario Regulation 278/05
as am. O. Reg. 493/09; 422/10 [ss. 1, 2 (French version)]; 479/10

Diving Operations
Ontario Regulation 629/94
as am O. Reg. 155/04; 32/14 [ss. 1-53, 54 (French version)]

Farming Operations
Ontario Regulation 414/05; as am O. Reg. 90/13; 298/13; 385/15

Firefighters—Protective Equipment
Ontario Regulation 714/94
as am. O. Reg. 449/97; 80/02; 24/09 [ss. 1, 2, 3 (French version)];
480/10

Health Care and Residential Facilities
Ontario Regulation 67/93
as am. O. Reg. 142/99; 631/05; 25/09 [ss. 1-9, 10 (French version)];
495/09; 94/10; 97/11; 169/11; 89/13

Industrial Establishments
Regulation 851
as am. O. Reg. 516/92; 630/94; 230/95; 450/97; 144/99; 284/99; 528/
00; 488/01; 280/05; 629/05; 565/06; 179/07; 494/09; 420/10 [ss. 1-
28, 29 (French version)]; 98/11; 382/15; 289/17

Inventory of Agents or Combinations of Agents for the Purpose of Section 34 of the Act
Regulation 852
as am. O. Reg. 208/91 (French version); 517/92

Joint Health and Safety Committees—Exemption from Requirements
Ontario Regulation 385/96
as am. O. Reg. 131/98; 19/09 (French version)

Mines and Mining Plants
R.R.O. 1990, Regulation 854

as am. O. Reg. 583/91; 584/91; 171/92; 384/92; 571/92; 693/92; 60/94; 779/94; 68/96; 272/97; 236/99; 486/99; 174/01; 251/01; 291/02; 31/04; 630/05; 84/07; 496/09; 99/11; 296/11; 92/13; 34/14; ss. 1-19, 20 (French version); 265/15; 383/15; 167/16

Needle Safety
Ontario Regulation 474/07
as am. O. Reg. 317/08; 21/09 (French version); 439/09

Noise
Ontario Regulation 381/15

Occupational Health and Safety Awareness and Training
Ontario Regulation 297/13
as am. O. Reg. 253/14; 84/17

Oil and Gas—Offshore
Regulation 855
as am. O. Reg. 566/06; 421/10 [ss. 1-19, 20 (French version)]; 384/15

Roll-Over Protective Structures
Regulation 856
as am. O. Reg. 357/91 (French version)

Teachers
Regulation 857
as am. O. Reg. 352/91 (French version)

University Academics and Teaching Assistants
Regulation 858
as am. O. Reg. 353/91 (French version)

Window Cleaning
Regulation 859
as am. O. Reg. 380/91 (French version); 523/92

Workplace Hazardous Materials Information System (WHMIS)
Regulation 860
as am. O. Reg. 356/91 (French version); 36/93; 168/16, ss. 1 (French version), 2, 3, 4(1), (2) (French version), (3), 5(1), (2), (3) (French version), (4), (5), 6-15

ACCIDENT PREVENTION, INVESTIGATION AND REPORTING[*]

---

[*] With contributions by Dilys Robertson, Don Buchanan and Joe Watkins (*J. Watkins & Associates Inc.*).

1.0 Work Refusals

The foundation for the Occupational Health and Safety Act (OHS Act) is the internal responsibility system (IRS), a principle designed to ensure that all workplace parties share a role in keeping workers safe. The OHS Act provides workers with the right to take immediate action in situations where they or another worker, are at risk of being injured. This includes a worker's right to refuse unsafe work.

1.1 Work Refusal Process

Workers initiating a work refusal must follow the procedures as set out in s. 43 of the Act.

Refer to Part V of the Act, including s. 43(3).

Refusal to work

43 (3) A worker may refuse to work or do particular work where he or she has reason to believe that,

(a) any equipment, machine, device or thing the worker is to use or operate is likely to endanger himself, herself or another worker;

(b) the physical condition of the workplace or the part thereof in which he or she works or is to work is likely to endanger himself or herself;

(b.1) workplace violence is likely to endanger himself or herself; or

(c) any equipment, machine, device or thing he or she is to use or operate or the physical condition of the workplace or the part thereof in which he or she works or is to work is in contravention of this Act or the regulations and such contravention is likely to endanger himself, herself or another worker.

Note that some workers have a limited right to refuse unsafe work, e.g., where the work is a normal condition of the worker's employment, or where the worker's job includes "duty of care" responsibilities. Refer to s. 43(1) and (2).

Examples of workers with limited rights to refuse include workers employed in police services, firefighting, correctional services, secure custody centres for young offenders, hospitals, long term care facilities, or ambulance services.

1.2 Worker Duty to Report Refusal

A worker must report the circumstances of their refusal to their employer or supervisor, in line with s. 43(4).

This parallels the worker's responsibilities to report contraventions of the Act or regulations and/or hazards under s. 28(1)(c) and (d) of the Act.

1.3 Work Refusal Procedure

> *Source, Ontario Ministry of Labour, 2018: This two-stage procedure is adapted, with only minor changes,*

from the work refusal process posted in flowchart format on the MOL website.	
First Stage	
• Worker considers work unsafe.	
• Worker refuses to work. • Worker reports the concern immediately to supervisor or employer, and to worker safety representative and/or management representative. • Worker stays in safe place.	
• **Employer or supervisor investigates** in the presence of the worker and the worker safety representative.	

Issue Resolved Worker goes back to work.	**Issue Not Resolved** [proceed to the second stage]

Second Stage	
• With reasonable grounds to believe work is still unsafe, worker continues to refuse and remains in safe place. • Worker or employer or someone representing worker or employer calls the Ministry of Labour (MOL).	
Ministry of Labour Inspector investigates in consultation with the worker, safety representative and supervisor or management representative.*	
Inspector gives decision to worker, management representative/supervisor and safety representative in writing.	
Changes are made if required or ordered. Worker returns to work.	

Pending the Ministry of Labour investigation:

- *The refusing worker may be offered other work if it doesn't conflict with a collective agreement*
- *Refused work may be offered to another worker, but management must inform the new worker that the offered work is the subject of a work refusal. This must be done in the presence of:*
  - o *a member of the joint health and safety committee who represents workers; or*
  - o *a health and safety representative, or*
  - o *a worker who because of his or her knowledge, experience and training is selected by the trade union that represents the worker or, if there is no trade union, by the workers to represent them*

2.0 Employer Duty to Report Injuries and Illness

There are specific notification and reporting requirements as detailed in ss. 51, 52 and 53 of the OHS Act pertaining to:

- fatalities and critical injuries;
- disabling injuries;
- occupational illnesses;
- workplace violence; and
- accidents, etc., at project mine or site.

2.1 Duty to Report Fatality or Critical Injury

Section 51 outlines the specific notification and reporting requirements where a person is killed or is critically injured from any cause at a workplace.

2.1.1 Definition of Critical Injury

As defined under the OHS Act (Regulation 834/90), a critical injury is an injury of a serious nature that:

- places life in jeopardy;
- produces unconsciousness;
- results in substantial loss of blood;
- involves the fracture of a leg or arm (but not a finger or toe);
- involves the amputation of a leg, arm, hand or foot (but not a finger or toe);
- consists of burns to a major portion of the body; or
- causes the loss of sight in an eye.

2.2 Immediate Notification Requirement and Written Report — Fatality or Critical Injury

With respect to the preservation of life, the employer or other workplace party should summon the life-saving assistance of emergency responders by dialing 9-1-1.

In line with s. 51(1), an employer must immediately report by telephone or other direct means to the MOL Contact Centre any fatalities or critical injuries; and submit a written report within 48 hours to a director of the MOL.

Notice of death or injury

51(1) Where a person is killed or critically injured from any cause at a workplace, the constructor, if any, and the employer shall notify an inspector, and the committee, health and safety representative and trade union, if any, immediately of the occurrence by telephone or other direct means and the employer shall, within forty-eight hours after the occurrence, send to a Director a written report of the circumstances of the occurrence containing such information and particulars as the regulations prescribe.

2.3 MOL Contact Centre

To report critical injuries or fatalities (involving workers and/ or non-workers), contact the MOL's Health and Safety Contact Centre.

Health & Safety Contact Centre
- Toll-free: 1-877-202-0008
- TTY: 1-855-653-9260
- Fax: 905-577-1316

☐ Call anytime to report critical injuries or fatalities.
☐ Call anytime to report work refusals (as per Stage 2 of work refusal flowchart).
☐ Call 8:30 a.m. — 5:00 p.m., Monday — Friday, for general inquiries about workplace health and safety.
☐ In an emergency, always call 911 immediately.

2.4 Summary: Immediate Actions After a Critical Injury or Fatality

1. Attend to the worker
   - arrange medical and emergency services, call 9-1-1 (and/or other on-site emergency response services)
2. Preserve and secure the accident site, including any wreckage

- You must preserve the accident scene, unless interfering with the wreckage is necessary for saving life, relieving human suffering or preventing unnecessary damage to equipment or other property, until permission has been given by the MOL Inspector.
3. Report the critical injury or fatality; immediately notify
   - the MOL Health and Safety Contact Centre, to reach a MOL Inspector;
   - the injured worker's family;
   - the JHSC or the worker health and safety representative; and
   - the union(s), if any.
4. Designate an employer representative for contacts with the MOL, including MOL Inspector.
5. Coordinate activities of MOL Inspector.
6. Record MOL Inspector's observations, comments, tests, results, measurements, and photographs.
7. Copy and retain all witness statements and documents given to MOL Inspector.
8. **Prepare and send a written report to a MOL Director within 48 hours after the incident**.

Ed. — *Also refer to Section 2.7 on page XXX for additional guidance on following your emergency response plan.*

2.5 Content of Written Report

An employer's written report of a fatality or critical injury must contain any information prescribed by regulations. This includes:

- the name, address and phone number of the employer (and constructor, if any);
- the type of work operation;
- the name, address and phone number of the person who was critically injured or killed;
- the time and place of the occurrence;
- a description of the occurrence and the bodily injury sustained;
- a description of the machinery or equipment involved, if any;
- the names, addresses and phone numbers of all witnesses to the occurrence;
- the name, address and phone number of the physician, if any, by whom the person was or is being attended; and
- **the steps taken to prevent a recurrence.**

2.6 Sector-Specific Reporting

Note that several of the sector-specific regulations under the OHS Act (e.g., construction, health care, diving) pinpoint the type of information that must be included when reporting to MOL. Most importantly, this includes the steps taken to prevent a recurrence.

This requirement is absent in some of the sector-specific regulations, e.g., industrial establishments, oil and gas, and mining. Although the MOL does not have a set form for reporting on the steps taken to prevent a recurrence, each written report must contain the information required by the relevant regulation. The employer should always consult the applicable sector-specific regulation to determine the exact information to be submitted.

An effective, thorough investigation is the best way to determine the most appropriate corrective actions following an occurrence, whether an injury-incident, fatality, occupational illness or near-miss.

2.7 Follow Your Emergency Response Plan

Employers should create, maintain and always be ready to follow the steps set out in their major incident/emergency response plan.

- First, you must ensure you have a major incident/emergency response plan in place. The plan should clearly address assigned roles and duties. Persons with assigned roles should be trained and know how to follow the plan, prior to any emergency event taking place.
- The plan should be regularly updated and training updates should occur when the plan changes.

2.7.1 Response

During the initial response, there is often a great deal of confusion and activity immediately following the significant event, e.g., emergency, fatality or critical injury.

It is up to the employer and management to establish controls and protect the scene. The measures and procedures required to establish control should be clearly identified in the emergency response plan.

In addition to the basic steps noted earlier in Section 2.5, review the following additional points to ensure your emergency response plan meets regulatory requirements and your organization's emergency response objectives.

RESPOND TO THE INCIDENT OR EMERGENCY PROMPTLY AND POSITIVELY

Management is responsible to take control at the scene.
- Qualified persons attend to the injured party.
- Call for emergency services and investigative authorities.
- Control potential secondary accidents; prevent further injuries or damage.
- Identify, isolate and preserve sources of evidence at the scene.
- Preserve the scene until directed otherwise by the MOL Inspector in charge.
- Submit the Employer's Report within 48 hours of the incident.

Your plan should include:

1. SUMMON ASSISTANCE: 9-1-1, medical, emergency & psycho-sociocare for all affected persons.

2. SECURE & PRESERVE the accident site.
You must preserve the accident scene, including any wreckage. You can only alter the scene if it is necessary to:
- save a life or relieve human suffering;
- maintain an essential public utility service or a public transportation system; or
- prevent unnecessary damage to equipment or other property.

Permission from a MOL Inspector must be obtained before interfering with, disturbing, destroying, altering or carrying away any wreckage, article or thing at the scene or connected with the occurrence.

3. LOCK OUT & TAG OUT the equipment and machinery. Assign a competent person. The Lock Out shuts down the equipment, the Tag Out tells everyone who shut down the equipment and when.

4. NOTIFY:
- the MOL Health and Safety Contact Centre;
- the JHSC or the worker health and safety representative; and
- the trade union(s), if any.

| 5. DESIGNATE an employer representative for contacts with the worker, worker's family and others as appropriate in the circumstances. |
| 6. DESIGNATE a knowledgeable employer representative for contacts with the MOL & MOL Inspector. The MOL will also be seeking assistance from the worker representative. |
| 7. CONTACT LEGAL COUNSEL — based on the needs and circumstances of the situation and prior to initiating an employer-led investigation. |
| 8. CO-ORDINATE activities as requested by the MOL Inspector. |
| 9. RECORD MOL Inspector's requests, observations, comments, and points of interest or focus. |
| 10. REQUEST A COPY and RETAIN all witness statements and documents provided to the MOL Inspector. |
| 11. PREPARE and SEND a written report to a MOL Director within 48 hours after the accident. |
| 12. COOPERATE with the MOL Inspector and the worker member of the JHSC or health and safety representative conducting an accident investigation. |

3.0 Fatality or Critical Injury Investigations

3.1 Criminal and Administrative Investigations

Immediately following a fatal or critical injury in the workplace, the MOL will attend the scene.

In the event they have not yet been contacted, the police may also attend to secure the scene or otherwise assist the MOL. The police are also charged with the responsibility to determine whether a breach of criminal law has occurred.

Criminal Code of Canada (Duty of persons directing work)

217.1 Everyone who undertakes, or has the authority, to direct how another person does work or performs a task is under a legal duty to take reasonable steps to prevent bodily harm to that person, or any other person, arising from that work or task.

The MOL will conduct a separate "administrative" investigation to determine whether there were issues of non-compliance under the OHS Act which contributed to the fatality or critical injury.

Section 62(2) of the OHS Act requires every person to provide assistance and cooperate fully with MOL Inspectors, including while they conduct inspections, investigations or otherwise carry out their duties under the Act.

The MOL will normally take the lead on workplace fatalities and critical injury investigations. Workplace parties should not formally interview witnesses or analyze evidence until permission has been granted from the MOL Inspector.

The MOL has up to one year to determine whether potential violations of the OHS Act contributed to the fatality or critical injury incident.

The workplace parties involved in the incident should note and understand that the MOL may use some or all of the one-year period before making a decision to lay charges or not.

3.2 Employer Investigations

An employer and their supervisors should be aware that the MOL and/or the police might conduct investigations to determine whether or not the employer and/or supervisors complied with the legislation.

Any report or investigation conducted by the employer or supervisors is subject to disclosure to the MOL and/or the police, and to the JHSC [in line with s. 25(2)(l)].

For situations involving complex or significant issues, the employer may wish to consider their options before initiating their own investigation.

As noted earlier, the employer is required to provide the MOL with a written report within 48 hours of the incident and this report must contain such information as prescribed by regulations. This written report is separate from an investigative report.

3.3 Worker Representative Investigations

Section 9(31) of the OHS Act provides that members of the JHSC who represent workers shall designate one or more such members to investigate cases where a worker is fatally or critically injured at a workplace from any cause.

Section 8(14) provides a similar provision for the worker health and safety representative to conduct an investigation, i.e., in workplaces where a JHSC is not required.

The findings of the worker representative's investigation are reported directly to a Director and the JHSC.

The JHSC may also decide, through their terms of reference, to investigate other incidents (in addition to incidents involving fatalities or critical injuries).

The worker representative investigating the incident should take time to prepare themselves mentally for what and whom they may be investigating.

In reality, fatalities or critical injuries can involve friends, co-workers and others well known to the investigator. This can be emotionally challenging at the time of the incident and throughout the investigator's involvement and beyond.

The MOL will be the lead agency during the investigation, thus allowing the worker representative time to determine their investigative steps.

The worker representative should consult with the MOL Inspector before commencing their investigation or interviewing witnesses.

It is helpful to keep in mind that the purpose of the MOL investigation is to determine compliance with the Act or Regulations, whereas the purpose of the worker representative's investigation is to identify contributing or underlying factors and make recommendations focussed on preventing a recurrence.

3.4 Accident/Incident Investigation Steps

Here is a summary of the main points in the investigation process:

☐ identify your purpose and role
☐ identify your legal authority to investigate
☐ develop an action plan
☐ investigate the incident
☐ identify the causes
☐ report the findings
☐ develop a plan for corrective action

☐ implement the plan
☐ evaluate the effectiveness of the corrective action
☐ make changes for continuous improvement

3.5 Incident Investigation Policy and Procedures

Use this short sample checklist to consider your accident investigation methods and forms.

☐ Written policy and procedure on accident investigations that sets out:
  • What types of incidents will be investigated?
  • Who will investigate — immediate supervisor, management, MOL and worker representative?
  • Responsibilities for reviewing and implementing corrective action.

☐ Are your investigations carried out according to a standard investigation system? Does that system include identifying underlying and contributing factors, and failures in the OH&S management system?

☐ Are appropriate personnel (e.g., all supervisors and members of the JHSC, or, for smaller workplaces, the worker health and safety representative) trained in basic principles of incident investigation, as well as company procedures and related forms, reports and checklists?

☐ Do you keep track of incident investigation training? Do you encourage such training widely, across departments, so that experienced employees can contribute to different types of investigations?

☐ Do you have appropriate forms, checklists or templates to help the investigation team effectively collect information during the investigation?

☐ Are you meeting legal requirements to involve/include JHSC members (or worker health and safety representative) in accident/incident/illness investigations?

☐ Do you review all your accident/incident/occupational illness results over time in order to identify repeat issues and common factors related to the incidents/illnesses?

☐ Do you have a plan in place for ongoing monitoring of the wellbeing of workplace parties following a significant incident?

For more guidance, check other resources such as the CCOHS website, which offers a range of investigation tips and resources.

- *http://www.ccohs.ca/oshanswers/hsprograms/investig.html*

3.5.1 Collecting Pertinent Information

- Identify the people, equipment, materials, process and environment relating to the incident.
- Interview witnesses in private.
- Interview near the incident location if feasible.
- Explain your purpose, authority and role.
- Ask open-ended questions and record the witness's response.
- Seek clarification as appropriate.
- Review the information provided; ask the witness to identify any changes, additions or deletions.
- Use visual aids (e.g., sketches, drawings, photographs) to show relative positions and before-and-after details.
- Analyze equipment, materials, workflow process and work environment to determine contributing factors.
- Examine workplace records to identify contributing factors such as training, maintenance or scheduling issues.

3.5.2 Root Cause Analysis

- Determine the significant factors or conditions that contributed to the incident. To the extent possible, do an initial analysis or evaluation of the immediate and underlying causes.
- Determine or consider the immediate causes or symptoms, e.g., unsafe conditions, unsafe acts, substandard practices or conditions, or a combination thereof.
- Determine other factors or underlying causes, such as job/system factors or personal factors.
- If possible, determine the specific cause(s) or most significant factors or conditions, in relation to the facts that are known or become evident, as the investigation proceeds.

3.5.3 Remedial Action

- Based on the initial circumstances at the site and any known facts or conditions, ensure that remedial actions are taken where necessary.
- Consider alternative hazard controls.

- Take temporary hazard prevention actions immediately, as needed.
- Take permanent preventive measures or actions as soon as possible.
- Document the incident, root cause and contributing factors within a detailed written report.

3.5.4 Share and Review Findings, Recommendations and Actions Taken

For each incident investigation, share the written report as required by the legislation, i.e., share with MOL and JHSC.

As appropriate for your organization and role, share the findings, recommendations and actions taken within the organization, e.g., share with supervisors and/or managers.

Address any need to do more follow-up work. For instance, conduct investigation review meetings to review steps in the investigation and implementation of any recommendations. In addition, be sure to monitor the implementation of recommendations, such as remedial or preventive actions, in order to ensure the expected outcomes (e.g., hazard elimination, prevention or control) are achieved.

4.0 Non-Fatal or Non-Critical Injury

4.1 Disabling Injury

A disabling injury is where a person is disabled from performing his or her usual work or requires medical attention.

4.1.1 Written Notice — Disabling Injury

Where an accident, explosion, fire or incident of workplace violence causes a disabling injury or where medical attention is required but no person dies or is critically injured because of that occurrence, within four days of the occurrence the employer shall provide written notice to:

- the JHSC or worker health and safety representative; and the trade union, if any.

If required by an inspector, the notice must also be provided to a Director of the MOL.

Refer to s. 52(1).

Notice of accident, explosion, fire or violence causing injury

52(1) If a person is disabled from performing his or her usual work or requires medical attention because of an accident, explosion, fire or incident of workplace violence at a workplace, but no person dies or is critically injured because of that occurrence, the employer shall, within four days of the occurrence, give written notice of the occurrence containing the prescribed information and particulars to the following:

1. The committee, the health and safety representative and the trade union, if any.

2. The Director, if an inspector requires notification of the Director.
The written notice must contain the information and particulars as prescribed in the applicable workplace regulation.

Typically, a notice under s. 52(1) of the Act, respecting an occurrence involving a worker, shall set out:

- the name, address and phone number of the employer/constructor;
- the type of work operation;
- the name, address and phone number of the person who was injured or ill
- the time and place of the occurrence;
- a description of the nature and circumstances of the occurrence
- nature of the injury, bodily harm, occupational disease or illness
- a description of the machinery or equipment involved, if any;
- the names, addresses and phone numbers of all witnesses to the occurrence;
- the name, address and phone number of the physician, if any, by whom the person was or is being attended;
- the name and address of each medical facility, if any, where the worker was or is being attended for the injury or illness; and
- **the steps taken to prevent a recurrence.**

The employer should consult the specific and applicable regulation to determine the exact information required to be submitted.

4.2 Occupational Illness

Generally, an occupational illness is a condition or illness that can be wholly or partly associated with a worker's past or present employment. It is defined in the OHS Act as:

s. 1(1) Occupational illness

A condition that results from exposure in a workplace to a physical, chemical or biological agent to the extent that the normal physiological mechanisms are affected and the health of the worker is impaired. It includes, but is not limited, to an occupational disease for which a worker is entitled to benefits under the Workplace Safety and Insurance Act,1997.

4.2.1 Written Notice — Occupational Illness

In line with s. 52(2) and (3) of the Act (and other regulations, e.g., Section 5 of the Health Care Regulation) an employer must report being informed of a worker's occupational illness or illness claim filed with the WSIB. The employer must report in writing to:

- a Director of the MOL;
- the JHSC or worker health and safety representative; and
- the union/s (if any).

The written notice must contain the information and particulars as prescribed in the applicable workplace regulation.

The written notice must be given within 4 days, and will typically include:

- the name, address and phone number of the employer;
- the nature of the illness and the circumstances which gave rise to the illness;
- a description of the cause or suspected cause of the illness;
- the period when the worker was affected by the illness;
- the name, address and phone number of the worker;
- the name, address and phone number of the physician by whom the person was or is being attended;
- name, address and phone number of each medical facility, if any, where the worker was or is being attended for the illness; and
- **a description of the steps taken to prevent a recurrence or further illness.**

4.3 Project Site or Mine Reporting Requirements

Under Section 53 of the OHS Act, construction projects, mines and mining plants must report non-injury incidents, such as unexpected events or dangerous occurrences (e.g., fire, explosion, cave-in, rockburst) where the incident could have caused an injury.

Written notice must be given to a MOL director, the JHSC (or worker health and safety representative) and the union, if any. This written notice must be given within 48 hours of the incident and must contain any prescribed information.

5.0 Workplace Safety and Insurance Act and the WSIB

In addition to reporting requirements under the OHS Act, there are concurrent reporting requirements under the Workplace Safety and Insurance Act.

The Workplace Safety and Insurance Board (WSIB) administers the Workplace Safety and Insurance Act.

5.1 WSIB Contact Information

Contact the WSIB Monday to Friday, from 7:30 a.m. to 5 p.m.
- **Tel: 1-800-387-0750 or 416-344-1000**
- TTY: 1-800-387-0050
- Fax: 416-344-4684 or 1-888-313-7373

For forms, resources, eServices and more, visit the WSIB website:
- *www.wsib.on.ca*

5.2 Employer Report to WSIB Following a Disabling or Critical Injury

When a disabling injury or critical injury occurs, the employer must:

1. Make sure first aid is given immediately.
2. Make sure there is a record of the first aid treatment/advice given to the worker.
3. Complete and give to the worker the *WSIB Treatment Memorandum Form 156* if the worker needs more than first aid treatment/advice.
4. Provide immediate transportation to a hospital, a doctor's office, or the worker's home, if necessary.
5. Complete the *WSIB Form 7 (Employer's Report of Injury/Disease)* if the worker needs more than first aid treatment/advice. Make sure to also ask the worker to file a claim and give written consent to the release of functional abilities information on the Form 7; the employee's signature should be included in Section B.)
6. Give the worker the designated worker's copy of the Form 7.
7. Return the completed Form 7 to the WSIB within three days of learning of the work-related injury or occupational disease. If the worker is unable or unwilling to sign, send in the Form 7 without the signature.

8. Pay full wages and benefits for the day or shift on which the injury occurred.
9. Cooperate in the worker's early and safe return to work.

5.2.1 About Employer's Report of Injury/Illness (Form 7)

As noted, a Form 7 (or eForm 7) must be completed and sent to the WSIB within three days of learning of a work-related injury or occupational disease.

Also note that on the Form 7, employers must report a work-related accident/illness if they learn that a worker:

- requires health care; and/or
  is absent from regular work;
- earns less than regular pay for regular work (e.g., only working partial hours);
- requires modified work at less than regular pay.

Reporting is also required if, following the date of the work-related accident/illness, the worker does not receive health care but requires modified work.

5.2.2 Using the eForm 7

Employers may choose to file a Form 7 online, using the eForm 7. This method is generally faster and more convenient.

Note: To file online, you will first need to sign up on the WSIB website for e-services, and then log-in each time.

Once an eForm7 is completed and submitted, you'll receive confirmation of your submission, and e-notices of any status changes later on. You can also submit any relevant documents for each claim file.

5.3 Worker's Report of Injury/Illness

In all cases of injury/illness, a worker must:

1. Get first aid right away.
2. Tell the employer of any injury or the possible onset of a work-related disease/condition.
3. File a claim for workplace insurance benefits (*Form 6 — Worker's Report of Injury/Disease; or file online using eForm 6*) promptly, when more than first aid treatment/advice is needed.
4. Sign the Form 6 and give a copy to the employer.
5. Choose a doctor or other qualified health professional. Do not change health professionals without permission from the WSIB.

6. Cooperate in health care treatment.
7. Cooperate in safe return to work.
8. Complete and return all WSIB forms promptly.
9. Report to the WSIB any changes in income, return to work status or medical condition.

5.3.1 About Employee Consent

Whether a worker signs a Form 6 or Form 7 (Section B), in either case the employee is agreeing to have their treating health professional (e.g., doctor) release functional abilities information to the employer.

For employers, make sure the employee understands that the written consent (signature) is necessary in order to receive benefits. The employee should also know their assigned claim number and that it should be quoted on all correspondence he or she may have with the Board.

5.3.2 Filing an eForm 6

To file an eForm 6 online, a worker can visit the WSIB website and follow the Form 6 application guide. To file an eForm 6, the WSIB advises that a worker will need:

* worker information (name, date of birth, address)
* employer information (name, address)
* accident/illness details (e.g., date of accident, injury/illness information)
* health care information (e.g., treatment date, location)
* employment information (e.g., work schedule, earnings)
* return to work information (e.g., modified work details)

5.4 Health Professional's Report (Form 8)

Note that at the time of a worker's initial visit to a health professional in regards to a workplace injury/illness, the health professional (e.g., doctor) sends in a separate form (Form 8) to the WSIB.

5.5 About Return to Work and Functional Abilities

Following a worker's initial post-injury visit to a health professional, *the employer or the worker* can later request a health professional to complete a *Functional Abilities Form (FAF) — 2647A*. As the worker gets closer to returning to work, completing this form helps to facilitate the return to work process.

Note, the WSIB suggests that, ideally, the FAF form should only be completed when the worker is functionally able to return to work. The form includes a section for employers to complete and requires the worker's signature.

One purpose of the form is to encourage communication between the employer and the worker about the work-related details of returning to work. In general, this includes:

- consideration of the worker's functional abilities for various tasks or movements, such as lifting, climbing, bending, walking, sitting, pulling or driving;
- identification of jobs that are suitable for the worker, or job accommodation(s); and
- timing or plans for return to work, e.g., a phased or immediate return.

5.5.1 Providing the FAF-2647A Form to a Health Professional

When an employer or worker decides to ask a treating health professional (e.g., doctor) to complete the FAF, the WSIB recommends these steps:

- **For an employer:** ensure the worker gives a copy of the FAF to the health professional; or, if necessary, send a copy of it to the health professional. (Do not send it to the WSIB; only the health professional does that.)
- **For a worker:** Bring a signed FAF to your health professional and ask them to complete it. By providing your signature (see Worker's Signature section on the FAF), this authorizes the health professional to release the functional abilities information to your employer.

When fully completed, **the health professional** (not the employer) submits the FAF to the WSIB.

(Note, although the worker's initial signed consent to the release of functional abilities information will already appear on the Form 6 or 7, the worker's signature on the FAF form is still required.)

For more guidance, refer to these guidance documents on the WSIB's website:

- FAF Form (the blank form notes responsibilities of workers, employers and health professionals)
- FAF Fact Sheet
- Guide to Completing the FAF

Note that health professionals who complete the WSIB's FAF are paid a fee of $40. This cost subsequently is reflected on the employer's accident cost statement.

5.5.2 Employer's Own Form

Some employers may prefer to use their own form (specific to their work environment) to gather functional abilities information. If the employer is using a non-WSIB form, they must pay the health professional directly for completing the form.

The WSIB advises that the employer form should not request diagnostic or confidential information, and should be limited to functional information.

5.6 In Case of Injury Poster (Form 82)

Employers are required to prominently display the WSIB's "In Case of Injury" Poster (Form 82) in their workplace. This poster is provided free of charge, in different sizes and languages. Employers can get the poster in printable .pdf format online (*www.wsib.on.ca*) or by calling the WSIB during regular business hours at 1-800-387-0750.

6.0 Effective Workplace Inspections

As part of your organization's systems for hazard identification, assessment, elimination and control, be sure to conduct regular workplace inspections.

Supervisors should be inspecting the workplace for hazards each day and with each new assignment given to a worker.

Worker representatives should be inspecting the physical condition of the workplace at least every 30 days, in line with ss. 8(9) or 9(26) of the OHS Act.

Use the following two sample checklists as a starting point. As appropriate, add to the lists or create a similar list that meets your workplace needs or conditions.

For all worksites and work undertakings, it's good practice to meet or exceed OHS Regulations, and follow best industry practices.

Your workplace inspections should be tailored to help you pinpoint any sub-standard practices or conditions, and lead to correction, compliance, or other improvements that reduce risk or hazards.

6.1 Worker Representatives and Workplace Inspections

JHSCs and worker health and safety representatives play an important part in conducting regular workplace inspections, to help identify and control workplace hazards. Your workplace inspection team can help to:
- plan and carry out inspections; and
- clearly report on findings.

For guidance on completing effective workplace inspections, consider any resources that may already be used within your organization, and then look at possible improvements or changes. For instance, the MOL website and other OHS-related organizations in Ontario have various resources and inspection checklists available for review online. Also consider other resources available from CCOHS or other Canadian jurisdictions.

6.2 Purposes

Some of the general purposes of inspections include:
- determining specific OHS-related concerns of workers and supervisors
- review of current jobs and tasks; including existing and potential hazards
- investigating and pinpointing underlying causes of hazards
- developing recommendations for corrective action
- monitoring of steps or actions that have been taken to control or eliminate a hazard, e.g., substitution or replacement, administrative controls, engineering controls, PPE

6.3 Inspect All Operations and Locations

Your workplace inspections should address all operations and locations. You will need to consider the work environment, equipment and tools, work processes and people. For each task or type of work, you'll need to know how people are working, whether the equipment and tools are safe, and whether people are following the correct processes.

Some examples of workplace hazards that your inspection team should be looking for include:
- general or specific safety hazards, e.g., inadequate machine guards, unsafe workplace conditions, unsafe work practices
- biological hazards, e.g., viruses, bacteria, fungi and parasites
- chemical hazards, e.g., via potential exposures to a liquid, solid, vapour, gas, dust, fume or mist

- ergonomic hazards, e.g., repetitive and forceful movements using power tools; awkward postures while working at a task or work station
- physical hazards, e.g., noise, vibration, heat, cold, electricity, radiation, pressure, weather conditions
- psychosocial hazards that can affect mental health or well-being such as overwork, stress, harassment or violence

Before beginning an inspection, consider what you will be reporting on. In many cases, you will first need:

- diagram(s) of different work area(s), e.g., project site layout, operations/plant layout, office floor plans, etc.
- equipment and tool inventory, including safety manuals, known hazards, etc.
- inventory of hazardous products or materials, e.g., WHMIS or TDG regulated products; gather the relevant Safety Data Sheets (SDSs)

Another pre-inspection task is to develop or update any practical checklists that your team can use to help keep the inspection on pace and to the point. Generally, a checklist should include:

- inspection responsibilities; naming who will do which part(s) of the inspection
- inspection activities, e.g., list of inspection steps and areas/processes to be inspected
- an area to record findings and add comments or notes

6.4 Inspection Team

In addition to JHSC members or worker health and safety representatives, an inspection team may include:

- a supervisor(s) who knows the work area being inspected; and
- others who may have relevant knowledge, training or certification, such as engineers, team leads, occupational hygienists or OHS professionals

Overall, your teams' expertise will ideally include a reasonable knowledge of:

- relevant regulations and procedures
- existing and potential hazards
- relevant work procedures and processes

In many cases, for team objectivity, it may be more appropriate to not include a work area's supervisor on the inspection team. The following excerpt from the CCOHS website offers this general guidance:

"If the supervisor of the area does not accompany the inspection team, the inspection team should consult the supervisor before leaving the area. Discuss each recommendation with the supervisor. Report items that the supervisor can immediately correct. Note these on the report as corrected. This documentation keeps the records clear and serves as a reminder to check the condition during the next inspection. Although a supervisor may interpret reporting as a criticism, the inspection team cannot fail to report hazards. Aim to be objective and maintain an attitude that is firm, friendly, and fair."

6.5 Inspection Reports

Using the checklists and other forms or documentation developed by your organization, the inspection team should make note of each observed unsafe condition or hazard, along with any relevant comments and recommended actions or methods of controlling or eliminating the hazard. For each hazard, describe the relevant details and the exact location. Note that many workplaces assign a priority to each identified hazard. For example:

- A = Major; requires immediate action
- B = Serious; requires short-term action
- C = Minor; requires long-term action

After each listed hazard, enter a "correction date" as appropriate. This helps to set a timeline or target for correction and encourages resolution of each identified hazard. Also note that each inspection team member should review the recommendations in the report. This type of teamwork can help to boost accuracy and clarity, and the overall effectiveness of the inspection.

All reports should be concise and factual. This allows the JHSC and the employer (e.g., managers/supervisors) to clearly understand the issue or hazard, consider the recommended corrective actions, and make further evaluations or decisions as may be necessary or appropriate.

6.6 Inspection Checklists

Design checklists or inspection sheets/forms that are most relevant to your organization. Two types of sample checklists are shown on the following pages.

Sample Inspection Checklist Number 1

General Physical Conditions

- Aisles and storage stacks: accessibility, marking, adequate dimensions
- Compressed gas cylinders: segregation in storage, weather protection and restraints
- Deluge showers and eye baths: water flow, temperature and drainage
- Electrical fixtures: wiring, cords, grounds and connections
- Exits: marking, visibility, lighting and unobstructed access
- Firefighting equipment: equipment and early detection systems, sprinklers, fire plugs, etc.
- Flammables and explosives: storage, ventilation and working supply
- Guards and safety devices: removable and fixed guards; safety devices or attachments; nip points, cutting & shear edges, presses, rotating parts and gear devices
- Hand tools: condition, storage and proper use
- Hoisting equipment: e.g., air hoists, hydraulic lifts, jacks, electric hoists, wire ropes, chains
- Ladders and climbing devices: condition, storage and proper use
- Machinery/power equipment and parts: e.g., agitators, grinders, forging presses, pulverizing machines, drilling machines
- Mechanical and power transmission systems: check for condition and guarding, e.g., shafts, bearings, gears, pulleys, drums, cables, belts, sprockets, ropes, chains
- Materials handling equipment and lifting devices: condition, proper use and storage
- Pressure vessels, boilers and pipes: check for leaks, condition and performance of objects subject to internal pressure from compression of liquids or gases
- Pumps, compressors, blowers and fans: check condition and performance of equipment that moves or compresses liquids, air, or gases
- Overhead structures and equipment: check for structural integrity and maintenance of equipment that may fall from above
- Scrap and refuse: accumulation, removal, storage and disposal

- Shafts, pits, sumps and floor openings: check for signage/hazard controls for any type of opening which is a tripping or fall hazard
- Stacking and storage: location, segregation, stability, damage, protection
- Vehicles and carrying equipment: check for safe performance/ maintenance of trucks, cars, motorized carts, and non-motorized equipment for transporting materials
- Walking, standing and working surfaces: guarding and condition; including floors, aisles, stairs, platforms, ramps, roads, scaffolds, ladders, desks, workbenches
- Warning and signal devices: check functionality of direct communication systems, e.g., radio, telephones, buzzers, bells, lights

Occupational/Environmental Health

- Caustic, corrosive and toxic materials: e.g., ensure use of WHMIS labels and WHMIS compliance, including storage, disposal and spill clean-up; also ensure TDG compliance for handling and transporting of dangerous goods
- Hazardous substances: e.g., provide information to affected employees about hazards substances, including SDSs and other aspects of WHMIS compliance
- Human factors engineering: e.g., effective application of ergonomics and hazard controls
- Noise exposure: e.g., meet regulatory requirements for measurement and controls
- Personal protective equipment: e.g., goggles, gloves, aprons, leggings, etc.; ensure sufficient PPE for the number of workers, suitable location of PPE, and compliance with regulations where select PPE is required
- Radiation exposure: e.g., effective measurement and controls
- Temperature extremes: e.g., preventive measures, measurement and controls
- Ventilation: e.g., ensure effective ventilation of toxic fumes, vapours, mists, smoke and gases

Sample Checklist Number 2
Checklist No. 2 is one type of checklist posted on the WorkSafeBC website. It is reprinted and included here, with permission.

Note that this type of checklist helps the inspection team to look for a variety of unsafe conditions and consider relevant safe work practices. With each inspection, corrective actions can be taken and supervisors informed of hazards and concerns. Your checklists should be customized, as appropriate, to your workplace and work areas.

Guards	Support and Structure
Inspect for: √ Missing guards on gears, belts, pulleys and shafts √ Missing guards on power saws √ Missing point of operation guards on all machines √ Grinding wheel guarded and tool rests adjusted √ Pinch points guarded against inadvertent contact	Inspect for: √ Faulty bracing, shoring √ Sharp-edged, jagged splinters √ Worn, cracked, broken conditions √ Slippery walking and gripping surfaces √ Uneven surfaces √ Missing hand rails and platform guardrails √ Broken steps creating potential for worker or equipment to trip, fall, roll, collapse, slide, etc. √ Protruding objects
Electrical	**Ventilation, Illumination, Noise, Radiation**
Inspect for: √ Ungrounded machines and equipment √ Low voltage leaks √ Obstructed switch panels √ Use of "lock-outs" for mechanics and electricians √ Close proximity to stop buttons on all machines	Inspect for: √ Excessive heat √ Use of unshielded X-rays √ Arc-flash without shielding √ Excessive dust √ Exposure to toxic dust, fumes, gases √ Gas leaks √ Excessive noise

√ Defective cords, plugs, receptacles √ Overloaded circuits √ Use of light duty extension cords instead of approved wiring √ Power cords across aisles, under rugs, etc. √ Use of low voltage systems or ground fault interrupters in wet locations	√ Poor ventilation for chemical use and storage √ Failure to protect workers from the above hazards

Miscellaneous Items	**Work Practices**
Inspect for: √ Poor housekeeping √ Proper storage of flammable liquids √ Exits clear for emergencies √ Adequate first aid supplies √ Fire extinguishers in working condition √ Damaged rigging √ Vehicle neglect √ Eye protection, head protection, breathing protection available √ Warning devices for work in streets √ New employees informed of work hazards	Inspect for: √ Missing guards on gears, belts, pulleys and shafts √ Failure to use PPE √ Horseplay √ Failure to follow safety/health rules and procedures √ Misuse of tools and equipment √ Failure to follow safe working procedures √ Poor housekeeping √ Other

7.0 Emergency Procedures

9-1-1 is the emergency number used to contact:
- Ambulance, Fire or Police

1. Don't Panic
2. Assess the situation
3. Determine the type of emergency

4. Dial 9-1-1

Be ready to provide the following information:

- your name (and call-back number, e.g., mobile phone)
- your organization
- type of emergency
- type of help needed

Do NOT hang up until told to do so by emergency personnel receiving the information.

8.0 Posting Requirements

Employers should be aware of legislated posting requirements, plus OHS training requirements such as the employer's duty to provide training in accordance with ss. 25 and 26 of the OHS Act.

Learn more about posting and training requirements on the MOL website at:

- *http://www.labour.gov.on.ca/english/atwork/posting_training.php*

Examples of some of the posting requirements include:

a. OHS Act: Employers are required to post a copy of the OHS Act in their workplaces.

b. Required Poster: All provincially regulated workplaces must display the MOL poster entitled *Health & Safety at Work: Prevention Starts Here*. The poster includes rights and responsibilities of workers, supervisors and employers, plus MOL contact information. Printed colour posters are available in English and French from Service Ontario free of charge or can be downloaded in English, French and 15 other languages.

c. OHS Policy: The OHS Act requires employers to prepare and review, at least annually, a written occupational health and safety policy, and to develop and maintain a program to implement that policy. The policy must be posted in the workplace.

Note that the OHS Act also requires employers to prepare and review, at least annually or more frequently as required, a policy with respect to workplace violence and a policy with respect to workplace harassment. These policies must be posted in the workplace, except for workplaces with five or fewer workers (unless ordered by a MOL Inspector.)

The WSIB (Workplace Safety and Insurance Act) also establishes specific posting requirements, e.g., the "In Case of Injury" poster. Contact the

WSIB for more information and/or visit the WSIB and MOL websites for guidance.

9.0 Due Diligence Checklist

Employers can get a sense of the state of due diligence in their company by asking the kinds of questions posed below. Although these questions are meant for employers, they can also be adapted and used by supervisors, safety leaders, JHSCs, and workers.

Due Diligence Checklist

☐ 1. Do you know, understand and follow your OHS duties set out in the OHS Act and regulations?

☐ 2. Have you implemented an effective OHS program to identify, assess and control hazards (following the hierarchy of controls: first, elimination of the hazard; second, use of engineering controls; third, use of administrative controls; and fourth, use of PPE)?

☐ 3. Are you informed on the potential sources of hazards and appropriate hazard controls from:

- OHS legislation?
- The experience of others (e.g., from industry standards and best practice)?
- Your own internal OHS program (e.g., from inspections, reports, investigations and employee concerns)?
- Any previous incidents in your organization?

☐ 4. Are your workers encouraged to bring forward their concerns and are those concerns treated seriously?

☐ 5. Do you develop appropriate systems of work within your OHS management system (e.g., OHS objectives, policies, standards, safety processes and procedures, etc.) that contribute to or are essential to safety?

☐ 6. Do you provide OHS information to workers including hazards, hazard controls, safety policies, rules, procedures and any applicable regulations?

☐ 7. Do you provide direction and instruction to employees on their work tasks?

☐ 8. Regarding your equipment, do you:

- Use the correct equipment for the job?
- Train operators and supervisors in the safe use of the equipment?
- Ensure that equipment is properly installed?
- Ensure that unsafe equipment is not used?

- Have equipment available that enables the work to be carried out safely?
- Abide by manufacturer's specifications?
- Consider safety factors when obtaining new equipment?

☐ 9. Regarding equipment inspections and maintenance:
- Is your equipment inspected at suitable, regular intervals?
- Once identified, are equipment deficiencies, defects and unsafe conditions promptly repaired or otherwise remedied?
- Is frequency of inspections based on experience, manufacturer's specifications, regulatory requirements and a hazard assessment?
- Are maintenance personnel competent to maintain equipment adequately?
- Is maintenance work planned and conducted in a safe fashion (e.g., equipment that is being serviced is locked out and safety devices are not bypassed)?
- Are preventive maintenance and regular servicing of equipment performed as appropriate and required?
- Do the maintenance systems include pre-use equipment checks, walk-arounds, identification of critical parts and items and maintenance procedures?
- Are workers empowered to refuse to use equipment that is not in good working order?

☐ 10. Regarding PPE and other protective devices:
- Is PPE and protective clothing appropriate to the hazard and in good repair?
- Are workers trained in the proper and safe use, care, fit-testing and maintenance of all PPE?
- Are protective devices in place and functional?
- Are protective devices secure and appropriate for the risk?
- Are guards and other safety devices adequately maintained?

☐ 11. Regarding training, do you:
- Provide the required orientation and training for your young or new workers?
- Use appropriate testing to verify that your training is effective?
- Provide ongoing training as needed for all employees; whether front-line or management?

☐ 12. Have you ensured that corrective and preventive actions have been taken as a result of incident investigations?

☐ 13. Do you take reasonable steps to ensure that your OHS program is working, committing appropriate resources toward OHS, requiring OHS accountability, and providing monitoring and correction through:
* Formal, planned observations with respect to specific tasks?
* General observation of work going on by a supervisor or manager in the field?
* Formal reports, such as near-miss and incident reports?
* Informal reports, such as verbal reports?
* Workplace inspections?
* Regular internal and external OHS program audits?

☐ 14. Have you documented and kept records on all the work you do to ensure workplace health and safety?

OCCUPATIONAL HEALTH AND SAFETY ACT

R.S.O. 1990, c. O.1, as am. S.O. 1992, c. 14, ss. 2, 3; 1992, c. 21, s. 63; 1993, c. 27, Sched.; 1994, c. 24, s. 35; 1994, c. 25, s. 83; 1994, c. 27, s. 120; 1995, c. 1, s. 84; 1995, c. 5, ss. 28-32; 1997, c. 4, s. 84; 1997, c. 16, s. 2; 1998, c. 8, ss. 49-60; 2001, c. 9, Sched. I, s. 3 [s. 3(2), (6) not in force at date of publication. Repealed 2006, c. 21, Sched. F, s. 10.1(1).]; 2001, c. 13, s. 22; 2001, c. 26; 2004, c. 3, Sched. A, s. 93; 2006, c. 19, Sched. D, s. 14, Sched. M, s. 5; 2006, c. 21, Sched. F, s. 136(1), Table 1; 2006, c. 34, Sched. C, s. 25; 2006, c. 35, Sched. C, s. 93; 2007, c. 8, s. 221; 2009, c. 23; 2009, c. 33, Sched. 20, s. 3; 2011, c. 1, Sched. 7, s. 2(1)-(3), (4)-(6) (Fr.), (7)-(12), (13) (Fr.), (14) (Fr.) [s. 2(4)-(6), (12)-(14) not in force at date of publication. Repealed 2015, c. 27, Sched. 4, s. 11.]; 2011, c. 11, ss. 1-18 [ss. 6, 18(1) not in force at date of publication; s. 8(3) conditions not yet satisfied.]; 2014, c. 10, Sched. 4; 2015, c. 27, Sched. 4, ss. 2-7; 2016, c. 2, Sched. 4;7 2016, c. 37, Sched. 16; 2017, c. 22, Sched. 1, s. 71, Sched. 3; 2017, c. 34, Sched. 30.

1. (1) Definitions — In this Act,

"**adjudicator**" [Repealed 1998, c. 8, s. 49(1).]

"**Agency**" [Repealed 1997, c. 16, s. 2(1).]

"**Board**" means the Ontario Labour Relations Board;

"**Building Code**" means any version of the *Ontario Building Code* that was in force at any time since it was made under the *Building Code Act, 1974*, the *Building Code Act* of the Revised Statutes of Ontario, 1980, the *Building Code Act* of the Revised Statutes of Ontario, 1990, the *Building Code Act, 1992* or a successor to the *Building Code Act, 1992*;

"**certified member**" means a committee member who is certified under section 7.6;

"Chief Prevention Officer" means the Chief Prevention Officer appointed under subsection 22.3(1);

"committee" means a joint health and safety committee established under this Act;

"competent person" means a person who,

> (a) is qualified because of knowledge, training and experience to organize the work and its performance,
>
> (b) is familiar with this Act and the regulations that apply to the work, and
>
> (c) has knowledge of any potential or actual danger to health or safety in the workplace;

"construction" includes erection, alteration, repair, dismantling, demolition, structural maintenance, painting, land clearing, earth moving, grading, excavating, trenching, digging, boring, drilling, blasting, or concreting, the installation of any machinery or plant, and any work or undertaking in connection with a project but does not include any work or undertaking underground in a mine;

"constructor" means a person who undertakes a project for an owner and includes an owner who undertakes all or part of a project by himself or by more than one employer;

"Deputy Minister" means the Deputy Minister of Labour;

"designated substance" means a biological, chemical or physical agent or combination thereof prescribed as a designated substance to which the exposure of a worker is prohibited, regulated, restricted, limited or controlled;

"Director" means an inspector under this Act who is appointed as a Director for the purposes of this Act;

"employer" means a person who employs one or more workers or contracts for the services of one or more workers and includes a contractor or subcontractor who performs work or supplies services and a contractor or subcontractor who undertakes with an owner, constructor, contractor or subcontractor to perform work or supply services;

"engineer of the Ministry" means a person who is employed by the Ministry and who is licensed as a professional engineer under the *Professional Engineers Act*;

"factory" means,

(a) a building or place other than a mine, mining plant or place where homework is carried on, where,

(i) any manufacturing process or assembling in connection with the manufacturing of any goods or products is carried on,

(ii) in preparing, inspecting, manufacturing, finishing, repairing, warehousing, cleaning or adapting for hire or sale any substance, article or thing, energy is,

(A) used to work any machinery or device, or

(B) modified in any manner,

(iii) any work is performed by way of trade or for the purposes of gain in or incidental to the making of any goods, substance, article or thing or part thereof,

(iv) any work is performed by way of trade or for the purposes of gain in or incidental to the altering, demolishing, repairing, maintaining, ornamenting, finishing, storing, cleaning, washing or adapting for sale of any goods, substance, article or thing, or

(v) aircraft, locomotives or vehicles used for private or public transport are maintained,

(b) a laundry including a laundry operated in conjunction with,

(i) a public or private hospital,

(ii) a hotel, or

(iii) a public or private institution for religious, charitable or educational purposes, and

(c) a logging operation;

"hazardous material" means a biological or chemical agent named or described in the regulations as a hazardous material;

"hazardous physical agent" means a physical agent named or described in the regulations as a hazardous physical agent;

"health and safety management system" means a coordinated system of procedures, processes and other measures that is designed to be implemented by employers in order to promote continuous improvement in occupational health and safety;

"health and safety representative" means a health and safety representative selected under this Act;

"homework" means the doing of any work in the manufacture, pre-paration, improvement, repair, alteration, assembly or completion of any article or thing or any part thereof by a person for wages in premises occupied primarily as living accommodation;

"industrial establishment" means an office building, factory, arena, shop or office, and any land, buildings and structures appertaining thereto;

"inspector" means an inspector appointed for the purposes of this Act and includes a Director;

"labour relations officer" means a labour relations officer appointed under the *Labour Relations Act, 1995*;

"licensee" means a person who holds a licence under Part III of the *Crown Forest Sustainability Act, 1994*;

"logging" means the operation of felling or trimming trees for commercial or industrial purposes or for the clearing of land, and includes the mea-suring, storing, transporting or floating of logs, the maintenance of haul roads, scarification, the carrying out of planned burns and the practice of silviculture;

"mine" means any work or undertaking for the purpose of opening up, proving, removing or extracting any metallic or non-metallic mineral or mineral-bearing substance, rock, earth, clay, sand or gravel;

"mining plant" means any roasting or smelting furnace, concentrator, mill or place used for or in connection with washing, crushing, grinding, sifting, reducing, leaching, roasting, smelting, refining, treating or re-search on any substance mentioned in the definition of **"mine"**;

"Minister" means the Minister of Labour;

"Ministry" means the Ministry of Labour;

"occupational illness" means a condition that results from exposure in a workplace to a physical, chemical or biological agent to the extent that the normal physiological mechanisms are affected and the health of the worker is impaired thereby and includes an occupational disease for which a worker is entitled to benefits under the *Workplace Safety and Insurance Act, 1997*;

"Office of the Employer Adviser" means the office continued under subsection 176(2) of the *Workplace Safety and Insurance Act, 1997*;

"Office of the Worker Adviser" means the office continued under subsection 176(1) of the *Workplace Safety and Insurance Act, 1997;***"owner"** includes a trustee, receiver, mortgagee in possession, tenant, lessee, or occupier of any lands or premises used or to be used as a workplace, and a person who acts for or on behalf of an owner as an agent or delegate;

"prescribed" means prescribed by a regulation made under this Act;

"project" means a construction project, whether public or private, including,

(a) the construction of a building, bridge, structure, industrial establishment, mining plant, shaft, tunnel, caisson, trench, excavation, highway, railway, street, runway, parking lot, cofferdam, conduit, sewer, watermain, service connection, telegraph, telephone or electrical cable, pipe line, duct or well, or any combination thereof,

(b) the moving of a building or structure, and

(c) any work or undertaking, or any lands or appurtenances used in connection with construction;

"regulations" means the regulations made under this Act;

"shop" means a building, booth or stall or a part of such building, booth or stall where goods are handled, exposed or offered for sale or where services are offered for sale;

"supervisor" means a person who has charge of a workplace or authority over a worker;

"trade union" means a trade union as defined in the *Labour Relations Act, 1995* that has the status of exclusive bargaining agent under that Act in respect of any bargaining unit or units in a workplace and includes an organization representing workers or persons to whom this Act applies where such organization has exclusive bargaining rights under any other Act in respect of such workers or persons;

"worker" means any of the following, but does not include an inmate of a correctional institution or like institution or facility who participates inside the institution or facility in a work project or rehabilitation program:

1. A person who performs work or supplies services for monetary compensation.

2. A secondary school student who performs work or supplies services for no monetary compensation under a work experience program authorized by the school board that operates the school in which the student is enrolled.

3. A person who performs work or supplies services for no monetary compensation under a program approved by a college of applied arts and technology, university, private career college or other post-secondary institution.

4. [Repealed 2017, c. 22, Sched. 1, s. 71(2).]

5. Such other persons as may be prescribed who perform work or supply services to an employer for no monetary compensation; ("travailleur")

"workplace" means any land, premises, location or thing at, upon, in or near which a worker works;

"workplace harassment" means,

(a) engaging in a course of vexatious comment or conduct against a worker in a workplace that is known or ought reasonably to be known to be unwelcome, or

(b) workplace sexual harassment;

"workplace sexual harassment" means,

(a) engaging in a course of vexatious comment or conduct against a worker in a workplace because of sex, sexual orientation, gender identity or gender expression, where the course of comment or conduct is known or ought reasonably to be known to be unwelcome, or

(b) making a sexual solicitation or advance where the person making the solicitation or advance is in a position to confer, grant or deny a benefit or advancement to the worker and the person knows or ought reasonably to know that the solicitation or advance is unwelcome;

"workplace violence" means,

(a) the exercise of physical force by a person against a worker, in a workplace, that causes or could cause physical injury to the worker,

(b) an attempt to exercise physical force against a worker, in a workplace, that could cause physical injury to the worker,

(c) a statement or behaviour that it is reasonable for a worker to interpret as a threat to exercise physical force against the worker, in a workplace, that could cause physical injury to the worker.

(2) Ship under repair — For the purposes of this Act and the regulations, a ship being manufactured or under repair shall be deemed to be a project.

(3) Limitation — An owner does not become a constructor by virtue only of the fact that the owner has engaged an architect, professional engineer or other person solely to oversee quality control at a project.

"Workplace harassment" — A reasonable action taken by an employer or supervisor relating to the management and direction of workers or the workplace is not workplace harassment.

1993, c. 27 Sched.; 1994, c. 24 s. 35; 1994, c. 25 s. 83(1); 1997, c. 16 s. 2; 1998, c. 8 s. 49; 2009, c. 23 s. 1; 2009, c. 33, Sched. 20, s. 3(1); 2011, c. 11 s. 1; 2014, c. 10, Sched. 4, s. 1; 2016, c. 2, Sched. 4, s. 1; 2016, c. 37, Sched. 16, s. 1; 2017, c. 22, Sched. 1, s. 71

Part I — Application

2. (1) Application to Crown — This Act binds the Crown and applies to an employee in the service of the Crown or an agency, board, commission or corporation that exercises any function assigned or delegated to it by the Crown.

(2) Application of other Acts — Despite anything in any general or special Act, the provisions of this Act and the regulations prevail.

3. (1) Application to private residences — This Act does not apply to work performed by the owner or occupant or a servant of the owner or occupant to, in or about a private residence or the lands and appurtenances used in connection therewith.

(2) Farming operations — Except as is prescribed and subject to the conditions and limitations prescribed, this Act or a Part thereof does not apply to farming operations.

(3) Teachers, etc. — Except as is prescribed and subject to the conditions and limitations prescribed, this Act or a Part thereof does not apply to,

(a) a person who is employed as a teacher as defined in the *Education Act*; or

(b) a person who is employed as a member or teaching assistant of the academic staff of a university or a related institution.

4. Self-employed persons — Subsection 25(1), clauses 26(1)(c), (e), (f) and (g), subsection 33(1) and sections 34, 37, 38, 39, 40, 41, 51, 52, 54, 57, 59, 60, 61, 62, 66, 67, 68 and 69, and the regulations in relation thereto, apply with necessary modifications to a self-employed person.

2001, c. 9 Sched. I, s. 3(1)

Part II — Administration

4.1 (1) Administration of Act — The Minister is responsible for the administration of this Act.

(2) Powers of Minister — In administering this Act, the Minister's powers and duties include the following:

    1. To promote occupational health and safety and to promote the prevention of workplace injuries and occupational diseases.

    2. To promote public awareness of occupational health and safety.

    3. To educate employers, workers and other persons about occupational health and safety.

    4. To foster a commitment to occupational health and safety among employers, workers and others.

    5. To make grants, in such amounts and on such terms as the Minister considers advisable, to support occupational health and safety.

(3) Duty to consider — In administering this Act, the Minister shall consider advice that is provided to the Minister under this Act.

2011, c. 11 s. 2

5. Delegation of powers — Where under this Act or the regulations any power or duty is granted to or vested in the Minister or the Deputy Minister, the Minister or Deputy Minister may in writing delegate that power or duty from time to time to any employee in the Ministry subject to such limitations, restrictions, conditions and requirements as the Minister or Deputy Minister may set out in the delegation.

2006, c. 35 Sched. C, s. 93(1)

6. (1) Appointment of inspectors and Directors — Such persons as may be necessary to administer and enforce this Act and the regulations may be appointed as inspectors by the Deputy Minister and the Deputy

Minister may designate one or more of the inspectors as a Director or Directors.

(2) Director may act as inspector — A Director may exercise any of the powers or perform any of the duties of an inspector under this Act or the regulations.

7. (1) Certificate of appointment — The Deputy Minister shall issue a certificate of appointment, bearing his or her signature or a facsimile thereof, to every inspector.

(2) Production of certificate — Every inspector, in the exercise of any powers or duties under this Act, shall produce his or her certificate of appointment upon request.

7.1 (1) Standards—training programs — The Chief Prevention Officer may establish standards for training programs required under this Act or the regulations.

(2) Approval—training program — The Chief Prevention Officer may approve a training program that is established before or after this subsection comes into force if the training program meets the standards established under subsection (1).

2011, c. 11 s. 3

7.2 (1) Standards—persons who provide training — The Chief Prevention Officer may establish standards that a person shall meet in order to become an approved training provider.

(2) Approval—persons who provide training — The Chief Prevention Officer may approve a person who meets the standards described in subsection (1) as a training provider with respect to one or more approved training programs.

2011, c. 11 s. 3

7.3 (1) Amendment of standard — The Chief Prevention Officer may amend a standard established under subsection 7.1(1) or 7.2(1).

(2) Publication of standards — The Chief Prevention Officer shall publish the standards established under subsections 7.1(1) and 7.2(1) promptly after establishing or amending them.

2011, c. 11 s. 3

7.4 (1) Time limit of approval — An approval given under subsection 7.1(2) or 7.2(2) is valid for the period that the Chief Prevention Officer specifies in the approval.

(2) Revocation, etc., of approval — The Chief Prevention Officer may revoke or amend an approval given under subsection 7.1(2) or 7.2(2).

(3) Information to be provided to Chief Prevention Officer — The Chief Prevention Officer may require any person who is seeking an approval or is the subject of an approval under subsection 7.1(2) or 7.2(2) to provide the Chief Prevention Officer with whatever information, records or accounts he or she may require pertaining to the approval and the Chief Prevention Officer may make such inquiries and examinations as he or she considers necessary.

2011, c. 11 s. 3

7.5 (1) Collection and use of training information — The Chief Prevention Officer may collect information about a worker's successful completion of an approved training program for the purpose of maintaining a record of workers who have successfully completed approved training programs.

(2) Disclosure by training provider — The Chief Prevention Officer may require an approved training provider to disclose to him or her the information described in subsection (1).

(3) Same — The Chief Prevention Officer may specify the time at which, and the form in which, the information shall be provided.

(4) Disclosure by Chief Prevention Officer — The Chief Prevention Officer may disclose information collected under subsection (1) to any person, including but not limited to a current or potential employer of a worker, if the worker consents to the disclosure.

2011, c. 11 s. 3

7.6 (1) Certification of members — The Chief Prevention Officer may,
    (a) establish training and other requirements that a committee member shall fulfil in order to become a certified member; and
    (b) certify a committee member who fulfils the requirements described in clause (a).

(2) Transition — A person who is certified under paragraph 5 of subsection 4(1) of the *Workplace Safety and Insurance Act, 1997* on the date section 20 of the *Occupational Health and Safety Statute Law Amendment Act, 2011* comes into force is deemed to be certified under this section.

2011, c. 11 s. 4

7.6.1 (1) Accreditation of health and safety management systems — The Chief Prevention Officer may accredit a health and safety management system if the system meets any applicable standards established under subsection (2).

(2) Standards — The Chief Prevention Officer may establish standards that a health and safety management system must meet in order to become an accredited health and safety management system.

(3) Amendment — The Chief Prevention Officer may amend standards established under subsection (2).

2016, c. 37, Sched. 16, s. 2

7.6.2 (1) Recognition of employers — The Chief Prevention Officer may give recognition to an employer in respect of one or more of its workplaces, upon the employer's application, if, (a) the employer satisfies the Chief Prevention Officer that it is a certified user of an accredited health and safety management system in its workplace or workplaces; and (b) the employer meets any applicable criteria established under subsection (2).

(2) Criteria — The Chief Prevention Officer may establish criteria that an employer must meet for the purposes of clause (1) (b).

(3) Amendment — The Chief Prevention Officer may amend criteria established under subsection (2).

2016, c. 37, Sched. 16, s. 2

7.6.3 (1) Validity of accreditations, recognitions — An accreditation given under subsection 7.6.1 (1) or a recognition given under subsection 7.6.2 (1) is valid for the period that the Chief Prevention Officer specifies in the accreditation or recognition.

(2) Revocation, etc., of accreditations, recognitions — The Chief Prevention Officer may revoke or amend an accreditation or recognition.

2016, c. 37, Sched. 16, s. 2

7.6.4 (1) Information re accreditations, recognitions — The Chief Prevention Officer may require any person who is seeking an accreditation under subsection 7.6.1 (1) or recognition under subsection 7.6.2 (1), or who is the subject of an accreditation or recognition, to provide the Chief

Prevention Officer with whatever information, records or accounts he or she may require pertaining to the accreditation or recognition and the Chief Prevention Officer may make such inquiries and examinations as he or she considers necessary.

(2) Disclosure by Director — A Director may communicate or allow to be communicated or disclosed any information that was collected under the authority of this Act or the regulations to the Chief Prevention Officer or to a delegate for the purposes of determining whether the employer should receive recognition or should keep such recognition.

(3) Same — Any disclosure of personal information that is authorized under subsection (2) shall be deemed to be in compliance with clause 42 (1) (d) of the *Freedom of Information and Protection of Privacy Act*.2016, c. 37, Sched. 16, s. 2

7.6.5 (1) Publication — The Chief Prevention Officer may publish or otherwise make available to the public information relating to health and safety management systems accredited under subsection 7.6.1 (1) and employers given recognition under subsection 7.6.2 (1), including the names of the systems and employers.

(2) Same — The Chief Prevention Officer shall publish the standards for accreditation of health and safety management systems and the criteria for recognition of employers promptly after establishing or amending them.
2016, c. 37, Sched. 16, s. 2

7.7 Delegation — The Chief Prevention Officer may delegate, in writing, any of his or her powers or duties under subsections 7.1 (2) and 7.2 (2), sections 7.4 and 7.5, clause 7.6 (1) (b), subsections 7.6.1 (1) and 7.6.2 (1), sections 7.6.3 and 7.6.4 and subsection 7.6.5 (1) to any person, including any person outside the Ministry, subject to such limitations, restrictions, conditions and requirements as the Chief Prevention Officer may set out in the delegation.
2011, c. 11, s. 5; 2016, c. 37, Sched. 16, s. 3

(2) Standards — The Chief Prevention Officer may establish standards that a health and safety management system must meet in order to become an accredited health and safety management system.
2011, c. 11 s. 5

8. (1) Mandatory selection of health and safety representative — At a project or other workplace where no committee is required under section

9 and where the number of workers regularly exceeds five, the constructor or employer shall cause the workers to select at least one health and safety representative from among the workers at the workplace who do not exercise managerial functions.

(2) Order appointing health and safety representatives — If no health and safety representative is required under subsection (1) and no committee is required under section 9 for a workplace, the Minister may, by order in writing, require a constructor or employer to cause the workers to select one or more health and safety representatives from among the workers at the workplace or part thereof who do not exercise managerial functions, and may provide in the order for the qualifications of such representatives.

(3) Idem — The Minister may from time to give such directions as the Minister considers advisable concerning the carrying out of the functions of a health and safety representative.

(4) What Minister shall consider — In exercising the power conferred by subsection (2), the Minister shall consider the matters set out in subsection 9(5).

(5) Selection of representatives — The selection of a health and safety representative shall be made by those workers who do not exercise managerial functions and who will be represented by the health and safety representative in the workplace, or the part or parts thereof, as the case may be, or, where there is a trade union or trade unions representing such workers, by the trade union or trade unions.

Proposed Addition — 8(5.1)-(5.3)

(5.1) Training requirement — Unless otherwise prescribed, a constructor or employer shall ensure that a health and safety representative selected under subsection (5) receives training to enable him or her to effectively exercise the powers and perform the duties of a health and safety representative.

(5.2) Same — The training described in subsection (5.1) shall meet such requirements as may be prescribed.

(5.3) Entitlement to be paid — A health and safety representative is deemed to be at work while he or she is receiving the training described in subsection (5.1), and the representative's employer shall pay the representative for the time spent, at the representative's regular or premium rate as may be proper.

2011, c. 11 s. 6 [Not in force at date of publication.]

(6) Inspections — Unless otherwise required by the regulations or by an order by an inspector, a health and safety representative shall inspect the physical condition of the workplace at least once a month.

(7) Idem — If it is not practical to inspect the workplace at least once a month, the health and safety representative shall inspect the physical condition of the workplace at least once a year, inspecting at least a part of the workplace in each month.

(8) Schedule of inspections — The inspection required by subsection (7) shall be undertaken in accordance with a schedule agreed upon by the constructor or employer and the health and safety representative.

(9) Inspections — The constructor, employer and workers shall provide a health and safety representative with such information and assistance as the member may require for the purpose of carrying out an inspection of the workplace.

(10) Idem — A health and safety representative has power to identify situations that may be a source of danger or hazard to workers and to make recommendations or report his or her findings thereon to the employer, the workers and the trade union or trade unions representing the workers.

(11) Powers of representatives — A health and safety representative has the power,

(a) to obtain information from the constructor or employer concerning the conducting or taking of tests of any equipment, machine, device, article, thing, material or biological, chemical or physical agent in or about a workplace for the purpose of occupational health and safety;

(b) to be consulted about, and be present at the beginning of, testing referred to in clause (a) conducted in or about the workplace if the representative believes his or her presence is required to ensure that valid testing procedures are used or to ensure that the test results are valid; and

(c) to obtain information from the constructor or employer respecting,

(i) the identification of potential or existing hazards of materials, processes or equipment, and

(ii) health and safety experience and work practices and standards in similar or other industries of which the constructor or employer has knowledge.

(12) Response to recommendations — A constructor or employer who receives written recommendations from a health and safety representative shall respond in writing within twenty-one days.

(13) Idem — A response of a constructor or employer under subsection (12) shall contain a timetable for implementing the recommendations the constructor or employer agrees with and give reasons why the constructor or employer disagrees with any recommendations that the constructor or employer does not accept.

(14) Notice of accident, inspection by representative — Where a person is killed or critically injured at a workplace from any cause, the health and safety representative may, subject to subsection 51(2), inspect the place where the accident occurred and any machine, device or thing, and shall report his or her findings in writing to a Director.

(15) Entitlement to time from work — A health and safety representative is entitled to take such time from work as is necessary to carry out his or her duties under subsections (6) and (14) and the time so spent shall be deemed to be work time for which the representative shall be paid by his or her employer at the representative's regular or premium rate as may be proper.

(16) Additional powers of certain health and safety representatives — A health and safety representative or representatives of like nature appointed or selected under the provisions of a collective agreement or other agreement or arrangement between the constructor or the employer and the workers, has, in addition to his or her functions and powers under the provisions of the collective agreement or other agreement or arrangement, the functions and powers conferred upon a health and safety representative by this section.

9. (1) Application — Subject to subsection (3), this section does not apply,

(a) to a constructor at a project at which work is expected to last less than three months; or

(b) to a prescribed employer or workplace or class of employers or workplaces.

(2) Joint health and safety committee — A joint health and safety committee is required,

(a) at a workplace at which twenty or more workers are regularly employed;

(b) at a workplace with respect to which an order to an employer is in effect under section 33; or

(c) at a workplace, other than a construction project where fewer than twenty workers are regularly employed, with respect to which a regulation concerning designated substances applies.

(3) Minister's order — Despite subsections (1) and (2), the Minister may, by order in writing, require a constructor or an employer to establish and maintain one or more joint health and safety committees for a workplace or a part thereof, and may, in such order, provide for the composition, practice and procedure of any committee so established.

(3.1) Same — Despite subsections (1) and (2), the Minister may, be order in writing, permit a constructor or an employer to establish and maintain one joint health and safety committee for more than one workplace or parts thereof, and may, in the order, provide for the composition, practice and procedure of any committee so established.

(3.2) Same — In an order under subsection (3.1), the Minister may,

(a) provide that the members of a committee who represent workers may designate a worker at a workplace who is not a member of the committee to inspect the physical condition of the workplace under subsection 9(23) and to exercise a committee member's rights and responsibilities under clause 43(4)(a) and subsections 43(7), (11) and (12); and

(b) require the employer to provide training to the worker to enable the worker to adequately perform the tasks or exercise the rights and responsibilities delegated by the committee.

(3.3) Same — If a worker is designated under clause (3.2)(a), the following apply:

1. The designated worker shall comply with this section as if the worker were a committee member while exercising a committee member's rights and responsibilities.

2. Subsections 9(35) and 43(13), section 55, clauses 62(5)(a) and (b) and subsection 65(1) apply to the designated worker as if the worker were a committee member while the worker exercises a committee member's rights and responsibilities.

3. The worker does not become a member of the committee as a result of the designation.

(4) Establishment of committee — The constructor or employer shall cause a joint health and safety committee to be established and maintained at the workplace unless the Minister is satisfied that a committee of like nature or an arrangement, program or system in which the workers participate was, on the 1st day of October, 1979, established and maintained pursuant to a collective agreement or other agreement or arrangement and that such committee, arrangement, program or system provides benefits for the health and safety of the workers equal to, or greater than, the benefits to be derived under a committee established under this section.

(5) What Minister shall consider — In exercising the power conferred by subsection (3) or (3.1), the Minister shall consider,

    (a) the nature of the work being done;

    (b) the request of a constructor, employer, a group of the workers the trade union or trade unions representing the workers in a workplace;

    (c) the frequency of illness or injury in the workplace or in the industry of which the constructor or employer is a part;

    (d) the existence of health and safety programs and procedures in the workplace and the effectiveness thereof; and

    (e) such other matters as the Minister considers advisable.

(6) Composition of committee — A committee shall consist of,

    (a) at least two persons, for a workplace where fewer than fifty workers are regularly employed; or

    (b) at least four persons or such greater number of people as may be prescribed, for a workplace where fifty or more workers are regularly employed.

(7) Idem — At least half the members of a committee shall be workers employed at the workplace who do not exercise managerial functions.

(8) Selection of members — The members of a committee who represent workers shall be selected by the workers they are to represent or, if a trade union or unions represent the workers, by the trade union or unions.

(9) Idem — The constructor or employer shall select the remaining members of a committee from among persons who exercise managerial functions for the constructor or employer and, to the extent possible, who do so at the workplace.

(10) Requirement for committee membership — A member of the committee who ceases to be employed at the workplace ceases to be a member of the committee.

(11) Committee to be co-chaired — Two of the members of a committee shall co-chair the committee, one of whom shall be selected by the members who represent workers and the other of whom shall be selected by the members who exercise managerial functions.

(12) Certification requirement — Unless otherwise prescribed, a constructor or employer shall ensure that at least one member of the committee representing the constructor or employer and at least one member representing workers are certified members.

(13) Idem — Subsection (12) does not apply with respect to a project where fewer than fifty workers are regularly employed or that is expected to last less than three months.

(14) Designation of member to be certified — If no member representing workers is a certified member, the workers or the trade unions who selected the members representing workers shall select from among them one or more who are to become certified.

(15) Designation of certified members — If there is more than one certified member representing workers, the workers or the trade unions who selected the members representing workers shall designate one or more certified members who then become solely entitled to exercise the rights and required to perform the duties under this Act of a certified member representing workers.

(16) Idem — If there is more than one certified member representing the constructor or employer, the constructor or employer shall designate one or more of them who then become solely entitled to exercise the rights and required to perform the duties under this Act of a certified member representing a constructor or an employer.

(17) Replacement of certified member — If a certified member resigns or is unable to act, the constructor or employer shall, within a reasonable time, take all steps necessary to ensure that the requirement set out in subsection (12) is met.

(18) Powers of committee — It is the function of a committee and it has power to,

(a) identify situations that may be a source of danger or hazard to workers;

(b) make recommendations to the constructor or employer and the workers for the improvement of the health and safety of workers;

(c) recommend to the constructor or employer and the workers the establishment, maintenance and monitoring of programs, measures and procedures respecting the health or safety of workers;

(d) obtain information from the constructor or employer respecting,

(i) the identification of potential or existing hazards of materials, processes or equipment, and

(ii) health and safety experience and work practices and standards in similar or other industries of which the constructor or employer has knowledge;

(e) obtain information from the constructor or employer concerning the conducting or taking of tests of any equipment, machine, device, article, thing, material or biological, chemical or physical agent in or about a workplace for the purpose of occupational health and safety; and

(f) be consulted about, and have a designated member representing workers be present at the beginning of, testing referred to in clause (e) conducted in or about the workplace if the designated member believes his or her presence is required to ensure that valid testing procedures are used or to ensure that the test results are valid.

(19) Idem — The members of the committee who represent workers shall designate one of them who is entitled to be present at the beginning of testing described in clause (18)(f).

(19.1) Powers of co-chairs — If the committee has failed to reach consensus about making recommendations under subsection (18) after attempting in good faith to do so, either co-chair of the committee has the power to make written recommendations to the constructor or employer.

(20) Response to recommendations — A constructor or employer who receives written recommendations from a committee or co-chair shall respond in writing within twenty-one days.

(21) Idem — A response of a constructor or employer under subsection (20) shall contain a timetable for implementing the recommendations the constructor or employer agrees with and give reasons why the constructor or employer disagrees with any recommendations that the constructor or employer does not accept.

(22) Minutes of proceedings — A committee shall maintain and keep minutes of its proceedings and make the same available for examination and review by an inspector.

(23) Inspections — Subject to subsection (24), the members of a committee who represent workers shall designate a member representing workers to inspect the physical condition of the workplace.

(24) Idem — If possible, the member designated under subsection (23) shall be a certified member.

(25) Idem — The members of a committee are not required to designate the same member to perform all inspections or to perform all of a particular inspection.

(26) Idem — Unless otherwise required by the regulations or by an order by an inspector, a member designated under subsection (23) shall inspect the physical condition of the workplace at least once a month.

(27) Idem — If it is not practical to inspect the workplace at least once a month, the member designated under subsection (23) shall inspect the physical condition of the workplace at least once a year, inspecting at least a part of the workplace in each month.

(28) Schedule of inspections — The inspection required by subsection (27) shall be undertaken in accordance with a schedule established by the committee.

(29) Inspections — The constructor, employer and the workers shall provide a member designated under subsection (23) with such information and assistance as the member may require for the purpose of carrying out an inspection of the workplace.

(30) Information reported to the committee — The member shall inform the committee of situations that may be a source of danger or hazard to workers and the committee shall consider such information within a reasonable period of time.

(31) Idem — The members of a committee who represent workers shall designate one or more such members to investigate cases where a worker is killed or critically injured at a workplace from any cause and one of those members may, subject to subsection 51(2), inspect the place where the accident occurred and any machine, device or thing, and shall report his or her findings to a Director and to the committee.

(32) Posting of names and work locations — A constructor or an employer required to establish a committee under this section shall post and keep posted at the workplace the names and work locations of the committee members in a conspicuous place or places where they are most likely to come to the attention of the workers.

(33) Meetings — A committee shall meet at least once every three months at the workplace and may be required to meet by order of the Minister.

(34) Entitlement to time from work — A member of a committee is entitled to,

    (a) one hour or such longer period of time as the committee determines is necessary to prepare for each committee meeting;

    (b) such time as is necessary to attend meetings of the committee; and

    (c) such time as is necessary to carry out the member's duties under subsections (26), (27) and (31).

(35) Entitlement to be paid — A member of a committee shall be deemed to be at work during the times described in subsection (34) and the member's employer shall pay the member for those times at the member's regular or premium rate as may be proper.

(36) Idem — A member of a committee shall be deemed to be at work while the member is fulfilling the requirements for becoming a certified member and the member's employer shall pay the member for the time spent at the member's regular or premium rate as may be proper.

(37) Exception — Subsection (36) does not apply with respect to workers who are paid by the Workplace Safety and Insurance Board for the time spent fulfilling the requirements for becoming certified.

(38) Additional powers of certain committees — Any committee of a like nature to a committee established under this section in existence in a workplace under the provisions of a collective agreement or other agreement or arrangement between a constructor or an employer and the workers has, in addition to its functions and powers under the provisions of the collective agreement or other agreement or arrangement, the functions and powers conferred upon a committee by this section.

(39) Dispute resolution — Where a dispute arises as to the application of subsection (2), or the compliance or purported compliance therewith by a constructor or an employer, the dispute shall be decided by the Minister after consulting the constructor or the employer and the workers or the trade union or trade unions representing the workers.

1993, c. 27 Sched.; 1994, c. 27 s. 120(1), (2); 1998, c. 8 s. 50; 2001, c. 9 Sched. I, s. 3(3); 2011, c. 11 s. 7

10. (1) Worker trades committee — If a committee is required at a project, other than a project where fewer than fifty workers are regularly employed or that is expected to last less than three months, the committee shall establish a worker trades committee for the project.

(2) Committee membership — The members of a worker trades committee shall represent workers employed in each of the trades at the workplace.

(3) Selection of members — The members of a worker trades committee shall be selected by the workers employed in the trades the members are to represent or, if a trade union represents the workers, by the trade union.

(4) Function of worker trades committee — It is the function of a worker trades committee to inform the committee at the workplace of the health and safety concerns of the workers employed in the trades at the workplace.

(5) Entitlement to time from work — Subject to subsection (6), a member of a worker trades committee is entitled to such time from work as is necessary to attend meetings of the worker trades committee and the time so spent shall be deemed to be work time for which the member shall be paid by the employer at the member's regular or premium rate as may be proper.

(6) Committee to determine maximum entitlement — The committee for a workplace shall determine the maximum amount of time for which members of a worker trades committee for the workplace are entitled to be paid under subsection (5) for each meeting of the worker trades committee.

11. (1) Consultation on industrial hygiene testing — The constructor or employer at a workplace shall consult a health and safety representative or the committee with respect to proposed testing strategies for investigating industrial hygiene at the workplace.

(2) Information — The constructor or employer shall provide information to a health and safety representative or the committee concerning testing strategies to be used to investigate industrial hygiene at the workplace.

(3) Attendance at testing — A health and safety representative or a designated committee member representing workers at a workplace is entitled to be present at the beginning of testing conducted with respect to industrial hygiene at the workplace if the representative or member believes his or her presence is required to ensure that valid testing procedures are used or to ensure that the test results are valid.

(4) Designation of member — The committee members representing workers shall designate one of them for the purpose of subsection (3).

12. (1) Summary to be furnished — For workplaces to which the insurance plan established under the *Workplace Safety and Insurance Act, 1997* applies, the Workplace Safety and Insurance Board, upon the request of an employer, a worker, committee, health and safety representative or trade union, shall send to the employer, and to the worker, committee, health and safety representative or trade union requesting the information an annual summary of data relating to the employer in respect of the number of work accident fatalities, the number of lost workday cases, the number of lost workdays, the number of non-fatal cases that required medical aid without lost workdays, the incidence of occupational illnesses, the number of occupational injuries, and such other data as the Board may consider necessary or advisable.

(2) Posting of copy of summary — Upon receipt of the annual summary, the employer shall cause a copy thereof to be posted in a conspicuous place or places at the workplace where it is most likely to come to the attention of the workers.

(3) Director to provide information — A Director shall, in accordance with the objects and purposes of this Act, ensure that persons and organizations concerned with the purposes of this Act are provided with information and advice pertaining to its administration and to the protection of the occupational health and occupational safety of workers generally.

1997, c. 16 s. 2(4)

13. [Repealed 1997, c. 16, s. 2(5).]

14. [Repealed 1997, c. 16, s. 2(6).]

15. [Repealed 1997, c. 16, s. 2(7).]

16. [Repealed 1997, c. 16, s. 2(8).]

17. [Repealed 1997, c. 16, s. 2(9).]

18. [Repealed 1997, c. 16, s. 2(10).]

19. [Repealed 1997, c. 16, s. 2(10).]

20. (1) Testimony in civil proceedings, etc. — Except with the consent of the Board, no member of the Board, nor its registrar, nor any of its other officers, nor any of its clerks or servants shall be required to give testimony in any civil proceeding or in any proceeding before the Board or in any proceeding before any other tribunal respecting information obtained in the discharge of their duties or while acting within the scope of their employment under this Act.

(2) Non-disclosure — No information or material furnished to or received by a labour relations officer under this Act shall be disclosed except to the Board or as authorized by the Board.

1998, c. 8 s. 51

21. (1) Advisory committees — The Minister may appoint committees, which are not committees as defined in subsection 1(1), or persons to assist or advise the Minister on any matter arising under this Act or to inquire into and report to the Minister on any matter that the Minister considers advisable.

(2) Remuneration and expenses — Any person appointed under subsection (1) who is not a public servant within the meaning of the *Public Service of Ontario Act, 2006* may be paid such remuneration and expenses as may be from time to time fixed by the Lieutenant Governor in Council.

2006, c. 35 Sched. C, s. 93(2)

22. (1) Contribution to defray cost — The Workplace Safety and Insurance Board shall require Schedule 1 and Schedule 2 employers under the *Workplace Safety and Insurance Act, 1997* to make payments to defray the cost of administering this Act and the regulations. The Lieutenant Governor in Council may fix the total payment to be made by all employers for that purpose.

(2) Same — The Workplace Safety and Insurance Board shall remit the money collected from employers under this section to the Minister of Finance.

1997, c. 16 s. 2(11)

22.1 (1) Powers under federal legislation — If a regulation under the *Canada Labour Code* incorporates by reference all or part of this Act or the regulations made under it, the Board and any person having powers under this Act may exercise any powers conferred by the regulation under the *Canada Labour Code*.

(2) Same — If a regulation under section 44 of the *Nuclear Safety and Control Act* (Canada) requires an employer to whom this Act applies to comply with all or part of this Act or the regulations made under it, the Board and any person having powers under this Act may exercise any powers conferred by the regulation under the *Nuclear Safety and Control Act* (Canada).

1998, c. 8 s. 52; 2011, c. 1 Sched. 7, s. 2(1)

Part II.1 — Prevention Council, Chief Prevention Officer and Designated Entities

[Heading added 2011, c. 11, s. 8(1).]

Prevention Council

[Heading added 2011, c. 11, s. 8(1).]

22.2 (1) Prevention Council — The Minister shall establish a council to be known as the Prevention Council in English and Conseil de la prévention in French.

(2) Composition — The Council shall be composed of such members as the Minister may appoint, and shall include representatives from each of the following groups:

    1. Trade unions and provincial labour organizations.

    2. Employers.

    3. Non-unionized workers, the Workplace Safety and Insurance Board and persons with occupational health and safety expertise.

(3) Same — In appointing members of the Council, the Minister shall ensure that,

    (a) an equal number of members are appointed to represent the groups described in paragraphs 1 and 2 of subsection (2); and

    (b) the group described in paragraph 3 of subsection (2) is represented by not more than one-third of the members of the Council.

(4) Appointment of members — The members of the Council shall be appointed for such term as may be determined by the Minister.

(5) Chair — The members of the Council shall choose a chair from among themselves by the date fixed by the Minister; if they fail to do so, the Minister shall designate a member as chair.

(6) Same — Subsection (5) applies on the first appointment of members and thereafter whenever the office of chair is vacant.

(7) Functions — The Council shall,

    (a) provide advice to the Minister on the appointment of a Chief Prevention Officer;

    (b) provide advice to the Chief Prevention Officer,

        (i) on the prevention of workplace injuries and occupational diseases,

        (ii) for the purposes of the provincial occupational health and safety strategy and the annual report under section 22.3, and

        (iii) on any significant proposed changes to the funding and delivery of services for the prevention of workplace injuries and occupational diseases;

    (c) provide advice on any other matter specified by the Minister; and

    (d) perform such other functions as may be specified by the Minister.

(8) For the purposes of subsection (7), any advice provided by the Council shall be communicated by the chair of the Council.

(9) Remuneration and expenses — Any member of the Council who is not a public servant within the meaning of the *Public Service of Ontario Act, 2006* may be paid such remuneration and expenses as may be from time to time fixed by the Lieutenant Governor in Council.

2011, c. 11 s. 8(1)

Chief Prevention Officer
[Heading added 2011, c. 11, s. 8(1).]

22.3 Chief Prevention Officer — (1) Functions — The Minister shall appoint a Chief Prevention Officer to,

(a) develop a provincial occupational health and safety strategy;

(b) prepare an annual report on occupational health and safety;

(c) exercise any power or duty delegated to him or her by the Minister under this Act;

(d) provide advice to the Minister on the prevention of workplace injuries and occupational diseases;

(e) provide advice to the Minister on any proposed changes to the funding and delivery of services for the prevention of workplace injuries and occupational diseases;

(f) provide advice to the Minister on the establishment of standards for designated entities under section 22.5;

(g) exercise the powers and perform the duties with respect to training that are set out in sections 7.1 to 7.5;

(h) establish requirements for the certification of persons for the purposes of this Act and certify persons under section 7.6 who meet those requirements;

(h.1) exercise the powers and perform the duties with respect to accreditation of health and safety management systems and re-cognition of employers that are set out in sections 7.6.1 to 7.6.5;

(i) exercise the powers and perform the duties set out in section 22.7; and

(j) exercise such other powers and perform such other duties as may be assigned to the Chief Prevention Officer under this Act.

(2) Appointment — The Chief Prevention Officer may be appointed for a term not exceeding five years and may be reappointed for successive terms not exceeding five years each.

(3) Occupational health and safety strategy — The Chief Prevention Officer shall develop a written provincial occupational health and safety strategy that includes,

(a) a statement of occupational health and safety goals;

(b) key performance indicators for measuring the achievement of the goals; and

(c) any other matter specified by the Minister.

(4) Advice of Prevention Council — The Chief Prevention Officer shall consult with the Prevention Council and shall consider its advice in developing the strategy.

(5) Strategy provided to Minister — The Chief Prevention Officer shall provide the strategy to the Minister on or before a day specified by the Minister.

(6) Minister's approval — The Minister may approve the strategy or refer it back to the Chief Prevention Officer for further consideration.

(7) Publication — After approving the strategy, the Minister shall publish it promptly.

(8) Annual report — The Chief Prevention Officer shall provide an annual written report to the Minister on occupational health and safety that includes a measurement of the achievement of the goals established in the strategy, and that contains such other information as the Minister may require.

(9) Advice of Prevention Council — The Chief Prevention Officer shall consult with the Prevention Council and shall consider its advice in developing the report.

(10) Report provided to Minister — The Chief Prevention Officer shall provide the annual report to the Minister on or before a day specified by the Minister.

(11) Publication — The Minister shall publish the Chief Prevention Officer's report promptly.

2011, c. 11 s. 8(1); 2016, c. 37, Sched. 16, s. 4

Changes to Funding and Delivery of Services
[Heading added 2011, c. 11, s. 8(1).]

22.4 (1) If Minister proposes change — If the Minister is considering a proposed change to the funding and delivery of services for the prevention of workplace injuries and occupational diseases, the Minister shall determine whether the proposed change would be a significant change.

(2) If proposed change significant — If the Minister determines that the proposed change is significant, the Minister shall seek advice from the Chief Prevention Officer with respect to the proposed change.

(3) If Chief Prevention Officer advising on change — If the Chief Prevention Officer is considering providing advice to the Minister concerning a proposed change to the funding and delivery of services for the prevention of workplace injuries and occupational diseases, the Chief Prevention Officer shall determine whether the proposed change would be a significant change.

(4) Prevention Council endorsement — If the Minister asks the Chief Prevention Officer for advice under subsection (2) or if the Chief Prevention Officer determines under subsection (3) that a proposed change would be a significant change, the Chief Prevention Officer shall,

> (a) ask the chair of the Prevention Council to state whether the Council endorses the proposed change; and
> (b) include that statement in the advice to the Minister.

(5) Matters to consider in determining if change is significant — The Minister and the Chief Prevention Officer shall consider such matters as may be prescribed when determining whether a proposed change to the funding and delivery of services for the prevention of workplace injuries and occupational diseases would be a significant change.

(6) Regulation — On the recommendation of the Minister, the Lieutenant Governor in Council may make regulations prescribing matters to be considered when determining whether a proposed change to the funding and delivery of services for the prevention of workplace injuries and occupational diseases would be a significant change.

(7) Same — Before recommending to the Lieutenant Governor in Council that a regulation be made under subsection (6), the Minister shall seek the advice of the Chief Prevention Officer and require the Chief Prevention Officer to seek the advice of the Prevention Council with respect to the matters to be prescribed.

2011, c. 11 s. 8(1)

Designated Entities

[Heading added 2011, c. 11, s. 8(2).]

22.5 (1) Eligible for grant — An entity that is designated under this section is eligible for a grant from the Ministry.

(2) Designation by Minister — The Minister may designate an entity as a safe workplace association or as a medical clinic or training centre specializing in occupational health and safety matters if the entity meets the standards established by the Minister.

(3) Standards — The Minister may establish standards that an entity shall meet before it is eligible to be designated.

(4) Same — The standards established under subsection (3) may address any matter the Minister considers appropriate, including governance, objectives, functions and operations.

(5) Same — The Minister may establish different standards for associations, clinics or centres serving different industries or groups.

(6) Duty to comply — A designated entity shall operate in accordance with the standards established under subsection (3) that apply to it, and in accordance with any other requirements imposed on it under section 22.6.

(7) Amendment of standard — The Minister may amend a standard established under subsection (3).

(8) Date for compliance with amended standard — If the Minister amends a standard established under subsection (3), the Minister shall establish a date by which designated entities to which the amended standard applies are required to comply with it.

(9) Publication of standards — The Minister shall promptly publish,

    (a) the standards established under subsection (3); and

    (b) standards amended under subsection (7), together with the compliance date described in subsection (8).

(10) Transition — When the Minister establishes and publishes standards under subsections (3) and (9) for the first time after the coming into force of subsection 8(2) of the *Occupational Health and Safety Statute Law Amendment Act, 2011*, the Minister shall establish a date for the purposes of subsections (11) and (12) and shall publish it together with the standards.

(11) Same — An entity that is designated as a safe workplace association or as a medical clinic or training centre specializing in occupational health and safety matters under section 6 of the *Workplace Safety and Insurance*

Act, 1997 on the date section 20 of the *Occupational Health and Safety Statute Law Amendment Act, 2011* comes into force is deemed to be designated for the purposes of this Act until the date established by the Minister under subsection (10).

(12) Same — The standards that are in place under section 6 of the *Workplace Safety and Insurance Act, 1997* on the date section 20 of the *Occupational Health and Safety Statute Law Amendment Act, 2011* comes into force continue to apply, with necessary modifications, and are deemed to be standards for the purposes of this section, until the date established by the Minister under subsection (10).

2011, c. 11 s. 8(2)

22.6 Effect of designation — (1) Directions — The Minister may direct a designated entity to take such actions as the Minister considers appropriate.

(2) Government directives — In addition to the directions the Minister may issue under subsection (1), the Minister may direct an entity to comply with such government directives as the Minister specifies.

(3) Failure to comply — If an entity has committed any failure described in paragraphs 1 to 3 of subsection 22.7(3), the Minister may,

(a) reduce or suspend grants to the entity while the non-compliance continues;

(b) assume control of the entity and responsibility for its affairs and operations;

(c) revoke the designation and cease to provide grants to the entity; or

(d) take such other steps as he or she considers appropriate.

2011, c. 11 s. 8(2)

22.7 (1) Compliance and monitoring of designated entities — The Chief Prevention Officer shall monitor the operation of designated entities and,

(a) may require a designated entity to provide such information, records or accounts as the Chief Prevention Officer specifies; and

(b) may make such inquiries and examinations as he or she considers necessary.

(2) Report to Minister — The Chief Prevention Officer shall report to the Minister on the compliance of designated entities with the standards established under section 22.5 and with any directions given by the Minister under section 22.6.

(3) Advice to Minister — Where the Chief Prevention Officer determines that any of the following have occurred, the Chief Prevention Officer shall report that determination to the Minister and may advise the Minister with respect to any action the Minister may decide to take under section 22.6:

1. A designated entity has failed to operate in accordance with a standard established under section 22.5 that applies to it.

2. A designated entity has failed to comply with a direction given by the Minister under section 22.6 or a requirement of the Chief Prevention Officer under clause (1)(a).

3. A designated entity has failed to co-operate in an inquiry or examination conducted by the Chief Prevention Officer under clause (1)(b).

2011, c. 11 s. 8(2)

22.8 (1) Appointment of administrator — For the purposes of assuming control of an entity and responsibility for its affairs and operations under clause 22.6(3)(b), the Minister may appoint an administrator.

(2) Term of appointment — The appointment of the administrator remains valid until it is terminated by the Minister.

(3) Powers and duties of administrator — The administrator has the exclusive right to exercise the powers and perform the duties of the board of directors and its officers and exercise the powers of its members.

(4) Same — In the appointment, the Minister may specify the powers and duties of the administrator and the terms and conditions governing those powers and duties.

(5) Additional power of administrator — The board of directors and officers may continue to act to the extent authorized by the Minister, but any such act is valid only if approved, in writing, by the administrator.

(6) Report, directions — The administrator shall report to the Minister as required by him or her and shall carry out his or her directions.

(7) Meeting of members — Before the termination of an administrator's appointment, the administrator may call a meeting of the members to elect a board of directors in accordance with the *Corporations Act*.

Proposed Amendment — Conditional Amendment — 22.8(7)

On the coming into force of 2010, c. 15, s. 24 [Not in force at date of publication.], s. 22.8(7) is replaced by the following:

> (7) **Meeting of members** — Before the termination of an administrator's appointment, the administrator may call a meeting of the members to elect a board of directors in accordance with the *Not-For-Profit Corporations Act, 2010*.
>
> 2011, c. 11 s. 8(3) [Conditions not yet satisfied.]

(8) Unincorporated entity — This section applies, with necessary modifications, to an entity that is not incorporated.

2011, c. 11 s. 8(2)

22.9 Delegation of powers and duties — Despite section 5, the Minister may delegate his or her powers or duties under sections 22.5, 22.6 and 22.8 only to the Chief Prevention Officer.

2011, c. 11 s. 8(2)

Part III — Duties of Employers and Other Persons

23. (1) Duties of constructor — A constructor shall ensure, on a project undertaken by the constructor that,

> (a) the measures and procedures prescribed by this Act and the regulations are carried out on the project;
>
> (b) every employer and every worker performing work on the project complies with this Act and the regulations; and
>
> (c) the health and safety of workers on the project is protected.

(2) Notice of project — Where so prescribed, a constructor shall, before commencing any work on a project, give to a Director notice in writing of the project containing such information as may be prescribed.

24. (1) Duties of licensees — A licensee shall ensure that,

> (a) the measures and procedures prescribed by this Act and the regulations are carried out with respect to logging in the licensed area;
>
> (b) every employer performing logging in the licensed area for the licensee complies with this Act and the regulations; and
>
> (c) the health and safety of workers employed by employers referred to in clause (b) is protected.

(2) Definition — In this section, "licensed area" means the lands on which the licensee is authorized to harvest or use forest resources.

1994, c. 25 s. 83(2)

25. (1) Duties of employers — An employer shall ensure that,

(a) the equipment, materials and protective devices as prescribed are provided;

(b) the equipment, materials and protective devices provided by the employer are maintained in good condition;

(c) the measures and procedures prescribed are carried out in the workplace;

(d) the equipment, materials and protective devices provided by the employer are used as prescribed; and

(e) a building, structure, or any part thereof, or any other part of a workplace, whether temporary or permanent, is capable of supporting any loads that may be applied to it,

(i) as determined by the applicable design requirements established under the version of the *Building Code* that was in force at the time of its construction,

(ii) in accordance with such other requirements as may be prescribed, or

(iii) in accordance with good engineering practice, if subclauses (i) and (ii) do not apply.

(2) Idem — Without limiting the strict duty imposed by subsection (1), an employer shall,

(a) provide information, instruction and supervision to a worker to protect the health or safety of the worker;

(b) in a medical emergency for the purpose of diagnosis or treatment, provide, upon request, information in the possession of the employer, including confidential business information, to a legally qualified medical practitioner and to such other persons as may be prescribed;

(c) when appointing a supervisor, appoint a competent person;

(d) acquaint a worker or a person in authority over a worker with any hazard in the work and in the handling, storage, use, disposal and transport of any article, device, equipment or a biological, chemical or physical agent;

(e) afford assistance and co-operation to a committee and a health and safety representative in the carrying out by the committee and the health and safety representative of any of their functions;

(f) only employ in or about a workplace a person over such age as may be prescribed;

(g) not knowingly permit a person who is under such age as may be prescribed to be in or about a workplace;

(h) take every precaution reasonable in the circumstances for the protection of a worker;

(i) post, in the workplace, a copy of this Act and any explanatory material prepared by the Ministry, both in English and the majority language of the workplace, outlining the rights, responsibilities and duties of workers;

(j) prepare and review at least annually a written occupational health and safety policy and develop and maintain a program to implement that policy;

(k) post at a conspicuous location in the workplace a copy of the occupational health and safety policy;

(l) provide to the committee or to a health and safety representative the results of a report respecting occupational health and safety that is in the employer's possession and, if that report is in writing, a copy of the portions of the report that concern occupational health and safety;

(m) advise workers of the results of a report referred to in clause (1) and, if the report is in writing, make available to them on request copies of the portions of the report that concern occupational health and safety; and.

(n) notify a Director if a committee or a health and safety representative, if any, has identified potential structural inadequacies of a building, structure, or any part thereof, or any other part of a workplace, whether temporary or permanent, as a source of danger or hazard to workers.

(3) **Idem** — For the purposes of clause (2)(c), an employer may appoint himself or herself as a supervisor where the employer is a competent person.

(3.1) **Same** — Any explanatory material referred to under clause (2)(i) may be published as part of the poster required under section 2 of the *Employment Standards Act, 2000*.

(4) Idem — Clause (2)(j) does not apply with respect to a workplace at which five or fewer workers are regularly employed.

(5) Idem — Clause (2)(n) does not apply to an employer that owns the workplace.

2009, c. 23, s. 2; 2011, c. 1, Sched. 7, s. 2(2); 2011, c. 11, s. 9; 2017, c. 34, Sched. 30, s. 1

25.1 (1) Footwear — An employer shall not require a worker to wear footwear with an elevated heel unless it is required for the worker to perform his or her work safely.

(2) Exception — Subsection (1) does not apply with respect to an employer of a worker who works as a performer in the entertainment and advertising industry.

(3) Definitions — In subsection (2),

"entertainment and advertising industry" means the industry of producing,

    (a) live or broadcast performances, or

    (b) visual, audio or audio-visual recordings of performances, in any medium or format;

"performance" means a performance of any kind, including theatre, dance, ice skating, comedy, musical productions, variety, circus, concerts, opera, modelling and voice-overs, and "performer" has a corresponding meaning.

2017, c. 22, Sched. 3, s. 1

26. (1) Additional duties of employers — In addition to the duties imposed by section 25, an employer shall,

    (a) establish an occupational health service for workers as prescribed;

    (b) where an occupational health service is established as prescribed, maintain the same according to the standards prescribed;

    (c) keep and maintain accurate records of the handling, storage, use and disposal of biological, chemical or physical agents as prescribed;

    (d) accurately keep and maintain and make available to the worker affected such records of the exposure of a worker to biological, chemical or physical agents as may be prescribed;

(e) notify a Director of the use or introduction into a workplace of such biological, chemical or physical agents as may be prescribed;

(f) monitor at such time or times or at such interval or intervals the levels of biological, chemical or physical agents in a workplace and keep and post accurate records thereof as prescribed;

(g) comply with a standard limiting the exposure of a worker to biological, chemical or physical agents as prescribed;

(h) establish a medical surveillance program for the benefit of workers as prescribed;

(i) provide for safety-related medical examinations and tests for workers as prescribed;

(j) where so prescribed, only permit a worker to work or be in a workplace who has undergone such medical examinations, tests or x-rays as prescribed and who is found to be physically fit to do the work in the workplace;

(k) where so prescribed, provide a worker with written instructions as to the measures and procedures to be taken for the protection of a worker; and

(l) carry out such training programs for workers, supervisors and committee members as may be prescribed.

(2) Idem — For the purposes of clause (1)(a), a group of employers, with the approval of a Director, may act as an employer.

(3) Idem — If a worker participates in a prescribed medical surveillance program or undergoes prescribed medical examinations or tests, his or her employer shall pay,

(a) the worker's costs for medical examinations or tests required by the medical surveillance program or required by regulation;

(b) the worker's reasonable travel costs respecting the examinations or tests; and

(c) the time the worker spends to undergo the examinations or tests, including travel time, which shall be deemed to be work time for which the worker shall be paid at his or her regular or premium rate as may be proper.

1994, c. 27 s. 120(3)

27. (1) Duties of supervisor — A supervisor shall ensure that a worker,

(a) works in the manner and with the protective devices, measures and procedures required by this Act and the regulations; and

(b) uses or wears the equipment, protective devices or clothing that the worker's employer requires to be used or worn;

(2) Additional duties of supervisor — Without limiting the duty imposed by subsection (1), a supervisor shall,

(a) advise a worker of the existence of any potential or actual danger to the health or safety of the worker of which the supervisor is aware;

(b) where so prescribed, provide a worker with written instructions as to the measures and procedures to be taken for protection of the worker; and

(c) take every precaution reasonable in the circumstances for the protection of a worker.

28. (1) Duties of workers — A worker shall,

(a) work in compliance with the provisions of this Act and the regulations;

(b) use or wear the equipment, protective devices or clothing that the worker's employer requires to be used or worn;

(c) report to his or her employer or supervisor the absence of or defect in any equipment or protective device of which the worker is aware and which may endanger himself, herself or another worker; and

(d) report to his or her employer or supervisor any contravention of this Act or the regulations or the existence of any hazard of which he or she knows.

(2) Idem — No worker shall,

(a) remove or make ineffective any protective device required by the regulations or by his or her employer, without providing an adequate temporary protective device and when the need for removing or making ineffective the protective device has ceased, the protective device shall be replaced immediately;

(b) use or operate any equipment, machine, device or thing or work in a manner that may endanger himself, herself or any other worker; or

(c) engage in any prank, contest, feat of strength, unnecessary running or rough and boisterous conduct.

(3) Consent to medical surveillance — A worker is not required to participate in a prescribed medical surveillance program unless the worker consents to do so.

29. (1) Duties of owners — The owner of a workplace that is not a project shall,

    (a) ensure that,

        (i) such facilities as are prescribed are provided,

        (ii) any facilities prescribed to be provided are maintained as prescribed,

        (iii) the workplace complies with the regulations, and

        (iv) no workplace is constructed, developed, reconstructed, altered or added to except in compliance with this Act and the regulations; and

    (b) where so prescribed, furnish to a Director any drawings, plans or specifications of any workplace as prescribed.

(2) Mine plans — The owner of a mine shall cause drawings, plans or specifications to be maintained and kept up to date not more than six months last past on such scale and showing such matters or things as may be prescribed.

(3) Plans of workplaces — Where so prescribed, an owner or employer shall,

    (a) not begin any, development, re, alteration, addition or installation to or in a workplace until the drawings, layout and specifications thereof and any alterations thereto have been filed with the Ministry for review by an engineer of the Ministry for compliance with this Act and the regulations; and

    (b) keep a copy of the drawings as reviewed in a convenient location at or near the workplace and such drawings shall be produced by the owner or employer upon the request of an inspector for his or her examination and inspection.

(4) Additional information — An engineer of the Ministry may require the drawings, layout and specifications to be supplemented by the owner or employer with additional information.

(5) Fees — Fees as prescribed for the filing and review of drawings, layout or specifications shall become due and payable by the owner or employer upon filing.

30. (1) Duty of project owners — Before beginning a project, the owner shall determine whether any designated substances are present at the project site and shall prepare a list of all designated substances that are present at the site.

(2) Tenders — If any work on a project is tendered, the person issuing the tenders shall include, as part of the tendering information, a copy of the list referred to in subsection (1).

(3) Idem — An owner shall ensure that a prospective constructor of a project on the owner's property has received a copy of the list referred to in subsection (1) before entering into a binding contract with the constructor.

(4) Duty of constructors — The constructor for a project shall ensure that each prospective contractor and subcontractor for the project has received a copy of the list referred to in subsection (1) before the prospective contractor or subcontractor enters into a binding contract for the supply of work on the project.

(5) Liability — An owner who fails to comply with this section is liable to the constructor and every contractor and subcontractor who suffers any loss or damages as the result of the subsequent discovery on the project of a designated substance that the owner ought reasonably to have known of but that was not on the list prepared under subsection (1).

(6) Idem — A constructor who fails to comply with this section is liable to every contractor and subcontractor who suffers any loss or damages as the result of the subsequent discovery on the project of a designated substance that was on the list prepared under subsection (1).

31. (1) Duties of suppliers — Every person who supplies any machine, device, tool or equipment under any rental, leasing or similar arrangement for use in or about a workplace shall ensure,

    (a) that the machine, device, tool or equipment is in good condition;

    (b) that the machine, device, tool or equipment complies with this Act and the regulations; and

    (c) if it is the person's responsibility under the rental, leasing or similar arrangement to do so, that the machine, device, tool or equipment is maintained in good condition.

(2) Architects and engineers — An architect as defined in the *Architects Act*, and a professional engineer as defined in the *Professional Engineers*

Act, contravenes this Act if, as a result of his or her advice that is given or his or her certification required under this Act that is made negligently or incompetently, a worker is endangered.

32. Duties of directors and officers of a corporation — Every director and every officer of a corporation shall take all reasonable care to ensure that the corporation complies with,

(a) this Act and the regulations;

(b) orders and requirements of inspectors and Directors; and

(c) orders of the Minister.

Part III.0.1 — Violence and Harassment
[Heading added 2009, c. 23, s. 3.]

32.0.1 (1) Policies, violence and harassment — An employer shall,

(a) prepare a policy with respect to workplace violence;

(b) prepare a policy with respect to workplace harassment; and

(c) review the policies as often as is necessary, but at least annually.

(2) Written form, posting — The policies shall be in written form and shall be posted at a conspicuous place in the workplace.

(3) Exception — Subsection (2) does not apply if the number of workers regularly employed at the workplace is five or fewer, unless an inspector orders otherwise.

2009, c. 23 s. 3; 2011, c. 1 Sched. 7, s. 2(3)

32.0.2 (1) Program, violence — An employer shall develop and maintain a program to implement the policy with respect to workplace violence required under clause 32.0.1(1)(a).

(2) Contents — Without limiting the generality of subsection (1), the program shall,

(a) include measures and procedures to control the risks identified in the assessment required under subsection 32.0.3(1) as likely to expose a worker to physical injury;

(b) include measures and procedures for summoning immediate assistance when workplace violence occurs or is likely to occur;

(c) include measures and procedures for workers to report incidents of workplace violence to the employer or supervisor;

(d) set out how the employer will investigate and deal with incidents or complaints of workplace violence; and

(e) include any prescribed elements.

2009, c. 23 s. 3

32.0.3 (1) Assessment of risks of violence — An employer shall assess the risks of workplace violence that may arise from the nature of the workplace, the type of work or the conditions of work.

(2) Considerations — The assessment shall take into account,

(a) circumstances that would be common to similar workplaces;

(b) circumstances specific to the workplace; and

(c) any other prescribed elements.

(3) Results — An employer shall,

(a) advise the committee or a health and safety representative, if any, of the results of the assessment, and provide a copy if the assessment is in writing; and

(b) if there is no committee or health and safety representative, advise the workers of the results of the assessment and, if the assessment is in writing, provide copies on request or advise the workers how to obtain copies.

(4) Reassessment — An employer shall reassess the risks of workplace violence as often as is necessary to ensure that the related policy under clause 32.0.1(1)(a) and the related program under subsection 32.0.2(1) continue to protect workers from workplace violence.

(5) Same — Subsection (3) also applies with respect to the results of the reassessment.

2009, c. 23 s. 3

32.0.4 Domestic violence — If an employer becomes aware, or ought reasonably to be aware, that domestic violence that would likely expose a worker to physical injury may occur in the workplace, the employer shall take every precaution reasonable in the circumstances for the protection of the worker.

2009, c. 23 s. 3

32.0.5 (1) Duties re violence — For greater certainty, the employer duties set out in section 25, the supervisor duties set out in section 27, and the worker duties set out in section 28 apply, as appropriate, with respect to workplace violence.

(2) Information — An employer shall provide a worker with,

(a) information and instruction that is appropriate for the worker on the contents of the policy and program with respect to workplace violence; and

(b) any other prescribed information or instruction.

(3) Provision of information — An employer's duty to provide information to a worker under clause 25(2)(a) and a supervisor's duty to advise a worker under clause 27(2)(a) include the duty to provide information, including personal information, related to a risk of workplace violence from a person with a history of violent behaviour if,

(a) the worker can be expected to encounter that person in the course of his or her work; and

(b) the risk of workplace violence is likely to expose the worker to physical injury.

(4) Limit on disclosure — No employer or supervisor shall disclose more personal information in the circumstances described in subsection (3) than is reasonably necessary to protect the worker from physical injury.

2009, c. 23 s. 3

32.0.6 (1) Program, harassment — An employer shall, in consultation with the committee or a health and safety representative, if any, develop and maintain a written program to implement the policy with respect to workplace harassment required under clause 32.0.1(1)(b).

(2) Contents — Without limiting the generality of subsection (1), the program shall,

(a) include measures and procedures for workers to report incidents of workplace harassment to the employer or supervisor;

(b) include measures and procedures for workers to report incidents of workplace harassment to a person other than the employer or supervisor, if the employer or supervisor is the alleged harasser;

(c) set out how incidents or complaints of workplace harassment will be investigated and dealt with;

(d) set out how information obtained about an incident or complaint of workplace harassment, including identifying information about any individuals involved, will not be disclosed unless the disclosure is necessary for the purposes of investigating or taking corrective action with respect to the incident or complaint, or is otherwise required by law;

(e) set out how a worker who has allegedly experienced workplace harassment and the alleged harasser, if he or she is a worker of the employer, will be informed of the results of the investigation and of any corrective action that has been taken or that will be taken as a result of the investigation; and

(f) include any prescribed elements.

2009, c. 23, s. 3; 2016, c. 2, Sched. 4, s. 2

32.0.7 (1) Duties re harassment — To protect a worker from workplace harassment, an employer shall ensure that,

(a) an investigation is conducted into incidents and complaints of workplace harassment that is appropriate in the circumstances;

(b) the worker who has allegedly experienced workplace harassment and the alleged harasser, if he or she is a worker of the employer, are informed in writing of the results of the investigation and of any corrective action that has been taken or that will be taken as a result of the investigation;

(c) the program developed under section 32.0.6 is reviewed as often as necessary, but at least annually, to ensure that it adequately implements the policy with respect to workplace harassment required under clause 32.0.1(1)(b), and

(d) such other duties as may be prescribed are carried out.

(2) Results of investigation not a report — The results of an investigation under clause (1)(a), and any report created in the course of or for the purposes of the investigation, are not a report respecting occupational health and safety for the purposes of subsection 25(2).

2009, c. 23, s. 3; 2016, c. 2, Sched. 4, s. 3

32.0.8 Information and instruction, harassment — An employer shall provide a worker with,

(a) information and instruction that is appropriate for the worker on the contents of the policy and program with respect to workplace harassment; and

(b) any other prescribed information.

2016, c. 2, Sched. 4, s. 3

Part III.1 — Codes of Practice

32.1 Definition — In this Part,

"legal requirement" means a requirement imposed by a provision of this Act or by a regulation made under this Act.

2001, c. 9 Sched. I, s. 3(4); 2011, c. 11 s. 10

32.2 (1) Approval of code of practice — The Minister may approve a code of practice and the approved code of practice may be followed to comply with a legal requirement specified in the approval.

(1.1) Same — An approval made under subsection (1) may be subject to such terms and conditions as the Minister considers appropriate and may be general or particular in its application.

(2) Withdrawal of approval — The Minister may withdraw an approval under subsection (1).

(3) Part III (Regulations) of the — *Legislation Act, 2006* not to apply Part III (Regulations) of the *Legislation Act, 2006* does not apply with respect to an approval under this section or the withdrawal of such an approval.

(4) Delegation — The Minister may delegate the Minister's power under this section to the Deputy Minister.

2001, c. 9 Sch. I, s. 3(4); 2006, c. 21 Sch. F, s. 136(1), Table 1; 2011, c. 11 s. 11

32.3 (1) Publication of approval, etc. — An approval or a withdrawal of an approval under section 32.2 shall be published in *The Ontario Gazette*.

(2) Effect of publication — Publication of an approval or withdrawal of approval in *The Ontario Gazette*,

    (a) is, in the absence of evidence to the contrary, proof of the approval or withdrawal of approval; and

    (b) shall be deemed to be notice of the approval or withdrawal of approval to everyone affected by it.

(3) Judicial notice — Judicial notice shall be taken of an approval or withdrawal of approval published in *The Ontario Gazette*.

2001, c. 9 Sched. I, s. 3(4)

32.4 Effect of approved code of practice — The following apply if a code of practice is approved under section 32.2:

    1. Subject to any terms or conditions set out in the approval, compliance with the approved code of practice is deemed to be compliance with the legal requirement.

2. A failure to comply with the approved code of practice is not, in itself, a breach of the legal requirement.

3. [Repealed 2011, c. 11, s. 12.]

2001, c. 9 Sched. I, s. 3(4); 2011, c. 11 s. 12

Part IV — Toxic Substances

33. (1) Orders of Director — Where a biological, chemical or physical agent or combination of such agents is used or intended to be used in the workplace and its presence in the workplace or the manner of its use is in the opinion of a Director likely to endanger the health of a worker, the Director shall by notice in writing to the employer order that the use, intended use, presence or manner of use be,

(a) prohibit;

(b) limited or restricted in such manner as the Director specifies; or

(c) subject to such conditions regarding administrative control, work practices, engineering control and time limits for compliance as the Director specifies.

(2) Contents of order — Where a Director makes an order to an employer under subsection (1), the order shall,

(a) identify the biological, chemical or physical agent, or combination of such agents, and the manner of use that is the subject-matter of the order; and

(b) state the opinion of the Director as to the likelihood of the danger to the health of a worker, and the Director's reasons in respect thereof, including the matters or causes which give rise to his or her opinion.

(3) Posting of order — The employer shall provide a copy of an order made under subsection (1) to the committee, health and safety representative and trade union, if any, and shall cause a copy of the order to be posted in a conspicuous place in the workplace where it is most likely to come to the attention of the workers who may be affected by the use, presence or intended use of the biological, chemical or physical agent or combination of agents.

(4) Appeal to Minister — Where the employer, a worker or a trade union considers that he, she or it is aggrieved by an order made under subsection (1), the employer, worker or trade union may by notice in writing given within fourteen days of the making of the order appeal to the Minister.

(5) Delegation — The Minister may, having regard to the circumstances, direct that an appeal under subsection (4) be determined on his or her behalf by a person appointed by the Minister for that purpose.

(6) Procedure — The Minister or, where a person has been appointed under subsection (5), the person so appointed, may give such directions and issue such orders as he or she considers proper or necessary concerning the procedures to be adopted or followed and shall have all the powers of a chair of a board of arbitration under subsection 48(12) of the *Labour Relations Act, 1995*.

(7) Substitution of findings — On an appeal, the Minister or, where a person has been appointed under subsection (5), the person so appointed, may substitute his or her findings for those of the Director and may rescind or affirm the order appealed from or make a new order in substitution therefor and such order shall stand in the place of and have the like effect under this Act and the regulations as the order of the Director, and such order shall be final and not subject to appeal under this section.

(8) Matters to be considered — In making a decision or order under subsection (1) or (7), a Director, the Minister or, where a person has been appointed under subsection (5), the person so appointed shall consider as relevant factors,

    (a) the relation of the agent, combination of agents or by-product to a biological or chemical agent that is known to be a danger to health;

    (b) the quantities of the agent, combination of agents or by-product used or intended to be used or present;

    (c) the extent of exposure;

    (d) the availability of other processes, agents or equipment for use or intended use;

    (e) data regarding the effect of the process or agent on health; and

    (f) any criteria or guide with respect to the exposure of a worker to a biological, chemical or physical agent or combination of such agents that are adopted by a regulation.

(9) Suspension of order by Minister, etc., pending disposition of appeal — On an appeal under subsection (4), the Minister or, where a person has been appointed under subsection (5), the person so appointed may suspend the operation of the order appealed from pending the disposition of the appeal.

(10) Remuneration of appointee — A person appointed under subsection (5) shall be paid such remuneration and expenses as the Minister, with the approval of the Lieutenant Governor in Council, determines.

(11) Application — This section does not apply to designated substances.

(12) No hearing required prior to issuing order — A Director is not required to hold or afford to an employer or any other person an opportunity for a hearing before making an order under subsection (1).

2001, c. 9 Sched. I, s. 3(5)

34. (1) New biological or chemical agents — Except for purposes of research and development, no person shall,

    (a) manufacture;

    (b) distribute; or

    (c) supply,

for commercial or industrial use in a workplace any new biological or chemical agent unless the person first submits to a Director notice in writing of the person's intention to manufacture, distribute or supply such new agent and the notice shall include the ingredients of such new agent and their common or generic name or names and the composition and properties thereof.

(2) Report on assessment — Where in the opinion of the Director, which opinion shall be made promptly, the introduction of the new biological or chemical agent referred to in subsection (1) may endanger the health or safety of the workers in a workplace, the Director shall require the manufacturer, distributor or supplier, as the case may be, to provide, at the expense of the manufacturer, distributor or supplier, a report or assessment, made or to be made by a person possessing such special, expert or professional knowledge or qualifications as are specified by the Director, of the agent intended to be manufactured, distributed or supplied and the manner of use including the matters referred to in subclauses 54(1)(o)(i) to (vii).

(3) Interpretation — For the purpose of this section, a biological or chemical agent is not considered to be new if, before a person manufactures, distributes or supplies the agent, it was used in a workplace other than the person's workplace or it is included in an inventory compiled or adopted by the Minister.

35. Designation of substances — Prior to a substance being designated under paragraph 23 of subsection 70(2), the Minister,

> (a) shall publish in *The Ontario Gazette* a notice stating that the substance may be designated and calling for briefs or submissions in relation to the designation; and
>
> (b) shall publish in *The Ontario Gazette* a notice setting forth the proposed regulation relating to the designation of the substance at least sixty days before the regulation is filed with the Registrar of Regulations.

36. [Repealed 2001, c. 9, Sched. I, s. 3(7).]

37. (1) Hazardous material identification and data sheets — An employer,

> (a) shall ensure that all hazardous materials present in the workplace are identified in the prescribed manner;
>
> (b) shall obtain or prepare, as may be prescribed, a current safety data sheet for all hazardous materials present in the workplace; and
>
> (c) shall ensure that the identification required by clause (a) and safety data sheets required by clause (b) are available in English and such other languages as may be prescribed.

(2) Prohibition — No person shall remove or deface the identification described in clause (1)(a) for a hazardous material.

(3) Hazardous material not to be used — An employer shall ensure that a hazardous material is not used, handled or stored at a workplace unless the prescribed requirements concerning identification, safety data sheets and worker instruction and training are met.

(4) Notice to Director — An employer shall advise a Director in writing if the employer, after making reasonable efforts, is unable to obtain a label or safety data sheet required by subsection (1).

(5) [Repealed 2015, c. 27, Sched. 4, s. 2.]

38. (1) Material safety data sheets to be made available — Making safety data sheets available — A copy of every current safety data sheet required by this Part in respect of hazardous materials in a workplace shall be,

2015, c. 27, Sched. 4, s. 2 Sched. 4, s. 2

> (a) made available by the employer in the workplace in such a manner as to allow examination by the workers;

(b) furnished by the employer to the committee or health and safety representative, if any, for the workplace or to a worker selected by the workers to represent them, if there is no committee or health and safety representative;

(c) furnished by the employer on request or if so prescribed to the medical officer of health of the health unit in which the workplace is located;

(d) furnished by the employer on request or if so prescribed to the fire department which serves the location in which the workplace is located; and

(e) filed by the employer with a Director on request or if so prescribed.

(1.1) Additional requirement — In addition to complying with subsection (1), the employer shall make a copy of a safety data sheet readily available to those workers who may be exposed to the hazardous material to which it relates.

(2) Public access — The medical officer of health, at the request of any person, shall request an employer to furnish a copy of a current safety data sheet.

(3) Same — At the request of any person, the medical officer of health shall make available to the person for inspection a copy of any safety data sheet requested by the person and in the possession of the medical officer of health.

(4) Idem — A medical officer of health shall not disclose the name of any person who makes a request under subsection (2) or (3).

(5) Electronic format — For greater certainty, a copy of a safety data sheet in an electronic format is a copy for the purposes of this section.

(6) Requirement to consult — An employer shall consult with the committee and the health and safety representative, if any, on making safety data sheets available in the workplace or furnishing them as required by clauses (1)(a) and (b) and subsection (1.1).

 2001, c. 9 Sched. I, s. 3(8), (9); 2015, c. 27, Sched. 4, s. 3

39. (1) Assessment for hazardous materials — Where so prescribed, an employer shall assess all biological and chemical agents produced in the workplace for use therein to determine if they are hazardous materials.

(2) Assessments to be made available — The assessment required by subsection (1) shall be in writing and a copy of it shall be,

(a) made available by the employer in the workplace in such a manner as to allow examination by the workers;

(b) furnished by the employer to the committee or health and safety representative, if any, for the workplace or to a worker selected by the workers to represent them, if there is no committee or health and safety representative.

40. (1) Confidential business information — An employer may file a claim for an exemption from disclosing,

(a) information required under this Part in a label or safety data sheet; or

(b) the name of a toxicological study used by the employer to prepare a safety data sheet,

on the grounds that it is confidential business information.

(2) Idem — An application under subsection (1) shall be made only in respect of such types of confidential business information as may be prescribed.

(3) Determination of claim — A claim for an exemption made under subsection (1) shall be determined in accordance with the process set out in the *Hazardous Materials Information Review Act* (Canada).

(4) Appeal — The employer or any worker of the employer or any trade union representing the workers of the employer may, in accordance with the appeal process set out in the *Hazardous Materials Information Review Act* (Canada), appeal a determination made under subsection (3) and the appeal shall be determined in accordance with that process.

(5) [Repealed 2015, c. 27, Sched. 4, s. 4(3).]

(6) Effect of claim — Information that an employer considers to be confidential business information is exempt from disclosure from the time a claim is filed under subsection (1) until the claim is finally determined and for three years thereafter, if the claim is found to be valid.

(7) Effect of determination — A determination made under this section applies for the purposes of this Part.

(8) [Repealed 2015, c. 27, Sched. 4, s. 4(4).]

2001, c. 9 Sched. I, s. 3(10); 2015, c. 27, Sched. 4, s. 4

40.1 (1) Information privileged — Subject to subsection (2), all information obtained by an employee in the Ministry from a person acting under the authority of the *Hazardous Materials Information Review Act* (Canada) is privileged and no employee in the Ministry shall knowingly, without consent in writing of the Chief Screening Officer appointed under that Act,

    (a) communicate or allow to be communicated to any person any information obtained; or

    (b) allow any person to inspect or to have access to any part of a book, record, writing or other document containing any information obtained.

(2) Exception — An employee in the Ministry may communicate or allow to be communicated information described in subsection (1) or allow inspection of or access to any part of a book, record, writing or other document containing any such information to or by,

    (a) another employee in the Ministry for the purpose of administering or enforcing this Act; or

    (b) a physician or a medical professional prescribed under the *Hazardous Materials Information Review Act* (Canada) who requests that information for the purpose of making a medical diagnosis of, or rendering medical treatment to, a person in an emergency.

(3) Conditions — No person who obtains any information under subsection (2) shall knowingly disclose that information to any other person or knowingly allow any other person to have access to that information except as may be necessary for the purposes mentioned in that subsection.

(4) Non-disclosure prevails — Despite subsection 63(1), the requirements in this section that information received from a person acting under the authority of the *Hazardous Materials Information Review Act* (Canada) not be disclosed prevail over any other law.

    1992, c. 14 s. 2(1); 2006, c. 35 Sched. C, s. 93(3), (4); 2015, c. 27, Sched. 4, s. 5

41. (1) Hazardous physical agents — A person who distributes or supplies, directly or indirectly, or manufactures, produces or designs a thing for use in a workplace that causes, emits or produces a hazardous physical agent when the thing is in use or operation shall ensure that such information as may be prescribed is readily available respecting the hazardous physical agent and the proper use or operation of the thing.

(2) Duty of employer — Where an employer has a thing described in subsection (1) in the workplace, the employer shall ensure that the information referred to in that subsection has been obtained and is,

(a) made available in the workplace for workers who use or operate the thing or who are likely to be exposed to the hazardous physical agent; and

(b) furnished by the employer to the committee or health and safety representative, if any, for the workplace or a worker selected by the workers to represent them, if there is no committee or health and safety representative.

(3) Notices — An employer to whom subsection (2) applies shall post prominent notices identifying and warning of the hazardous physical agent in the part of the workplace in which the thing is used or operated or is to be used or operated.

(4) Idem — Notices required by subsection (3) shall contain such information as may be prescribed and shall be in English and such other language or languages as may be prescribed.

42. (1) Instruction and training — In addition to providing information and instruction to a worker as required by clause 25(2)(a), an employer shall ensure that a worker exposed or likely to be exposed to a hazardous material or to a hazardous physical agent receives, and that the worker participates in, such instruction and training as may be prescribed.

(2) Consultation — The instruction and training to be given under subsection (1) shall be developed and implemented by the employer in consultation with the committee or health and safety representative, if any, for the workplace.

(3) Review — An employer shall review, in consultation with the committee or health and safety representative, if any, for the workplace, the training and instruction provided to a worker and the worker's familiarity therewith at least annually.

(4) Idem — The review described in subsection (3) shall be held more frequently than annually, if,

(a) the employer, on the advice of the committee or health and safety representative, if any, for the workplace, determines that such reviews are necessary; or

(b) there is a change in circumstances that may affect the health or safety of a worker.

Part V — Right to Refuse or to Stop Work Where Health or Safety in Danger

43. (1) Application — This section does not apply to a worker described in subsection (2),

(a) when a circumstance described in clause (3)(a), (b), (b.1) or (c) is inherent in the worker's work or is a normal condition of the worker's employment; or

(b) when the worker's refusal to work would directly endanger the life, health or safety of another person.

(2) Idem — The worker referred to in subsection (1) is,

(a) a person employed in, or a member of, a police force to which the *Police Services Act* applies;

(b) a firefighter as defined in subsection 1(1) of the *Fire Protection and Prevention Act, 1997*;

(c) a person employed in the operation of,

(i) a correctional institution or facility,

(ii) a place of secure custody designated under section 24.1 of the *Young Offenders Act* (Canada), whether in accordance with section 88 of the *Youth Criminal Justice Act* (Canada) or otherwise,

(iii) a place of temporary detention under the *Youth Criminal Justice Act* (Canada), or

(iv) a similar institution, facility or place;

(d) a person employed in the operation of,

(i) a hospital, sanatorium, long-term care home, psychiatric institution, mental health centre or rehabilitation facility,

(ii) a residential group home or other facility for persons with behavioural or emotional problems or a physical, mental or developmental disability,

(iii) an ambulance service or a first aid clinic or station,

(iv) a laboratory operated by the Crown or licensed under the *Laboratory and Specimen Collection Centre Licensing Act*, or

(v) a laundry, food service, power plant or technical service or facility used in conjunction with an institution, facility or service described in subclause (i) to (iv).

(3) Refusal to work — A worker may refuse to work or do particular work where he or she has reason to believe that,

(a) any equipment, machine, device or thing the worker is to use or operate is likely to endanger himself, herself or another worker;

(b) the physical condition of the workplace or the part thereof in which he or she works or is to work is likely to endanger himself or herself;

(b.1) workplace violence is likely to endanger himself or herself; or

(c) any equipment, machine, device or thing he or she is to use or operate or the physical condition of the workplace or the part thereof in which he or she works or is to work is in contravention of this Act or the regulations and such contravention is likely to endanger himself, herself or another worker.

(4) Report of refusal to work — Upon refusing to work or do particular work, the worker shall promptly report the circumstances of the refusal to the worker's employer or supervisor who shall forthwith investigate the report in the presence of the worker and, if there is such, in the presence of one of,

(a) a committee member who represents workers, if any;

(b) a health and safety representative, if any; or

(c) a worker who because of knowledge, experience and training is selected by a trade union that represents the worker, or if there is no trade union, is selected by the workers to represent them, who shall be made available and who shall attend without delay.

(5) Worker to remain in safe place and available for investigation — Until the investigation is completed, the worker shall remain,

(a) in a safe place that is as near as reasonably possible to his or her work station; and

(b) available to the employer or supervisor for the purposes of the investigation.

(6) Refusal to work following investigation — Where, following the investigation or any steps taken to deal with the circumstances that caused the worker to refuse to work or do particular work, the worker has reasonable grounds to believe that,

> (a) the equipment, machine, device or thing that was the cause of the refusal to work or do particular work continues to be likely to endanger himself, herself or another worker;
>
> (b) the physical condition of the workplace or the part thereof in which he or she works continues to be likely to endanger himself or herself;
>
> (b.1) workplace violence continues to be likely to endanger himself or herself; or
>
> (c) any equipment, machine, device or thing he or she is to use or operate or the physical condition of the workplace or the part thereof in which he or she works or is to work is in contravention of this Act or the regulations and such contravention continues to be likely to endanger himself, herself or another worker, the worker may refuse to work or do the particular work and the employer or the worker or a person on behalf of the employer or worker shall cause an inspector to be notified thereof.

(7) Investigation by inspector — An inspector shall investigate the refusal to work in consultation with the employer or a person representing the employer, the worker, and if there is such, the person mentioned in clause (4)(a), (b) or (c).

(8) Decision of inspector — The inspector shall, following the investigation referred to in subsection (7), decide whether a circumstance described in clause (6)(a), (b), (b.1) or (c) is likely to endanger the worker or another person.

(9) Idem — The inspector shall give his or her decision, in writing, as soon as is practicable, to the employer, the worker, and, if there is such, the person mentioned in clause (4)(a), (b) or (c).

(10) Worker to remain in safe place and available for investigation — Pending the investigation and decision of the inspector, the worker shall remain, during the worker's normal working hours, in a safe place that is as near as reasonably possible to his or her work station and available to the inspector for the purposes of the investigation.

(10.1) Exception — Subsection (10) does not apply if the employer, subject to the provisions of a collective agreement, if any,

(a) assigns the worker reasonable alternative work during the worker's normal working hours; or

(b) subject to section 50, where an assignment of reasonable alternative work is not practicable, gives other directions to the worker.

(11) Duty to advise other workers — Pending the investigation and decision of the inspector, no worker shall be assigned to use or operate the equipment, machine, device or thing or to work in the workplace or in the part of the workplace being investigated unless, in the presence of a person described in subsection (12), the worker has been advised of the other worker's refusal and of his or her reasons for the refusal.

(12) Idem — The person referred to in subsection (11) must be,

(a) a committee member who represents workers and, if possible, who is a certified member;

(b) a health and safety representative; or

(c) a worker who because of his or her knowledge, experience and training is selected by the trade union that represents the worker or, if there is no trade union, by the workers to represent them.

(13) Entitlement to be paid — A person shall be deemed to be at work and the person's employer shall pay him or her at the regular or premium rate, as may be proper,

(a) for the time spent by the person carrying out the duties under subsections (4) and (7) of a person mentioned in clause (4)(a), (b) or (c); and

(b) for time spent by the person carrying out the duties under subsection (11) of a person described in subsection (12).

1997, c. 4 s. 84; 2001, c. 9 Sched. I, s. 3(11); 2001, c. 13 s. 22; 2006, c. 19 Sched. D, s. 14; 2007, c. 8 s. 221; 2009, c. 23 s. 4

44. (1) Definition — In sections 45 to 48, "dangerous circumstances" means a situation in which,

(a) a provision of this Act or the regulations is being contravened;

(b) the contravention poses a danger or a hazard to a worker; and

(c) the danger or hazard is such that any delay in controlling it may seriously endanger a worker.

(2) Non-application — Sections 45 to 49 do not apply to,

(a) a workplace at which workers described in clause 43(2)(a), (b) or (c) are employed; or

(b) a workplace at which workers described in clause 43(2)(d) are employed if a work stoppage would directly endanger the life, health or safety of another person.

45. (1) Bilateral work stoppage — A certified member who has reason to believe that dangerous circumstances exist at a workplace may request that a supervisor investigate the matter and the supervisor shall promptly do so in the presence of the certified member.

(2) Investigation by second certified member — The certified member may request that a second certified member representing the other workplace party investigate the matter if the first certified member has reason to believe that dangerous circumstances continue after the supervisor's investigation and remedial actions, if any.

(3) Idem — The second certified member shall promptly investigate the matter in the presence of the first certified member.

(4) Direction following investigation — If both certified members find that the dangerous circumstances exist, the certified members may direct the constructor or employer to stop the work or to stop the use of any part of a workplace or of any equipment, machine, device, article or thing.

(5) Constructor's or employer's duties — The constructor or employer shall immediately comply with the direction and shall ensure that compliance is effected in a way that does not endanger a person.

(6) Investigation by inspector — If the certified members do not agree whether dangerous circumstances exist, either certified member may request that an inspector investigate the matter and the inspector shall do so and provide the certified members with a written decision.

(7) Cancellation of direction — After taking steps to remedy the dangerous circumstances, the constructor or employer may request the certified members or an inspector to cancel the direction.

(8) Idem — The certified members who issued a direction may jointly cancel it or an inspector may cancel it.

(9) Delegation by certified member — In such circumstances as may be prescribed, a certified member who represents the constructor or employer shall designate a person to act under this section in his or her stead when the certified member is not available at the workplace.

46. (1) Declaration against constructor, etc. — A certified member at a workplace or an inspector who has reason to believe that the procedure for stopping work set out in section 45 will not be sufficient to protect a constructor's or employer's workers at the workplace from serious risk to their health or safety may apply to the Board for a declaration or recommendation described in subsection (5), or both.

(2) [Repealed 1998, c. 8, s. 53(2).]

(3) Minister a party — The Minister is entitled to be a party to a proceeding before the Board.

(4) Board procedure, etc. — Subsections 61(2) to (3.13) and subsection 61(8) apply, with necessary modifications, with respect to applications under this section.

(5) Declaration and recommendation — If the Board finds that the procedure for stopping work set out in section 45 will not be sufficient to protect the constructor's or employer's workers at the workplace from serious risk to their health or safety, the Board,

> (a) may issue a declaration that the constructor or employer is subject to the procedure for stopping work set out in section 47 for the period specified; and
>
> (b) may recommend to the Minister that an inspector be assigned to oversee the health and safety practices of the constructor or employer at the workplace on a full-time or part-time basis for a specified period.

(6) Criteria — In making a finding under subsection (5), the Board shall determine, using the prescribed criteria, whether the constructor or employer has demonstrated a failure to protect the health and safety of workers and shall consider such other matters as may be prescribed.

(7) Decision final — The decision of the Board on an application is final.

(8) Costs of inspector — The employer shall reimburse the Province of Ontario for the wages, benefits and expenses of an inspector assigned to the employer as recommended by the Board.

1998, c. 8 s. 53

47. (1) Unilateral work stoppage — This section applies, and section 45 does not apply, to a constructor or an employer,

> (a) against whom the Board has issued a declaration under section 46; or

(b) who advises the committee at a workplace in writing that the constructor or employer adopts the procedures set out in this section respecting work stoppages.

(2) Direction re work stoppage — A certified member may direct the constructor or employer to stop specified work or to stop the use of any part of a workplace or of any equipment, machine, device, article or thing if the certified member finds that dangerous circumstances exist.

(3) Constructor's or employer's duties — The constructor or employer shall immediately comply with the direction and shall ensure that compliance is effected in a way that does not endanger a person.

(4) Investigation by constructor, etc. — After complying with the direction, the constructor or employer shall promptly investigate the matter in the presence of the certified member.

(5) Investigation by inspector — If the certified member and the constructor or employer do not agree whether dangerous circumstances exist, the constructor or employer or the certified member may request that an inspector investigate the matter and the inspector shall do so and provide them with a written decision.

(6) Cancellation of direction — After taking steps to remedy the dangerous circumstances, the constructor or employer may request the certified member or an inspector to cancel the direction.

(7) Idem — The certified member who made the direction or an inspector may cancel it.

1998, c. 8 s. 54

48. (1) Entitlement to investigate — A certified member who receives a complaint that dangerous circumstances exist is entitled to investigate the complaint.

(2) Entitlement to be paid — The time spent by a certified member in exercising powers and carrying out duties under this section and sections 45 and 47 shall be deemed to be work time for which the member's employer shall pay the member at the regular or premium rate as may be proper.

49. (1) Complaint re direction to stop work — A constructor, an employer, a worker at the workplace or a representative of a trade union that represents workers at the workplace may file a complaint with the Board if he, she or it has reasonable grounds to believe that a certified member at the workplace recklessly or in bad faith exercised or failed to exercise a power under section 45 or 47.

(2) Limitation — A complaint must be filed not later than 30 days after the event to which the complaint relates.

(3) Minister a party — The Minister is entitled to be a party to a proceeding before the Board.

(3.1) Board procedure, etc. — Subsections 61(2) to (3.13) and subsection 61(8) apply, with necessary modifications, with respect to complaints under this section.

(4) Determination of complaint — The Board shall make a decision respecting the complaint and may make such order as it considers appropriate in the circumstances including an order decertifying a certified member.

(5) Decision final — The decision of the Board is final.

1998, c. 8 s. 55

Part VI — Reprisals by Employer Prohibited

50. (1) No discipline, dismissal, etc., by employer — No employer or person acting on behalf of an employer shall,

    (a) dismiss or threaten to dismiss a worker;

    (b) discipline or suspend or threaten to discipline or suspend a worker;

    (c) impose any penalty upon a worker; or

    (d) intimidate or coerce a worker, because the worker has acted in compliance with this Act or the regulations or an order made thereunder, has sought the enforcement of this Act or the regulations or has given evidence in a proceeding in respect of the enforcement of this Act or the regulations or in an inquest under the *Coroners Act*.

(2) Arbitration — Where a worker complains that an employer or person acting on behalf of an employer has contravened subsection (1), the worker may either have the matter dealt with by final and binding settlement by arbitration under a collective agreement, if any, or file a complaint with the Board in which case any rules governing the practice and procedure of the Board apply with all necessary modifications to the complaint.

(2.1) Referral by inspector — Where the circumstances warrant, an inspector may refer a matter to the Board if the following conditions are met:

    1. The worker has not had the matter dealt with by final and binding settlement by arbitration under a collective agreement or filed a complaint with the Board under subsection (2).

    2. The worker consents to the referral.

(2.2) Same — Any rules governing the practice and procedure of the Board apply with all necessary modifications to a referral made under subsection (2.1).

(2.3) Referral not an order — A referral made under subsection (2.1) is not an order or decision for the purposes of section 61.

(3) Inquiry by Board — The Board may inquire into any complaint filed under subsection (2) or referral made under subsection (2.1) and section 96 of the *Labour Relations Act, 1995*, except subsection (5), applies with all necessary modifications as if such section, except subsection (5), is enacted in and forms part of this Act.

(4) Same — On an inquiry by the Board into a complaint filed under subsection (2) or a referral made under subsection (2.1), sections 110, 114 and 116 of the *Labour Relations Act, 1995* apply with all necessary modifications.

(4.1) Rules to expedite proceedings — The chair of the Board may make rules under subsection 110(18) of the *Labour Relations Act, 1995* to expedite proceedings relating to a complaint filed under subsection (2) or a referral made under subsection (2.1).

(4.2) Same — Subsections 110(19), (20), (21) and (22) of the *Labour Relations Act, 1995* apply, with necessary modifications, to rules made under subsection (4.1).

(5) Onus of proof — On an inquiry by the Board into a complaint filed under subsection (2) or a referral made under subsection (2.1), the burden of proof that an employer or person acting on behalf of an employer did not act contrary to subsection (1) lies upon the employer or the person acting on behalf of the employer.

(6) Jurisdiction when complaint by public servant — The Board shall exercise jurisdiction under this section when a complaint filed under subsection (2) or a referral made under subsection (2.1) is in respect of a worker who is a public servant within the meaning of the *Public Service of Ontario Act, 2006*.

(7) Board may substitute penalty — Where on an inquiry by the Board into a complaint filed under subsection (2) or a referral made under subsection (2.1), the Board determines that a worker has been discharged or otherwise disciplined by an employer or the collective agreement, as the case may be, does not contain a specific penalty for the infraction, the Board may substitute such other penalty for the discharge or discipline as to the Board seems just and reasonable in all the circumstances.

(8) Exception — Despite subsections (2) and (2.1), a person who is subject to a rule or code of discipline under the *Police Services Act* shall have his or her complaint in relation to an alleged contravention of subsection (1) dealt with under that Act.

1992, c. 21 s. 63; 1995, c. 1 s. 84; 1998, c. 8 s. 56; 2006, c. 35 Sched. C, s. 93(5); 2011, c. 11 s. 13

50.1 (1) Offices of the Worker and Employer Advisers — Office of the Worker Adviser — In addition to the functions set out in section 176 of the *Workplace Safety and Insurance Act, 1997*, the Office of the Worker Adviser has the functions prescribed for the purposes of this Part, with respect to workers who are not members of a trade union.

(2) Office of the Employer Adviser — In addition to the functions set out in the section 176 of the *Workplace Safety and Insurance Act, 1997*, the Office of the Employer Adviser has the functions prescribed for the purposes of this Part, with respect to employers that have fewer than 100 employees or such other number as may be prescribed.

(3) Costs — In determining the amount of the costs that may be incurred by each office under subsection 176(3) of the *Workplace Safety and Insurance Act, 1997*, the Minister shall take into account any functions prescribed for the purposes of this Part.

2011, c. 11 s. 14

Part VII — Notices

51. (1) Notice of death or injury — Where a person is killed or critically injured from any cause at a workplace, the constructor, if any, and the employer shall notify an inspector, and the committee, health and safety representative and trade union, if any, immediately of the occurrence by telephone or other direct means and the employer shall, within forty-eight hours after the occurrence, send to a Director a written report of the circumstances of the occurrence containing such information and particulars as the regulations prescribe.

(2) Preservation of wreckage — Where a person is killed or is critically injured at a workplace, no person shall, except for the purpose of,

    (a) saving life or relieving human suffering;

    (b) maintaining an essential public utility service or a public transportation system; or

    (c) preventing unnecessary damage to equipment or other property,

interfere with, disturb, destroy, alter or carry away any wreckage, article or thing at the scene of or connected with the occurrence until permission so to do has been given by an inspector.

2011, c. 1 Sched. 7, s. 2(7)

52. (1) Notice of accident, explosion, fire or violence causing injury — If a person is disabled from performing his or her usual work or requires medical attention because of an accident, explosion, fire or incident of workplace violence at a workplace, but no person dies or is critically injured because of that occurrence, the employer shall, within four days of the occurrence, give written notice of the occurrence containing the prescribed information and particulars to the following:

    1. The committee, the health and safety representative and the trade union, if any.

    2. The Director, if an inspector requires notification of the Director.

(2) Notice of occupational illness — If an employer is advised by or on behalf of a worker that the worker has an occupational illness or that a claim in respect of an occupational illness has been filed with the Workplace Safety and Insurance Board by or on behalf of the worker, the employer shall give notice in writing, within four days of being so advised, to a Director, to the committee or a health and safety representative and to the trade union, if any, containing such information and particulars as are prescribed.

(3) Idem — Subsection (2) applies with all necessary modifications if an employer is advised by or on behalf of a former worker that the worker has or had an occupational illness or that a claim in respect of an occupational illness has been filed with the Workplace Safety and Insurance Board by or on behalf of the worker.

1997, c. 16 s. 2(12), (13); 2001, c. 9 Sched. I, s. 3(12); 2009, c. 23 s. 5

53. (1) Accident, etc., at project site or mine — If an accident, premature or unexpected explosion, fire, flood or inrush of water, failure of any equipment, machine, device, article or thing, cave-in, subsidence, rockburst, or other prescribed incident occurs at a project site, mine, mining plant or other prescribed location, the person determined under subsection,

(2) shall within two days after the occurrence, give notice in writing with the prescribed information and particulars,

    (a) to the committee, health and safety representative and trade union, if any; and

    (b) to a Director, unless a report under section 51 or a notice under section 52 has already been given to a Director.

(2) Person required to notify — The person required to give notice under subsection (1) is,

    (a) if the incident takes place at a project site, the constructor of the project;

    (b) if the incident occurs at a mine or a mining plant, the employer of a worker who works in the mine or plant; or

    (c) if the incident occurs at a prescribed location, the person prescribed for that location.

                  2011, c. 1, Sched. 7, s. 2(8); 2017, c. 34, Sched. 30, s. 2

53.1 Additional notices — In addition to the notice requirements set out in sections 51, 52 and 53, the regulations may specify additional notice requirements that must be met in the circumstances described in those sections, including specifying who is required to provide the notice, the timeframe in which it shall be provided and the information and particulars it must contain.

                    2017, c. 34,   Sched. 30, s. 3

Part VIII — Enforcement

54. (1) Powers of inspector — An inspector may, for the purposes of carrying out his or her duties and powers under this Act and the regulations,

(a) subject to subsection (2), enter in or upon any workplace at any time without warrant or notice;

(b) take up or use any machine, device, article, thing, material or biological, chemical or physical agent or part thereof;

(c) require the production of any drawings, specifications, licence, document, record or report, and inspect, examine and copy the same;

(d) upon giving a receipt therefor, remove any drawings, specifications, licence, document, record or report inspected or examined for the purpose of making copies thereof or extracts therefrom, and upon making copies thereof or extracts therefrom, shall promptly return the same to the person who produced or furnished them;

(e) conduct or take tests of any equipment, machine, device, article, thing, material or biological, chemical or physical agent in or about a workplace and for such purposes, take and carry away such samples as may be necessary;

(f) require in writing an employer to cause any tests described in clause (e) to be conducted or taken, at the expense of the employer, by a person possessing such special expert or professional knowledge or qualifications as are specified by the inspector and to provide, at the expense of the employer, a report or assessment by that person;

(g) in any inspection, examination, inquiry or test, be accompanied and assisted by or take with him or her any person or persons having special, expert or professional knowledge of any matter, take photographs, and take with him or her and use any equipment or materials required for such purpose;

(h) make inquiries of any person who is or was in a workplace either separate and apart from another person or in the presence of any other person that are or may be relevant to an inspection, examination, inquiry or test;

(i) require that a workplace or part thereof not be disturbed for a reasonable period of time for the purposes of carrying out an examination, investigation or test;

(j) require that any equipment, machine, device, article, thing or process be operated or set in motion or that a system or procedure be carried out that may be relevant to an examination, inquiry or test;

(k) require in writing an employer to have equipment, machinery or devices tested, at the expense of the employer, by a professional engineer and to provide, at the expense of the employer, a report bearing the seal and signature of the professional engineer stating that the equipment, machine or device is not likely to endanger a worker;

(l) require in writing that any equipment, machinery or device not be used pending testing described in clause (k);

(m) require in writing an owner, constructor or employer to provide, at the expense of the owner, constructor or employer, a report bearing the seal and signature of a professional engineer stating,

(i) the load limits of a building, structure, or any part thereof, or any other part of a workplace, whether temporary or permanent,

(ii) that a building, structure, or any part thereof, or any other part of a workplace, whether temporary or permanent, is capable of supporting or withstanding the loads being applied to it or likely to be applied to it, or

(iii) that a building, structure, or any part thereof, or any other part of a workplace, whether temporary or permanent, is capable of supporting any loads that may be applied to it,

(A) as determined by the applicable design requirements established under the version of the *Building Code* that was in force at the time of its construction,

(B) in accordance with such other requirements as may be prescribed, or

(C) in accordance with good engineering practice, if sub-subclauses (A) and (B) do not apply;

(n) require in writing an owner of a mine or part thereof to provide, at the owner's expense, a report in writing bearing the seal and signature of a professional engineer stating that the ground stability of, the mining methods and the support or rock reinforcement used in the mine or part thereof is such that a worker is not likely to be endangered;

(o) require in writing, within such time as is specified, a person who is an employer, manufacturer, producer, importer, distributor or supplier to produce records or information, or to provide, at the expense of the person, a report or evaluation made or to be made by a person or organization having special, expert or professional knowledge or qualifications as are specified by the inspector of any process or biological, chemical or physical agents or combination of such agents present, used or intended for use in a workplace and the manner of use, including,

(i) the ingredients thereof and their common or generic name or names,

(ii) the composition and the properties thereof,

(iii) the toxicological effect thereof,

(iv) the effect of exposure thereto whether by contact, inhalation or ingestion,

(v) the protective measures used or to be used in respect thereof,

(vi) the emergency measures used or to be used to deal with exposure in respect thereof, and

(vii) the effect of the use, transport and disposal thereof; and

(p) require the production of any materials concerning the content, frequency and manner of instruction of any training program and inspect, examine and copy the materials and attend any such program.

(2) Entry to dwellings — An inspector may only enter a dwelling or that part of a dwelling actually being used as a workplace with the consent of the occupier or under the authority of a warrant issued under this Act or the *Provincial Offences Act*.

(3) Representative to accompany inspector — Where an inspector makes an inspection of a workplace under the powers conferred upon him or her under subsection (1), the constructor, employer or group of employers shall afford a committee member representing workers or a health and safety representative, if any, or a worker selected by a trade union or trade unions, if any, because of knowledge, experience and training, to represent it or them and, where there is no trade union, a worker selected by the workers because of knowledge, training and experience to represent them, the opportunity to accompany the inspector during his or her physical inspection of a workplace, or any part or parts thereof.

(4) Consultation with workers — Where there is no committee member representing workers, no health and safety representative or worker selected under subsection (3), the inspector shall endeavour to consult during his or her physical inspection with a reasonable number of the workers concerning matters of health and safety at their work.

(5) Entitlement to time from work — The time spent by a committee member representing workers, a health and safety representative or a worker selected in accordance with subsection (3) in accompanying an inspector during his or her physical inspection, shall be deemed to be work time for which he or she shall be paid by his or her employer at his or her regular or premium rate as may be proper.

2001, c. 26 s. 1; 2011, c. 11 s. 15

55. Order for inspections — Subject to subsections 8(6) and 9(26), an inspector may in writing direct a health and safety representative or a member designated under subsection 9(23) to inspect the physical condition of all or part of a workplace at specified intervals.

2009, c. 33 Sched. 20, s. 3(2)

55.1 Order for written policies — In the case of a workplace at which the number of workers regularly employed is five or fewer, an inspector may in writing order that the policies with respect to workplace violence and workplace harassment required under section 32.0.1 be in written form and posted at a conspicuous place in the workplace.

2009, c. 23 s. 6; 2011, c. 1 Sched. 7, s. 2(9)

55.2 Order for written assessment, etc. — An inspector may in writing order that the following be in written form:

    1. The assessment of the risks of workplace violence required under subsection 32.0.3(1).

    2. A reassessment required under subsection 32.0.3(4).

2009, c. 23 s. 6

55.3 (1) Order for workplace harassment investigation — An inspector may in writing order an employer to cause an investigation described in clause 32.0.7(1)(a) to be conducted, at the expense of the employer, by an impartial person possessing such knowledge, experience or qualifications as are specified by the inspector and to obtain, at the expense of the employer, a written report by that person.

(2) Report — A report described in subsection (1) is not a report respecting occupational health and safety for the purposes of subsection 25(2).

2016, c. 2, Sched. 4, s. 4

56. (1) Warrants—investigative techniques, etc. — On application without notice, a justice of the peace or a provincial judge may issue a warrant authorizing an inspector, subject to this section, to use any investigative technique or procedure or to do any thing described in the warrant if the justice of the peace or provincial judge, as the case may be, is satisfied by information under oath that there are reasonable grounds to believe that an offence against this Act or the regulations has been or is being committed and that information and other evidence concerning the offence will be obtained through the use of the technique or procedure or the doing of the thing.

(1.1) Expert help — The warrant may authorize persons who have special, expert or professional knowledge to accompany and assist the inspector in the execution of the warrant.

(1.2) Terms and conditions of warrant — The warrant shall authorize the inspector to enter and search the place for which the warrant was issued and, without limiting the powers of the justice of the peace or the provincial judge under subsection (1), the warrant may, in respect of the alleged offence, authorize the inspector to,

(a) seize or examine and copy any drawings, specifications, licence, document, record or report;

(b) seize or examine any equipment, machine, device, article, thing, material or biological, chemical or physical agent;

(c) require a person to produce any item described in clause (a) or (b);

(d) conduct or take tests of any equipment, machine, device, article, thing, material or biological, chemical or physical agent, and take and carry away samples from the testing;

(e) take measurements of and record by any means the physical circumstances of the workplace; and

(f) make inquiries of any person either separate and apart from another person or in the presence of any other person.

(1.3) Duration — The warrant is valid for 30 days or for such shorter period as may be specified in it.

(1.4) Other terms and conditions — The warrant may contain terms and conditions in addition to those provided for in subsections (1) to (1.3) as the justice of the peace or provincial judge, as the case may be, considers advisable in the circumstances.

(1.5) Further warrants — A justice of the peace or provincial judge may issue further warrants under subsection (1).

(1.6) Powers, duties not restricted — Nothing in this section restricts any power or duty of an inspector under this Act or the regulations.

(2) Possession — The inspector may remove the thing seized under a warrant from the place from which it was seized or may detain it in that place.

(3) Notice of receipt — The inspector shall inform the person from whom the thing is seized as to the reason for the seizure and shall give the person a receipt for it.

(4) Report to justice — The inspector shall bring a thing seized under the authority of this section before a provincial judge or justice of the peace or, if that is not reasonably possible, shall report the seizure to a provincial judge or justice of the peace.

(5) Procedure — Sections 159 and 160 of the *Provincial Offences Act* apply with necessary modifications in respect of a thing seized under the authority of this section.

2001, c. 26 s. 2

56.1 (1) Power of inspector to seize — An inspector who executes a warrant issued under section 56 may seize or examine and copy any drawings, specifications, licence, document, record or report or seize or examine any equipment, machine, device, article, thing, material or biological, chemical or physical agent, in addition to those mentioned in the warrant, that he or she believes on reasonable grounds will afford evidence in respect of an offence under this Act or the regulations.

(2) Searches in exigent circumstances — Although a warrant issued under section 56 would otherwise be required, an inspector may exercise any of the powers described in subsection 56(1) without a warrant if the conditions for obtaining the warrant exist but by reason of exigent circumstances it would be impracticable to obtain the warrant.

(3) Report to justice, etc. — Subsections 56(3), (4) and (5) apply with necessary modifications to a thing seized under this section.

2001, c. 26 s. 3

57. (1) Orders by inspectors where non-compliance — Where an inspector finds that a provision of this Act or the regulations is being contravened, the inspector may order, orally or in writing, the owner, constructor, licensee, employer, or person whom he or she believes to be in charge of a workplace or the person whom the inspector believes to be the contravener to comply with the provision and may require the order to be carried out forthwith or within such period of time as the inspector specifies.

(2) Idem — Where an inspector makes an oral order under subsection (1), the inspector shall confirm the order in writing before leaving the workplace.

(3) Contents of order — An order made under subsection (1) shall indicate generally the nature of the contravention and where appropriate the location of the contravention.

(4) Compliance plan — An order made under subsection (1) may require a constructor, a licensee or an employer to submit to the Ministry a compliance plan prepared in the manner and including such items as required by the order.

(5) Idem — The compliance plan shall specify what the constructor, licensee or employer plans to do to comply with the order and when the constructor, licensee or employer intends to achieve compliance.

(6) Orders by inspector where worker endangered — Where an inspector makes an order under subsection (1) and finds that the contravention of this Act or the regulations is a danger or hazard to the health or safety of a worker, the inspector may,

(a) order that any place, equipment, machine, device, article or thing or any process or material shall not be used until the order is complied with;

(b) order that the work at the workplace as indicated in the order shall stop until the order to stop work is withdrawn or cancelled by an inspector after an inspection;

(c) order that the workplace where the contravention exists be cleared of workers and isolated by barricades, fencing or any other means suitable to prevent access thereto by a worker until the danger or hazard to the health or safety of a worker is removed.

(7) Resumption of work pending inspection — Despite clause (6)(b), a constructor, a licensee or an employer who gives notice to an inspector of compliance with an order made under subsection (6) may resume work pending an inspection and decision by an inspector respecting compliance with the order if, before the resumption of work, a committee member representing workers or a health and safety representative, as the case may be, advises an inspector that in his or her opinion the order has been complied with.

(8) Additional orders — In addition to the orders that may be made under subsection (6), where an inspector makes an order under subsection (1) for a contravention of section 37 or 41 or a Director has been advised of an employer's inability to obtain a current safety data sheet, the inspector may order that the hazardous material shall not be used or that the thing that causes, emits or produces the hazardous physical agent not be used or operated until the order is withdrawn or cancelled.

(9) Posting of notice — Where an inspector makes an order under this section, he or she may affix to the workplace, or to any equipment, machine, device, article or thing, a copy thereof or a notice of the order, in a form obtained from the Ministry and no person, except an inspector, shall remove such copy or notice unless authorized to do so by an inspector.

(10) Same — Where an inspector makes an order in writing or issues a report of his or her inspection to an owner, constructor, licensee, employer or person in charge of the workplace,

(a) the owner, constructor, licensee, employer or person in charge of the workplace shall forthwith cause a copy or copies of it to be posted in a conspicuous place or places at the workplace where it is most likely to come to the attention of the workers and shall furnish a copy of the order or report to the health and safety representative and the committee, if any; and

(b) if the order or report resulted from a complaint of a contravention of this Act or the regulations and the person who made the complaint requests a copy of it, the inspector shall cause a copy of it to be furnished to that person.

(11) No hearing required prior to making order — An inspector is not required to hold or afford to an owner, constructor, licensee, employer or any other person an opportunity for a hearing before making an order.

2001, c. 9 Sched. I, s. 3(13); 2011, c. 1 Sched. 7, s. 2(10); 2015, c. 27,
Sched. 4, s. 6

58. Entry into barricaded area — Where an order is made under clause 57(6)(c), no owner, constructor, employer or supervisor shall require or permit a worker to enter the workplace except for the purpose of doing work that is necessary or required to remove the danger or hazard and only where the worker is protected from the danger or hazard.

59. (1) Notice of compliance — Within three days after a constructor or employer who has received an order under section 57 believes that compliance with the order has been achieved, the constructor or employer shall submit to the Ministry a notice of compliance.

(2) Idem — The notice shall be signed by the constructor or employer and shall be accompanied by,

> (a) a statement of agreement or disagreement with the contents of the notice, signed by a member of the committee representing workers or by a health and safety representative, as the case may be; or
>
> (b) a statement that the member or representative has declined to sign the statement referred to in clause (a).

(3) Idem — The constructor or employer shall post the notice and the order issued under section 57 for a period of fourteen days following its submission to the Ministry in a place or places in the workplace where it is most likely to come to the attention of workers.

(4) Compliance achieved — Despite the submission of a notice compliance, a constructor or employer achieves compliance with an order under section 57 when an inspector determines that compliance has been achieved.

60. Injunction proceedings — In addition to any other remedy or penalty therefor, where an order made under subsection 57(6) is contravened, such contravention may be restrained upon an application made without notice to a judge of the Superior Court of Justice made at the instance of a Director.

2001, c. 9 Sched. I, s. 3(14)

61. (1) Appeals from order of an inspector — Any employer, constructor, licensee, owner, worker or trade union which considers himself, herself or itself aggrieved by any order made by an inspector under this

Act or the regulations may appeal to the Board within 30 days after the making of the order.

(2) Parties — The following are parties to the appeal:

1. The appellant.

2. In the case of an appeal by an employer, the employer's workers and each trade union representing any of the workers.

3. In the case of an appeal by a worker or trade union representing a worker, the worker's employer.

4. A Director.

5. Such other persons as the Board may specify.

(3) Inquiry by labour relations officer — The Board may authorize a labour relations officer to inquire into an appeal.

(3.1) Same — The labour relations officer shall forthwith inquire into the appeal and endeavour to effect a settlement of the matters raised in the appeal.

(3.2) Report to Board — The labour relations officer shall report the results of his or her inquiry and endeavours to the Board.

(3.3) Hearings — Subject to the rules made under subsection (3.8), the Board shall hold a hearing to consider the appeal unless the Board makes an order under subsection (3.4).

(3.4) Orders after consultation — The Board may make any interim or final order it considers appropriate after consulting with the parties.

(3.5) Same — The *Statutory Powers Procedure Act* does not apply with respect to a consultation the Board makes under subsection (3.4).

(3.6) Practice and procedure — The Board shall determine its own practice and procedure but shall give full opportunity to the parties to present their evidence and to make their submissions.

(3.7) Rules of practice — The chair may make rules governing the Board's practice and procedure and the exercise of its powers, and prescribing such forms as the chair considers advisable.

(3.8) Expedited appeals — The chair of the Board may make rules to expedite appeals and such rules,

(a) may provide that the Board is not required to hold a hearing; and

(b) may limit the extent to which the Board is required to give full opportunity to the parties to present their evidence and to make their submissions.

(3.9) Effective date of rules — Rules make under subsection (3.8) come into force on such dates as the Lieutenant Governor in Council may by order determine.

(3.10) Conflict with — *Statutory Powers Procedure Act* Rules made under this section apply despite anything in the *Statutory Powers Procedure Act*.

(3.11) Rules not regulations — Rules made under this section are not regulations within the meaning of Part III (Regulations) of the *Legislation Act, 2006*.

(3.12) Quorum — The chair or a vice-chair of the Board constitutes a quorum for the purposes of this section and is sufficient for the exercise of the jurisdiction and powers of the Board under this section.

(3.13) Entering premises — For the purposes of an appeal under this section, the Board may enter any premises where work is being or has been done by workers or in which the employer carries on business, whether or not the premises are those of the employer, and inspect and view any work, material, machinery, appliance or article therein, and interrogate any person respecting any matter and post therein any notice that the Board considers necessary to bring to the attention of persons having an interest in the appeal.

(4) Powers of the Board — On an appeal under this section, the Board may substitute its findings for those of the inspector who made the order appealed from and may rescind or affirm the order or make a new order in substitution therefor, and for such purpose has all the powers of an inspector and the order of the Board shall stand in the place of and have the like effect under this Act and the regulations as the order of the inspector.

(5) Order, extended meaning — In this section, an order of an inspector under this Act or the regulations includes any order or decision made or given or the imposition of any terms or conditions therein by an inspector under the authority of this Act or the regulations or the refusal to make an order or decision by an inspector.

(6) Decision of Board final — A decision of the Board under this section is final.

(7) Suspension of order by Board pending disposition of appeal — On an appeal under subsection (1), the Board may suspend the operation of the order appealed from pending the disposition of the appeal.

(8) Reconsideration — The Board may at any time, if it considers it advisable to do so, reconsider any decision, order, direction, declaration or ruling made by it under this section and may vary or revoke any such decision, order, direction, declaration or ruling.

   1998, c. 8 s. 57; 2006, c. 21 Sched. F, s. 136(1), Table 1; 2011, c. 1 Sched. 7, s. 2(11)

62. (1) Obstruction of inspector — No person shall hinder, obstruct, molest or interfere with or attempt to hinder, obstruct, molest or interfere with an inspector in the exercise of a power or the performance of a duty under this Act or the regulations or in the execution of a warrant issued under this Act or the *Provincial Offences Act* with respect to a matter under this Act or the regulations.

(2) Assistance — Every person shall furnish all necessary means in the person's power to facilitate any entry, search, inspection, investigation, examination, testing or inquiry by an inspector,

    (a) in the exercise of his or her powers or the performance of his or her duties under this Act or the regulations; or

    (b) in the execution of a warrant issued under this Act or the *Provincial Offences Act* with respect to a matter under this Act or the regulations.

(3) False information, etc. — No person shall knowingly furnish an inspector with false information or neglect or refuse to furnish information required by an inspector,

    (a) in the exercise of his or her powers or the performance of his or her duties under this Act or the regulations; or

    (b) in the execution of a warrant issued under this Act or the *Provincial Offences Act* with respect to a matter under this Act or the regulations.

(4) Monitoring devices — No person shall interfere with any monitoring equipment or device in a workplace.

(5) Obstruction of committee, etc. — No person shall knowingly,

    (a) hinder or interfere with a committee, a committee member or a health and safety representative in the exercise of a power or performance of a duty under this Act;

(b) furnish a committee, a committee member or a health and safety representative with false information in the exercise of a power or performance of a duty under this Act; or

(c) hinder or interfere with a worker selected by a trade union or trade unions or a worker selected by the workers to represent them in the exercise of a power or performance of a duty under this Act.

2001, c. 26 s. 4

63. (1) Information confidential — Except for the purposes of this Act and the regulations or as required by law,

(a) an inspector, a person accompanying an inspector or a person who, at the request of an inspector, makes an examination, test or inquiry, shall not publish, disclose or communicate to any person any information, material, statement, report or result of any examination, test or inquiry acquired, furnished, obtained, made or received under the powers conferred under this Act or the regulations;

(b) [Repealed 1992, c. 14, s. 2(2).]

(c) no person shall publish, disclose or communicate to any person any secret manufacturing process or trade secret acquired, furnished, obtained, made or received under the provisions of this Act or the regulations;

(d) [Repealed 1992, c. 14, s. 2(3).]

(e) no person to whom information is communicated under this Act and the regulations shall divulge the name of the informant to any person; and

(f) no person shall disclose any information obtained in any medical examination, test or x-ray of a worker made or taken under this Act except in a form calculated to prevent the information from being identified with a particular person or case.

(2) Employer access to health records — No employer shall seek to gain access, except by an order of the court or other tribunal or in order to comply with another statute, to a health record concerning a worker without the worker's written consent.

(3) Compellability, civil suit — An inspector or a person who, at the request of an inspector, accompanies an inspector, or a person who makes an examination, test, inquiry or takes samples at the request of an inspector, is not a compellable witness in a civil suit or any proceeding, except an inquest under the *Coroners Act*, respecting any information, material, statement or test acquired, furnished, obtained, made or received under this Act or the regulations.

(3.1) Compellability of witnesses — Persons employed in the Office of the Worker Adviser or the Office of the Employer Adviser are not compellable witnesses in a civil suit or any proceeding respecting any information or material furnished to or obtained, made or received by them under this Act while acting within the scope of their employment.

(3.2) Exception — If the Office of the Worker Adviser or the Office of the Employer Adviser is a party to a proceeding, a person employed in the relevant Office may be determined to be a compellable witness.

(3.3) Production of documents — Persons employed in the Office of the Worker Adviser or the Office of the Employer Adviser are not required to produce, in a proceeding in which the relevant Office is not a party, any information or material furnished to or obtained, made or received by them under this Act while acting within the scope of their employment.

(4) Power of Director to disclose — A Director may communicate or allow to be communicated or disclosed information, material, statements or the result of a test acquired, furnished, obtained, made or received under this Act or the regulations.

(5) Medical emergencies — Subsection (1) does not apply so as to prevent any person from providing any information in the possession of the person, including confidential business information, in a medical emergency for the purpose of diagnosis or treatment.

(6) Conflict — This section prevails despite anything to the contrary in the *Personal Health Information Protection Act, 2004*.

1992, c. 14 s. 2(2), (3); 2004, c. 3 Sched. A, s. 93; 2011, c. 11 s. 16

64. Copies of reports — A Director may, upon receipt of a request in writing from the owner of a workplace who has entered into an agreement to sell the same and upon payment of the fee or fees prescribed, furnish to the owner or a person designated by the owner copies of reports or orders of an inspector made under this Act in respect of the workplace as to its compliance with subsection 29(1).

65. (1) Immunity — No action or other proceeding for damages, prohibition or mandamus shall be instituted respecting any act done in good faith in the execution or intended execution of a person's duties under this Act or in the exercise or intended exercise of a person's powers under this

Act or for any alleged neglect or default in the execution or performance in good faith of the person's duties or powers if the person is,

(a) an employee in the Ministry or a person who acts as an advisor for the Ministry;

(b) an employee in the Office of the Worker Adviser or the Office of the Employer Adviser;

(c) the Board or a labour relations officer;

(d) a health and safety representative or a committee member; or

(e) a worker selected by a trade union or trade unions or by workers to represent them.

(f) [Repealed 1997, c. 16, s. 2(15).]

(2) **Liability of Crown** — Subsection (1) does not, by reason of subsections 5(2) and (4) of the *Proceedings Against the Crown Act*, relieve the Crown of liability in respect of a tort committed by a Director, the Chief Prevention Officer, an inspector or an engineer of the Ministry to which it would otherwise be subject and the Crown is liable under that Act for any such tort in a like manner as if subsection (1) had not been enacted.

1995, c. 5 s. 32; 1997, c. 16 s. 2(14), (15); 1998, c. 8 s. 58; 2006, c. 35 Sched. C, s. 93(6); 2011, c. 11 s. 17

Part IX — Offences and Penalties

66. (1) Penalties — Every person who contravenes or fails to comply with,

(a) a provision of this Act or the regulations;

(b) an order or requirement of an inspector or a Director; or

(c) an order of the Minister,

is guilty of an offence and on conviction is liable to a fine of not more than $100,000 or to imprisonment for a term of not more than twelve months, or to both.

(2) **Idem** — If a corporation is convicted of an offence under subsection (1), the maximum fine that may be imposed upon the corporation is $1,500,000 and not as provided therein.

(3) **Defence** — On a prosecution for a failure to comply with,

(a) subsection 23(1);

(b) clause 25(1)(b), (c) or (d); or

(c) subsection 27(1), it shall be a defence for the accused to prove that every precaution reasonable in the circumstances was taken.

(4) Accused liable for acts or neglect of managers, agents, etc. — In a prosecution of an offence under any provision of this Act, any act or neglect on the part of any manager, agent, representative, officer, director or supervisor of the accused, whether a corporation or not, shall be the act or neglect of the accused.

2017, c. 34,　Sched. 30, s. 4

67. (1) Certified copies of documents, etc., as evidence — In any proceeding or prosecution under this Act,

(a) a copy of an order or decision purporting to have been made under this Act or the regulations and purporting to have been signed by the Minister or an inspector;

(b) a document purporting to be a copy of a notice, drawing, record or other document, or any extract therefrom given or made under this Act or the regulations and purporting to be certified by an inspector;

(c) a document purporting to certify the result of a test or an analysis of a sample of air and setting forth the concentration or amount of a biological, chemical or physical agent in a workplace or part thereof and purporting to be certified by an inspector; or

(d) a document purporting to certify the result of a test or an analysis of any equipment, machine, device, article, thing or substance and purporting to be certified by an inspector,

is evidence of the order, decision, writing or document, and the facts appearing in the order, decision, writing or document without proof of the signature or official character of the person appearing to have signed the order or the certificate and without further proof.

(2) Service of orders and decisions — In any proceeding or prosecution under this Act, a copy of an order or decision purporting to have been made under this Act or the regulations and purporting to have been signed by the Minister, a Director or an inspector may be served,

(a) personally in the case of an individual or in case of a partnership upon a partner, and in the case of a corporation, upon the president, vice-president, secretary, treasurer or a director, or upon the manager or person in charge of the workplace; or

(b) by registered letter addressed to a person or corporation mentioned in clause (a) at the last known place of business of the person or corporation, and the same shall be deemed to be good and sufficient service thereof.

68. (1) Place of trial — An information in respect of an offence under this Act may, at the election of the informant, be heard, tried and determined by the Ontario Court of Justice sitting in the county or district in which the accused is resident or carries on business although the subject-matter of the information did not arise in that county or district.

(2) Provincial judge required — The Attorney General or an agent for the Attorney General may by notice to the clerk of the court having jurisdiction in respect of an offence under this Act require that a provincial judge preside over the proceeding.

2001, c. 9 Sched. I, s. 3(15)

68.1 (1) Publication re convictions — If a person, including an individual, is convicted of an offence under this Act, a Director may publish or otherwise make available to the general public the name of the person, a description of the offence, the date of the conviction and the person's sentence.

(2) Internet publication — Authority to publish under subsection (1) includes authority to publish on the Internet.

(3) Disclosure — Any disclosure made under subsection (1) shall be deemed to be in compliance with clause 42(1)(e) of the *Freedom of Information and Protection of Privacy Act*.

2006, c. 19 Sched. M, s. 5; 2006, c. 34 Sched. C, s. 25

69. Limitation on prosecutions — No prosecution under this Act or the regulations shall be instituted more than one year after the later of,

 (a) the occurrence of the last act or default upon which the prosecution is based; or

 (b) the day upon which an inspector becomes aware of the alleged offence.

2017, c. 34,   Sched. 30, s. 5

Part X — Regulations

70. (1) Regulations — The Lieutenant Governor in Council may make such regulations as are advisable for the health or safety of persons in or about a workplace.

(2) Idem — Without limiting the generality of subsection (1), the Lieutenant Governor in Council may make regulations,

1. defining any word or expression used in this Act or the regulations that is not defined in this Act;

2. designating or defining any industry, workplace, employer or class of workplaces or employers for the purposes of this Act, a part of this Act, or the regulations or any provision thereof;

3. exempting any workplace, industry, activity, business, work, trade, occupation, profession, constructor, employer or any class thereof from the application of a regulation or any provision thereof;

4. limiting or restricting the application of a regulation or any provision thereof to any workplace, industry, activity, business, work, trade, occupation, profession, constructor, employer or any class thereof;

5. exempting an employer from the requirements of clause 37(1)(a) or (b) with respect to a hazardous material;

6. respecting any matter of thing that is required or permitted to be regulated or prescribed under this Act;

7. respecting any matter or thing, where a provision of this Act requires that the matter or thing be done, used or carried out or provided as prescribed;

8. respecting any matter or thing, where it is a condition precedent that a regulation be made prescribing the matter or thing before this Act or a provision of this Act has any effect;

9. providing for and prescribing fees and the payment or refund of fees;

10. prescribing classes of workplaces for which and circumstances under which a committee shall consist of more than four persons and in each case prescribing the number of persons;

11. prescribing employers or workplaces or classes thereof for the purposes of clause 9(1)(b);

12. exempting any workplace, industry, activity, business, work, trade, occupation, profession, constructor or employer or any class thereof from the application of subsection 9(2);

13. respecting the conditions for eligibility, qualifications, selection and term of committee members, including certified members, and the operation of the committee;

Proposed Addition — 70(2), paras. 13.1, 13.2

13.1 exempting any class of workplaces from the requirement set out in subsection 8(5.1);

13.2 requiring that the training of health and safety representatives under subsection 8(5.1) meet such requirements as may be prescribed;

2011, c. 11 s. 18(1) [Not in force at date of publication.]

14. exempting any class of workplaces from the requirement set out in subsection 9(12);

15. prescribing elements that any policy required under this Act must contain;

16. regulating or prohibiting the installation or use of any machine, device or thing or any class thereof;

17. requiring that any equipment, machine, device, article or thing used bear the seal of approval of an organization designated by the regulations to test and approve the equipment, machine, device, article or thing and designating organizations for such purposes;

18. prescribing classes of employers who shall establish and maintain a medical surveillance program in which workers may volunteer to participate;

19. governing medical surveillance programs;

20. respecting the reporting by physicians and others of workers affected by any biological, chemical or physical agents or combination thereof;

21. regulating or prohibiting atmospheric conditions to which any worker may be exposed in a workplace;

22. prescribing methods, standards or procedures for determining the amount, concentration or level of any atmospheric condition or any biological, chemical or physical agent or combination thereof in a workplace;

23. prescribing any biological, chemical or physical agent or combination thereof as a designated substance;

24. prohibiting, regulating, restricting, limiting or controlling the handling of, exposure to, or the use and disposal of any designated substance;

25. adopting by reference, in whole or in part, with such changes as the Lieutenant Governor in Council considers necessary, any code

or standard and requiring compliance with any code or standard that is so adopted;

26. adopting by reference any criteria or guide in relation to the exposure of a worker to any biological, chemical or physical agent or combination thereof;

27. enabling a Director by notice in writing to designate that any part of a project shall be an individual project for the purposes of this Act and the regulations and prescribing to whom notice shall be given;

28. permitting the Minister to approve laboratories for the purpose of carrying out and performing sampling, analyses, tests and examinations, and requiring that sampling, analyses, examinations and tests be carried out and performed by a laboratory approved by the Minister;

29. requiring and providing for the registration of employers of workers;

30. providing for the establishment, equipment, operation and maintenance of mine rescue stations, as the Minister may direct, and providing for the payment of the cost thereof and the recovery of such cost from the mining industry;

31. prescribing training programs that employers shall provide;

31.1 requiring that training programs provided by employers meet such requirements as may be prescribed;

32. increasing the number of certified members required on a committee;

33. prescribing restrictions, prohibitions or conditions with respect to workers or workplaces relating to the risks of workplace violence;

34. prescribing forms and notices and providing for their use;

35. prescribing building standards for industrial establishments;

36. prescribing by name or description any biological or chemical agent as a hazardous material and any physical agent as a hazardous physical agent;

37. prohibiting an employer from altering a label on a hazardous material in prescribed circumstances;

38. [Repealed 2015, c. 27, Sched. 4, s. 7(1).]

39. requiring an employer to disclose to such persons as may be prescribed the source of toxicological data used by the employer to prepare a safety data sheet;

40. prescribing the format and contents of a safety data sheet;

41. prescribing by class of employer the intervals at which a health and safety representative or a committee member designated under subsection 9(23) shall inspect all or part of a workplace;

42. establishing criteria for determining, for the purpose of section 51, whether a person is critically injured;

43. prescribing first aid requirements to be met and first aid services to be provided by employers and constructors;

44. prescribing, for the purpose of clause 26(1)(i), medical examinations and tests that a worker is required to undergo to ensure that the worker's health will not affect his or her ability to perform his or her job in a manner that might endanger others;

45. prescribing classes of workplace with respect to which section 45 does not apply;

46. prescribing the qualifications of persons whom a certified member may designate under subsection 45(9);

47. prescribing, for the purpose of subsection 46(6), criteria for determining whether a constructor or employer has demonstrated a failure to protect the health and safety of workers;

48. prescribing matters to be considered by the Board in deciding upon an application under section 46;

49. prescribing classes of workplace with respect to which section 47 does not apply.

50. requiring an employer to designate a person in a workplace to act as a workplace co-ordinator with respect to workplace violence and workplace harassment, and prescribing the functions and duties of the co-ordinator;

51. in the case of a worker described in subsection 43(2), specifying situations in which a circumstance described in clause 43(3)(a), (b), (b.1) or (c) shall be considered, for the purposes of clause 43(1)(a), to be inherent in the worker's work or a normal condition of employment;

52. varying or supplementing subsections 43(4) to (13) with respect to the following workers, in circumstances when section 43 applies to them:

> i. workers to whom section 43 applies by reason of a regulation made for the purposes of subsection 3(3), and
>
> ii. workers described in subsection 43(2).

53. providing for such transitional matters as the Lieutenant Governor in Council considers necessary or advisable in connection with the implementation of section 22.5;

54. prescribing the functions of the Office of the Worker Adviser for the purposes of Part VI;

55. prescribing the functions of the Office of the Employer Adviser for the purposes of Part VI;

56. prescribing a number of employees for the purposes of subsection 50.1(2).

1997, c. 16 s. 2(16); 1998, c. 8 s. 59; 2001, c. 9 Sched. I, s. 3(16); 2009, c. 23 s. 7; 2011, c. 11 s. 18(2)-(4); 2015, c. 27, Sched. 4, s. 7

71. (1) Regulations, taxi industry — The Lieutenant Governor in Council may make regulations governing the application of the duties and rights set out in Part III.0.1 to the taxi industry.

(2) Same — Without limiting the generality of subsection (1), the Lieutenant Governor in Council may make regulations,

(a) specifying that all or any of the duties set out in Part III.0.1 apply for the purposes of the regulations, with such modifications as may be necessary in the circumstances;

(b) specifying who shall be considered an employer for the purposes of the regulations and requiring that person to carry out the specified duties;

(c) specifying who shall be considered a worker for the purposes of the regulations;

(d) specifying what shall be considered a workplace for the purposes of the regulations.

2009, c. 23 s. 8

ONT. REG. 632/05 — CONFINED SPACES

made under the *Occupational Health and Safety Act*

O. Reg. 632/05, as am. O. Reg. 23/09, ss. 1-3, 4 (Fr.); 492/09;
95/11; 346/15

1. Definitions — In this Regulation,

"**acceptable atmospheric levels**" means that,

(a) the atmospheric concentration of any explosive or flammable gas or vapour is less than,

    (i) 25 per cent of its lower explosive limit, if paragraph 1 of subsection 19(4) applies,

    (ii) 10 per cent of its lower explosive limit, if paragraph 2 of subsection 19(4) applies,

    (iii) 5 per cent of its lower explosive limit, if paragraph 3 of subsection 19(4) applies,

(b) the oxygen content of the atmosphere is at least 19.5 per cent but not more than 23 per cent by volume,

(c) in the case of a workplace that is not a project, the exposure to atmospheric contaminants does not exceed any applicable limit set out in Regulation 833 of the Revised Regulations of Ontario, 1990 (*Control of Exposure to Biological or Chemical Agents*) made under the Act or Ontario Regulation 490/09 (*Designated Substances*) made under the Act, and

(d) in the case of a workplace that is a project, the exposure to atmospheric contaminants does not exceed any applicable limit set out in Regulation 833 of the Revised Regulations of Ontario, 1990 (*Control of Exposure to Biological or Chemical Agents*) made under the Act;

"**adequate**", when used in relation to a procedure, plan, material, device, object or thing, means that it is,

(a) sufficient for both its intended and its actual use, and

(b) sufficient to protect a worker from occupational illness or occupational injury;

"adequately" has a meaning that corresponds to the meaning of **"adequate"**;

"assessment" means an assessment of hazards with respect to one or more confined spaces in a workplace, as described in section 6;

"atmospheric hazards" means,

(a) the accumulation of flammable, combustible or explosive agents,

(b) an oxygen content in the atmosphere that is less than 19.5 per cent or more than 23 per cent by volume, or

(c) the accumulation of atmospheric contaminants, including gases, vapours, fumes, dusts or mists, that could,

(i) result in acute health effects that pose an immediate threat to life, or

(ii) interfere with a person's ability to escape unaided from a confined space;

"cold work" means work that is not capable of producing a source of ignition;

"confined space" means a fully or partially enclosed space,

(a) that is not both designed and constructed for continuous human occupancy, and

(b) in which atmospheric hazards may occur because of its construction, location or contents or because of work that is done in it;

"emergency work" means work performed in connection with an unforeseen event that involves an imminent danger to the life, health or safety of any person;

"hot work" means work that is capable of producing a source of ignition;

"lead employer" means an employer who contracts for the services of one or more other employers or independent contractors in relation to one or more confined spaces that are located,

(a) in the lead employer's own workplace, or

(b) in another employer's workplace;

"plan" means a plan for one or more confined spaces in a workplace, as described in section 7;

"program" means a program for one or more confined spaces in a workplace, as described in section 5;

"purging" means displacing contaminants from a confined space;

"related work" means work that is performed near a confined space in direct support of work inside the confined space.

O. Reg. 492/09 s. 1; 95/11 s. 1; 346/15, s. 1

2. Application — Subject to section 3, this Regulation applies to all workplaces to which the *Occupational Health and Safety Act* applies.

3. Exceptions —

(1) This Regulation does not apply to work performed underwater by a diver during a diving operation as defined in Ontario Regulation 629/94 (*Diving Operations*) made under the Act.

(2) Sections 4 to 7 and 9 to 21 of this Regulation do not apply to emergency work performed by,

> (a) a firefighter as defined in subsection 1(1) of the *Fire Protection and Prevention Act, 1997*; or
>
> (b) a person who,
>
> > (i) holds a certificate under the *Technical Standards and Safety Act, 2000* designating him or her as a gas technician, and
> >
> > (ii) is working under the direction of a fire department, as defined in the *Fire Protection and Prevention Act, 1997*.

(3) A worker described in subsection (2) who performs emergency work shall be adequately protected by,

> (a) personal protective equipment, clothing and devices provided by the worker's employer;
>
> (b) training under section 8 provided by that employer; and
>
> (c) written procedures and other measures developed by that employer.

O. Reg. 23/09 s. 1; 95/11 s. 2

4. Confined spaces with multi-employer involvement —

(1) This section applies if the workers of more than one employer perform work in the same confined space or related work with respect to the same confined space.

(2) Before any worker enters the confined space or begins related work with respect to the confined space, the lead employer or, in the case of a project, the constructor, shall prepare a co-ordination document to ensure that the duties imposed on employers by sections 5 to 7, 9 to 12 and 14 to 20 are performed in a way that protects the health and safety of all workers who perform work in the confined space or related work with respect to the confined space.

(3) Without restricting the generality of subsection (2), in the case of a workplace that is not a project, the co-ordination document may provide for the performance of a duty or duties referred to in that subsection by one or more employers on behalf of one or more other employers with respect to some or all of the workers.

(4) A copy of the co-ordination document shall be provided to,

    (a) each employer of workers who perform work in the same confined space or related work with respect to the same confined space;

    (b) in the case of a workplace that is not a project, the joint health and safety committee or health and safety representative, if any, for each employer of workers who perform work in the same confined space or related work with respect to the same confined space; and

    (c) in the case of a workplace that is a project, the joint health and safety committee or health and safety representative, if any, for the project.

O. Reg. 95/11 s. 3

5. Program —

(1) If a workplace includes a confined space that workers may enter to perform work, the employer shall ensure that a written program for the confined space is developed and maintained in accordance with this Regulation before a worker enters the confined space.

(2) A program described in subsection (1) may apply to one or more confined spaces.

(3) In the case of a workplace that is not a project, the program described in subsection (1) shall be developed and maintained in consultation with the joint health and safety committee or the health and safety representative, if any.

(4) A program described in subsection (1) shall be adequate and shall provide for,

(a) a method for recognizing each confined space to which the program applies;

(b) a method for assessing the hazards to which workers may be exposed, in accordance with section 6;

(c) a method for the development of one or more plans, in accordance with section 7;

(d) a method for the training of workers, in accordance with section 8 or section 9.1, as the case may be; and

(e) an entry permit system that sets out the measures and procedures to be followed when work is to be performed in a confined space to which the program applies.

(5) In the case of a workplace that is not a project, the employer shall provide a copy of the program to the joint health and safety committee or the health and safety representative, if any.

(6) In the case of a workplace that is a project, the employer shall provide a copy of the program to the constructor, who shall provide a copy of it to the project's joint health and safety committee or the health and safety representative, if any.

(7) The employer or constructor, as the case may be, shall ensure that a copy of the program is available to,

(a) any other employer of workers who perform work to which the program relates; and

(b) every worker who performs work to which the program relates, if the workplace has no joint health and safety committee or health and safety representative.

O. Reg. 95/11 s. 4

6. Assessment —

(1) Before any worker enters a confined space, the employer shall ensure that an adequate assessment of the hazards related to the confined space has been carried out.

(2) The assessment shall be recorded in writing and shall consider, with respect to each confined space,

(a) the hazards that may exist due to the design, construction, location, use or contents of the confined space; and

(b) the hazards that may develop while work is done inside the confined space.

(3) The record of the assessment may be incorporated into an entry permit under section 10.

(4) If two or more confined spaces are of similar construction and present the same hazards, their assessments may be recorded in a single document, but each confined space shall be clearly identified in the assessment.

(5) The employer shall appoint a person with adequate knowledge, training and experience to carry out the assessment and shall maintain a record containing details of the person's knowledge, training and experience.

(6) The assessment shall contain the name of the person who carries out the assessment.

(7) The person shall sign and date the assessment and provide it to the employer.

(8) On request, the employer shall provide copies of the assessment and of the record mentioned in subsection (5) to,

> (a) the joint health and safety committee or the project's joint health and safety committee, as the case may be, or the health and safety representative, if any; or
>
> (b) every worker who performs work to which the assessment relates, if the workplace has no joint health and safety committee or health and safety representative.

(9) The employer shall ensure that the assessment is reviewed as often as is necessary to ensure that the relevant plan remains adequate.

O. Reg. 95/11 s. 5

7. Plan —

(1) Before any worker enters a confined space, the employer shall ensure that an adequate written plan, including procedures for the control of hazards identified in the assessment, has been developed and implemented by a competent person for the confined space.

(2) The plan may be incorporated into an entry permit under section 10.

(3) The plan shall contain provisions for,

> (a) the duties of workers;
>
> (b) co-ordination in accordance with section 4, if applicable;
>
> (c) on-site rescue procedures, in accordance with section 11;

(d) rescue equipment and methods of communication, in accordance with section 12;

(e) personal protective equipment, clothing and devices, in accordance with section 13;

(f) isolation of energy and control of materials movement, in accordance with section 14;

(g) attendants, in accordance with section 15;

(h) adequate means for entering and exiting, in accordance with section 16;

(i) atmospheric testing, in accordance with section 18;

(j) adequate procedures for working in the presence of explosive or flammable substances, in accordance with section 19; and

(k) ventilation and purging, in accordance with section 20.

(4) One plan may deal with two or more confined spaces that are of similar construction and present the same hazards as identified by the assessment.

(5) The employer shall ensure that the plan is reviewed as often as is necessary to ensure that it remains adequate.

8. Hazard recognition and other general training—workplaces other than projects —

(0.1) This section does not apply to workplaces that are projects.

(1) Every worker who enters a confined space or who performs related work shall be given adequate training for safe work practices for working in confined spaces and for performing related work, including training in the recognition of hazards associated with confined spaces.

(2) The employer shall appoint a person with adequate knowledge, training and experience to conduct the training.

(3) The employer shall ensure that training under this section is developed in consultation with the joint health and safety committee or the health and safety representative, if any.

(4) The employer shall ensure that training under this section is reviewed, in consultation with the joint health and safety committee or the health and safety representative, if any, whenever there is a change in circumstances that may affect the safety of a worker who enters a confined space in the workplace, and in any case at least once annually.

(5) The employer shall maintain up-to-date written records showing who provided and who received training under this section, the nature of the training and the date when it was provided.

(6) The records may be incorporated into an entry permit under section 10.

(7) Training under this section may be combined with training under section 9.

O. Reg. 95/11 s. 6

9. Plan-specific training—workplaces other than projects —

(0.1) This section does not apply to workplaces that are projects.

(1) The employer shall ensure that every worker who enters a confined space or who performs related work,

    (a) receives adequate training, in accordance with the relevant plan, to work safely and properly; and

    (b) follows the plan.

(2) The employer shall maintain up-to-date written records showing who provided and who received training under this section, and the date when it was provided.

(3) The records may be incorporated into an entry permit under section 10.

(4) Training under this section may be combined with training under section 8.

O. Reg. 95/11 s. 7

9.1 Training—projects —

(1) This section applies only to workplaces that are projects.

(2) The employer shall ensure that every worker who enters a confined space or who performs related work receives adequate training to perform the work safely, in accordance with the relevant plan.

(3) Training under subsection (2) shall include training in,

    (a) the recognition of hazards associated with confined spaces; and

    (b) safe work practices for working in confined spaces and for performing related work.

632/05

(4) The employer shall maintain up-to-date written records showing who provided and who received training under this section and the date when it was provided.

(5) The employer shall provide the training records under subsection (4) to the project's joint health and safety committee or health and safety representative, if any, on request.

(6) The records may be incorporated into an entry permit under section 10.

O. Reg. 95/11 s. 8

10. Entry permits —

(1) The employer shall ensure that a separate entry permit is issued each time work is to be performed in a confined space, before any worker enters the confined space.

(2) An entry permit shall be adequate and shall include at least the following:

    1. The location of the confined space.

    2. A description of the work to be performed there.

    3. A description of the hazards and the corresponding control measures.

    4. The time period for which the entry permit applies.

    5. The name of the attendant described in section 15.

    6. A record of each worker's entries and exits.

    7. A list of the equipment required for entry and rescue, and verification that the equipment is in good working order.

    8. Results obtained in atmospheric testing under section 18.

    9. If the work to be performed in the confined space includes hot work, adequate provisions for the hot work and corresponding control measures.

(3) Before each shift, a competent person shall verify that the entry permit complies with the relevant plan.

(4) The employer shall ensure that the entry permit, during the time period for which it applies, is readily available to every person who enters the confined space and to every person who performs related work with respect to the confined space.

11. On-site rescue procedures —

(1) The employer shall ensure that no worker enters or remains in a confined space unless, in accordance with the relevant plan, adequate written on-site rescue procedures that apply to the confined space have been developed and are ready for immediate implementation.

(2) Before a worker enters a confined space, the employer shall ensure that an adequate number of persons trained in the matters listed in subsection (3) are available for immediate implementation of the on-site rescue procedures mentioned in subsection (1).

(3) The persons shall be trained in,

 (a) the on-site rescue procedures mentioned in subsection (1);

 (b) first aid and cardio-pulmonary resuscitation; and

 (c) the use of the rescue equipment required in accordance with the relevant plan.

12. Rescue equipment and methods of communication —

(1) The employer shall ensure that the rescue equipment identified in the relevant plan is,

 (a) readily available to effect a rescue in the confined space;

 (b) appropriate for entry into the confined space; and

 (c) inspected as often as is necessary to ensure it is in good working order, by a person with adequate knowledge, training and experience who is appointed by the employer.

(2) The inspection under clause (1)(c) shall be recorded in writing by the person, and the record of the inspection may be incorporated into the entry permit under section 10.

(3) The employer shall establish methods of communication that are appropriate for the hazards identified in the relevant assessment, and shall make them readily available for workers to communicate with the attendant described in section 15.

13. Personal protective equipment, clothing and devices — The employer shall ensure that each worker who enters a confined space is provided with adequate personal protective equipment, clothing and devices, in accordance with the relevant plan.

14. Isolation of energy and control of materials movement — The employer shall, in accordance with the relevant plan, ensure that each worker entering a confined space is adequately protected,

(a) against the release of hazardous substances into the confined space,

    (i) by blanking or disconnecting piping, or

    (ii) if compliance with subclause (i) is not practical in the circumstances for technical reasons, by other adequate means;

(b) against contact with electrical energy inside the confined space that could endanger the worker,

    (i) by disconnecting, de-energizing, locking out and tagging the source of electrical energy, or

    (ii) if compliance with subclause (i) is not practical in the circumstances for technical reasons, by other adequate means;

(c) against contact with moving parts of equipment inside the confined space that could endanger the worker,

    (i) by disconnecting the equipment from its power source, de-energizing the equipment, locking it out and tagging it, or

    (ii) if compliance with subclause (i) is not practical in the circumstances for technical reasons, by immobilizing the equipment by blocking or other adequate means; and

(d) against drowning, engulfment, entrapment, suffocation and other hazards from free-flowing material, by adequate means.

O. Reg. 23/09 s. 2

15. Attendant —

(1) Whenever a worker is to enter a confined space, the employer shall ensure that an attendant,

    (a) is assigned;

    (b) is stationed outside and near,

        (i) the entrance to the confined space, or

        (ii) if there are two or more entrances, the one that will best allow the attendant to perform his or her duties under subsection (2);

    (c) is in constant communication with all workers inside the confined space, using the means of communication described in the relevant plan; and

    (d) is provided with a device for summoning an adequate rescue response.

(2) The attendant shall not enter the confined space at any time and shall, in accordance with the relevant plan,

(a) monitor the safety of the worker inside;

(b) provide assistance to him or her; and

(c) summon an adequate rescue response if required.

16. Means for entering and exiting — An adequate means for entering and exiting shall be provided for all workers who enter a confined space, in accordance with the relevant plan.

17. Preventing unauthorized entry — If there is a possibility of unauthorized entry into a confined space, the employer, or in the case of a project, the constructor, shall ensure that each entrance to the confined space,

(a) is adequately secured against unauthorized entry; or

(b) has been provided with adequate barricades, adequate warning signs regarding unauthorized entry, or both.

O. Reg. 95/11 s. 9

18. Atmospheric testing —

(1) The employer shall appoint a person with adequate knowledge, training and experience to perform adequate tests as often as necessary before and while a worker is in a confined space to ensure that acceptable atmospheric levels are maintained in the confined space in accordance with the relevant plan.

(2) If the confined space has been both unoccupied and unattended, tests shall be performed before a worker enters or re-enters.

(3) The person performing the tests shall use calibrated instruments that are in good working order and are appropriate for the hazards identified in the relevant assessment.

(4) The employer shall ensure that the results of every sample of a test are recorded, subject to subsection (5).

(5) If the tests are performed using continuous monitoring, the employer shall ensure that test results are recorded at adequate intervals.

(6) The tests shall be performed in a manner that does not endanger the health or safety of the person performing them.

(7) In this section,

"**sample**" means an individual reading of the composition of the atmosphere in the confined space;

"**test**" means a collection of samples.

19. Explosive and flammable substances —

(1) This section applies only in respect of atmospheric hazards described in clause (a) of the definition of "atmospheric hazards" in section 1.

(2) The employer shall ensure that this section is complied with, by ventilation, purging, rendering the atmosphere inert or other adequate means, in accordance with the relevant plan.

(3) The employer shall ensure that no worker enters or remains in a confined space that contains or is likely to contain an airborne combustible dust or mist whose atmospheric concentration may create a hazard of explosion.

(4) The employer shall ensure that no worker enters or remains in a confined space that contains or is likely to contain an explosive or flammable gas or vapour, unless one of the following applies:

　　1. The worker is performing only inspection work that does not produce a source of ignition. In the case of an explosive or flammable gas or vapour, the atmospheric concentration is less than 25 per cent of its lower explosive limit, as determined by a combustible gas instrument.

　　2. The worker is performing only cold work. In the case of an explosive or flammable gas or vapour, the atmospheric concentration is less than 10 per cent of its lower explosive limit, as determined by a combustible gas instrument.

　　3. The worker is performing hot work. All the following conditions are satisfied:

　　　　i. In the case of an explosive or flammable gas or vapour, the atmospheric concentration is less than 5 per cent of its lower explosive limit, as determined by a combustible gas instrument.

　　　　ii. The atmosphere in the confined space does not contain, and is not likely to contain while a worker is inside, an oxygen content greater than 23 per cent by volume.

　　　　iii. The atmosphere in the confined space is monitored continuously.

iv. The entry permit includes adequate provisions for hot work and corresponding control measures.

v. An adequate warning system and exit procedure are provided to ensure that workers have adequate warning and are able to exit the confined space safely if either or both of the following occur:

A. In the case of an explosive or flammable gas or vapour, the atmospheric concentration exceeds 5 per cent of its lower explosive limit.

B. The oxygen content of the atmosphere exceeds 23 per cent by volume.

(5) Subsections (3) and (4) do not apply if,

(a) the atmosphere in the confined space,

(i) has been rendered inert by adding an inert gas, and

(ii) is monitored continuously to ensure that it remains inert; and

(b) a worker entering the confined space uses,

(i) adequate respiratory protective equipment,

(ii) adequate equipment to allow persons outside the confined space to locate and rescue the worker if necessary, and

(iii) such other equipment as is necessary to ensure the worker's safety.

(6) The equipment mentioned in subclauses (5)(b)(i), (ii) and (iii) shall be inspected by a person with adequate knowledge, training and experience, appointed by the employer, and shall be in good working order before the worker enters the confined space.

O. Reg. 23/09 s. 3

20. Ventilation and purging —

(1) This section applies only in respect of atmospheric hazards described in clause (b) or (c) of the definition of "atmospheric hazards" in section 1.

(2) If atmospheric hazards exist or are likely to exist in a confined space, the confined space shall be purged, ventilated or both, before any worker enters it, to ensure that acceptable atmospheric levels are maintained in the confined space while any worker is inside.

(3) If mechanical ventilation is required to maintain acceptable atmospheric levels, an adequate warning system and exit procedure shall also

be provided to ensure that workers have adequate warning of ventilation failure and are able to exit the confined space safely.

(4) If compliance with subsection (2) is not practical in the circumstances for technical reasons,

(a) compliance with subsection (3) is not required; and

(b) a worker entering the confined space shall use,

(i) adequate respiratory protective equipment,

(ii) adequate equipment to allow persons outside the confined space to locate and rescue the worker if necessary, and

(iii) such other equipment as is necessary to ensure the worker's safety.

(5) The equipment mentioned in subclauses (4)(b)(i), (ii) and (iii) shall be inspected by a person with adequate knowledge, training and experience, appointed by the employer, and shall be in good working order before the worker enters the confined space.

21. Records —

(1) In the case of a workplace that is not a project, the employer shall retain every assessment, plan, co-ordination document under section 4, record of training under subsection 8(5) or 9(2), entry permit under section 10, record of an inspection under subsection 12(2) and record of a test under section 18, including records of each sample, for the longer of the following periods:

1. One year after the document is created.

2. The period that is necessary to ensure that at least the two most recent records of each kind that relate to a particular confined space are retained.

(2) In the case of a workplace that is a project, the constructor or employer, as the case may be,

(a) shall keep available for inspection at the project every assessment, plan, co-ordination document under section 4, record of training under subsection 9.1(4), entry permit under section 10, record of an inspection under subsection 12(2) and record of a test under section 18, including records of each sample; and

(b) shall retain the documents described in clause (a) for one year after the project is finished.

(3) If section 4 applies,

(a) the documents described in subsection (1) shall be retained by the employer responsible for creating them; and

(b) the documents described in clause (2)(a) shall be retained by the constructor or employer, as the case may be, responsible for creating them.

O. Reg. 95/11 s. 10

22. Commencement — This Regulation comes into force on September 30, 2006.

TABLE 1 [Repealed O. Reg. 492/09, s. 2.]

[Repealed O. Reg. 492/09, s. 2.]

ONT. REG. 213/91 — CONSTRUCTION PROJECTS

made under the *Occupational Health and Safety Act*

O. Reg. 213/91, as am. O. Reg. 631/94; 143/99; 571/99; 145/00; 527/00; 85/04; 627/05; 628/05; 443/09; 96/11; 88/13; 252/14; 345/15; 242/16; 471/16; 142/17, ss. 1-42, 43 (Fr.).

Part I — General

Interpretation and Application

1. (1) In this Regulation,

"adequate", in relation to a procedure, plan, material, device, object or thing, means,

    (a) sufficient for both its intended and its actual use, and

    (b) sufficient to protect a worker from occupational illness or occupational injury,

and **"adequately"** has a corresponding meaning;

"allowable unit stress", in relation to a material, means,

    (a) the allowable unit stress assigned to a material by the standards required under the Building Code, or

    (b) if no allowable unit stress is assigned under clause (a), the allowable unit stress for the material as determined by a professional engineer in accordance with good engineering practice;

"approved", in relation to a form, means approved by the Minister;

"blocker truck" means a truck that weighs at least 6,800 kilograms and has four-way flashers and a mounted flashing arrowboard sign;

"boom" means the projecting part of a backhoe, shovel, crane or similar lifting device from which a load is likely to be supported;

"Building Code" [Repealed O. Reg. 345/15, s. 1(2).];

"caisson" means,

105

(a) a casing below ground or water level whether or not it is designed to contain air at a pressure greater than atmospheric pressure,

(b) an excavation, including a waterwell but not a well within the
meaning of the *Oil, Gas and Salt Resources Act*, drilled by an auger
and into which a person may enter;

"cofferdam" means a structure constructed entirely or partially below
water level or below the level of the groundwater table and intended to
provide a work place that is free of water;

"competent worker", in relation to specific work, means a worker who,

(a) is qualified because of knowledge, training and experience to
perform the work,

(b) is familiar with the *Occupational Health and Safety Act* and with
the provisions of the regulations that apply to the work, and

(c) has knowledge of all potential or actual danger to health or
safety in the work;

"conduit" means a sewer, a water main, a duct or cable for a telegraphic,
telephonic, television or electrical service, a pipe or duct for the transportation of any solid, liquid or gas or any combination of these items and
includes a service connection made or intended to be made thereto;

"confined space" [Repealed O. Reg. 628/05, s. 1.]

"Construction Health and Safety Branch" [Revoked O. Reg. 145/00, s.
1(3).]

"crash truck" means a blocker truck that is equipped with a crash-at-
tenuating device;

"critical weld" means, in relation to a suspended work platform, a weld
the failure of which could result in the complete or partial collapse of the
suspended work platform;

"excavation" means the hole that is left in the ground, as a result of
removing material;

"excavation depth" means the vertical dimension from the highest point
of the excavation wall to a point level with the lowest point of the excavation;

"excavation width" means the least horizontal dimension between the two
opposite walls of the excavation;

"fall arrest system" means an assembly of components joined together so that when the assembly is connected to a fixed support, it is capable of arresting a worker's fall;

"fall restricting system" means a type of fall arrest system that has been designed to limit a worker's fall to a specified distance;

"falsework", in relation to a form or structure, means the structural support and bracing used to support all or part of the form or structure;

"fixed support" means a permanent or temporary structure or a component of such a structure that can withstand all loads and forces the structure or component is intended to support or resist and is sufficient to protect a worker's health and safety, and includes equipment or devices that are securely fastened to the structure or component;

"flammable liquid" means a liquid with a flash point below 37.8 degrees celsius and a vapour pressure not exceeding 275 kilopascals absolute at 37.8 degrees celsius;

"form" means the mould into which concrete or another material is to be placed;

"formwork" means a system of forms connected together;

"freeway" means a controlled-access highway that has a continuous dividing median and a normal posted speed limit of 90 kilometres per hour or more;

"full body harness" means a device that can arrest an accidental vertical or near vertical fall of a worker and which can guide and distribute the impact forces of the fall by means of leg and shoulder strap supports and an upper dorsal suspension assembly which, after the arrest, will not by itself permit the release or further lowering of the worker;

"generic installation drawing"   means a drawing and related documentation, if any, that,

    (a) identifies components, configurations and load limitations of a suspended work platform system or powered boatswain's chair,

    (b) is intended to be used at any location where all of the requirements in the drawing and documentation are satisfied, and

    (c) bears the seal and signature of a professional engineer confirming that a suspended work platform system or boatswain's chair installed in accordance with the drawing would be in compliance with the requirements of this Regulation;

213/91

"guardrail system" means an assembly of components joined together to provide a barrier to prevent a worker from falling from the edge of a surface;

"highway" means a common and public highway, street, avenue, parkway, driveway, square, place, bridge, viaduct or trestle, any part of which is intended for or used by the general public for the passage of vehicles;

"longitudinal buffer area" means the area of a project between the end of a lane closure taper and the start of a work area;

"magazine" means a place in which explosives are stored or kept, whether above or below ground;

"multi-point suspended scaffold" [Repealed O. Reg. 242/16, s. 2(1).]

"multi-point suspended work platform" means a suspended work platform more than 750 millimetres in width or a system of suspended work platforms in which any one platform is more than 750 millimetres in width that is supported from an overhead fixed support system by at least three primary load-carrying means of suspension to maintain the stability of the work platform or system of work platforms;

"non-destructive test" means one of the following methods of testing or examining a material, component or part to evaluate its condition without subjecting it to physical distortion, damage or destruction:

1. Eddy current testing.
2. Magnetic particle testing.
3. Liquid penetrant testing.
4. Radiographic testing.
5. Ultrasonic testing;

"professional engineer" means a person who is a professional engineer within the meaning of the *Professional Engineers Act*;

"public way" means a highway or other street, avenue, parkway, driveway, square, place, bridge, viaduct, or other open space to which the public has access, as of right or by expressed or implied invitation;

"rated platform capacity" means the combined weight of occupants, tools, equipment and other material that the manufacturer has indicated can be safely carried by a suspended work platform, work platform module or boatswain's chair;

"roadway" means the travelled portion of a highway;

"rotary foundation drill rig" means a drill rig used for boring holes in soil for the placement of foundations or earth retention structures but does not include a drill rig that,

(a) is used for geotechnical sampling,

(b) is used for drilling water, oil or gas wells,

(c) is a rock drill or a diamond drill,

(d) is a digger derrick,

(e) is used for digging holes for posts, concrete forming tubes, poles or light standards,

(f) is a pile driver without an auger,

(g) is a horizontal boring machine, or

(h) is a tunnel boring machine;

"safety belt" means a belt worn around the waist of a worker and all the fittings for the belt appropriate for the use being made of it;

"safety factor" means the ratio of the failure load to the specified load or rated load;

"safety net" means a safety net that complies with section 26.8, and is located and supported in such a way that it arrests the fall of a worker who may fall into it without endangering the worker;

"service shaft" means a shaft by which people or materials are passed into or out of a tunnel under construction;

"shaft" means an excavation with a longitudinal axis at an angle greater than 45 degrees from the horizontal that is used to pass people or materials into or out of a tunnel or that leads to a tunnel or that is used as an access to a boring or augering operation;

"sheathing" means the members of shoring that are placed up against the walls of an excavation to directly resist the pressure exerted from the walls of the excavation;

"sign truck" means a vehicle that has,

(a) four-way flashers and a mounted flashing arrowboard sign, or

(b) a portable trailer with a mounted flashing arrowboard sign;

"site-specific installation drawing" means a drawing and related documentation, if any, that identifies components, configurations and load limitations of a suspended work platform system or powered boatswain's chair for use at a specific site;

"**strut**" means a transverse member of shoring that directly resists pressure from a wale;

"**suitable**", in relation to a procedure, material, device, object or thing, means sufficient to protect a worker from damage to the worker's body or health;

"**suspended work platform system**" means an access system comprising one or more overhead fixed supports, one or more suspension lines, hoisting devices, if any, and one or more work platforms that can be moved vertically, but it does not include a boatswain's chair or a multi-point suspended work platform;

"**tower crane**" means a travelling, fixed or climbing mechanical device or structure that has,

    (a) a boom, a jib or both,

    (b) a power-driven drum and wire rope to raise, lower or move material, and

    (c) a vertical mast;

"**travel restraint system**" means an assembly of components capable of restricting a worker's movement on a work surface and preventing the worker from reaching a location from which he or she could fall;

"**traverse**", when used in relation to a multi-point suspended work platform, means to move the platform horizontally, in a controlled manner, along the building or structure to which it is attached;

"**trench**" means an excavation where the excavation depth exceeds the excavation width;

"**tunnel**" means a subterranean passage into which a person may enter that is made by excavating beneath the overburden;

"**underground**", in relation to work, means inside a shaft, tunnel or caisson;

"**vehicle**" means a vehicle propelled by mechanical power and includes a trailer, a traction engine and a road-building machine;

"**wale**" means a longitudinal member of the shoring that is placed against the sheathing to directly resist the pressure from the sheathing;

"**work belt**" means a belt that has a back support pad and a connecting hook at the front and that is capable of supporting a worker.

(1.1) Every non-destructive test required by this Regulation shall be carried out and interpreted by a person who has been certified by Natural Resources Canada to the appropriate level in accordance with CAN/CGSB Standard 48.9712-2014, Non-destructive Testing — Qualification and Certification of Personnel.

(2) In this Regulation, a short form listed in Column 1 of the Table to this subsection has the same meaning as the term set out opposite to it in Column 2.

TABLE

Item	Column 1	Column 2
	Short forms	Corresponding terms
1.	ANSI	American National Standards Institute
2.	CSA	Canadian Standards Association
3.	CAN	National Standards of Canada

O. Reg. 631/94 s. 1; 145/00 s. 1; 85/04 s. 1; 628/05 s. 1; 345/15 s. 1; 242/16, s. 2; 142/17, s. 1

1.1 In this Regulation, a requirement that something be done in accordance with good engineering practice includes a requirement that it be done in a manner that protects the health and safety of all workers.

O. Reg. 85/04 s. 2

1.2 In this Regulation, a requirement that a design, drawing, instruction, report, specification, opinion or other document be prepared by a professional engineer includes a requirement that he or she sign and seal it.

O. Reg. 85/04 s. 2

2. This Part applies with respect to all projects.

Alternative Methods and Materials

3. An employer, owner or constructor may vary a procedure required by this Regulation or the composition, design, size or arrangement of a material, object, device or thing as required by this Regulation,

(a) if the procedure, composition, design, size or arrangement as varied affords protection for the health and safety of workers that is at least equal to the protection that would otherwise be given; and

(b) if the employer, owner or constructor gives written notice of the varied procedure, composition, design, size or arrangement to the joint health and safety committee or the health and safety representative, if any, for the work place.

Designation of a Project

4. A Director may designate in writing a part of a project as a project and the designated project is considered to be a project for the purposes of the Act and this Regulation.

O. Reg. 145/00 s. 2

Registration and Notices

5. (1) Before beginning work at a project, each contructor and employer engaged in construction shall complete an approved registration form.

(2) The constructor shall ensure that,

(a) each employer at the project provides to the constructor a completed approved registration form; and

(b) a copy of the employer's completed form is kept at the project while the employer is working there.

O. Reg. 145/00 s. 3

6. (1) This section applies with respect to a project if,

(a) the total cost of labour and materials for the project is expected to exceed $50,000;

(b) the work is the erection or structural alteration of a building more than two storeys or more than 7.5 metres high;

(c) the work is the demolition of a building at least four metres high with a floor area of at least thirty square metres;

(d) the work is the erection, structural alteration or structural repair of a bridge, an earth-retaining structure or a water-retaining structure more than three metres high or of a silo, chimney or a similar structure more than 7.5 metres high;

(e) work in compressed air is to be done at the project;

(f) a tunnel, caisson, cofferdam or well into which a person may enter is to be constructed at the project;

(g) a trench into which a person may enter is to be excavated at the project and the trench is more than 300 metres long or more than 1.2 metres deep and over thirty metres long;

(g.1) the work is the construction, over frozen water, slush or wetlands, of an ice road for vehicles, machinery or equipment; or

(h) a part of the permanent or temporary work is required by this Regulation to be designed by a professional engineer.

(2) A constructor shall comply with subsection (3) or (4) before beginning work at the project.

(3) The constructor shall complete an approved notification form and file it at the Ministry office located nearest to the project or submit it electronically on a website of the government of Ontario.

(4) If the constructor believes that the work at the project will not take more than 14 days, the constructor may provide the relevant information to an inspector at the Ministry office located nearest to the project,

(a) by faxing the completed form to the inspector; or

(b) by providing the information that would be required to complete the form to the inspector by telephone.

(5) Despite subsection (2), the constructor may begin work at a project before complying with subsection (3) or (4) if the following conditions are met:

1. It is necessary to do the work immediately to prevent injury to people or damage to property.

2. Before beginning the work, the constructor gives an inspector notice of the information required in the form by telephone or fax.

(6) The constructor shall keep the completed notification form posted in a conspicuous place at the project or available at the project for review by an inspector.

(7) [Revoked O. Reg. 145/00, s. 4.]

O. Reg. 145/00 s. 4; 345/15 s. 2; 242/16, s. 3

7. If section 6 does not apply to a project but the project includes work on a trench more than 1.2 metres deep into which a worker may enter, the constructor shall, before any work at the project is begun, give notice in person, by telephone or by fax to the Ministry office located nearest to the project.

O. Reg. 145/00 s. 5

7.1 (1) This section applies with respect to a project at which a suspended work platform system is to be used.

(2) At least 48 hours before a suspended work platform system is used for the first time at a project, the constructor shall complete an approved notification form and provide it to the Ministry by faxing it or delivering it in person to the Ministry office located nearest to the project or submitting it electronically on a website of the government of Ontario.

(3) Despite subsection (2), the constructor may put a suspended work platform system into use before providing the approved notification form if the following conditions are met:

    1. It is necessary to use the suspended work platform system immediately to prevent injury to people or damage to property.

    2. Before using the suspended work platform system, the constructor gives an inspector at the Ministry office located nearest to the project oral notice, by telephone or in person, that the system will be used.

(4) If a constructor uses a suspended work platform system under subsection (3), the constructor shall, within 24 hours of beginning to use the suspended work platform system, provide a completed approved notification form to the Ministry in a manner described in subsection (2).

(5) The constructor shall keep a copy of the completed notification form in a conspicuous location at the project.

O. Reg. 242/16, s. 4

Accident Notices and Reports under Sections 51-53 of the Act

8. A written report under subsection 51(1) of the Act respecting an occurrence in which a person is killed or critically injured shall set out,

    (a) the name and address of the constructor and the employer, if the person involved is a worker;

    (b) the nature and the circumstances of the occurrence, and the bodily injury sustained by the person;

    (c) a description of the machinery or equipment involved;

    (d) the time and place of the occurrence;

    (e) the name and address of the person involved;

    (f) the names and addresses of all witnesses to the occurrence;

(g) the name and address of any legally qualified medical practitioner, by whom the person was or is being attended for the injury; and

(h) the steps taken to prevent a recurrence.

O. Reg. 145/00 s. 6; 142/17, s. 2

9. (1) A notice under subsection 52(1) of the Act respecting an occurrence involving a worker shall set out,

(a) the name, address and type of business of the employer;

(b) the nature and the circumstances of the occurrence and the bodily injury or illness sustained by the worker;

(c) a description of the machinery or equipment involved;

(d) the time and place of the occurrence;

(e) the name and address of the worker involved;

(f) the names and addresses of all witnesses to the occurrence;

(g) the name and address of any legally qualified medical practitioner by whom the worker was or is being attended for the injury or illness;

(g.1) the name and address of each medical facility, if any, where the worker was or is being attended for the injury or illness; and

(h) the steps taken to prevent a recurrence.

(2) A notice under subsection 52(2) of the Act (information and particulars respecting a worker's occupational illness) shall contain the following information:

1. The employer's name, address and type of business.

2. The nature of the illness.

3. The worker's name and address.

4. The name and address of any legally qualified medical practitioner by whom the worker was or is being attended for the illness.

5. The name and address of each medical facility, if any, where the worker was or is being attended for the illness.

6. A description of the steps taken to prevent a recurrence or further illness.

O. Reg. 145/00 s. 7; 142/17, s. 3

10. (1) An employer shall keep in the employer's permanent records a record of any accident, explosion or fire involving a worker that causes injury requiring medical attention but does not disable the worker from performing his or her usual work.

(2) The records shall include particulars of,

    (a) the nature and circumstances of the occurrence, and the injury sustained by the worker;

    (b) the time and place of the occurrence;

    (c) the name and address of the injured worker; and

    (d) the steps taken to prevent a recurrence.

(3) An employer to whom subsection (1) applies shall make the record available to an inspector upon request.

O. Reg. 142/17, s. 4

11. (1) The following incidents are prescribed for the purpose of section 53 of the Act:

    1. A worker falling a vertical distance of three metres or more.

    2. A worker falling and having the fall arrested by a fall arrest system other than a fall restricting system.

    3. A worker becoming unconscious for any reason.

    4. Accidental contact by a worker or by a worker's tool or equipment with energized electrical equipment, installations or conductors.

    5. Accidental contact by a crane, similar hoisting device, backhoe, power shovel or other vehicle or equipment or its load with an energized electrical conductor rated at more than 750 volts.

    6. Structural failure of all or part of falsework designed by, or required by this Regulation to be designed by, a professional engineer.

    7. Structural failure of a principal supporting member, including a column, beam, wall or truss, of a structure.

    8. Failure of all or part of the structural supports of a scaffold.

    9. Structural failure of all or part of an earth- or water-retaining structure, including a failure of the temporary or permanent supports for a shaft, tunnel, caisson, cofferdam or trench.

    10. Failure of a wall of an excavation or of similar earthwork with respect to which a professional engineer has given a written opinion that the stability of the wall is such that no worker will be endangered by it.

    11. Overturning or the structural failure of all or part of a crane or similar hoisting device.

(2) A notice under section 53 of the Act shall set out the circumstances of the occurrence and the steps taken to prevent a recurrence.

O. Reg. 85/04 s. 3; 627/05 s. 1

12. (1) This section applies with respect to an occurrence for which a report under subsection 51(1) of the Act or a notice under section 52 or 53 of the Act is given, if the occurrence involves a failure of all or part of,

(a) temporary or permanent works;

(b) a structure;

(c) a wall of an excavation or of a similar earthwork for which a professional engineer has given a written opinion that the stability of the wall is such that no worker will be endangered by it; or

(d) a crane or similar hoisting device.

(2) A constructor or employer who submits a report under subsection 51(1) of the Act (notice of death or injury) or gives a notice under section 52 or 53 of the Act (notice of accident, etc.) shall also provide, within 14 days after the occurrence, a professional engineer's written opinion stating the cause of the occurrence.

O. Reg. 145/00 s. 8; 142/17, s. 5

General Requirements

13. (1) A constructor shall post in a conspicuous place at a project and keep posted while work is done at the project a notice setting out,

(a) the constructor's name and if the constructor carries on business in a different name, the business name;

(b) the address and telephone number of the constructor's head office or principal place of business in Ontario; and

(c) the address and telephone number of the nearest office of the Ministry.

(2) Within forty-eight hours after a health and safety representative or joint health and safety committee members are selected for a project, a constructor shall add to the notice the name, trade and employer of the health and safety representative or of each of the committee members.

O. Reg. 145/00 s. 9

14. (1) A constructor shall appoint a supervisor for every project at which five or more workers will work at the same time.

(2) The supervisor shall supervise the work at all times either personally or by having an assistant, who is a competent person, do so personally.

(3) A supervisor or a competent person appointed by the supervisor shall inspect all machinery and equipment, including fire extinguishing equipment, magazines, electrical installations, communication systems, sanitation and medical facilities, buildings and other structures, temporary supports and means of access and egress at the project to ensure that they do not endanger any worker.

(4) An inspection shall be made at least once a week or more frequently as the supervisor determines is necessary in order to ensure that the machinery and equipment referred to in subsection (3) do not endanger any worker.

(5) A competent person shall perform tests and observations necessary for the detection of hazardous conditions on a project.

15. (1) An employer of five or more workers on a project shall appoint a supervisor for the workers.

(2) The supervisor shall supervise the work at all times either personally or by having an assistant, who is a competent person, do so personally.

O. Reg. 145/00 s. 10

16. At a project, no person younger than 16 years of age shall,
    (a) be employed in or about the workplace; or
    (b) be permitted to be present in or about the workplace while work is being performed.

O. Reg. 145/00 s. 11

17. (1) A constructor shall establish for a project written procedures to be followed in the event of an emergency and shall ensure that the procedures are followed at the project.

(2) The constructor shall review the emergency procedures with the joint health and safety committee or the health and safety representative for the project, if any.

(3) The constructor shall ensure that the emergency procedures are posted in a conspicuous place at the project.

O. Reg. 145/00 s. 11

18. The constructor shall ensure that every worker at the project has ready access to a telephone, two-way radio or other system of two-way communication in the event of an emergency.

O. Reg. 145/00 s. 11

19. If, under this Regulation, a record is required to be kept available for inspection at a project, the constructor or employer, as the case may be, shall keep the record for at least one year after the project is finished.

Part II — General Construction

Application

20. This Part applies with respect to all projects.

Protective Clothing, Equipment and Devices

21. (1) A worker shall wear such protective clothing and use such personal protective equipment or devices as are necessary to protect the worker against the hazards to which the worker may be exposed.

(2) A worker's employer shall require the worker to comply with subsection (1).

(3) A worker required to wear protective clothing or use personal protective equipment or devices shall be adequately instructed and trained in the care and use of the clothing, equipment or device before wearing or using it.

22. (1) Every worker shall wear protective headwear at all times when on a project.

(2) Protective headwear shall be a safety hat that,
 (a) consists of a shell and suspension that is adequate to protect a person's head against impact and against flying or falling small objects; and
 (b) has a shell which can withstand a dielectric strength test at 20,000 volts phase to ground.

23. (1) Every worker shall wear protective footwear at all times when on a project.

(2) Protective footwear shall be a safety shoe or safety boot,
 (a) with a box toe that is adequate to protect the wearer's toes against injury due to impact and is capable of resisting at least 125 joules impact; and
 (b) with a sole or insole that is adequate to protect the wearer's feet against injury due to puncture and is capable of resisting a pene-

tration load of 1.2 kilonewtons when tested with a Deutsche Industrie Norm standard pin.

O. Reg. 345/15 s. 3

24. A worker shall use protection appropriate in the circumstances when there is a risk of eye injury to the worker.

25. A worker shall use protection appropriate in the circumstances when there is a risk of injury on a project from contact between the worker's skin and,

(a) a noxious gas, liquid, fume or dust;

(b) an object that may puncture, cut or abrade the skin;

(c) a hot object, hot liquid or molten metal; or

(d) radiant heat.

26. Sections 26.1 to 26.9 apply where a worker may be exposed to any of the following hazards:

1. Falling more than 3 metres.

2. Falling more than 1.2 metres, if the work area is used as a path for a wheelbarrow or similar equipment.

3. Falling into operating machinery.

4. Falling into water or another liquid.

5. Falling into or onto a hazardous substance or object.

6. Falling through an opening on a work surface.

O. Reg. 145/00 s. 12; 85/04 s. 4; 345/15 s. 4

26.1(1) A worker shall be adequately protected by a guardrail system that meets the requirements of subsections 26.3(2) to (8).

(2) Despite subsection (1), if it is not practicable to install a guardrail system as that subsection requires, a worker shall be adequately protected by the highest ranked method that is practicable from the following ranking of fall protection methods:

1. A travel restraint system that meets the requirements of section 26.4.

2. A fall restricting system that meets the requirements of section 26.5.

3. A fall arrest system, other than a fall restricting system designed for use in wood pole climbing, that meets the requirements of section 26.6.

4. A safety net that meets the requirements of section 26.8.

(3) The components of any system listed in subsection (2) shall be designed by a professional engineer in accordance with good engineering practice, and shall meet the requirements of any of the following National Standards of Canada standards that are applicable:

    1. CAN/CSA-Z259.1-05: Body Belts and Saddles for Work Positioning and Travel Restraint.

    2. CAN/CSA-Z259.2.5-12: Fall Arresters and Vertical Lifelines.

    3. CAN/CSA-Z259.2.2-98 (R2004): Self-Retracting Devices for Personal Fall-Arrest Systems.

    4. CAN/CSA-Z259.2.3-99 (R2004): Descent Control Devices.

    5. CAN/CSA-Z259.10-06: Full Body Harnesses.

    6. CAN/CSA-Z259.11-05: Energy Absorbers and Lanyards.

    7. CAN/CSA-Z259.12-01 (R2006): Connecting Components for Personal Fall Arrest Systems (PFAS).

    8. CAN/CSA-Z259.14-01 (R2007): Fall Restrict Equipment for Wood Pole Climbing.

(4) Before any use of a fall arrest system or a safety net by a worker at a project, the worker's employer shall develop written procedures for rescuing the worker after his or her fall has been arrested.

            O. Reg. 145/00 s. 12; 85/04 s. 5; 443/09 s. 1; 345/15 s. 5

26.2(1) An employer shall ensure that a worker who may use a fall protection system is adequately trained in its use and given adequate oral and written instructions by a competent person.

(1.1) In addition to the requirements of subsection (1), an employer shall ensure that a worker who may use a fall protection system meets the working at heights training requirements of Ontario Regulation 297/13 (*Occupational Health and Safety Awareness and Training*).

(2) The employer shall ensure that the person who provides the training and instruction referred to in subsection (1) prepares a written training and instruction record for each worker and signs the record.

(3) The training and instruction record shall include the worker's name and the dates on which training and instruction took place.

(4) The employer shall make the training and instruction record for each worker available to an inspector on request.

                  O. Reg. 145/00 s. 13; 252/14 s. 1

26.3(1) Despite paragraph 1 of section 26, a guardrail system that meets the requirements of this section shall be used if a worker has access to the perimeter or an open side of any of the following work surfaces and may be exposed to a fall of 2.4 metres or more:

    1. A floor, including the floor of a mezzanine or balcony.

    2. The surface of a bridge.

    3. A roof while formwork is in place.

    4. A scaffold platform or other work platform, runway or ramp.

(2) One of the following precautions shall be used to prevent a worker from falling through an opening on a work surface:

    1. A guardrail system that meets the requirements of this section.

    2. A protective covering that,

        i. completely covers the opening,

        ii. is securely fastened,

        iii. is adequately identified as covering an opening,

        iv. is made from material adequate to support all loads to which the covering may be subjected, and

        v. is capable of supporting a live load of at least 2.4 kilonewtons per square metre without exceeding the allowable unit stresses for the material used.

(3) The guardrail system or protective covering required under subsection (1) or (2) may be removed temporarily to perform work in or around the opening if a worker is adequately protected and signs are posted in accordance with subsections 44(1) and (2).

(4) The following are the specifications for a guardrail system:

    1. It shall have a top rail, an intermediate rail and a toe board.

    2. The intermediate rail may be replaced by material that can withstand a point load of 450 newtons applied in a lateral or vertical downward direction.

    3. Subject to subsection 116(8), the top of the guardrail system shall be located at least 0.9 metres but not more than 1.1 metres above the surface on which the system is installed.

    4. The intermediate rail shall be located midway between the top rail and the toe board.

    4.1 The toe board shall extend from the surface to which the guardrail system is attached to a height of at least 89 millimetres.

213/91

5. If the guardrail system is located at the perimeter of a work surface, the distance between the edge of the surface and the guardrail system shall not be greater than 300 millimetres.

(5) A guardrail system shall be capable of resisting anywhere along the length of the system the following loads when applied separately, without exceeding the allowable unit stress of each material used:

1. A point load of 675 newtons applied in a lateral direction to the top rail.

2. A point load of 450 newtons applied in a vertical downward direction to the top rail.

3. A point load of 450 newtons applied in a lateral or vertical downward direction to the intermediate rail, or midway between the top rail and the toe board.

4. A point load of 225 newtons applied in a lateral direction to the toe board.

(6) The distance between any two adjacent posts of the guardrail system may be greater than 2.4 metres only if the system is capable of resisting the loads specified in subsection (5) increased in proportion to the greater distance between the posts.

(7) The following additional requirements apply to a guardrail system that is made of wood:

1. The wood shall be spruce, pine or fir (S-P-F) timber of construction grade quality or better and shall not have any visible defect affecting its load-carrying capacity.

2. The wood shall be free of sharp objects such as splinters and protruding nails.

3. The system shall have posts that are at least 38 millimetres by 89 millimetres, are securely fastened to the surface and are spaced at intervals of not more than 2.4 metres.

4. The top rail and the intermediate rail shall each be at least 38 millimetres by 89 millimetres.

(7.1) If a guardrail system that is made of wood is constructed and installed so that it is capable of resisting all loads that it may be subjected to by a worker, the following do not apply:

1. The requirement in paragraph 2 of subsection (4) that the replacement material can withstand a point load of 450 newtons.

2. Subsections (5) and (6).

(8) The following additional requirements apply to a guardrail system that is made of wire rope:

　　1. The top rail and intermediate rail shall be made of wire rope that is at least 10 millimetres in diameter, and the rope shall be kept taut by a turnbuckle or other device.

　　2. The outward deflection of the top rail and intermediate rail resulting from the loads specified in subsection (5) shall not extend beyond the edge of a work surface.

　　3. The system shall have vertical separators at intervals of not more than 2.4 metres and horizontal supports at intervals of not more than 9 metres.

　　4. [Repealed O. Reg. 443/09, s. 2(6).]

O. Reg. 145/00 s. 14; 443/09 s. 2; 345/15 s. 6

26.4(1) A travel restraint system shall consist of a full body harness with adequate attachment points or a safety belt.

(2) The full body harness or safety belt shall be attached by a lifeline or lanyard to a fixed support that meets the requirements of section 26.7.

(3) The travel restraint system shall be inspected by a competent worker before each use.

(4) If a component of the travel restraint system is found to be defective on inspection, the defective component shall immediately be taken out of service.

O. Reg. 145/00 s. 14

26.5(1) A fall restricting system that is not designed for use in wood pole climbing shall consist of an assembly of components that is,

　　(a) attached to an independent fixed support that meets the requirements of section 26.7; and

　　(b) designed and arranged in accordance with the manufacturer's instructions and so that a worker's free fall distance does not exceed 0.6 metres.

(2) A fall restricting system that is designed for use in wood pole climbing,

　　(a) shall consist of an assembly of components that is designed and arranged in accordance with the manufacturer's instructions; and

　　(b) shall not allow pole slippage in excess of the distances set out in the applicable National Standards of Canada standard referred to in subsection 26.1(3).

(3) A fall restricting system shall be inspected by a competent worker before each use.

(4) If a component of the fall restricting system is found to be defective on inspection, the component shall be taken out of service immediately.

(5) If a worker who is using the fall restricting system falls or slips more than the distance determined under clause (1)(b) or (2)(b), as the case may be, the system shall be taken out of service immediately and shall not be used again by a worker unless all components of the system have been certified by the manufacturer as being safe for reuse.

O. Reg. 145/00 s. 14; 85/04 s. 6

26.6(1) A fall arrest system shall consist of a full body harness with adequate attachment points and a lanyard equipped with a shock absorber or similar device.

(2) The fall arrest system shall be attached by a lifeline or by the lanyard to an independent fixed support that meets the requirements of section 26.7.

(3) The fall arrest system shall be arranged so that a worker cannot hit the ground or an object or level below the work.

(4) Despite subsection (1), the fall arrest system shall not include a shock absorber if wearing or using one could cause a worker to hit the ground or an object or level below the work.

(5) The fall arrest system shall not subject a worker who falls to a peak fall arrest force greater than 8 kilonewtons.

(6) The fall arrest system shall be inspected by a competent worker before each use.

(7) If a component of the fall arrest system is found to be defective on inspection, the defective component shall immediately be taken out of service.

(8) If a worker who is using the fall arrest system falls, the system shall be immediately removed from service and shall not be used again by a worker unless all components of the system have been certified by the manufacturer as being safe for re-use.

(9) Subsections (1) to (8) do not apply to fall restricting systems designed for use in wood pole climbing.

O. Reg. 145/00 s. 14; 85/04 s. 7

26.7(1) A permanent anchor system shall be used as the fixed support in a fall arrest system, fall restricting system or travel restraint system if the following conditions are met:

    1. The anchor system has been installed according to the *Building Code*.

    2. It is safe and practical to use the anchor system as the fixed support.

(2) If the conditions set out in subsection (1) are not met, a temporary fixed support shall be used that meets the following requirements:

    1. Subject to paragraph 2, a support used in a fall arrest system shall be capable of supporting a static force of at least 8 kilonewtons without exceeding the allowable unit stress for each material used.

    2. If a shock absorber is also used in the fall arrest system, the support shall be capable of supporting a static force of at least 6 kilonewtons without exceeding the allowable unit stress for each material used.

    3. Subject to paragraph 4, a support used in a fall restricting system must be capable of supporting a static force of at least 6 kilonewtons without exceeding the allowable unit stress for each material used.

    4. Paragraph 3 does not apply to a support that is used in accordance with the manufacturer's written instructions and is adequate to protect a worker.

    5. A support used in a travel restraint system shall be capable of supporting a static force of at least 2 kilonewtons without exceeding the allowable unit stress for each material used.

(3) Despite the requirements listed in subsection (2), the support capacity of a temporary fixed support used in a fall protection system may be determined by dynamic testing in accordance with good engineering practice to ensure that the temporary fixed support has adequate capacity to arrest a worker's fall.

(4) A fixed support shall not have any sharp edges that could cut, chafe or abrade the connection between it and another component of the system.

(5) Subsections (1) to (4) do not apply to fall restricting systems designed for use in wood pole climbing.

                           O. Reg. 145/00 s. 14; 85/04 s. 8

26.8(1) A safety net shall be designated, tested and installed in accordance with ANSI/ASSE Standard A10.11-2010, Safety Requirements for Personnel and Debris Nets.

(2) The safety net shall be installed by a competent worker.

(3) A professional engineer or a competent person under the engineer's supervision shall inspect and test the installation of the safety net before it is put in service.

(4) The engineer shall document the inspection and testing of the safety net.

(5) A copy of the document shall be kept at the project while the safety net is in service.

O. Reg. 145/00 s. 14; 85/04 s. 9; 345/15 s. 7

26.9(1) This section applies to a lanyard or lifeline that is part of a travel restraint system or a fall arrest system.

(2) The following requirements apply to a lanyard or a lifeline:

    1. It shall not be used in such a way that it is likely to be cut, chafed or abraded.

    2. It shall not be subjected to extreme temperature, flame, abrasive or corrosive materials or other hazards that may damage it.

    3. The free end of the lanyard or lifeline shall be kept clear of equipment and machinery.

(3) Only one person at a time may use a lanyard.

(4) The connecting ends of a lanyard shall be wrapped around a protective thimble and adequately fastened with a swaged fitting or eye splice supplied by the manufacturer of the lanyard.

(5) A horizontal or vertical lifeline shall be kept free from splices or knots, except knots used to connect it to a fixed support.

(6) Only one person at a time may use a vertical lifeline.

(7) A vertical lifeline shall,

    (a) extend to the ground; or

    (b) have a positive stop that prevents the rope grab or other similar device from running off the end of the lifeline.

(8) The following requirements apply to a horizontal lifeline system:

    1. It shall be designed by a professional engineer in accordance with good engineering practice.

2. The design may be a standard design or a custom design.

3. The design shall,

    i. show the arrangement of the system including the anchorage or fixed support system,

    ii. indicate the components used,

    iii. state the number of workers that can safely be attached to it,

    iv. set out instructions for installation or erection, and

    v. show the design loads for the system.

4. The system shall be installed or erected, and maintained, in accordance with the professional engineer's design.

5. Before each use, the system shall be inspected by a professional engineer or a competent worker designated by a supervisor.

6. The constructor shall keep the design at the project while the system is in use.

O. Reg. 145/00 s. 14; 242/16, s. 5

26.10 [Revoked O. Reg. 85/04, s. 10.]

26.11 [Revoked O. Reg. 85/04, s. 10.]

27. (1) Despite subsections 26.1(1) and (2), if the following conditions are met, a worker shall wear a lifejacket or other personal flotation device that is adequate:

1. The worker is exposed to a risk of drowning on a project.

2. It is not reasonably possible to install a guardrail system as subsection 26.1(1) requires.

3. It is not reasonably possible to protect the worker adequately by means of a fall protection method as subsection 26.1(2) requires.

(2) If a worker may drown at a project,

    (a) at least two workers trained to perform rescue operations shall be available to perform rescue operations;

    (b) rescue equipment shall be provided in a suitable location on or near the project; and

    (c) all workers on the project shall be advised of the rescue procedures to be followed and their role, if any, in carrying out a rescue.

(3) The rescue equipment shall include,

    (a) a seaworthy boat equipped with a lifebuoy attached to a buoyant heaving line not less than 15 metres in length and a boat hook; and

(b) [Repealed O. Reg. 443/09, s. 3(2).]

(c) an alarm system capable of warning a worker of the necessity of carrying out a rescue operation.

(4) The boat shall be power-driven if the water is likely to be rough or swift.

(5) The alarm system shall be activated when a rescue operation is necessary.

(6) [Repealed O. Reg. 443/09, s. 3(3).]

O. Reg. 443/09 s. 3

Hygiene

28. (1) A reasonable supply of potable drinking water shall be kept readily accessible at a project for the use of workers.

(2) Drinking water shall be supplied from a piping system or from a clean, covered container with a drain faucet.

(3) Workers shall be given a sanitary means of drinking the drinking water.

(4) Workers shall not be required to share a common drinking cup to drink water.

29. (1) In this section,

"facilities" means toilet, urinal and clean-up facilities;

"non-sewered flush toilet facilities" [Revoked O. Reg. 527/00, s. 1.]

"service", when used as a verb, means to have waste pumped out and to have the facilities replenished where necessary.

"sewered toilet facilities" [Revoked O. Reg. 527/00, s. 1.]

(2) [Revoked O. Reg. 527/00, s. 1.]

(3) The constructor shall ensure,

(a) that facilities are provided or arranged for workers before work has started at a project; and

(b) that workers at the project have reasonable access to these facilities.

(4) Subject to subsections (5) and (6), the facilities shall be located not more than 180 metres, measured horizontally, from the project work area.

(5) If work is being performed in a tunnel, the facilities shall be located not more than 180 metres, measured horizontally, from the entrance to the tunnel.

(6) The facilities may be located not more than 3 kilometres from the work area if transportation to the facilities is provided for workers where reasonably required.

(7) If the project is the construction of a building, the facility shall be located not more than 9 metres, measured vertically, from the level at which work is being performed, in addition to meeting the requirement set out in subsection (4).

(8) The location of the facilities under subsection (7) may be varied if the arrangement affords reasonable accessibility for workers.

(9) If the location of the facilities is varied under subsection (8), the constructor shall document in writing the location and the reasons for the variance, and shall provide the document to,

    (a) the joint health and safety committee or the health and safety representative, if any, for the workplace; or

    (b) the workers, if there is no committee or representative for the workers.

(10) The constructor shall,

    (a) inform workers of the location of the facilities; and

    (b) post the location of the facilities in a conspicuous place at the project if it is practical to do so.

(11) The facilites shall be serviced, cleaned and sanitized as frequently as necessary to maintain them in a clean and sanitary condition.

(12) The constructor shall keep at the project for the duration of the project,

    (a) a record of the servicing, cleaning and sanitizing of the facilities; and

    (b) a copy of the document required under subsection (9), if any.

(13) Facilities that are not under the constructor's control satisfy the requirements of this section only if the constructor has received permission from the facilities' owner for workers to use the facilities.

              O. Reg. 145/00 s. 15; 527/00 s. 1; 142/17, s. 6

29.1(0.1) In this section,

"non-sewered flush toilet facilities" means water flush toilets or chemical flush toilets that have the features listed in subsection (0.2);

"sewered toilet facilities" means water flush toilets that are connected to a sanitary sewer system and equipped with a trap in accordance with the applicable provisions of the Building Code.

(0.2) The features referred to in the definition of "non-sewered flush toilet facilities" in subsection (0.1) are:

1. The toilets are not connected to a sanitary sewer system.
2. They are equipped with a trap or a positive seal separating stored waste from the bowl.
3. The waste is first flushed from the bowl with water or with water containing chemical additives. Then the waste is deposited into a container and chemically treated sufficiently for the container's maximum capacity.

(1) Each toilet facility shall meet the following requirements:

1. There shall be a toilet with an open-front toilet seat.
2. There shall be a toilet paper holder and an adequate supply of toilet paper. If the facility is intended for use by female workers, there shall be a disposal receptacle for sanitary napkins.
3. The facility shall afford the user privacy and protection from weather and from falling objects. There shall be a self-closing door that can be locked from inside the facility.
4. The facility shall be,
    i. illuminated by natural or artificial light,
    ii. adequately heated, if that is possible, and
    iii. adequately ventilated.
5. If the facility is intended for use by males only or by females only, it shall have a sign indicating that fact.
6. The facility shall be kept in good repair at all times.

(2) Separate toilet facilities shall be provided for male and female workers, unless the facilities are intended to be used by only one worker at a time.

(3) Sewered toilet facilities or non-sewered flush toilet facilities shall be provided at a project, subject to subsection (4).

(4) If a project is being carried out in a remote unpopulated area and it is not reasonably possible to provide the toilet facilities required under subsection (3), other types of toilet facilities that come as close as possible to having the features of non-sewered flush toilet facilities shall be provided instead.

(5) When water flush toilets or non-recirculating chemical flush toilets are provided, the minimum number of toilets required at the project is as follows:

TABLE 1

Item	Column 1 Minium number of toilets	Column 2 Number of workers regularly employed at the project
1.	1	1-15
2.	2	16-30
3.	3	31-45
4.	4	46-60
5.	4, plus 1 additional toilet for each additional group of 15 or fewer workers	61 or more

(6) If the toilets are located in a multiple water flush toilet facility and are intended to be used by male workers, water flush urinals may be substituted for a maximum of two-thirds of the number of toilets required by subsection (5).

(7) When toilets other than water flush toilets or non-recirculating chemical flush toilets are provided, the minimum number of toilets required at the project is as follows:

TABLE 2

Item	Column 1 Minium number of toilets	Column 2 Number of workers regularly employed at the project
1.	1	1-10
2.	2	11-20
3.	3	21-30
4.	4	31-40
5.	4, plus 1 additional toilet for each additional group of 15 or fewer workers	41 or more

(8) If the toilets are located in a portable single-unit toilet facility intended for use by male workers, there shall be at least one urinal for each toilet.

(9) Portable urinals equipped with clean-up facilities are permitted in addition to the requirements of this section.

O. Reg. 145/00 s. 15; 527/00 s. 2; 345/15 s. 8; 142/17, s. 7

29.2(1) Each single-toilet facility shall be provided with its own clean-up facility.

(1.1) In a multiple-toilet facility at a project, one clean-up facility shall be provided for every two toilets.

(2) Each clean-up facility shall meet the following requirements:

1. Subject to subsection (3), the facility shall have a wash basin with running water. Both hot and cold running water shall be available if reasonably possible.

2. Soap or hand cleanser shall be provided.

3. Paper towels or a hand dryer shall be provided. If paper towels are provided, there shall be a waste disposal receptacle nearby.

(3) If is is not reasonably possible to have a wash basin with running water at a clean-up facility, hand cleanser that can be used without water shall be provided instead.

O. Reg. 145/00 s. 15; 527/00 s. 3

30. Workers who handle or use corrosive, poisonous or other substances likely to endanger their health shall be provided with washing facilities with clean water, soap and individual towels.

General Requirements

31. (1) Every part of a project, including a temporary structure,

(a) shall be designed and constructed to support or resist all loads and forces to which it is likely to be subjected without exceeding the allowable unit stress for each material used; and

(b) shall be adequately braced to prevent any movement that may affect its stability or cause its failure or collapse.

(2) If two structural steel columns or structural steel beams are connected to a common column or common beam,

(a) the connection shall be made using a clipped double connection; or

(b) the first column or beam shall be secured in a seated connection.

(3) No part of a project, including a temporary structure, shall be subjected to a load in excess of the load it is designed and constructed to bear.

32. (1) During the construction of a building, temporary or permanent flooring shall be installed progressively as the building is erected.

(2) Temporary flooring,

(a) shall consist of material that, without exceeding the allowable unit stress for the material used, is capable of supporting,

(i) any load to which it is likely to be subjected, and

(ii) a load of at least 2.4 kilonewtons per square metre;

(b) shall be securely fastened to and supported on girders, beams or other structural members that are capable of supporting any load likely to be applied to the flooring without exceeding the allowable unit stress for the structural members; and

(c) shall extend over the whole area of the surface on or above which work is being carried out.

(3) Temporary flooring shall not be subjected to a load in excess of the load that it is designed and constructed to bear.

33. (1) Subject to subsection (2), work on a building shall not be carried out at a distance higher than the higher of two storeys or the first column splice above the temporary or permanent flooring.

(2) If the vertical distance between the tiers of column splices on a building exceeds two storeys, work shall not be carried out higher than three storeys above the temporary or permanent flooring.

(3) This section does not apply to work carried out by a worker,

    (a) who is working from a scaffold;

    (b) whose fall would be arrested by means of a safety net without endangering the worker; or

    (c) who is using a fall arrest system attached to the project.

34. (1) If material may fall on a worker, overhead protection shall be provided,

    (a) at every means of access to and egress from a building or other structure under construction; and

    (b) above every area where work is being carried out.

(2) Overhead protection shall consist of material capable of supporting 2.4 kilonewtons per square metre without exceeding the allowable unit stress for the material used.

Housekeeping

35. (1) Waste material and debris shall be removed to a disposal area and reusable material shall be removed to a storage area as often as is necessary to prevent a hazardous condition arising and, in any event, at least once daily.

(2) Rubbish, debris and other materials shall not be permitted to fall freely from one level to another but shall be lowered by a chute, in a container or by a crane or hoist.

(3) Despite subsection (2), rubbish, debris and other materials from demolition on a project may be permitted to fall or may be dropped into an enclosed designated area to which people do not have access.

(4) A chute,

    (a) shall be adequately constructed and rigidly fastened in place;

(b) if it has a slope exceeding a gradient of one in one, shall be enclosed on its four sides;

(c) shall have a gate at the bottom end if one is necessary to control the flow of material; and

(d) shall discharge into a container or an enclosed area surrounded by barriers.

(5) The entrance to a chute,

(a) shall be constructed to prevent spilling over when rubbish, debris and other materials are being deposited into the chute;

(b) if it is at or below floor level, shall have a curb that is at least 100 millimetres high;

(c) shall not be more than 1.2 metres high;

(d) shall be kept closed when the chute is not in use; and

(e) shall be designed so that any person will be discouraged from entering it.

36. If a formwork tie, reinforcing steel, a nail or another object protruding from concrete or another surface may endanger a worker, the protrusion shall be removed, cut off at the surface or otherwise protected as soon as practicable.

37. (1) Material or equipment at a project shall be stored and moved in a manner that does not endanger a worker.

(2) No material or equipment to be moved by a crane or similar hoisting device shall be stored under or in close proximity to an energized outdoor overhead electrical conductor.

38. Blocking, support chains, metal bands, wire rope and rigging components shall be removed from material or equipment in a manner that does not endanger a worker.

39. Material and equipment at a project shall be piled or stacked in a manner that prevents it from tipping, collapsing or rolling.

40. (1) No material shall be stored, stacked or piled closer than 1.8 metres to,

(a) an opening in a floor or roof;

(b) the open edge of a floor, roof or balcony; or

(c) an excavation.

(2) Subsection (1) does not apply with respect to material in a building or a completely enclosed part of a building that is used solely for storing and distributing materials.

(3) Subsection (1) does not apply with respect to small masonry units including bricks, blocks and similar objects,

    (a) that can be handled by one worker;

    (b) that are to be used at the edge of a floor, a roof, an excavation or an opening in a floor or roof; and

    (c) that are stacked in a pile whose height is less than the distance from the face of the pile to the edge of the floor, roof, excavation or opening in a floor or roof.

O. Reg. 142/17, s. 8

41. A combustible, corrosive or toxic substance shall be stored in a suitable container.

42. (1) A storage cylinder for compressed gas shall be secured in an upright position.

(2) The control valve of a storage cylinder for compressed gas, other than a cylinder connected to a regulator, supply line or hose, shall be covered by a protective cap that is secured in its proper position.

(3) A spent storage cylinder shall not be stored inside a building.

(4) No storage cylinder for propane shall be placed closer than three metres to a source of ignition or fire.

(5) Subsection (4) does not apply to a storage cylinder,

    (a) that forms part of hand-held propane equipment;

    (b) that forms part of a lead pot used in plumbing or electrical work;

    (c) that forms part of a propane-powered or propane-heated vehicle; or

    (d) that is protected from a source of ignition by a barrier, wall or other means of separation.

43. (1) A flammable liquid or gas shall be stored in a building or storage tank that is suitable for the purpose and, if practicable, not less than 100 metres from a magazine for explosives.

(2) No more than one work day's normal supply of a flammable liquid shall be stored in a building or structure on a project unless it is stored,

(a) in a container that is suitable for the particular hazards of the liquid; and

(b) in a controlled access area or a room,

(i) that has sufficient window area to provide explosion relief to the outside, and

(ii) that is remote from the means of egress from the building or structure.

(3) A portable container used to store or transport flammable liquids,

(a) shall be approved for use for that liquid by a recognized testing laboratory; and

(b) shall have a label stating the use for which the container is approved and the name of the testing laboratory which gave the approval required by clause (a).

44. (1) Signs meeting the requirements of subsection (2) shall be posted in prominent locations and in sufficient numbers to warn workers of a hazard on a project.

(2) A sign shall contain the word "DANGER" written in legible letters that are at least 150 millimetres in height and shall state that entry by any unauthorized person to the area where the hazard exists is forbidden.

(3) Without limiting the generality of subsection (1), a sign shall be posted,

(a) adjacent to a hoisting area;

(b) under a boatswain's chair or a suspended work platform;

(c) at the outlet from a chute;

(d) at a means of access to a place where there may be a noxious gas, vapour, dust or fume, noxious substance or a lack of oxygen; and

(e) where there is a potential hazard from an energized overhead electrical conductor at more than 750 volts.

(4) No person shall enter an area in which a sign is posted other than a worker authorized to work in the area.

O. Reg. 242/16, s. 6; 142/17, s. 9

45. (1) The areas in which a worker is present and the means of access to and egress from those areas shall be adequately lit.

(2) A light bulb used in a temporary lighting system shall be enclosed by a mechanical protection device.

46. **(1)** A project shall be adequately ventilated by natural or mechanical means,

(a) if a worker may be injured by inhaling a noxious gas, vapour, dust or fume or from a lack of oxygen; or

(b) if a gas, vapour, dust or fume may be capable of forming an explosive mixture with air.

(2) If it is not practicable to provide natural or mechanical ventilation in the circumstances described in clause (1)(a), respiratory protective equipment suitable for the hazard shall be provided to and used by the workers.

47. **(1)** This section does not apply to an internal combustion engine operated in a tunnel.

(2) No internal combustion engine shall be operated in an excavation or in a building or other enclosed structure unless there is an adequate supply of air for combustion and,

(a) the exhaust gases and fumes from the engine are adequately discharged directly outside the excavation, building or other enclosed structure to a point sufficiently remote to prevent the return of the gases and fumes; or

(b) there is adequate natural or mechanical ventilation to ensure that exhaust gases and fumes from the engine will not accumulate in the excavation, building or other enclosed structure.

(3) An excavation or a building or other enclosed structure in which an internal combustion engine is being operated shall be tested for airborne concentrations of carbon monoxide to ensure that the concentrations do not exceed the applicable limits as determined in accordance with section 4 of Regulation 833 of the Revised Regulations of Ontario, 1990 (*Control of Exposure to Biological or Chemical Agents*), made under the Act.

(4) The testing under subsection (3) shall be carried out by a competent worker in accordance with a written testing strategy, which shall be developed by the employer in consultation with the joint health and safety committee or a health and safety representative, if any.

(5) An internal combustion engine under this section shall be maintained and used in accordance with section 93.

O. Reg. 345/15 s. 9

48. (1) When a drum, tank, pipeline or other container is to be repaired or altered,

> (a) its internal pressures shall be adjusted to atmospheric pressure before any fastening is removed;
>
> (b) it shall be drained, cleaned and ventilated or otherwise rendered free from any explosive, flammable or harmful substance; and
>
> (c) it shall not be refilled during repair or alteration if the substance which is to be placed in it may vaporize or ignite.

(2) Clauses (1)(a) and (b) do not apply with respect to a pipeline if hot-tapping and boxing-in are carried out by a competent worker under controlled conditions that provide for the protection of all persons.

Temporary Heat

49. (1) A fuel-fired heating device shall be located, protected and used in such a way that there is no risk of igniting a tarpaulin or similar temporary enclosure or combustible materials adjacent to it.

(2) No fuel-fired heating device shall be used in a confined or enclosed space unless there is an adequate supply of air for combustion and adequate general ventilation.

(3) A fuel-fired heating device shall be protected from damage and from overturning.

(4) No fuel-fired heating device shall be located so as to restrict any means of egress.

(5) A fuel-fired heating device that generates noxious products of combustion shall discharge the products of combustion outside the building or structure in which it is located.

50. All fuel supply lines shall be constructed, guarded or placed in such a way as to be protected from damage.

51. (1) Temporary steam-piping shall be installed and supported so as not to endanger a worker.

(2) Temporary steam-piping shall be insulated or otherwise protected if a worker is likely to come into contact with it.

Fire Safety

52. (1) Fire extinguishing equipment shall be provided at readily accessible and adequately marked locations at a project.

(1.1) Every worker who may be required to use fire extinguishing equipment shall be trained in its use.

(2) Without limiting subsection (1), at least one fire extinguisher shall be provided,

    (a) where flammable liquids or combustible materials are stored, handled or used;

    (b) where oil-fired or gas-fired equipment, other than permanent furnace equipment in a building, is used;

    (c) where welding or open-flame operations are carried on; and

    (d) on each storey of an enclosed building being constructed or altered.

(3) At least one fire extinguisher shall be provided in a workshop for each 300 or fewer square metres of floor area.

(4) Clause (2)(d) and subsection (3) do not apply to a building,

    (a) that is to be used as a detached or semi-detached single-family dwelling;

    (b) that has two storeys or less and is to be used as a multiple family dwelling; or

    (c) that has one storey with no basement or cellar.

O. Reg. 145/00 s. 16

53. (1) Fire extinguishing equipment shall be of a suitable type and size to permit the evacuation of workers during a fire.

(2) Every fire extinguisher,

    (a) shall be a type whose contents are discharged under pressure; and

    (b) shall have an Underwriters' Laboratories of Canada rating of at least 4A40BC.

54. (1) Fire extinguishing equipment shall be protected from physical damage and from freezing.

(2) After a fire extinguisher is used, it shall be refilled or replaced immediately.

55. Every fire extinguisher shall be inspected for defects or deterioration at least once a month by a competent worker who shall record the date of the inspection on a tag attached to it.

56. No work shall be carried out at a height of 84 metres or more in a building unless the building has temporary or permanent fire pumps that provide a minimum water flow of 1,890 litres per minute at a discharge pressure of at least 450 kilopascals at and above the 84-metre height.

O. Reg. 145/00 s. 17

57. (1) As construction proceeds in a building with two or more storeys, a permanent or temporary standpipe shall be installed such that the distance between the standpipe and the uppermost work level is no more than two storeys at any given time.

(2) Subsection (1) does not apply to work carried out in a building which is not required by the Building Code to have a permanent standpipe.

(3) A permanent standpipe,

(a) shall have sufficient hose outlets to permit every part of the building to be protected by a hose not longer than twenty-three metres;

(b) shall have a connection for the use of the local fire department located on the street side of the building not more than 900 millimetres and not less than 300 millimetres above ground level and to which there is clear access at all times; and

(c) shall be maintained so as to be readily operable if required to be used.

(4) Every hose outlet in a permanent standpipe shall have a valve.

(5) Every hose used with a permanent standpipe,

(a) shall be at least thirty-eight millimetres in diameter;

(b) shall have a combination straight stream and fog nozzle; and

(c) shall be stored on a rack in such a way as to protect it from damage and keep it available for immediate use.

(6) If a temporary standpipe has been installed, it shall not be disconnected until the permanent standpipe is connected, so that there is always a standpipe in service.

(7) A temporary standpipe shall be maintained so that it is readily operable.

(8) A temporary standpipe shall have at least one hose outlet per floor, with a valve and a hose attached to each hose outlet and a nozzle attached to each hose.

(9) In addition to the requirements of subsection (8), there shall be a connection to which there is clear access at all times, located betweeen 30 and 90 centimetres above ground level on a side of the building that faces the street.

(10) A hose outlet on a temporary standpipe,

(a) shall have a valve; and

(b) shall be capable of accepting a hose that is 38 millimetres in diameter.

(11) If a temporary standpipe is installed in a building under construction, the constructor shall post at the project, or have available for review, a floor plan of the building indicating,

(a) the location of the hose outlets on each floor;

(b) the location of the point on the perimeter of each floor that is furthest from the hose outlet on that floor; and

(c) the location of each exit on each floor.

(12) The constructor shall give a copy of the floor plan to the fire department located nearest to the project.

O. Reg. 145/00 s. 18; 142/17, s. 10

58. No flammable liquid shall be transferred from one container to another by the direct application of air under pressure.

Dust Control
[Heading added O. Reg. 145/00, s. 19.]

59. If the dissemination of dust is a hazard to a worker, the dust shall be adequately controlled or each worker who may be exposed to the hazard shall be provided with adequate personal protective equipment.

O. Reg. 145/00 s. 19

Confined Spaces

60. [Repealed O. Reg. 628/05, s. 2.]

61. [Repealed O. Reg. 628/05, s. 2.]

62. [Repealed O. Reg. 628/05, s. 2.]

63. [Repealed O. Reg. 628/05, s. 2.]

Public Way Protection

64. (1) No work shall be carried out on a building or structure located 4.5 metres or less from of a public way unless a covered way is constructed over the part of the public way that is adjacent to the project.

(2) Subsection (1) does not apply with respect to a building or structure if the work being done is enclosed.

(3) A covered way,

    (a) shall have an unobstructed height of not less than 2.4 metres;

    (b) shall have an unobstructed width of not less than 1.1 metres or, if it is over a sidewalk that is less than 1.1 metres wide, have a width equal to the width of the sidewalk;

    (c) shall be capable of supporting any load likely to be applied to it and capable of supporting a load of at least 2.4 kilonewtons per square metre;

    (d) shall have a weather-tight roof;

    (e) shall have the side adjacent to the project covered with a partition that has a smooth surface on the public way side;

    (f) shall have a railing one metre high from ground level on the street side; and

    (g) shall have adequate lighting within the public way.

O. Reg. 142/17,   s. 11

65. If work on a project may endanger a person using a public way, a sturdy fence at least 1.8 metres in height shall be constructed between the public way and the project.

66. Machinery, equipment and material that is being used, left or stored where it may be a hazard to traffic on a public way shall be marked by flashing devices.

O. Reg. 145/00 s. 20

Traffic Control
[Heading added O. Reg. 145/00, s. 21.]

67. (1) In this section,

"barricade" means a device that provides a visual indicator of the path a motorist is supposed to take;

"barrier" means a device that provides a physical limitation through which a vehicle would not normally pass, and includes a concrete barrier;

"mobile operation" means work, including a paving operation, that is done on a highway or the shoulder of a highway and moves along at speeds of less than 30 kilometers per hour.

(2) If a worker at a project on a highway may be endangered by vehicular traffic unrelated to the project, the project shall make use of as many of the following measures as is necessary to adequately protect the worker:
1. Barriers.
2. Barricades.
3. Delineators.
4. Lane control devices.
5. Warning signs.
6. Flashing lights.
7. Flares.
8. Traffic control devices.
9. Blocker trucks.
10. Crash trucks.
11. Sign trucks.
12. Speed control devices.
13. Longitudinal buffer areas.

(3) In addition to the measures listed in subsection (2) but subject to section 68, a worker may be used to direct traffic.

(4) Every employer shall develop in writing and implement a traffic protection plan for the employers' workers at a project if any of them may be exposed to a hazard from vehicular traffic.

(5) The traffic protection plan,
  (a) shall specify the vehicular traffic hazards and the measures described in subsection (2) to be used to protect workers; and
  (b) shall be kept at the project and made available to an inspector or a worker on request.

(6) A worker who is required to set up or remove measures described in subsection (2) on a roadway or a shoulder of a roadway,
  (a) shall be a competent worker;
  (b) shall not perform any other work while setting up or removing the measures; and

(c) shall be given adequate written and oral instruction, in a language that he or she understands, with respect to setting up or removing the measures.

(7) Adequate barriers shall be installed to protect workers at a project from vehicular traffic if the project,

(a) is on a freeway;

(b) is not a mobile operation; and

(c) is expected to require more than five days to complete.

(8) [Repealed O. Reg. 345/15, s. 11(2).]

(9) [Repealed O. Reg. 345/15, s. 11(2).]

(10) If it is not practical to install barriers as subsection (7) requires, or if the project is expected to require five days or less to complete, crash trucks shall be adequately positioned to protect workers.

(11) If work on a shoulder of a freeway is expected to take less than 30 minutes to complete, a vehicle with four-way flashers and a 360-degree beacon light shall be provided.

(12) The following measures shall be taken to protect a worker at a project if the project is on a freeway and involves a mobile operation:

1. An adequate number of crash trucks shall be adequately positioned between vehicular traffic and workers in order to adequately protect workers at the project.

2. If the operation involves intermittent stops averaging 30 minutes or less, an adequate number of barricades or delineators shall be adequately positioned between vehicular traffic and the worker.

3. If the operation involves intermittent stops averaging more than 30 minutes,

    i. an adequate longitudinal buffer area shall be provided if physically possible,

    ii. the lane on which work is being done shall be adequately identified with lane closure signs and a lane closure taper, and

    iii. an adequate number of barricades or delineators shall be adequately positioned between vehicular traffic and the work area.

O. Reg. 145/00, s. 21; 345/15, s. 11; 242/16, s. 7

68. The following requirements apply with respect to a sign used by a worker to direct vehicular traffic:

1. It shall be octagonal in shape, measure 450 milimetres betweeen opposite sides, and be mounted on a pole that is 1.2 metres long.

2. It shall be made of material with at least the rigidity of plywood that is six millimetres thick.

3. On one side it shall be high-intensity retro-reflective grade red in colour, with the word "STOP" written in legible high-intensity retro-reflective grade white letters 150 millimetres high in a central position on the sign.

4. On the other side it shall be high-intensity retro-reflective micro-prismatic fluorescent chartreuse in colour, with a black diamond-shaped border that is at least 317 millimetres by 317 millimetres, and with the word "SLOW" written in legible black letters 120 millimetres high in a central position on the sign.

5. It shall be maintained in a clean and legible condition.

O. Reg. 145/00 s. 22; 142/17, s. 12

69. (1) This section applies with respect to directing vehicular traffic that may be a hazard to workers on a public way.

(2) A worker shall not direct vehicular traffic for more than one lane in the same direction.

(3) A worker shall not direct vehicular traffic if the normal posted speed limit of the public way is more than 90 kilometres per hour.

(4) A worker who is required to direct vehicular traffic,

    (a) shall be a competent worker;

    (b) shall not perform any other work while directing vehicular traffic;

    (c) shall be positioned in such a way that he or she is endangered as little as possible by vehicular traffic; and

    (d) shall be given adequate written and oral instructions, in a language that he or she understands, with respect to directing vehicular traffic, and those instructions shall include a description of the signals that are to be used.

(5) The written instructions referred to in clause (4)(d) shall be kept at the project.

O. Reg. 145/00 s. 23

69.1(1) A worker who may be endangered by vehicular traffic shall wear a garment that covers at least his or her upper body and has the following features:

1. The garment shall be fluorescent blaze or international orange in colour.

2. On the front and the back, there shall be two yellow stripes that are 5 centimetres wide. The yellow area shall total at least 500 square centimetres on the front and at least 570 square centimetres on the back.

3. On the front, the stripes shall be arranged vertically and centred and shall be approximately 225 millimetres apart, measured from the centre of each stripe. On the back, they shall be arranged in a diagonal "X" pattern.

4. The stripes shall be retro-reflective and fluorescent.

(2) If the garment is a vest, it shall have adjustable fit.

(3) A nylon vest to which this section applies shall also have a side and front tear-away feature.

(4) In addition, a worker who may be endangered by vehicular traffic during night-time hours shall wear retro-reflective silver stripes encircling each arm and leg, or equivalent side visibility-enhancing stripes with a minimum area of 50 square centimetres per side.

O. Reg. 145/00 s. 23; 345/15 s. 12

Access to and Egress from Work Areas

70. (1) Access to and egress from a work area located above or below ground level shall be by stairs, runway, ramp or ladder.

(2) Subsection (1) does not apply to a work platform within the meaning of section 136.1 that is able to be moved to give access to a floor, roof or platform or to ground level.

O. Reg. 242/16, s. 8

71. Adequate means of egress shall be provided from a work area to permit the evacuation of workers during an emergency.

72. A work area, a route to and from a work area and a scaffold platform on which work is being performed shall be maintained at all times in a condition that does not endanger workers and, without limiting the generality of the foregoing,

(a) shall be kept clear of obstructions;

(b) shall be kept clear of snow, ice or other slippery material; and

(c) shall be treated with sand or similar material when necessary to ensure a firm footing.

Platforms, Runways and Ramps

73. (1) Runways, ramps and platforms other than scaffold platforms shall meet the requirements of this section.

(2) A runway, ramp or platform shall be designed, constructed and maintained to support or resist, without exceeding the allowable unit stresses for the materials of which it is made,

    (a) all loads and forces to which it is likely to be subjected; and

    (b) at least 2.4 kilonewtons per square metre.

(3) No runway, ramp or platform shall be loaded in excess of the load that it is designed and constructed to bear.

(4) A runway, ramp or platform shall be at least 460 millimetres wide and shall be securely fastened in place.

74. (1) A ramp shall have,

    (a) a slope not exceeding a gradient of 1 in 3; and

    (b) if its slope exceeds a gradient of 1 in 8, cross cleats made from nineteen millimetres by thirty-eight millimetres boards that are securely nailed to the ramp and spaced at regular intervals not exceeding 500 millimetres.

(2) Subsection (1) does not apply to a ramp installed in the stairwell of a building not exceeding two storeys in height if the ramp,

    (a) has a slope not exceeding a gradient of 1 in 1; and

    (b) has cross cleats made from thirty-eight millimetres by thirty-eight millimetres boards that are securely nailed to the ramp and spaced at regular intervals not exceed 300 millimetres.

Stairs and Landings

75. (1) No work shall be performed in a building or structure that will be at least two storeys high when it is finished unless stairs are installed in accordance with this section.

(2) As the construction of a building or structure progresses, permanent or temporary stairs shall be installed up to,

    (a) the uppermost work level; or

213/91

(b) if stairs would interfere with work on the uppermost work level, no more than two storeys or nine metres below the uppermost work level, whichever distance is shorter

(3) Subsection (2) does not apply with respect to,

(a) a part of a building or structure in which only the structural steel beams or columns are erected; or

(b) a structure to which a permanent ladder is attached before the structure is raised into position.

O. Reg. 142/17,   s. 13

76. (1) Temporary stairs and landings shall be designed, constructed and maintained to support a live load of 4.8 kilonewtons per square metre without exceeding the allowable unit stresses for each material used.

(2) No temporary stair or landing shall be loaded in excess of the load it is designed and constructed to bear.

77. (1) No work shall be performed in a building or structure with stairs unless the stairs meet the requirements of this section.

(2) Stairs shall have,

(a) a clear width of at least 500 millimetres;

(b) treads and risers of uniform width, length and height;

(c) subject to subsection (3), stringers with a maximum slope of 50 degrees from the horizontal;

(d) landings that are less than 4.5 metres apart measured vertically;

(e) a securely fastened and supported wooden handrail on the open sides of each flight; and

(f) a guardrail on the open side of each landing.

(3) The stringers of prefabricated stairs erected inside a tower formed by scaffold frame sections shall have a maximum slope of 60 degrees from the horizontal.

(4) A wooden handrail shall measure thirty-eight millimetres by eighty-nine millimetres and shall be free of loose knots, sharp edges, splinters and shakes.

(5) Skeleton steel stairs shall have temporary wooden treads securely fastened in place that are made of suitable planking extending the full width and breadth of the stairs and landings.

Ladders

78. In sections 78 to 84,

"extension trestle ladder" means a self-supporting portable ladder that is adjustable in length, consisting of a trestle ladder base, a vertically adjustable extension section and an adequate means of locking the ladder base and extension section together;

"platform ladder" means a self-supporting portable ladder that is not adjustable in length, where the highest standing level is a platform;

"single ladder" means a non-self-supporting portable ladder that is not adjustable in length and having only one section;

"step-ladder" means a self-supporting portable ladder that is not adjustable in length, having flat steps and a hinged back, and whose back section is either a single ladder or other supporting device, but does not include a step stool or platform ladder;

"step stool" means a self-supporting, portable, fixed or foldable ladder, not adjustable in length, and having,

    (a) a height of 800 millimetres or less, excluding side rails, if any, above the top cap,

    (b) flat steps, but no pail shelf, and

    (c) a ladder top cap that can be stood or stepped on;

"top step" means the first step below the top cap of a step-ladder or, if there is no top cap, the first step below the top of the rails;

"trestle ladder" means a self-supporting portable ladder, non-adjustable in length, having two sections and hinged at the top so as to be able to form equal angles with the base.

O. Reg. 345/15 s. 13

79. A ladder shall be designed, constructed and maintained so as not to endanger a worker and shall be capable of withstanding all loads to which it may be subjected.

O. Reg. 345/15 s. 13

80. (1) A portable ladder at a project shall be manufactured and shall meet the design, performance, test and marking requirements of a Grade 1, Grade 1A or Grade 1AA ladder in the CSA Standard Z11-12, Portable Ladders.

(2) Despite subsection (1), a portable single ladder that is custom-built for use at a project may be used at the project if the ladder has,

(a) rungs spaced at 300 millimetres on centres;

(b) side rails at least 300 millimetres apart; and

(c) a maximum length, measured along its side rail, of not more than nine metres.

(3) If a portable single ladder under subsection (2) is made of wood, the ladder shall also,

(a) be made of wood that is straight-grained and free of loose knots, sharp edges, splinters and shakes; and

(b) not be painted or coated with an opaque material that obscures the wood grain or interferes with inspections of the ladder.

(4) If the rungs of a ladder under subsection (3) are of the cleat type, the ladder shall also,

(a) have side rails that are not less than 400 millimetres but not more than 610 millimetres apart;

(b) have side rails that measure not less than,

(i) 38 millimetres by 89 millimetres if the ladder is 5.8 metres long or less, or

(ii) 38 millimetres by 140 millimetres if the ladder is more than 5.8 metres long;

(c) have rungs that measure not less than,

(i) 19 millimetres by 64 millimetres if the side rails are 400 millimetres apart, or

(ii) 19 millimetres by 89 millimetres if the side rails are more than 400 millimetres apart; and

(d) have rungs braced by filler blocks that are at least 19 millimetres thick and located between the rungs.

(5) If a ladder under subsection (3) is a double-width wooden ladder, the ladder shall also,

(a) have three evenly-spaced rails that measure at least 38 millimetres by 140 millimetres;

(b) have rungs that,

(i) measure at least 38 millimetres by 89 millimetres,

(ii) extend the full width of the ladder, and

(iii) are braced by filler blocks that are at least 19 millimetres thick; and

(c) be at least 1.5 metres wide but not more than 2 metres wide.

O. Reg. 345/15   s. 13

81. (1) A portable ladder,

    (a) shall be free from defective or loose rungs;

    (b) shall be placed on a firm and level footing or support surface; and

    (c) shall not be used in an elevator shaft or a similar hoisting area when the shaft or area is being used for hoisting.

(2) A non-self-supporting portable ladder shall be situated so that its base is not less than one-quarter, and not more than one-third, of the length of the ladder from a point directly below the top of the ladder and at the same level as the base of the ladder, if the ladder is not securely fastened to prevent its movement.

(3) A portable ladder or ladder section shall not be tied or fastened to another ladder or ladder section to increase its length unless the manufacturer's instructions allow for this.

(4) A manufactured portable ladder shall be used in accordance with the manufacturer's instructions.

O. Reg. 345/15   s. 13

82. (1) This section applies if a portable ladder is used as a means of access and egress between,

    (a) levels of a building or structure;

    (b) the ground or grade level to a building or structure; or

    (c) different work surface levels.

(2) The ladder,

    (a) shall extend at the upper level at least 900 millimetres above the landing surface;

    (b) shall, subject to subsection (3), have a clear space of at least 150 millimetres behind every rung;

    (c) shall be located so that an adequate landing surface that is clear of obstructions is available at the top and bottom of the ladder for access and egress; and

    (d) shall be secured at the top and bottom to prevent movement of the ladder.

(3) Clause (2)(b) does not apply to a ladder lying on an excavation wall that is sloped, as required by section 234.

O. Reg. 345/15   s. 13

83. (1) When a step-ladder is being used, its legs shall be fully spread open and its spreaders shall be locked.

(2) No worker shall stand or step on,

(a) the top cap, top step or pail shelf of a step-ladder;

(b) the top cap or top step of a combination ladder when it is used as a step-ladder;

(c) the top step of the extension section of an extension trestle ladder; or

(d) the top step of a trestle ladder.

O. Reg. 345/15 s. 13

84. (1) Subject to subsection (2), an access ladder fixed in position,

(a) shall be vertical;

(b) shall have rest platforms at not more than nine metre intervals;

(c) shall be offset at each rest platform;

(d) where the ladder extends over five metres above grade, floor or landing, shall have a safety cage commencing not more than 2.2 metres above grade, floor or landing and continuing at least 90 centimetres above the top landing with openings to permit access by a worker to rest platforms or to the top landing;

(e) shall have side rails that extend 90 centimetres above the landing;

(f) shall have rungs that are at least 15 centimetres from the wall and spaced at regular intervals;

(g) shall have an adequate landing surface that is clear of obstructions at the top and bottom of the ladder for access and egress;

(h) shall be free from defective or loose rungs; and

(i) shall not be used in an elevator shaft or a similar hoisting area when the shaft or area is being used for hoisting.

(2) Clauses (1)(b), (c) and (d) do not apply to any access ladder on a tower, water tank, chimney or similar structure that has a safety device that will provide protection should a worker using the ladder fall.

O. Reg. 631/94 s. 2; 345/15 s. 14(3)

Guardrails and Protective Coverings

85. [Revoked O. Reg. 145/00, s. 24.]

86. [Revoked O. Reg. 145/00, s. 24.]

Forms, Formwork, Falsework and Re-Shoring

87. (1) Formwork, falsework and re-shoring shall be designed, constructed, supported and braced so that they are capable of withstanding all loads and forces likely to be applied to them,

    (a) without exceeding the allowable working loads established for any component of the structure; and

    (b) without causing uplift, sliding, overturning or lateral displacement of the system.

(2) No formwork, falsework or re-shoring shall be loaded in excess of the load that it is designed and constructed to bear.

(3) The allowable working load of the formwork, falsework or re-shoring shall be established,

    (a) by a professional engineer in accordance with good engineering practice; or

    (b) by testing the principal components to their ultimate strength in a manner that simulates the actual loading conditions to which the formwork, falsework or re-shoring is likely to be subjected and by applying a reduction factor, in accordance with good engineering practice, to the values of ultimate strength.

(4) The results of the testing in clause (3)(b) shall be verified and certified by a professional engineer and made available to an inspector upon request.

(5) If single post shores are placed more than one tier high, the junction of each tier shall be braced against a fixed support in at least two directions in order to prevent any lateral movement.

88. Formwork and falsework shall not be removed unless,

    (a) the concrete is strong enough to support itself and any loads that may be applied to the structure; or

    (b) the concrete and the structure are adequately re-shored.

89. (1) This section applies with respect to formwork, falsework and re-shoring that includes,

    (a) a tubular metal frame;

    (b) a column whose effective length is dependent upon lateral restraints between the ends of the column;

    (c) shores placed one upon another to form a supporting system that is more than one tier in height;

213/91

(d) shores which are three metres or more in height;

(e) a truss;

(f) members so connected to one another that a load applied to one member may alter or induce stress in another member; or

(g) a unitized modular formwork or falsework structure intended to be moved as a unit.

(2) Formwork and falsework shall be designed by a professional engineer in accordance with good engineering practice and be installed or erected in accordance with the design drawings.

(3) Formwork and falsework shall, before the placement of concrete, be inspected by a professional engineer or by a competent worker designated in writing by the professional engineer.

(4) The person carrying out the inspection shall state in writing whether the formwork and falsework is installed or erected in accordance with the design drawings for it.

(5) The constructor shall keep the design drawings and the statements on the project while the formwork or the falsework is in use.

90. Re-shoring shall be designed by a professional engineer in accordance with good engineering practice and be erected in accordance with the design drawings.

91. Falsework and re-shoring,

(a) shall have sound and rigid footings capable of carrying the maximum load to which the footings may be subjected without settlement or deformation of the soil or structure below the footings; and

(b) shall be adequately protected to prevent deformation caused by frost heave.

92. (1) Design drawings by a professional engineer for the formwork, falsework or re-shoring,

(a) if a manufactured system is used, shall identify the components;

(b) if non-manufactured system components are used, shall show the size, grade and specifications of the non-manufactured system components;

(c) shall show the design loads for the structure and shall detail the bracing and external ties required to adequately support the design loads;

(d) if the structure is a unitized modular formwork or falsework structure intended to be lifted or moved as a unit, shall show the attachment points for rigging and hoisting; and

(e) shall set out the erection instructions that are specified by the manufacturer or by the professional engineer.

(f) [Revoked O. Reg. 85/04, s. 11.]

(2) The constructor shall keep the design drawings on the project while the formwork, falsework or re-shoring is in use.

O. Reg. 85/04 s. 11

Equipment, General

93. (1) All vehicles, machinery, tools and equipment shall be maintained in a condition that does not endanger a worker.

(2) No vehicle, machine, tool or equipment shall be used,

(a) while it is defective or hazardous;

(b) when the weather or other conditions are such that its use is likely to endanger a worker; or

(c) while it is being repaired or serviced, unless the repair or servicing requires that it be operated.

(3) All vehicles, machines, tools and equipment shall be used in accordance with any operating manuals issued by the manufacturers.

(4) For vehicles, machines, tools and equipment rated at greater than 10 horsepower, copies of any operating manuals issued by the manufacturers shall be kept readily available at the project.

O. Reg. 145/00 s. 25

94. (1) All mechanically-powered vehicles, machines, tools and equipment rated at greater than 10 horsepower shall be inspected by a competent worker to determine whether they can handle their rated capacity and to identify any defects or hazardous conditions.

(2) The inspections shall be performed before the vehicles, machines, tools or equipment are first used at the project and thereafter at least once a year or more frequently as recommended by the manufacturer.

O. Reg. 145/00 s. 26

95. (1) Every replacement part for a vehicle, machine, tool or equipment shall have at least the same safety factor as the part it is replacing.

(2) No modification to, extension to, repair to or replacement of a part of a vehicle, machine, tool or equipment shall result in a reduction of the safety factor of the vehicle, machine, tool or equipment.

96. **(1)** No worker shall operate a vehicle or powered machine, tool or equipment at a project unless he or she is competent to do so.

(2) However, a worker being trained in the operation of a vehicle or powered machine, tool or equipment may operate it while being instructed and supervised by a competent person.

O. Reg. 145/00 s. 26; 345/15 s. 15

97. **(1)** Every vehicle other than a trailer shall be equipped with brakes and a seat or other place for the vehicle operator.

(2) No person other than the operator shall ride on a vehicle unless a seat is provided for the use of, and is used by, the person.

98. The means of access to any operator's station in a vehicle, machine or equipment shall not endanger the operator and shall have skid-resistant walking, climbing and work surfaces.

99. A cab or screen shall be provided to protect a worker who is exposed to an overhead hazard while operating a vehicle.

100. **(1)** No vehicle, machine or equipment shall be drawn or towed by another vehicle on a project unless there are two separate means of attachment to the vehicle drawing or towing it.

(2) Subsection (1) does not apply with respect to a vehicle being drawn or towed in which there is an operator and that has brakes that are able to stop the vehicle with its load, if any.

(3) Each means of attachment referred to in subsection (1) shall be constructed and attached in such a way that the failure of one means of attachment does not permit the vehicle, machine or equipment being drawn or towed to become detached from the other vehicle.

101. **(1)** No worker shall remain on or in a vehicle, machine or equipment while it is being loaded or unloaded if the worker might be endangered by remaining there.

(2) Such action as may be necessary to prevent an unattended vehicle, machine or equipment from being started or set in motion by an unauthorized person shall be taken.

(3) An unattended vehicle, machine or equipment shall have its brakes applied and its wheels blocked to prevent movement when the vehicle, machine or equipment is on sloping ground or is adjacent to an excavation.

102. No operator shall leave unattended the controls of,

    (a) a front-end loader, backhoe or other excavating machine with its bucket raised;

    (b) a bulldozer with its blade raised;

    (c) a fork-lift truck with its forks raised; or

    (d) a crane or other similar hoisting device with its load raised.

103. (1) No worker shall operate a shovel, backhoe or similar excavating machine in such a way that it or part of its load passes over a worker.

(2) No worker shall operate a crane or similar hoisting device in such a way that part of its load passes over another worker unless the other worker is receiving the load or is engaged in sinking a shaft.

(3) If practicable, a worker who is receiving a load or is engaged in sinking a shaft shall be positioned so that no load or part of a load carried by a crane or similar hoisting device passes over the worker.

(4) Subsections (2) and (3) do not apply in respect of a multi-tiered load as defined in section 103.1 if written procedures have been developed and implemented for the particular project in accordance with that section.

O. Reg. 627/05 s. 2

103.1(1) In this section,

"move" includes raise and lower;

"multi-tiered load" means two or three individually rigged structural steel pieces that are,

    (a) suspended so that they remain horizontal,

    (b) aligned vertically, and

    (c) moved simultaneously by a crane;

"multi-tiered load hoisting operation" means the moving of one or more multi-tiered loads by one crane at a project;

"procedures" means the procedures prepared under subsection (7).

(2) A multi-tiered load,

    (a) shall not contain structural steel pieces that are bundled together;

(b) shall not contain more than three structural steel pieces;

(c) shall not use one structural steel piece to support another;

(d) shall have each structural steel piece independently slung back to the main load hook or master link;

(e) shall be lowered only by a crane using power-controlled lowering.

(3) A crane shall be used to move only one multi-tiered load at a time.

(4) A crane shall not be used for a multi-tiered load if it is contrary to the crane manufacturer's specifications or limitations to do so.

(5) No worker shall be in an area where a multi-tiered load hoisting operation is taking place unless he or she is directly engaged in the operation.

(6) Before a multi-tiered load hoisting operation is begun at a project, written procedures to ensure the safety of workers engaged in the operation shall be developed and implemented.

(7) The procedures shall be prepared by a professional engineer in accordance with good engineering practice and shall,

(a) include design drawings that illustrate the arrangement and dimensions of the structural steel pieces, the assembly of rigging components and devices, and all attachment points;

(b) identify the crane and its rated load-carrying capacity, and identify and specify its limitations and restrictions, if any;

(c) describe the method of determining the weight of the structural steel pieces;

(d) specify the maximum load per lift and the maximum reach of the crane per lift;

(e) identify all factors that could affect the safety of the multi-tiered load hoisting operation, such as wind speed, weather conditions, potential overlapping of cranes and other restrictions;

(f) state the measures to be taken to control and secure multi-tiered loads while they are being moved;

(g) specify any circumstances that would require additional work, including inspections, to be performed by a professional engineer to ensure the safety of any worker engaged in the multi-tiered load hoisting operation; and

(h) identify all critical parts of the rigging and of the rigged structural steel pieces that are to be inspected before each lift, and set out the inspection criteria to be followed.

(8) The employer responsible for a multi-tiered load hoisting operation shall,

(a) create a document that identifies the workers engaged in the multi-tiered load hoisting operation by name and job title and states their respective duties;

(b) ensure that, before the multi-tiered load hoisting operation is begun, a copy of the procedures is provided to and reviewed with each worker engaged in the operation;

(c) ensure that the procedures are implemented, and are followed throughout the multi-tiered load hoisting operation;

(d) ensure that any deviations from the procedures are approved by a professional engineer, in writing, before any multi-tiered load is moved; and

(e) unless the professional engineer who prepared the procedures specifies otherwise, appoint a competent worker to ensure that the procedures, including the inspections described in clause (7)(h), are followed before any multi-tiered load is moved.

(9) The employer responsible for a multi-tiered load hoisting operation shall keep a copy of the following available for inspection at the project until the operation is completed:

1. The procedures.
2. The document described in clause (8)(a).
3. Any approvals given under clause (8)(d).

(10) Before the first multi-tiered load hoisting operation is started at a project, the constructor shall give notice to the Ministry office located nearest the project, in person, by telephone, by fax or by electronic means.

O. Reg. 627/05 s. 3; 142/17, s. 14

104. (1) Every project shall be planned and organized so that vehicles, machines and equipment are not operated in reverse or are operated in reverse as little as possible.

(2) Vehicles, machines and equipment at a project shall not be operated in reverse unless there is no practical alternative to doing so.

(3) Operators of vehicles, machines and equipment shall be assisted by signallers if either of the following applies:

1. The operator's view of the intended path of travel is obstructed.

2. A person could be endangered by the vehicle, machine or equipment or by its load.

(4) Subsection (3) also applies to shovels, backhoes and similar excavating machines and to cranes and similar hoisting devices.

(5) The operator and the signaller shall,

(a) jointly establish the procedures by which the signaller assists the operator; and

(b) follow those procedures.

(6) If subsection (3) applies to the project and it is not possible to carry out the project without some operation of vehicles and equipment in reverse, signs shall be posted at the project in conspicuous places warning workers of the danger.

O. Reg. 145/00 s. 27

105. A dump truck shall be equipped with an automatic audible alarm that signals when the truck is being operated in reverse.

O. Reg. 145/00 s. 27

106. (1) A signaller shall be a competent worker and shall not perform other work while acting as a signaller.

(1.1) The signaller shall wear a garment that covers at least his or her upper body and has the following features:

1. The garment shall be fluorescent blaze or international orange in colour.

2. On the front and the back, there shall be two yellow stripes that are 5 centimetres wide. The yellow area shall total at least 500 square centimetres on the front and at least 570 square centimetres on the back.

3. On the front, the stripes shall be arranged vertically and centred and shall be approximately 225 millimetres apart, measured from the centre of each stripe. On the back, they shall be arranged in a diagonal "X" pattern.

4. The stripes shall be retro-reflective and fluorescent.

(1.2) If the garment is a vest, it shall have adjustable fit.

(1.3) A nylon vest to which this section applies shall also have a side and front tear-away feature.

(1.4) In addition, a signaller who may be endangered during night-time hours shall wear retro-reflective silver stripes encircling each arm and leg, or equivalent side visibility-enhancing stripes with a minimum area of 50 square centimetres per side.

(1.5) The employer shall,

(a) ensure that the signaller has received adequate oral training in his or her duties and has received adequate oral and written instructions in a language that he or she understands; and

(b) keep the written instructions at the project.

(2) A signaller,

(a) shall be clear of the intended path of travel of the vehicle, machine or equipment, crane or similar hoisting device, shovel, backhoe or similar excavating machine or its load;

(b) shall be in full view of the operator of the vehicle, machine or equipment, crane or similar hoisting device, shovel, backhoe or similar excavating machine;

(c) shall have a clear view of the intended path of travel of the vehicle, machine or equipment, crane or similar hoisting device, shovel, backhoe or similar excavating machine or its load; and

(d) shall watch the part of the vehicle, machine or equipment or crane or similar hoisting device, shovel, backhoe or similar excavating machine or its load whose path of travel the operator cannot see.

(3) The signaller shall communicate with the operator by means of a telecommunication system or, where visual signals are clearly visible to the operator, by means of prearranged visual signals.

O. Reg. 145/00 s. 28; 345/15 s. 16

107. No worker shall use as a work place a platform, bucket, basket, load, hook or sling that is capable of moving and that is supported by a fork-lift truck, front-end loader or similar machine.

108. Blocking shall be installed to prevent the collapse or movement of part or all of a piece of equipment that is being dismantled, altered or repaired if its collapse or movement may endanger a worker.

109. Every gear, pulley, belt, chain, shaft, flywheel, saw and other mechanically-operated part of a machine to which a worker has access shall be guarded or fenced so that it will not endanger a worker.

110. (1) Safety chains, cages or other protection against blown-off side or lock rings shall be used when inflating a tire mounted on a rim.

(2) If a cage is used, the tire shall be inflated by remote means.

111. (1) A lifting jack shall have its rated capacity legibly cast or stamped on it in a place where it can be readily seen.

(2) A lifting jack shall be equipped with a positive stop to prevent over-travel or, if a positive stop is not practicable, with an overtravel indicator.

112. (1) Every chain-saw shall have a chain that minimizes kickback and a device to stop the chain in the event of a kickback.

(1.1) No worker shall use a chain-saw unless he or she has been adequately trained in its use.

(1.2) No worker shall use a chain-saw unless he or she is wearing,

 (a) adequate personal protective equipment and clothing, including gloves, and

 (b) adequate eye protection and hearing protection.

(2) A worker shall hold a chain-saw firmly when starting it and firmly in both hands when using it.

(3) The chain of a chain saw shall be stopped when not cutting.

O. Reg. 145/00 s. 29

113. No object or material shall be placed, left or stored in a location or manner that may endanger a worker.

114. A hose that may whip shall be attached to a rope or chain in order to prevent whipping.

115. No barrel, box or other loose object shall be used as a work place or as a support for a ladder, scaffold or work platform.

116. (1) No stilts shall be present at or used on a project except in accordance with this section.

(2) No leg extensions, other than stilts, shall be present at or used on a project.

(3) Subject to subsection (4), stilts may be used on a project for work in residential units and residential common areas only if they are used for the following purposes:

 1. Drywall finishing work.
 2. Installation of insulation.

3. Installation of vapour barriers.

(4) Stilts shall not be used on a scaffold or to climb up or down stairs.

(5) Stilts used in accordance with this section shall,
 (a) be commercially manufactured;
 (b) be made of unpainted metal;
 (c) have a non-slip surface on the bottom of each base plate;
 (d) be in good working condition; and
 (e) be suitable for their intended use.

(6) Stilts may be used to a maximum height of 76 centimetres as measured from the work surface that the user of the stilts would otherwise stand on to the top of the foot plate.

(7) Stilts may be used on a work surface only if the work surface satisfies the following conditions:
 1. It is made of rigid material.
 2. It is either level or does not have a slope of more than three per cent.
 3. All openings on the work surface are adequately covered or guarded.
 4. All open sides of the work surface are adequately guarded.
 5. It is free of debris or anything else that may be a hazard to a worker on stilts.
 6. All obstructions that cannot be removed are adequately guarded, placed or secured to prevent a worker on stilts from being injured.

(8) If stilts are used in a work area for which sections 26.1 and 26.3 require a guardrail system, the guardrail system shall be modified by adding,
 (a) an additional top rail,
  (i) 76 centimetres above the existing top rail, or
  (ii) at a height above the existing top rail equal to the height of the stilts being used in the work area; and
 (b) an intermediate rail that is located midway between the additional top rail and the existing top rail.

(9) A modified guardrail system described in subsection (8) shall be capable of resisting any load it could be subjected to by a worker on stilts.

(10) An employer shall ensure that a worker who uses stilts is trained in their use by completing an adequate training program that,

213/91

165

(a) enables the worker to demonstrate proficiency in the safe and proper use of stilts; and

(b) provides instruction on the relevant requirements of this Regulation; and

(c) provides instruction on,

    (i) mounting and dismounting,

    (ii) adjusting stilts to suit the individual worker and the work,

    (iii) walking on and working with stilts while maintaining balance and stability,

    (iv) inspecting stilts for damage and defects,

    (v) maintaining, servicing and storing stilts,

    (vi) conducting an inspection of the work area before commencing work to identify hazards for stilts use,

    (vii) correcting any hazardous conditions identified under subclause (vi), and

    (viii) setting up tools and materials to ensure they are adequately accessible when using stilts.

(11) No worker shall use stilts at a project unless he or she has successfully completed a program described in subsection (10) and carries proof of completing the program at all times when using the stilts.

(12) A worker using stilts at a project shall inspect the stilts for damage, wear, corrosion and other defects the first time each day that the worker uses the stilts.

(13) An employer shall ensure that a worker does not use stilts that are damaged, worn, corroded or defective and no worker shall use such stilts.

(14) Stilts shall be stored, serviced and maintained in accordance with the manufacturer's instructions.

O. Reg. 443/09 s. 4

Explosive Actuated Fastening Tool

117. (1) No worker shall use an explosive actuated fastening tool unless he or she has been adequately trained in its use.

(2) When using an explosive actuated fastening tool, the worker shall carry proof of her or her training in its use.

(3) No worker shall use an explosive actuated fastening tool unless he or she is wearing,

(a) adequate personal protective equipment; and

(b) adequate eye protection.

O. Reg. 145/00 s. 30

118. A worker using an explosive actuated fastening tool shall inspect it before using it to ensure,

(a) that it is clean;

(b) that all moving parts operate freely;

(c) that its barrel is free from obstruction; and

(d) that it is not defective.

119. (1) No worker shall use an explosive actuated fastening tool unless it has a suitable protective guard,

(a) that is at least seventy-five millimetres in diameter;

(b) that is mounted at right angles to the barrel of the tool; and

(c) that is centred on the muzzle end of the tool, if practicable.

(2) An explosive actuated fastening tool shall be inoperable unless,

(a) its muzzle end is held against a surface using a force at least 22 newtons greater than the force equivalent of the weight of the tool measured in newtons;

(b) when a protective guard is centred on the muzzle end of the tool, the bearing surface of the guard is not tilted more than eight degrees from the work surface.

(3) Subsection (1) and clause (2)(b) do not apply with respect to an explosive actuated fastening tool if the velocity of a fastener fired from it does not exceed 90 metres per second measured at a distance of two metres from its muzzle end when propelled by the maximum commercially-available explosive load it is chambered to accept.

(4) An explosive actuated fastening tool that is designed to require dismantling into separate parts for loading shall be inoperable unless the separate parts are locked together.

(5) An explosive actuated fastening tool shall have a firing mechanism that prevents the tool from being fired if it is dropped or while it is being loaded or prepared for firing.

(6) The firing movement for an explosive actuated fastening tool shall be a separate action from the operation of bringing the tool into firing position.

(7) An explosive actuated fastening tool shall not be capable of being fired until the operator performs the two separate actions described in subsection (6).

O. Reg. 145/00 s. 31; 142/17, s. 15

120. (1) Every explosive actuated fastening tool shall be stored in a locked container when not in use.

(2) No explosive actuated fastening tool shall be left unattended when out of its container.

(3) No explosive actuated fastening tool shall be loaded unless it is being prepared for immediate use.

(4) No explosive actuated fastening tool, whether or not it is loaded, shall be pointed at a person.

121. (1) Every explosive load for an explosive actuated fastening tool,

(a) shall be marked or labelled so that a worker can easily identify its strength; and

(b) shall be stored in a locked container unless it is required for immediate use.

(2) No explosive load for an explosive actuated fastening tool,

(a) shall be stored in a container with explosive loads of other strengths; or

(b) shall be left unattended where it may be available to a worker who is not qualified to operate an explosive actuated fastening tool.

(3) A misfired explosive load removed from an explosive actuated fastening tool shall be placed in a water-filled container on the project until the misfired explosive load is removed from the project.

Welding and Cutting

122. (1) Cylinders, piping and fittings used in welding and cutting shall be protected against damage.

(2) No cylinder of compressed gas used in welding and cutting shall be dropped, hoisted by slings or magnets or transported or stored in a horizontal position.

(3) The valve of a cylinder shall be closed when the cylinder is spent or is not being used.

123. Precautions to prevent a fire shall be taken when using a blow torch or welding or cutting equipment or a similar piece of equipment.

124. (1) No arc welding electrode or ground lead shall be hung over a compressed gas cylinder.

(2) An area where electric welding is carried on shall be kept free of electrode stubs and metal scrap.

(3) Receptacles for electrode stubs shall be provided and used.

Access at Heights
[Heading added O. Reg. 242/16, s. 9.]

125. (1) Where work cannot be done on or from the ground or from a building or other permanent structure without hazard to workers, a worker shall be provided with a scaffold, a suspended work platform, a boatswain's chair or a multi-point suspended work platform that meets the requirements of this Regulation.

(2) A worker who is on or under a scaffold, a suspended work platform system or a multi-point suspended work platform while it is being erected, altered or dismantled shall be on a part of the scaffold, suspended work platform system or multi-point suspended work platform that meets the requirements of this Regulation.

O. Reg. 242/16, s. 9

Scaffolds and Work Platforms

126. (1) Every scaffold shall be designed and constructed to support or resist,

    (a) two times the maximum load or force to which it is likely to be subjected, without exceeding the allowable unit stresses for the materials of which it is made; and

    (b) four times the maximum load or force to which it is likely to be subjected without overturning.

(2) Despite clause (1)(a), a scaffold with structural components whose capacity can only be determined by testing shall be designed and constructed to support or resist three times the maximum load or force to which it is likely to be subjected without causing the failure of any component.

(3) No scaffold shall be loaded in excess of the load that it is designed and constructed to bear.

127. (1) The failure load of a scaffold which consists of structural components whose capacity cannot be determined by testing shall be established by testing the components in a manner that simulates the actual loading conditions for which each of the components is fabricated.

(2) A professional engineer shall verify and certify the results of a test and the corresponding rated load of the scaffold.

(3) The constructor shall make available to an inspector upon request a copy of the certification by the professional engineer.

128. (1) Every scaffold,

    (a) shall have uprights braced diagonally in the horizontal and vertical planes to prevent lateral movement;

    (b) shall have horizontal members that are adequately secured to prevent lateral movement and that do not have splices between the points of support;

    (c) shall have footings, sills or supports that are sound, rigid and capable of supporting at least two times the maximum load to which the scaffold may be subjected without settlement or deformation that may affect the stability of the scaffold;

    (d) shall have all fittings and gear, including base plates or wheels, installed in accordance with the manufacturer's instructions;

    (e) shall have connecting devices between frames that provide positive engagement in tension and compression;

    (f) shall have safety catches on all hooks; and

    (g) shall be adequately secured at vertical intervals not exceeding three times the least lateral dimension of the scaffold, measured at the base, to prevent lateral movement.

(2) A scaffold shall be constructed of suitable structural materials and, if lumber is used, it shall be construction grade or Number 1 Grade spruce.

(3) A scaffold mounted on pneumatic tires shall not be supported by the pneumatic tires while the scaffold is being erected, used or dismantled.

(4) If tubular metal frames are used to support masonry units on a scaffold platform, each frame leg shall have a minimum working load of,

    (a) twenty-two kilonewtons for standard frames; and

    (b) 16.7 kilonewtons for walk-through frames.

129. (1) A scaffold mounted on castors or wheels,

(a) shall be equipped with a suitable braking device on each castor or wheel; and

(b) shall have the brakes applied when a worker is on the scaffold.

(2) A scaffold mounted on castors or wheels shall be equipped with guy wires or outriggers to prevent its overturning if the height of the scaffold platform exceeds three times the least lateral dimension of the scaffold,

(a) measured at the base of the scaffold; or

(b) if outriggers are used, measured between the outriggers.

(3) No scaffold mounted on castors or wheels that has a scaffold platform more than 2.4 metres above the base shall be moved when a worker is on it unless,

(a) the worker is wearing a full body harness as part of a fall arrest system attached to a fixed support; and

(b) the scaffold is being moved on a firm level surface.

130. (1) A scaffold shall be designed by a professional engineer and shall be erected in accordance with the design if the scaffold exceeds,

(a) fifteen metres in height above its base support; or

(b) ten metres in height above its base support if the scaffold is constructed of a tube and clamp system.

(2) Design drawings for a scaffold shall set out erection instructions and the rated loads for the scaffold.

(3) A professional engineer or a competent worker designated by the supervisor of the project shall inspect the scaffold before it is used to ensure that it is erected in accordance with the design drawings.

(4) The person carrying out an inspection shall state in writing whether the scaffold is erected in accordance with the design drawings.

(5) The constructor shall keep at a project the design drawings and the written statement for a scaffold while the scaffold is erected.

O. Reg. 85/04 s. 12

131. Only a competent worker shall supervise the erection, alteration and dismantling of a scaffold.

132. (1) A professional engineer shall inspect and give a written opinion as to the structural adequacy of a centre pole scaffold used in silo construction when required by subsection (2).

(2) An inspection shall be performed on the earlier of,

(a) the twenty-fourth time the scaffold is erected following the most recent inspection; or

(b) for a scaffold used in the construction of,

(i) a monolithic silo, two years after the scaffold is erected or after the most recent inspection, and

(ii) a stave silo, one year after the scaffold is erected or after the most recent inspection.

(3) The employer responsible for constructing the silo shall keep with a scaffold every written opinion by a professional engineer concerning the scaffold while it is in use on a project.

(4) The employer responsible for constructing the silo shall record information about the frequency of use of the scaffold in a log book which shall be kept with the scaffold while it is in use on a project.

133. (1) This section applies with respect to a worker who is installing reinforcing steel on a vertical surface consisting of horizontal reinforcing steel bars.

(2) A scaffold shall be provided for a worker who is working more than 3.7 metres above the ground or a floor.

(3) If a scaffold cannot be erected, a worker shall use and wear a work belt.

(4) No worker who is climbing the vertical surface shall carry reinforcing steel bars.

134. (1) Every scaffold platform and other work platform shall be designed, constructed and maintained to support or resist, without exceeding the allowable unit stresses for the material of which it is constructed,

(a) all loads and forces to which it is likely to be subjected; and

(b) at least 2.4 kilonewtons per square metre.

(2) Each component of a scaffold platform or other work platform shall be capable of supporting a load of at least 2.2 kilonewtons without exceeding the allowable unit stress for each material used.

(3) No scaffold platform or other work platform shall be loaded in excess of the load that it is designed and constructed to bear.

135. (1) A scaffold platform or other work platform,

(a) shall be at least 460 millimetres wide;

213/91

(b) if it is 2.4 metres or more above a floor, roof or other surface, consist of planks laid tightly side by side for the full width of the scaffold;

(c) shall be provided with a guardrail as required by section 26.3;

(d) shall be provided with a means of access as required by section 70;

(e) shall not have any unguarded openings; and

(f) shall have each component secured against slipping from its supports.

(2) A scaffold platform or other work platform made of sawn lumber planks shall have planks of number 1 grade spruce that do not have any defect affecting their load-carrying capacity and,

(a) that bear a legible grade identification stamp or are permanently identified as being number 1 grade spruce;

(b) that are at least forty-eight millimetres thick by 248 millimetres wide;

(c) that are arranged so that their span does not exceed 2.1 metres;

(d) that overhang their supports by not less than 150 millimetres and not more than 300 millimetres; and

(e) that are cleated or otherwise secured against slipping.

O. Reg. 527/00 s. 4

136. (1) Cubes of masonry units on a scaffold platform shall be placed directly over the scaffold frame.

(2) If it is not practicable to comply with subsection (1), the masonry units shall be placed on the scaffold platform in a manner that conforms with the load capability provisions of the scaffold platform as set out in section 134.

(3) The surface of an outrigger bracket platform used by a masonry worker shall be not more than one metre below the associated material storage platform.

(4) Masonry units to be installed in a building or structure shall be distributed along the scaffold platform before being used.

136.0.1 (1) The distance between the platform of an outrigger scaffold and the wall beyond which the scaffold extends shall not exceed 75 millimetres.

(2) The outrigger beams of an outrigger scaffold shall be secured against horizontal and vertical movement.

O. Reg. 242/16, s. 10

Suspended Work Platforms and Boatswain's Chairs
[Heading amended O. Reg. 242/16, s. 11.]

Interpretation and Application
[Heading added O. Reg. 242/16, s. 11.]

136.1 In sections 137 to 142.06,

"allowable suspended load" means the combined weight of a suspended work platform or boatswain's chair, the hoisting device or devices, the rated platform capacity and the suspended portion of the suspension line or lines;

"anchorage connector" means a component or a system of components of a fixed support that secures a suspended work platform or boatswain's chair and its associated suspension lines and lifelines to the fixed support;

"CSA Standard Z271-10" means Canadian Standards Association (CSA) Standard Z271-10, Safety Code for Suspended Platforms;

"work platform" means a built or manufactured work surface that, as the context requires, is intended to be used as or is in use as the work area of a suspended work platform system, but does not include a boatswain's chair.

O. Reg. 85/04, s. 13; 242/16, s. 11

136.2 Sections 137 to 142.06 do not apply to multi-point suspended work platforms.

O. Reg. 242/16, s. 11

General Requirements: Design
[Heading added O. Reg. 242/16, s. 11.]

137. (1) Every suspended work platform system or powered boatswain's chair, including all components and connections of the suspended work platform system or boatswain's chair, shall be designed by a professional engineer in accordance with,

    (a) good engineering practice;

    (b) CSA Standard Z271-10, with the exception of clauses 6.1.1(b) and 6.1.2;

    (c) the requirements of this section; and

(d) for a suspended work platform, the requirements of section 137.1.

(2) For the purposes of clause (1)(b), every reference to the National Building Code of Canada in CSA Standard Z271-10 shall be deemed to be a reference to the Building Code.

(3) Every suspended work platform system or powered boatswain's chair shall be designed to be able to support or resist,

(a) the rated platform capacity; and

(b) any other loads likely to be applied to it, including the loads specified in clause 6.1.5 (Design loads from forces imposed on a platform) of CSA Standard Z271-10.

(4) The design of a suspended work platform system or powered boatswain's chair shall take into account the potential increased loads due to wind on all components of the suspended work platform system or powered boatswain's chair if shielding, tarpaulins, enclosures, signs, banners or other similar items were used or attached.

(5) The design of a work platform or boatswain's chair shall use the factored load combination calculated in accordance with subsection (6).

(6) The factored load combination shall be calculated as follows:

$$p \, (a_D \, D + y \, a_L \, L)$$

where,

p is an impact factor of 1.25,

a_D is a dead load factor 1.25,

D is the dead load,

y is an importance factor of 1.9,

a_L is a live load factor of 1.5, and

L is the live load.

(7) [Repealed O. Reg. 242/16, s. 11.]

(8) [Repealed O. Reg. 242/16, s. 11.]

(9) [Repealed O. Reg. 242/16, s. 11.]

(10) [Repealed O. Reg. 242/16, s. 11.]

(11) [Repealed O. Reg. 242/16, s. 11.]

O. Reg. 242/16, s. 11

137.1 (1) In addition to the requirements set out in section 137, a suspended work platform shall be designed in accordance with the requirements of this section.

(2) A work platform shall not have a span of greater than 30 metres between adjacent points of suspension.

(3) The rated platform capacity for a suspended work platform shall use the relevant minimum live load determined as follows:

1. If the span of the work platform between adjacent points of suspension is 12 metres or less, the minimum live load shall be 340 kilograms.

2. If the span of the work platform between adjacent points of suspension is greater than 12 metres but not more than 15 metres, the minimum live load shall be 450 kilograms.

3. If the span of the work platform between adjacent points of suspension is greater than 15 metres but not more than 20 metres, the minimum live load shall be 680 kilograms.

4. If the span of the work platform between adjacent points of suspension is greater than 20 metres but not more than 25 metres, the minimum live load shall be 900 kilograms.

5. If the span of the work platform between adjacent points of suspension is greater than 25 metres but not more than 30 metres, the minimum live load shall be 1,130 kilograms.

(4) There shall be an additional load allowance for any construction debris or abrasive blasting grit to a depth of at least 25 millimetres and for other materials that may accumulate or be placed on the work platform as a result of the work.

(5) In the case of a modular suspended work platform system, all connections used to transfer a load from one module to another shall be designed to withstand at least the design loads as specified in this section, and any other external loads or forces.

(6) Despite section 26.3, a guardrail system on a work platform shall meet the requirements of clause 6.4 (Guardrail System) of CSA Standard Z271-10, with the exception of clause 6.4.1(b).

O. Reg. 242/16, s. 11

137.2 Design drawings for a work platform shall,

(a) set out the size and specifications of all the components of the work platform, including the type and grade of all materials to be used;

(b) state the maximum rated platform capacity of the work platform;

(c) state welding specifications for all welds used on the work platform, including weld length, weld locations and welding fillers to be used; and

(d) identify all critical welds used on the work platform.

O. Reg. 242/16, s. 11

137.3 (1) A work platform shall not be used unless the requirements of this section have been satisfied.

(2) In the case of a work platform designed before January 1, 2017, a professional engineer shall prepare a report that confirms that the structural integrity of the work platform is at least equal to the structural integrity of a work platform designed in accordance with sections 137 and 137.1.

(3) In the case of a work platform designed on or after January 1, 2017, a professional engineer shall prepare a report that,

(a) confirms that the work platform meets the requirements of sections 137 and 137.1;

(b) confirms that the suspended work platform's design and configuration have been tested to and meet the performance requirements set out in sections 7 to 11 of the ANSI/UL 1322-2004 Standard, "Fabricated Scaffold Planks and Stages", for the rated platform capacity and worst-case configurations;

(c) provides the results of the tests described in clause (b);

(d) subject to subsection (4), provides proof that the manufacturer of a suspended work platform or suspended work platform module has been certified to International Standard ISO 9001, Quality management systems — Requirements; and

(e) includes, if required under subsection (4), the quality assurance report described in clause (4)(c).

(4) If there is no proof available that the manufacturer has been certified to ISO 9001, a professional engineer shall,

(a) ensure that every critical weld of the work platform is subjected to a non-destructive test;

(b) examine all components of the work platform to ensure they are manufactured in accordance with the design drawings referred to in section 137.2;

(c) prepare a written quality assurance report that,

(i) confirms that every critical weld and every structural component referred to in subsection 139.1(2) is correctly manufactured and has no defects, and

(ii) includes the results of non-destructive tests described in clause (a) and the examination described in clause (b).

(5) The work platform shall be assembled in accordance with the manufacturer's instructions for assembly.

(6) While a work platform is in use at a project, the employer shall,

(a) make available to an inspector on request, the design drawings for the work platform; and

(b) keep at the project and make available to an inspector on request, the report prepared under subsection (2) or (3) and the manufacturer's instructions for assembly of the work platform.

O. Reg. 242/16, s. 11

General Requirements: Worker Training
[Heading added O. Reg. 242/16, s. 11.]

138. (1) An employer shall ensure that a worker successfully completes a training program that meets the requirements set out in subsection (2) at the following times:

1. Before the worker uses a suspended work platform system or boatswain's chair for the first time.

2. As often as is necessary, but at least every three years, after the worker uses a suspended work platform system or boatswain's chair for the first time.

(2) The training program referred to in subsection (1) shall,

(a) consist of adequate oral and written instruction for using a suspended work platform system or boatswain's chair, including instruction on,

(i) the regulations under the Act that apply to the work,

(ii) fall hazards related to the use of the suspended work platform system or boatswain's chair,

      (iii) selecting, putting on, using and inspecting personal protective equipment, and its components, that the worker is required to wear,

      (iv) identifying and using fixed supports for a suspended work platform system or boatswain's chair and for the worker's fall arrest system,

      (v) the components, functions and limitations of a suspended work platform system or boatswain's chair, tiebacks and operational controls,

      (vi) reading and using roof plans and work plans,

      (vii) the load limitations of the suspended work platform system or boatswain's chair, and

      (viii) elements of emergency rescue from a suspended work platform system or boatswain's chair; and

   (b) require the worker to demonstrate proficiency in,

      (i) selecting, putting on, using and inspecting the personal protective equipment the worker is required to use,

      (ii) rigging procedures and tying adequate knots,

      (iii) locating fixed supports that are identified in a roof plan,

      (iv) safely operating the suspended work platform system or boatswain's chair, and

      (v) operating the controls of the suspended work platform system or boatswain's chair in accordance with the manufacturer's instructions.

(3) The employer shall ensure that the person who provides the training program referred to in subsection (1) prepares and signs a written record for every worker who successfully completes the program and shall provide such written proof to the worker.

(4) A worker shall have the written proof described in subsection (3) readily available at a project.

O. Reg. 242/16, s. 11

138.1 (1) An employer shall designate a competent worker to be responsible for the installation and inspection of a suspended work platform system or boatswain's chair before it is put into service for the first time.

(2) The employer shall ensure that the competent worker successfully completes a training program that meets the requirements set out in subsection (3) at the following times:

1. Before the competent worker installs or inspects the installation of a suspended work platform or boatswain's chair for the first time.

2. As often as is necessary, but at least every three years, after the worker installs or inspects the installation of a suspended work platform or boatswain's chair for the first time.

(3) The training program referred to in subsection (2) shall,

    (a) consist of adequate oral and written instruction on,

        (i) rigging,

        (ii) methods to secure beams and equipment,

        (iii) fixed supports,

        (iv) principles of suspension lines, hoisting devices and load limits,

        (v) manufacturers' instructions for assembling, installing and disassembling suspended work platform systems or boatswain's chairs,

        (vi) reading and using roof plans and work plans,

        (vii) securing suspended work platform systems or boatswain's chairs to the face of a building, and

        (viii) electrical systems; and

    (b) require the competent worker to demonstrate proficiency in,

        (i) installing and torquing rigging hardware in accordance with the manufacturer's instructions,

        (ii) inspecting cable and terminations in accordance with the manufacturer's instructions,

        (iii) tying of adequate numbers of different knots,

        (iv) properly setting up a suspended work platform system or boatswain's chair in accordance with roof plans, work plans and the manufacturer's instructions, including,

            (A) selection and use of fixed supports,

            (B) set up of equipment,

            (C) use of hoists, including reeving cables,

            (D) use of descent controls and emergency controls,

            (E) impact of different work plans on set up of equipment, and

            (F) protection of public ways.

(4) The employer shall ensure that the person who provides the training program referred to in subsection (2) prepares and signs a written record

for every competent worker who successfully completes the program and shall provide such written proof to the competent worker.

(5) A competent worker shall have the written proof described in subsection (4) readily available at a project.

O. Reg. 242/16, s. 11; 142/17, s. 16

General Requirements: Testing
[Heading added O. Reg. 242/16, s. 11.]

139. (1) An employer shall ensure that, prior to the first use of a suspended work platform system at a project, the entire system, including its suspension lines, has been inspected, tested and maintained in accordance with this Regulation, the manufacturer's instructions, and clause 11 (Inspection and Testing) and Clause 12 (Maintenance) of CSA Standard Z271-10.

(2) The employer shall ensure that the inspection, testing and maintenance referred to in subsection (1) is completed by,

    (a) a competent worker; or

    (b) if the CSA Standard Z271-10 requires the inspection or test be performed by a person with specific qualifications, such person.

(3) [Repealed O. Reg. 242/16, s. 11.]

(4) [Repealed O. Reg. 242/16, s. 11.]

(5) [Repealed O. Reg. 242/16, s. 11.]

(6) [Repealed O. Reg. 242/16, s. 11.]

(7) [Repealed O. Reg. 242/16, s. 11.]

(8) [Repealed O. Reg. 242/16, s. 11.]

O. Reg. 85/04, s. 14; 242/16, s. 11

139.1 (1) Every supplier of and every employer who owns or uses a work platform shall ensure that the testing requirements in this section are met.

(2) For the purposes of this section, the types of structural components of a work platform are categorized in the following groups:

    1. Group 1, which is composed of trusses, corner or angled sections and platform modules.

    2. Group 2, which is composed of stirrups, module connectors and end frames.

(3) At least annually, a representative sample of each type of structural component shall be randomly selected and subjected to non-destructive testing in accordance with the following:

1. For each type of Group 1 structural component, the representative sample shall be composed of the number set out in Column 2 of the Table to this subsection opposite the total number of that type of component, set out in Column 1, in the supplier's or employer's entire inventory or fleet of suspended work platforms.

2. For each type of Group 2 structural component, the representative sample shall be composed of the number set out in Column 3 of the Table to this subsection opposite the total number of that type of component, set out in Column 1, in the supplier's or employer's entire inventory or fleet of suspended work platforms.

3. Every critical weld on each structural component as selected as part of the representative sample shall be subjected to non-destructive testing.

TABLE

Item	Column 1 Total number of the type of structural component in a supplier or employer's entire inventory or fleet of suspended work platforms	Column 2 Group 1: number of representative samples of the type of structural component to be tested	Column 3 Group 2: number of representative samples of the type of structural component to be tested
1.	2-15	2	2
2.	16-50	3	5
3.	51-150	5	8
4.	151-500	8	13
5.	500 or greater	13	20

(4) If any defect is found as a result of the testing conducted under subsection (3), a professional engineer shall review the interpretation of the test results to determine,

    (a) whether the defect affects the structural integrity of the structural component; and

    (b) if the defect does affect the structural integrity of the structural component, whether the defective component is to be rejected from further use permanently or pending its repair.

(5) The professional engineer shall prepare a written report of the review and determination made under subsection (4).

(6) If a defective structural component is rejected from further use, either permanently or pending repair, a representative sample that is composed of four times the number of each type of structural component that composed the original representative sample under subsection (3) shall be subjected to testing described in paragraph 3 of subsection (3).

(7) If any defect is found as a result of the testing conducted under subsection (6), subsections (4) to (6) apply, with necessary modifications.

(8) All other parts of a suspended work platform not listed in subsection (2) shall be inspected for damage at least once within the 12-month period preceding its use on a project and at least once annually while in use on a project.

O. Reg. 242/16, s. 11; 142/17, s. 17

General Requirements: Equipment
[Heading added O. Reg. 242/16, s. 11.]

140. (1) An employer who uses a suspended work platform system shall ensure that there are permanent equipment logs respecting components of the suspended work platform system and that the logs,

    (a) comply with clause 13 (Equipment Log) of CSA Standard Z271-10; and

    (b) include a record of the inspections, tests, repairs, modifications and maintenance performed on the components.

(2) The employer shall make the permanent equipment logs available to an inspector on request.

O. Reg. 242/16, s. 11

Pre-Use Requirements: Fixed Supports, Roof Plans, Work Plans and Installation
[Heading added O. Reg. 242/16, s. 11.]

141. (1) The supplier of or employer who owns a suspended work platform system shall ensure that all of its components are marked or labelled in accordance with clause 10.2 (Markings) of CSA Standard Z271-10.

(2) The supplier of or employer who owns a suspended work platform system shall ensure that each of the following structural components of every work platform is marked with a unique identifier:

1. A truss.
2. An end frame.
3. A stirrup.
4. A module connector.
5. A corner or angled section.

(3) Despite subsection (2), if a work platform module is manufactured as a single unit, it may be marked with a single unique identifier.

O. Reg. 242/16, s. 11

141.1 (1) Every fixed support shall be designed by a professional engineer in accordance with the requirements of this section.

(2) A fixed support shall be designed and constructed to support all loads to which it may be subjected.

(3) The design of a fixed support shall use the factored loads calculated in accordance with subsection (4).

(4) The following values of load factors, as described in the provisions of the Building Code that address Limit States Design, shall be applied to calculate the factored loads for an outrigger and supporting structure, excluding anchorage connectors:

1. Live load factor = 3.0.
2. Dead load factor = 1.25.

(5) A component of a fixed support that may be subject to overturning shall be designed and constructed to support at least four times its allowable suspended load or force.

(6) Subject to subsection (7), an anchorage connector shall be designed to resist,

(a) the application of 22.2 kilonewtons in any direction without fracture of any component or pullout from the fixed support; and

(b) a test loading of 11.1 kilonewtons without permanent deformation of any component when subjected to the test loading in the direction or directions that generate the most critical effect on the fixed support with respect to stability and strength.

(7) For a suspended work platform system with a span between adjacent points of suspension of greater than 12 metres and up to 30 metres, the anchorage connectors for supporting the suspended work platform system shall be designed in accordance with good engineering practice to support the allowable suspended load and the minimum live loads for the length of the suspended work platform to be used, as set out in subsection 137.1(3).

O. Reg. 242/16, s. 11; 142/17, s. 18

141.2 (1) Every owner of a building or structure where a suspended work platform system or boatswain's chair is to be used shall ensure that there is a roof plan for the building or structure and ensure that the plan,

(a) contains drawings and layout diagrams that show the positions of all fixed supports on the building or structure;

(b) indicates whether the fixed supports are adequate for the purposes of attaching work platforms, boatswain's chairs and lifelines;

(c) meets the requirements of clause 10.1.2 (Roof Plan) of CSA Standard Z271-10; and

(d) has been approved in writing by a professional engineer.

(2) The owner shall post a legible copy of the roof plan near every entrance to the roof or top level of the building or structure where the suspended work platform system or boatswain's chair is to be used.

(3) The owner shall provide a copy of the roof plan to the constructor for a project at the building or structure.

(4) The constructor shall ensure that every employer whose workers are to use the suspended work platform system or boatswain's chair at the building or structure has received a copy of the roof plan.

(5) No employer or constructor shall permit a worker to use a suspended work platform system or boatswain's chair on a building or structure unless the employer or constructor has received a copy of the roof plan and, if required, the design drawings and written procedures prepared under subsection 141.3(2).

O. Reg. 242/16, s. 11

141.3 (1) If the roof plan required under section 141.2 indicates that the fixed supports on the building or structure are not adequate for the purposes of attaching a suspended work platform system or boatswain's chair and lifelines, if any, the owner shall provide the constructor for a project at the building or structure with any structural drawings for the building or structure that the owner has control over.

(2) The constructor shall ensure that a professional engineer prepares, using any structural drawings provided by the owner under subsection (1), design drawings and written procedures that indicate the manner in which the suspended work platform system or boatswain's chair and lifelines, if any, must be supported from the building or structure during the relevant project.

(3) The constructor shall ensure that every employer whose workers are to use the suspended work platform system or boatswain's chair and lifelines, if any, at the building or structure has received a copy of the design drawings and written procedures.

O. Reg. 242/16, s. 11

141.4 (1) The owner of a building or structure shall ensure that all fixed supports identified in the roof plan are inspected, maintained and tested in accordance with clause 11 (Inspection and Testing) of CSA Standard Z271-10 and the manufacturer's instructions.

(2) Without limiting the generality of subsection (1), the owner shall ensure that a fixed support identified in the roof plan is inspected by a professional engineer,

　　(a) before being used for the first time after it is installed and after every time that it is repaired or modified;

　　(b) as often as necessary and at least as often as recommended by the manufacturer of the fixed support;

　　(c) at least once within the 12-month period preceding its use; and

　　(d) if a professional engineer, an employer, a supervisor or a worker advises the owner that there are reasonable grounds to believe the fixed support is defective or not adequate to support the suspended work platform, boatswain's chair or lifeline.

(3) An owner who has been advised under clause (2)(d) shall ensure that the fixed support in question is not used until the requirements in subsections (4) and (5) are met, as applicable.

(4) The professional engineer who performs an inspection under subsection (2) shall prepare a written report that,

(a) indicates whether the fixed support meets the requirements of section 141.1 and is adequate for the purposes of attaching a suspended work platform, boatswain's chair or lifeline; and

(b) if the fixed support is not adequate, indicates the defects and hazardous conditions of the fixed support.

(5) A fixed support that has been identified in the report of the professional engineer as having a defect or hazardous condition shall not be used until the owner of the building or structure ensures that,

(a) the defect or hazardous condition of the fixed support has been repaired, modified or corrected; and

(b) the fixed support has been inspected and tested by a professional engineer in accordance with clause 11.3.3 (Anchorage connectors) of CSA Standard Z271-10 and the professional engineer has determined the fixed support to be adequate to support a suspended work platform, boatswain's chair or lifeline.

(6) The owner of the building or structure shall, respecting a fixed support,

(a) keep a permanent record, in accordance with clause 13 (Equipment Log) of CSA Standard Z271-10, of all inspections, tests, repairs, modifications and maintenance of the fixed support as long as the fixed support is used;

(b) make the record available, on request, to an inspector; and

(c) make the record available, on request, to a constructor of a project where workers are to use a suspended work platform system or boatswain's chair and lifelines, if any.

(7) No employer or constructor shall permit a worker to use a fixed support unless the employer or constructor has ensured that the fixed support has been inspected, maintained and tested as required by this section and, if applicable, the requirements in subsections (4) and (5) are met.

O. Reg. 242/16, s. 11

141.5 (1) Before a suspended work platform system or boatswain's chair is put into service for the first time on a project, the employer shall ensure that a competent person,

213/91

(a) prepares written procedures for the rescue of workers from a suspended work platform system or boatswain's chair in an emergency;

(b) conducts a risk assessment of the work to be undertaken to identify hazards that may arise from use of the suspended work platform system or boatswain's chair with reference to the nature of the workplace, the type of work and the conditions of work; and

(c) prepares a written, site-specific work plan that complies with subsection (2) and, if it is a work plan respecting a suspended work platform system, also complies with subsection (3).

(2) A site-specific work plan for a suspended work platform system or boatswain's chair shall include, at a minimum,

(a) measures and procedures to protect the health and safety of workers using the suspended work platform system or boatswain's chair;

(b) procedures to install, move and dismantle the suspended work platform system or boatswain's chair;

(c) an assessment as to whether the suspended work platform system or boatswain's chair can be installed according to a generic installation drawing or whether it must be installed according to a site-specific installation drawing;

(d) the rated platform capacity of the suspended work platform, suspended work platform module or boatswain's chair;

(e) the weight of all materials, tools and equipment allowed to be on the suspended work platform or boatswain's chair;

(f) how all suspension lines and lifelines are to be attached to the fixed supports shown in any roof plan required under section 141.2;

(g) an identification of the hazards related to material hoisting, cutting, grinding and sandblasting associated with the work;

(h) an identification of all electrical hazards, including minimum distances when approaching electrical conductors;

(i) protection for the public and workers who may be below the suspended work platform or boatswain's chair;

(j) overhead protection for workers on a suspended work platform or boatswain's chair from any work being conducted above the suspended work platform or boatswain's chair;

(k) measures to be taken to protect workers using a suspended work platform system or boatswain's chair from weather and other conditions that may endanger them;

(l) a copy of the written procedures for the emergency rescue of workers from a suspended work platform or boatswain's chair in an emergency established under clause (1)(a);

(m) the maximum number of workers allowed on a suspended work platform, suspended work platform module or boatswain's chair;

(n) information about methods of fall protection, including installation, that may be used for the protection of workers using a suspended work platform or boatswain's chair; and

(o) information about ready access to a two-way communication system, such as radio, telephone or other similar means, to be provided to a worker using a suspended work platform system or boatswain's chair.

(3) In addition to the elements described in subsection (2), a site-specific plan for a suspended work platform system shall include, at a minimum,

(a) how the work platform is to be arranged in any location at which the platform is to be used on the project;

(b) a weight distribution plan to ensure loading across the work platform or suspended work platform module surface does not exceed the design capacity;

(c) the maximum amount or weight of debris, grit and other materials allowed to accumulate on the suspended work platform, and their permissible locations on the work platform; and

(d) an assessment as to whether a device may be used to transfer material to and from the work platform and, if it may, directions on how it is to be used.

(4) The employer shall keep at the project, and make available to an inspector on request, the site-specific work plan.

(5) The employer shall,

(a) ensure that the site-specific work plan is implemented at the project; and

(b) before a worker begins installing or using a suspended work platform system or boatswain's chair at the project, provide the worker with a copy of the site-specific work plan and review it with the worker.

O. Reg. 242/16, s. 11

213/91

141.6 (1) Only a designated competent worker who has successfully completed the training program under section 138.1 shall install, alter or dismantle a suspended work platform system or boatswain's chair.

(2) A suspended work platform system or boatswain's chair, including all components and connections of the suspended work platform system or boatswain's chair, shall be erected, installed, used and dismantled in accordance with the manufacturer's instructions and,

(a) a generic installation drawing; or

(b) in the case of a suspended work platform system, a site-specific drawing if not all of the requirements in the generic installation drawing can be satisfied or if one of the circumstances set out in subsection (3) applies.

(3) The following are circumstances for the purposes of clause (2)(b):

1. There will be stacked or tiered work platforms.

2. will be a work platform that, including its components, weighs more than 525 kilograms.

3. There will be a work platform that has a span greater than 12 metres between adjacent points of suspension.

4. There will be a work platform that has more than two primary suspension lines.

5. More than two hoisting devices will be used to move a work platform.

6. There will be a work platform that has any shielding, tarpaulin, enclosure, sign or banner on it that may increase the wind loads on the components of the suspended work platform system.

7. The vertical distance between the top of a suspension line and the lowest point on the street, ground or other horizontal surface under a work platform will exceed 150 metres.

O. Reg. 242/16, s. 11

141.7 (1) This section applies if a generic installation drawing is used under clause 141.6(2)(a).

(2) A designated competent worker who has successfully completed the training program under section 138.1 shall inspect a suspended work platform system or powered boatswain's chair to determine whether the installed suspended work platform system or installed powered boatswain's chair complies with the drawing,

(a) before it is put into service after it has been installed for the first time on a project; and

(b) if it is relocated at the project, at the new location before it is put into service.

(3) The designated competent worker shall provide a written report of the inspection indicating whether the installed suspended work platform system or installed powered boatswain's chair complies with the drawing.

(4) The suspended work platform system or powered boatswain's chair shall not be put into service unless the designated competent worker's report indicates that the suspended work platform system or boatswain's chair has been installed in accordance with the drawing.

(5) While the suspended work platform system or powered boatswain's chair is at the project, the employer shall keep at the project, and make available to an inspector on request, the generic installation drawing and every report prepared by a designated competent worker under subsection (3).

O. Reg. 242/16, s. 11

141.8 (1) This section applies if a site-specific installation drawing is used under clause 141.6(2)(b).

(2) The site-specific installation drawing shall be prepared by a professional engineer.

(3) A professional engineer shall inspect a suspended work platform after it has been installed for the first time at a project and before it is put into service and shall prepare a written report indicating whether the suspended work platform complies with the drawing.

(4) A suspended work platform shall not be put into service unless the professional engineer's report indicates it has been installed in accordance with the drawing.

(5) If a suspended work platform system is relocated at a project, a deviation from the site-specific drawing is permitted if the deviation is approved by a professional engineer.

(6) A suspended work platform system shall not be put into service at the new location unless,

(a) the suspended work platform system was inspected,

(i) if the installation at the new location was in accordance with the site-specific drawing, by either a professional en-

191

gineer or by a designated competent worker who has successfully completed the training program under section 138.1,
or

    (ii) if the installation at the new location was in accordance
    with the site-specific installation drawing and a deviation
    from it was approved by a professional engineer, by a pro-
    fessional engineer; and

(b) a report prepared under subsection (7) or (8) indicates that the
suspended work platform system has been installed in accordance
with the drawing and approved deviations, if any.

(7) In the case of an inspection under subclause 6(a)(i), the professional
engineer or designated competent worker shall provide a written report of
the inspection indicating whether the installed suspended work platform
system complies with the drawing.

(8) In the case of an inspection under subclause 6(a)(ii), the professional
engineer shall provide a written report of the inspection indicating whether the installed suspended work platform system complies with the
drawing and approved deviations.

(9) While the suspended work platform system is at the project, the employer shall keep at the project, and make available to an inspector on
request, the site-specific installation drawing, any approved deviations
and every report prepared under this section.

O. Reg. 242/16, s. 11

Project-Specific Use Requirements
[Heading added O. Reg. 242/16, s. 11.]

142. The employer shall ensure that the rated platform capacity of a
suspended work platform, work platform module or boatswain's chair is
posted conspicuously on the suspended work platform, work platform
module or boatswain's chair, as the case may be.

O. Reg. 242/16, s. 11

142.01 (1) A suspended work platform system or boatswain's chair and
the suspension lines of the suspended work platform system or boatswain's chair shall be attached to a fixed support in accordance with the
manufacturer's instructions.

(2) Every suspension line of a suspended work platform or boatswain's chair shall,

(a) be made of wire rope, subject to subsection 142.03(1);

(b) be vertical from the fixed support, including the outrigger beam;

(c) be parallel to every other suspension line, if any;

(d) extend to the ground or have a positive stop that prevents the suspended work platform or boatswain's chair from running off the end of the suspension line or lines;

(e) have each connecting end wrapped around a protective thimble and adequately fastened;

(f) be capable, along with its attachment components, of supporting at least 10 times the maximum load to which it may be subjected; and

(g) have fastenings and terminations that are,

(i) corrosion-resistant,

(ii) capable of developing at least 80 per cent of the rated breaking strength of the suspension line itself,

(iii) recommended by the manufacturer for use with suspended work platforms or boatswain's chairs, and

(iv) installed in accordance with the manufacturer's instructions.

(3) A U-type rope clamp shall not be used on a suspension line or tie-back.

(4) A hoisting device on a suspended work platform system or boatswain's chair shall,

(a) have legible operating and safety instructions affixed to it in a conspicuous location; and

(b) meet the requirements of clause 8 (Hoisting) of CSA Standard Z271-10.

(5) A suspended work platform system or boatswain's chair shall not be loaded in such a manner as to exceed the rated platform capacity for its work platform or individual platform module, or the rated hoist capacity.

(6) A work platform or boatswain's chair shall not be suspended or used at any time the wind speed exceeds 40 kilometres per hour.

(7) If an outrigger beam is to be used as a fixed support, it shall,

(a) be tied back and securely fastened to the building or structure, or a component of the building or structure, by a secondary cable or wire rope capable of supporting the allowable suspended load;

(b) be secured against horizontal and vertical movement;

(c) have securely attached counterweights that are designed and manufactured for the purpose; and

(d) have adequate legible instructions, provided by the manufacturer or a professional engineer, for the use of the counterweights affixed to the outrigger beam.

O. Reg. 242/16, s. 11

142.02 (1) All wire rope terminations of the suspension line of a suspended work platform system or boatswain's chair, including swaged socket and poured socket terminations, spliced eye terminations and turnback eye terminations shall, after installation onto the wire rope and prior to being used for the first time, be tested,

(a) in accordance with the recommendations of the manufacturer of the wire rope or termination; and

(b) to no more than 50 per cent of the wire rope's nominal or minimum rated breaking strength.

(2) While the suspended work platform system or boatswain's chair is at the project and the termination remains in service, an employer shall keep at the project, and make available to an inspector on request, a record of the tests described in subsection (1).

(3) The wire rope termination of a suspension line shall be protected from contact with the line's hoisting device.

O. Reg. 242/16, s. 11

142.03 (1) The suspension line of a boatswain's chair shall be made of wire rope unless the boatswain's chair is equipped with a descent control device.

(2) Every suspension line of a boatswain's chair shall be protected from abrasion.

(3) Every suspension line of a boatswain's chair that is made of organic or polymer fibres shall be,

(a) permanently marked with the date on which it was first put into use;

(b) doubled from the fixed support of the line to the ground or egress level;

(c) tested by a recognized testing laboratory two years after the date on which it was first put into use and then once every 12 months thereafter to assess whether,

213/91

(i) it has experienced abrasion, and

(ii) is capable of developing at least 80 per cent of the rated breaking strength of the suspension line itself; and

(d) discarded,

(i) if the test required under clause (c) determines that it does not have a breaking strength of at least 10 times the static load that the line is intended to support,

(ii) in accordance with the manufacturer's recommendations, or

(iii) when it is no longer safe for use.

(4) A boatswain's chair shall have a seat or seating area that is at least 600 millimetres long and 250 millimetres wide.

(5) If the seat or seating area is supported by a sling, the sling shall be constructed of wire rope at least nine millimetres in diameter which crosses under the seat or sitting area.

(6) If a boatswain's chair has a descent control device,

(a) the distance between the boatswain's chair and the fixed support shall not exceed 90 metres; and

(b) a worker on the boatswain's chair shall not use a corrosive substance, or mechanical grinding or flame-cutting equipment if the suspension line is not made of wire rope.

O. Reg. 242/16, s. 11

142.04 (1) Before a suspended work platform system or boatswain's chair is used for the first time each day, a competent worker shall identify any defects or hazardous conditions and document them in writing.

(2) The suspended work platform system or boatswain's chair shall not be used until the defects or hazardous conditions have been corrected or removed.

(3) The employer shall keep a copy of each document prepared by a competent worker under subsection (1) and make it available to an inspector on request.

O. Reg. 242/16, s. 11

142.05 (1) An employer shall ensure that a competent worker performs a functional test of a work platform or powered boatswain's chair to ensure that it is operating in accordance with the manufacturer's instructions,

(a) before it is used for the first time after it is installed at the project;

(b) if it is relocated at the project, at the new location before it is put into service; and

(c) before it is used for the first time each day.

(2) If a functional test performed under subsection (1) reveals defects or hazardous conditions, the work platform or powered boatswain's chair shall not be used until the defects or hazardous conditions have been corrected or removed.

(3) The work platform or powered boatswain's chair shall not be raised more than 30 centimetres during the functional test unless it has a hoisting device equipped with a remote operating device.

O. Reg. 242/16, s. 11

142.06 (1) A worker who is on or is getting on or off a suspended work platform or boatswain's chair shall wear a full body harness connected to a fall arrest system.

(2) Every worker on a suspended work platform or boatswain's chair shall have an effective means of summoning assistance in case of emergency.

(3) Every lifeline used with a suspended work platform or boatswain's chair shall,

(a) be suspended independently of the suspended work platform or boatswain's chair;

(b) be securely attached to a fixed support so that the failure of the suspended work platform or boatswain's chair will not cause the lifeline to fail;

(c) be protected from damage and abrasion; and

(d) if subject to wind conditions,

(i) not be suspended a vertical distance of more than 150 metres below the fixed support, and

(ii) if suspended a vertical distance of more than 100 metres below the fixed support, be restrained at or near the mid-point.

(4) Despite clauses (3)(a) and (b), the lifeline may be securely fastened to a work platform if,

(a) all or part of the suspended work platform has more than one means of suspension; and

(b) the suspended work platform is designed, assembled and maintained such that the failure of one means of suspension will not result in the complete or partial collapse of the suspended work platform.

(5) A suspended work platform shall have hangers located at least 150 millimetres but no more than 450 millimetres from the ends of the platform that are securely attached to it.

(6) If the suspension height of a suspended work platform is 15 metres or greater, the suspended work platform shall, if practicable, be restrained to the exterior face of the building or structure that it is suspended from unless the suspended work platform is being raised or lowered.

(7) If a suspended work platform is stationary and its guardrail adjacent to the face of the building or structure has been removed or lowered, the suspended work platform shall be restrained to the building or structure.
O. Reg. 242/16, s. 11; 471/16, s. 1

Multi-Point Suspended Work Platforms
[Heading added O. Reg. 85/04, s. 15; Amended O. Reg. 242/16, s. 1(2).]

142.1 Sections 142.2 to 142.8 apply to every multi-point suspended work platform.
O. Reg. 85/04 s. 15; 242/16, s. 1(1)

142.2(1) A multi-point suspended work platform and all its components shall be designed by a professional engineer in accordance with good engineering practice and with this section.

(2) A multi-point suspended work platform shall be designed to support, in addition to its dead load, live loads uniformly distributed over the platform surface of at least,

(a) 2.4 kilonewtons per square metre if the platform is to be used for masonry work;

(b) 3.6 kilonewtons per square metre if the platform is to be used for demolition work or for storage of masonry units or other related material or equipment; or

(c) 1.2 kilonewtons per square metre in any other case.

(3) In addition to the loads specified in subsection (2), a multi-point suspended work platform shall be able to support or resist,

213/91

(a) 1.1 kilonewtons concentrated on an area measuring 0.3 metres by 0.3 metres that is located on the platform at the position having the most adverse effect on the component under consideration;

(b) the wind load determined in accordance with the applicable provisions of the *Building Code*, based on a one in ten probability of being exceeded in any one year; and

(c) any other loads likely to be applied to it.

(4) The wind load referred to in clause (3)(b) may be reduced by 30 per cent if the professional engineer who designs the multi-point suspended work platform determines that it is appropriate to do so and indicates in writing that he or she has made the determination.

(5) Subject to clause (2)(c) and subsections (3) and (4), the professional engineer who designs the scaffold shall determine the minimum specified loads for erecting, dismantling, traversing, or otherwise moving the multi-point suspended work platform.

(6) If a multi-point suspended work platform is to be used for abrasive blasting operations, there shall be an additional load allowance for the accumulation of grit on the platform to a depth of at least 25 millimetres.

(7) Subject to subsection (8), in designing a multi-point suspended work platform and its structural members, the following values of load factors, as described in the applicable provisions of the *Building Code* related to Limit States Design, shall be applied to the load requirements referred to in subsections (2) to (6):

1. Live load factor = 3.0.
2. Dead load factor = 1.5.
3. Wind load factor = 1.5.

(8) In designing the suspension and anchorage system of a multi-point suspended work platform,

(a) the value of the live load factor shall be 4.0;

(b) the value of the dead load factor shall be 2.0; and

(c) the value of the wind load factor shall be 2.0.

(9) Despite subsections (7) and (8), a multi-point suspended work platform and its components may be designed by working stress design if the safety factors for the multi-point suspended work platform and the structural members are at least equal to what would otherwise be provided under those subsections.

(10) Despite subsections (7) and (8), if the failure load of a component has been determined by testing, the minimum safety factors shall be,

    (a) 3.0 for components of the multi-point suspended work platform;

    (b) 4.0 for components of the suspension and anchorage system; and

    (c) 10.0 for wire ropes, cables or chains used for hoisting, traversing or otherwise moving the multi-point suspended work platform.

(11) The failure load of a component referred to in subsection (10) shall be verified in writing by a professional engineer.

(12) A multi-point suspended work platform shall be designed, constructed and maintained in such a way that,

    (a) the failure of one means of support or suspension will not cause any part of the platform to collapse or fail, under the most adverse loading condition as determined by the professional engineer who designs the multi-point suspended work platform; and

    (b) compliance with subsections (7), (8), (9) and (10) is maintained in all fixed and moving conditions.

(13) The design of a multi-point suspended work platform shall include adequate movement-limiting devices to be used when traversing or otherwise moving it.

(14) Before a multi-point suspended work platform is erected, the constructor shall ensure that the professional engineer responsible for the structural integrity of the permanent building or structure from which the multi-point suspended work platform is suspended provides a written report approving the design loads imposed on the building or structure by the multi-point suspended work platform.

(15) Design drawings for a multi-point suspended work platform shall include,

    (a) a statement by the professional engineer that the design meets the requirements of this Regulation;

    (b) the size and specifications of all components, including the type and grade of all materials to be used;

    (c) the load factors and safety factors for the multi-point suspended work platform and all its components;

    (d) all the specified loads, including the loads during erection, dismantling, traversing and otherwise moving; and

(e) the procedures for erection, dismantling, traversing and otherwise moving.

(16) The design drawings shall be followed, subject to subsection (17).

(17) A deviation from the design drawings is permitted if the deviation,

(a) is approved, in advance and in writing, by a professional engineer; and

(b) complies with this Regulation.

O. Reg. 85/04 s. 15; 242/16, ss. 1(1), 12; 142/17, s. 19

142.3(1) Before erecting or dismantling a multi-point suspended work platform, the constructor shall give notice, in person, by telephone, by fax or by electronic means, to the Ministry office located nearest the project.

(2) A multi-point suspended work platform shall be inspected by a professional engineer to determine whether it complies with the design drawings, or the design drawings subject to any deviations approved under subsection 142.2(17), as the case may be,

(a) after it is erected but before it is first used; and

(b) if the work platform is moved to another anchorage position, before it is used there.

(3) The inspection under subsection (2) shall include a determination of whether all components are in adequate condition.

(4) The professional engineer who conducts the inspection under subsection (2) shall prepare a written report of the inspection.

(5) The written report is a positive report if it indicates that,

(a) the multi-point suspended work platform complies with the design drawings, or the design drawings subject to any deviations approved under subsection 142.2(17), as the case may be; and

(b) all components are in adequate condition.

(6) Subsections (1), (2), (3), (4) and (5) do not apply to a multi-point suspended work platform whose platform area is six square metres or less.

(7) A competent worker shall inspect a multi-point suspended scaffold each day before it is used.

O. Reg. 85/04 s. 15; 242/16, ss. 1(1), 13

142.4 The constructor shall keep at the project a copy of,

(a) the written report under subsection 142.2(14);

(b) the design drawings under subsection 142.2(15);

(c) any written approvals under subsection 142.2(17); and

(d) the written reports under subsection 142.3(4).

O. Reg. 85/04 s. 15

142.5(1) A multi-point suspended work platform shall be erected, dismantled, traversed or otherwise moved only by a competent worker under the supervision of a competent person and in accordance with the design drawings, or the design drawings subject to any deviations approved under subsection 142.2(17), as the case may be.

(2) Before a worker is on a multi-point suspended work platform for the first time, the employer shall provide the worker with adequate oral and written instructions for using the multi-point suspended work platform, including,

(a) the manufacturer's instructions or a professional engineer's instructions;

(b) instructions on the load limitations;

(c) instructions in, and a hands-on demonstration of, the proper operation of the multi-point suspended work platform.

(3) A worker who is to erect, dismantle, traverse or otherwise move a multi-point suspended work platform shall, in addition to the instructions set out in subsection (2), be given instructions in the procedures described in clause 142.2(15)(e).

(4) No person shall use a multi-point suspended work platform until the design drawings described in subsection 142.2(15) have been given to the constructor and the following documents have been prepared and given to the constructor:

1. The report described in subsection 142.2(14).

2. A positive report described in subsections 142.3(4) and (5), if applicable.

3. Any approval described in subsection 142.2(17), if applicable.

O. Reg. 85/04 s. 15; 242/16, ss. 1(1), 13

142.6(1) A multi-point suspended work platform shall not be loaded in excess of the specified loads indicated on the design drawings for the multi-point suspended work platform or boatswain's chair.

(2) Signs indicating the specified live loads shall be posted in conspicuous places on the multi-point suspended work platform.

O. Reg. 85/04 s. 15; 242/16, ss. 1(1), 13

142.7(1) A worker who is on a multi-point suspended work platform while it is being erected, dismantled, traversed or otherwise moved shall use a fall arrest system that is,

    (a) connected to a fixed support independent from the multi-point suspended work platform; and

    (b) designed, constructed and maintained in accordance with this Regulation.

(2) Despite subsection (1), a worker is not required to use a fall arrest system while the multi-point suspended work platform is stationary if guardrails are installed in accordance with section 26.3.

O. Reg. 85/04 s. 15; 242/16, ss. 1(1), 13

142.8(1) The constructor of a project where a multi-point suspended work platform is used shall keep a written record of all inspections, tests, repairs, modifications and maintenance performed on the multi-point suspended work platform and make copies of the record available to an inspector upon request.

(2) The record referred to in subsection (1) shall,

    (a) be kept up to date;

    (b) include the signature, name and business address of each person who performs an inspection, test, repair, modification or maintenance; and

    (c) be kept at the project while the multi-point suspended work platform is there.

O. Reg. 85/04 s. 15; 242/16, ss. 1(1), 13

Elevating Work Platforms

143. (1) Subject to subsection (2), every elevating work platform, including elevating rolling work platforms, self-propelled elevating work platforms, boom-type elevating work platforms and vehicle-mounted aerial devices shall comply with section 144.

(2) Subsection (1) does not apply to,

    (a) suspended scaffolds or suspended work platforms; and

    (b) buckets or baskets suspended from or attached to the boom of a crane.

144. (1) An elevating work platform shall be designed by a professional engineer in accordance with good engineering practice,

(a) to meet the requirements of the applicable National Standards of Canada standard, set out in the Table to subsection (6); and

(b) to support a minimum of 1.3 kilonewtons rated working load as determined in accordance with the applicable National Standards of Canada standard set out in the Table to subsection (6).

(2) An elevating work platform shall be manufactured in accordance with the design referred to in subsection (1).

(3) An elevating work platform,

(a) shall be tested in accordance with the National Standards of Canada standard set out in the Table to subsection (6); and

(b) shall be inspected each day before use, in accordance with the manufacturer's instructions by a worker trained in accordance with section 147.

(4) An elevating work platform shall only be used if a professional engineer has certified in writing that it complies with the National Standards of Canada standard set out in the Table to subsection (6).

(5) The certification required by subsection (4) shall include the details of testing.

(6) The National Standards of Canada standard applicable to the type of elevating work platform listed in Column 1 of the Table to this subsection are the standards set out opposite it in Column 2.

TABLE

COLUMN 1	COLUMN 2
Type of elevating work platform	National Standards of Canada standard
Elevating Rolling Work Platform	CAN3-B354.1-M82
Self-Propelled Elevating Work Paltform	CAN3-B354.2-M82 and CAN3-B354.3-M82
Boom-Type Elevating Work Platform	CAN3-B354.4-M82
Vehicle-Mounted Aerial Device	CAN/CSA-C225-10

213/91

(7) An elevating work platform shall be equipped with guardrails.

(8) An elevating work platform shall have signs that are clearly visible to an operator at its controls indicating,

    (a) the rated working load;

    (b) all limiting operating conditions including the use of outriggers, stabilizers and extendable axles;

    (c) the specific firm level surface conditions required for use in the elevated position;

    (d) such warnings as may be specified by the manufacturer;

    (e) other than for a boom-type elevating work platform, the direction of machine movement for each operating control;

    (f) the name and number of the National Standards of Canada standard to which it was designed; and

    (g) the name and address of the owner.

O. Reg. 345/15, s. 17

145. **(1)** The owner of an elevating work platform shall maintain it such that the safety factors of the original design are maintained.

(2) The owner of an elevating work platform shall keep a permanent record of all inspections, tests, repairs, modifications and maintenance performed on it.

(3) The permanent record required by subsection (2),

    (a) shall be kept up-to-date;

    (b) shall include complete records from the more recent of,

        (i) the date of purchase, or

        (ii) May 10, 1991; and

    (c) shall include the signature and name of the person who performed the inspection, test, repair, modification or maintenance.

O. Reg. 142/17, s. 20

146. A maintenance and inspection record tag,

    (a) shall be provided and attached to the elevating work platform near the operator's station; and

    (b) shall include,

        (i) the date of the last maintenance and inspection,

        (ii) the signature and name of the person who performed the maintenance and inspection, and

        (iii) an indication that the maintenance has been carried out in accordance with the manufacturer's recommendations.

147. (1) A worker who operates an elevating work platform shall, before using it for the first time, be given oral and written instruction on the operation and be trained to operate that class of elevating work platform.

(2) The instruction and training required by subsection (1) shall include,

    (a) the manufacturer's instruction;

    (b) instruction in the load limitations;

    (c) instruction in and a hands-on demonstration of the proper use of all controls; and

    (d) instruction in the limitations on the kinds of surfaces on which it is designed to be used.

148. (1) An elevating work platform,

    (a) shall not be loaded in excess of its rated working load;

    (b) shall be used and moved only in accordance with the manufacturer's written instructions;

    (c) shall not be loaded or used in such a manner as to affect its stability or endanger a worker;

    (d) shall not be moved unless all workers on it are protected from ejection by being attached to an adequate anchorage point on the elevating work platform by a method of fall protection; and

    (e) shall not be used, in the case of a self-propelled or vehicle-mounted boom-type elevating work platform or a vehicle-mounted aerial device, unless all workers on it are attached to an adequate anchorage point on the elevating work platform by a method of fall protection.

(2) Clause (1)(d) does not apply to,

    (a) a mast climbing work platform or a mast climbing transport platform if the platform has guardrails protecting all open sides of the platform where a worker is exposed to a hazard of falling 2.4 metres or more; and

    (b) a vehicle-mounted aerial device if the non-conductive requirements of the basket prevent the placement of an anchorage attachment inside the basket.

(3) [Repealed O. Reg. 242/16, s. 14(2).]

                    O. Reg. 345/15 s. 18; 242/16, s. 14; 142/17, s. 21

149. An operator's manual for an elevating work platform shall be kept with it while it is on a project.

Cranes, Hoisting and Rigging

150. (1) Subject to subsection (2), no worker shall operate a crane or similar hoisting device unless the worker holds a certificate of qualification issued under the *Ontario College of Trades and Apprenticeship Act, 2009*, that is not suspended, or the worker is an apprentice and is working pursuant to a training agreement registered under that Act, that is not suspended, in the trade of,

    (a) hoisting engineer—mobile crane operator 1, if the worker is operating a crane or similar hoisting device capable of raising, lowering or moving any material that weighs more than 30,000 pounds;

    (b) hoisting engineer—mobile crane operator 1 or hoisting engineer—mobile crane operator 2, if the worker is operating a crane or similar hoisting device capable of raising, lowering or moving only material that weighs more than 16,000 pounds but no more than 30,000 pounds; or

    (c) hoisting engineer—tower crane operator, if the worker is operating a tower crane.

(1.1) Subsection (1) does not apply when a worker is using excavation equipment to place pipes into a trench.

(2) No worker shall operate a crane or similar hoisting device, other than one described in subsection (1), unless,

    (a) the worker has written proof of training indicating that he or she is trained in the safe operation of the crane or similar hoisting device; or

    (b) the worker is being instructed in the operation of the crane or similar hoisting device and is accompanied by a person who meets the requirements of clause (a).

(3) A worker shall carry his or her proof of training while operating a crane or similar hoisting device.

O. Reg. 631/94; 88/13 s. 1

151. (1) No crane or similar hoisting device shall be subjected to a load greater than its rated load-carrying capacity.

(2) The manufacturer of a crane or similar hoisting device or a professional engineer shall determine its rated load-carrying capacity in accordance with,

(a) for a mobile crane, Canadian Standards Association Standard Z150-1974 Safety Code for Mobile Cranes; and

(b) for a tower crane, Canadian Standards Association Standard Z248-1976 Code for Tower Cranes.

(3) Every crane or similar hoisting device shall have affixed to it a load rating plate,

(a) that the operator can read while at the controls; and

(b) that contains enough information for the operator to determine the load that can be lifted for each configuration of the crane.

(4) A luffing boom crane, other than a tower crane, shall have affixed to it a boom angle indicator that the operator can read while at the controls.

152. (1) The owner of a crane or similar hoisting device shall keep a permanent record of all inspections of, tests of, repairs to, modifications to and maintenance of the crane or similar hoisting device.

(2) The owner of a crane or similar hoisting device shall prepare a log book for it for use at a project that shall include the record referred to in subsection (1) covering the period that is the greater of,

(a) the immediately preceding twelve months; and

(b) the period the crane or similar hoisting device is on the project.

(3) The log book shall be kept with the crane or similar hoisting device.

(4) The owner of a crane or similar hoisting device shall retain and make available to the constructor on request copies of all log books and records for the crane or similar hoisting device.

153. (1) No worker shall use as a workplace a platform, bucket, basket, load, hook, sling or similar device that is capable of moving and is supported by a cable attached to the boom of a crane or similar hoisting device, except in accordance with this section.

(2) A crane may be used to raise, support or lower a worker only if,

(a) conventional access equipment cannot be used;

(b) the platform that the worker is on,

(i) is designed by a professional engineer in accordance with good engineering practice,

(ii) is constructed in accordance with the design drawings,

(iii) is equipped with more than one means of suspension or support,

(iv) is equipped with anchor points for the attachment of the worker's fall arrest system,

(v) is equipped with a guardrail in accordance with section 26.3,

(vi) is suspended from, or supported by, a direct attachment to the boom of the crane,

(vii) is designed, constructed and maintained so that the failure of one means of support or suspension will not cause the collapse of all or part of the platform, and

(viii) has its maximum rated load capacity legibly and permanently marked in a conspicuous place on it; and

(c) the crane,

(i) is equipped with fail-safe mechanisms that will prevent the boom and the suspended platform from free falling in the event of a power source or system failure or the inadvertent release of any operating controls,

(ii) is not used to hoist material while the platform is being used to support a worker,

(iii) is not loaded in excess of 25 per cent of its maximum rated load,

(iv) has a revised load rating chart prepared by a professional engineer in accordance with good engineering practice and affixed in a conspicuous place on the crane,

(v) has, on its hoist line, hooks equipped with self-closing safety catches at the point where the platform is suspended, and

(vi) is equipped with an automatic limit switch that prevents the platform and load from reaching beyond the highest permissible position specified by the crane manufacturer.

(3) Any modifications or repairs to the boom of the crane shall be made in accordance with the instructions of the crane manufacturer or a professional engineer.

(4) Every worker on the platform shall wear a full body harness connected independently to anchor points on the platform and used in conjunction with a lanyard fitted with a shock absorber.

(5) The design drawings of the platform shall,

(a) set out the size and specifications of all components of the platform, including the type and grade of materials used for it;

(b) state the maximum live load of the platform;

(c) specify the model and type of crane to be used in conjunction with the platform; and

(d) include a statement that, in the opinion of the professional engineer who designed the platform, the design meets the requirements of clauses (a), (b) and (c).

(e) [Revoked O. Reg. 85/04, s. 16.]

(6) Before the platform is used, a competent worker shall inspect it and verify in writing that it has been constructed in accordance with the design drawings.

(7) No person shall use the platform until the verification required under subsection (6) is given.

(8) Before the crane is first used to lift persons, and at least once every 12 months after the first test, a professional engineer shall ensure that the crane be subjected to non-destructive testing to ensure the structural integrity of the crane.

(9) A competent worker shall visually inspect the crane's structural elements and the rigging equipment for defects before each use of the crane.

(10) The employer shall ensure that an adequate means of communication between the worker on the platform and the crane operator is established, maintained and used.

(11) Before beginning any hoisting operation under this section, the constructor shall notify by telephone an inspector in the office of the Ministry of Labour nearest to the project.

(12) The employer shall ensure that every worker involved with the hoisting operation receives adequate instructions about the requirements, restrictions and hazards associated with the hoisting operation.

(13) The employer shall develop adequate emergency rescue procedures and communicate these in writing to all workers involved with the hoisting operation.

(14) The constructor shall keep all design drawings, test reports, written statements and certification documents required under this section with the crane at all times during the hoisting operation.

(15) On request, the constructor shall provide an inspector with copies of any document described in subsection (14).

O. Reg. 631/94 s. 4; 527/00 s. 5; 85/04 s. 16; 242/16, s. 15

154. (1) A crane or similar hoisting device shall be set up, assembled, extended and dismantled only by a competent worker acting in accordance with the written instructions of the manufacturer and in such a manner as to not endanger any person or property.

(2) No crane or similar hoisting device shall include sections that are not designed for it or that are damaged.

(3) No crane or similar hoisting device shall includes nuts, bolts, pins or fastenings that are not the size and quality specified by the manufacturer.

155. Unless otherwise specified by its manufacturer, a crane or similar hoisting device,

　　(a) shall be equipped with a device to indicate whether its turntable is level; and

　　(b) shall be operated with its turntable level.

156. An outrigger or stabilizing device used on a crane or similar hoisting device,

　　(a) shall be extended to meet load capacity chart requirements; and

　　(b) shall rest on blocking able to support the crane or similar hoisting device and its maximum load without failure or without deformation or settlement which affects its stability.

Rotary Foundation Drill Rigs
[Heading added O. Reg. 345/15, s. 19.]

156.1(1) Before the start of any drilling operation on a project with a rotary foundation drill rig,

　　(a) an inspection of the work area shall be conducted to identify,

　　　　(i) potential hazards, including utilities, services, obstructions, structures and soil conditions that may endanger a worker engaged in, or in the vicinity of, the drilling operation, and

　　　　(ii) buildings and structures adjacent to, or in the vicinity of, the drilling operation that may be affected by it;

　　(b) any hazards identified under subclause (a)(i) shall be removed if practicable;

　　(c) if it is not practicable to remove the hazards identified under subclause (a)(i),

        (i) if practicable, they shall be disconnected or inactivated so as not to endanger workers engaged in, or in the vicinity of, the drilling operation, and

        (ii) they shall be located and marked by signs; and

    (d) a written report shall be prepared that indicates,

        (i) all of the hazards identified under subclause (a)(i),

        (ii) which hazards have not been removed, and

        (iii) which hazards have been disconnected or inactivated.

(2) The constructor shall keep a copy of the report mentioned under clause (1)(d) at the project until the drilling operation is completed, and make the report available, upon request, to an inspector and an employer responsible for the drilling operation.

O. Reg. 345/15   s. 19

156.2(1) Before a drilling operation begins, the employer responsible for it shall,

    (a) develop written measures and procedures in accordance with subsection (2) to protect the health and safety of workers engaged in, or in the vicinity of, the drilling operation; and

    (b) have a copy of these written measures and procedures provided to, and reviewed with, the workers engaged in the drilling operation.

(2) The written measures and procedures required under subsection (1) shall include, at a minimum, details of,

    (a) the measures and procedures to be implemented to protect workers from all unremoved hazards;

    (b) the procedures to be implemented for the assembly, erection, disassembly, alteration and operation of the drilling equipment;

    (c) the safe work areas that have been designated for,

        (i) the drilling operation,

        (ii) the staging, disassembly and alteration of the drilling equipment, and

        (iii) the storage of any excavated soil and material;

    (d) the procedures to be implemented for removing excavated soil and material;

    (e) the restricted access zone that has been designated around the drilling operation to restrict or prevent access by persons or equipment;

(f) the fall protection measures, in addition to those required under sections 26.1 to 26.9, to be implemented to prevent workers from falling into a drill hole or being engulfed by collapsing soil around a drill hole, while or after the hole is drilled; and

(g) the communications system to be used among the drill rig operator, the drill rig front-end worker and other workers in the restricted access zone, or a system of prearranged visual signals to be used among them if those signals are clearly visible and understood by them.

(3) Workers shall follow the written measures and procedures.

O. Reg. 345/15 s. 19

156.3 Sections 156.4 and 156.5 apply when a drilling operation at a project uses a rotary foundation drill rig that can exert a ground pressure of 200 kiloPascals or more under its tires, crawlers or outrigger pads in any configuration, including during its operational activities.

O. Reg. 345/15 s. 19

156.4(1) Before a drilling operation described in section 156.3 begins, a professional engineer shall,

(a) design a supporting surface for the drill rig in accordance with good engineering practice to adequately support the drill rig during all drilling and drill rig set-up activities;

(b) designate and design a path of travel for the drill rig to use on the project to ensure the path of travel safely supports the drill rig; and

(c) prepare a written report described in subsection (2).

(2) The written report required under clause (1)(c) shall include, at a minimum, details of,

(a) the project and its location;

(b) the designs and specifications for the supporting surface and path of travel;

(c) any operating restrictions imposed by the drill rig manufacturer's instructions, including the maximum safe ground slope for the drilling operation;

(d) the existing soil conditions, all associated hazards to workers' health and safety and the precautions to be taken to protect workers from the hazards associated with the soil conditions;

(e) the minimum load-bearing capacity of the supporting surface required for each activity to be undertaken by the drill rig;

(f) the surface preparation required for the supporting surface and path of travel to safely support the drill rig during its operation and travel;

(g) the parts of the drill rig and the attachments of the drill rig that are permitted on the supporting surface;

(h) the precautions to be taken to ensure that the drilling operation and movement of the drill rig on the path of travel,

> (i) do not damage or affect the stability of any building, structure, property or public way adjacent to, or in the vicinity of, the drilling operation, and

> (ii) do not endanger a person using any building, structure, property or public way adjacent to, or in the vicinity of, the drilling operation;

(i) the frequency of inspections of the supporting surface and the path of travel of the drill rig, and the type of inspection required, to ensure they remain stable, do not deteriorate and continue to function as designed by the professional engineer, and any specific weather or other conditions that could affect the supporting surface or path of travel that would require additional inspections to be conducted; and

(j) the qualifications of the person who conducts the inspections of the supporting surface and path of travel and whether the person needs to be a professional engineer, a person under the direction of a professional engineer, a competent worker or another person with specified qualifications.

(3) The supporting surface and path of travel for the drill rig shall be prepared or constructed in accordance with the professional engineer's written report.

(4) No deviation from the written report is permitted unless the deviation is approved, in advance and in a written report, by a professional engineer.

(5) The supporting surface and path of travel for the drill rig shall be inspected by a professional engineer after they are prepared or constructed and before the drill rig is assembled and erected on the supporting surface or uses the path of travel to confirm that they were prepared or constructed in accordance with the professional engineer's report.

(6) The professional engineer shall prepare a written report of the results of the inspection under subsection (5).

(7) While a rotary foundation drill rig is in service at a drilling operation described in section 156.3, the employer responsible for the drilling operation shall ensure that,

(a) the supporting surface and path of travel are regularly inspected in accordance with, and by the person identified by, the report described in subsection (2); and

(b) a written report of the inspections and results are kept at the project and made available to an inspector upon request.

(8) The constructor and employer responsible for the drilling operation shall keep at the project a copy of all reports described in this section and make them available to an inspector upon request until the drilling operation is completed.

O. Reg. 345/15 s. 19

156.5(1) Before a drilling operation described in section 156.3 begins, the employer responsible for it shall,

(a) develop a drilling procedure for the drill rig in accordance with subsection (2) and have it approved by a professional engineer; and

(b) have a copy of the drilling procedure provided to, and reviewed with, the workers engaged in the drilling operation.

(2) The drilling procedure shall be in writing and shall include, at a minimum, details of,

(a) the sequence of activities of the drilling operation to be followed including, if applicable, the delivery of concrete, rebar, steel piles and other materials related to the drilling operation;

(b) the procedures to be implemented for removing excavated soil and material from an auger or drilling tool and away from the supporting surface of the drill rig;

(c) the location to be used for storing excavated soil and material so that it does not endanger workers;

(d) the working area and designated path of travel to be used for any machinery or equipment used in the vicinity of the drilling operation so that the machinery or equipment does not affect the stability and integrity of the supporting surface of the drill rig;

(e) the measures and procedures to be implemented during the drilling operation to ensure that unremoved hazards do not endanger workers; and

(f) the areas that have been designated at, or in the vicinity of, the drilling operation where,

    (i) only persons authorized by the employer are allowed to enter, and

    (ii) no persons or equipment are allowed to enter.

(3) While a rotary foundation drill rig is in service at a drilling operation described in section 156.3, the employer responsible for the drilling operation shall ensure that,

(a) the drilling procedure described in subsection (2) is implemented; and

(b) the drilling procedure is followed by the workers engaged in, and in the vicinity of, the drilling operation.

O. Reg. 345/15 s. 19

156.6(1) An employer shall ensure that a worker who operates a rotary foundation drill rig,

(a) is qualified in accordance with section 156.7;

(b) has completed a training program that meets the requirements of section 156.9, or is participating in a training program that meets such requirements and is being instructed on the operation of the drill rig;

(c) has demonstrated to the employer that the worker has adequate knowledge and proficiency in operating the drill rig to be used at the project; and

(d) is authorized by the employer to operate the drill rig at the project.

(2) The employer shall maintain a record of the training program described in section 156.9 provided to the worker that includes,

(a) the worker's name and the training dates; and

(b) the name and signature of the training provider.

(3) The employer shall make the training record available to an inspector upon request.

O. Reg. 345/15 s. 19

156.7(1) No worker shall operate a rotary foundation drill rig except in accordance with this section.

(2) The worker shall,

(a) have completed a training program that meets the requirements of section 156.9 and have written proof of training available at the project to an inspector upon request; or

(b) be participating in a training program that meets the requirements of section 156.9 and is being instructed on the operation of the drill rig.

(3) If a worker is operating a drill rig with an effective torque equal to or greater than 50 kilonewton metres, the worker shall have a certificate of qualification or written proof of training as required by section 156.8 available at the project to an inspector upon request.

O. Reg. 345/15 s. 19

156.8(1) No worker shall operate a rotary foundation drill rig with an effective torque greater than 270 kilonewton metres unless the worker,

(a) holds a certificate of qualification issued under the *Ontario College of Trades and Apprenticeship Act, 2009*, that is not suspended, in the trade of hoisting engineer — mobile crane operator 1; or

(b) is an apprentice who is working pursuant to a training agreement registered under the *Ontario College of Trades and Apprenticeship Act, 2009*, that is not suspended, in the trade of hoisting engineer — mobile crane operator 1.

(2) No worker shall operate a rotary foundation drill rig with an effective torque greater than 190 kilonewton metres but less than or equal to 270 kilonewton metres unless the worker,

(a) holds a certificate of qualification issued under the *Ontario College of Trades and Apprenticeship Act, 2009*, that is not suspended, in the trade of hoisting engineer — mobile crane operator 1, or hoisting engineer — mobile crane operator 2; or

(b) is an apprentice who is working pursuant to a training agreement registered under the *Ontario College of Trades and Apprenticeship Act, 2009*, that is not suspended, in the trade of hoisting engineer — mobile crane operator 1, or hoisting engineer — mobile crane operator 2.

(3) No worker shall operate a rotary foundation drill rig with an effective torque equal to or greater than 50 kilonewton metres but less than or equal to 190 kilonewton metres unless the worker,

(a) holds a certificate of qualification issued under the *Ontario College of Trades and Apprenticeship Act, 2009*, that is not suspended, in the trade of hoisting engineer — mobile crane operator 1, or hoisting engineer — mobile crane operator 2;

(b) is an apprentice who is working pursuant to a training agreement registered under the *Ontario College of Trades and Apprenticeship Act, 2009*, that is not suspended, in the trade of hoisting engineer — mobile crane operator 1, or hoisting engineer — mobile crane operator 2; or

(c) has written proof that the worker has completed a training program on the operation of a 0-8 ton mobile crane that included instruction on,

    (i) the relevant requirements of this Regulation,

    (ii) how to use the manufacturer's operating manuals,

    (iii) minimum distances when approaching an overhead electrical conductor,

    (iv) communications and signals,

    (v) types of mobile cranes and their components, including wire and synthetic rope, hydraulics, rigging and rigging hardware,

    (vi) pre-operational inspections and checks, and

    (vii) safe work practices related to mobile cranes, including crane set-up, load charts, assembly and disassembly of manual boom extensions, basic crane operation and maintenance.

O. Reg. 345/15 s. 19

156.9 A training program for the operation of a rotary foundation drill rig shall include instruction on,

    (a) the relevant requirements of this Regulation and the drill rig manufacturer's operating manual;

    (b) safe work practices;

    (c) communications and signals;

    (d) pre-operational inspections and checks;

    (e) site assessment;

    (f) drill rig set-up, securing and operation; and

    (g) equipment maintenance.

O. Reg. 345/15 s. 19

Tower Cranes

157. (1) No tower crane shall be erected at a project except in accordance with this section.

(2) The foundations supporting a tower crane shall be designed by a professional engineer in accordance with the crane manufacturer's specifications and shall be constructed in accordance with the design.

(3) The shoring and bracing that support a tower crane or tie it in place shall be designed by a professional engineer in accordance with the crane manufacturer's specifications and shall be installed in accordance with the design.

(4) The structural engineer responsible for the structural integrity of the building or structure shall review the design drawings for the foundation, shoring and bracing for a tower crane before the crane is erected at a project to ensure the structural integrity of the building or structure.

(5) The structural engineer who reviews the design drawings shall sign the drawings upon approving them.

(6) The constructor shall keep at the project while a tower crane is erected a copy of the signed design drawings for its foundation, shoring and bracing and any written opinion about the drawings by a structural engineer.

158. (1) Before a tower crane is erected at a project, a professional engineer shall ensure that the structural elements and components of the crane be subjected to non-destructive testing to ensure the structural integrity of the crane.

(2) The professional engineer conducting an inspection or under whose direction an inspection is done shall prepare a written report of the test results.

(3) The constructor shall keep the report at the project while the crane is erected.

O. Reg. 631/94 s. 5; 85/04 s. 17; 242/16, s. 16

159. (1) A professional engineer or a competent worker designated by a professional engineer shall visually inspect for defects the structural elements and components of a tower crane,

(a) after the crane is erected and before it is used; and

(b) after the inspection under clause (a), at intervals not greater than twelve months.

(2) No tower crane shall be used until any defects found during an inspection are repaired in accordance with the instructions of the crane's manufacturer or a professional engineer.

(3) A professional engineer or a competent worker designated by a professional engineer shall inspect a tower crane that has been repaired to ensure that the defects are corrected.

(4) The professional engineer conducting an inspection or under whose direction the inspection is done shall prepare a written report of the test results.

(5) The constructor shall keep the report at a project while the crane is erected.

O. Reg. 85/04 s. 18

160. (1) A tower crane shall have automatic limit switches and automatic overload limit devices that prevent,

(a) overloading at relative radii;

(b) a load on the crane from reaching beyond the highest permissible position specified by the manufacturer; and

(c) the trolley from reaching beyond the permissible travel limit specified by the manufacturer.

(2) In addition to automatic limit switches and overload limit devices, a tower crane shall have such other switches and devices as the manufacturer specifies.

161. (1) A competent worker shall perform operational tests on a tower crane to ensure that its automatic limit switches and overload limit devices are installed and functioning in accordance with the manufacturer's specifications, if any.

(2) Operational tests shall be done,

(a) after the tower crane is erected on the project and before it is used; and

(b) at one-week intervals after the test under clause (a) while the crane is erected on the project.

(3) Overload limit devices for a tower crane shall be tested using test blocks designed for the purpose that have their weight clearly marked on them.

(4) The test blocks shall be kept on the project while the crane is erected.

162. (1) A tower crane boom shall be able to slew freely when the crane is unattended except when,

(a) the boom may collide with another crane, a structure or another object; or

(b) to slew freely would be contrary to the written procedures of the crane's manufacturer.

(2) When a tower crane boom is not permitted to slew freely it shall be secured in accordance with the written procedures of the crane's manufacturer.

163. (1) Subject to subsection (2), the operator's cabin of a tower crane shall be located on and attached to or positioned on the crane in accordance with the instructions of the crane's manufacturer for the specific model and configuration of the crane and in such a manner that in the event of a failure of the boom, the cabin will not be crushed against the mast.

(2) The operator's cabin shall not be located on or attached to the boom unless,

(a) the cabin and its attachments have been specifically designed and fabricated for that purpose by the original manufacturer of the crane in accordance with good engineering practice;

(b) the boom of the crane cannot affect or be affected by the operation of another crane or make contact with a structure or equipment;

(c) the crane is not overlapped by any part of another crane;

(d) because of specific site conditions, the location of the cabin on the boom provides greater visibility for the operator than does the manufacturer's standard cabin location;

(e) the means of access to the cabin or other locations on the boom is by a catwalk constructed of skid resistant expanded metal or similar material and fitted with solidly constructed guardrails and devices which provide fall protection for the operator;

(f) the structural, environmental and ergonomic design of the cabin is equal to or greater than that of the crane's manufacturer's standard cabin design; and

(g) the proposed location and attachment method provide a structural and mechanical safety factor equal to or greater than that of a cabin located on the crane mast or attached to the slewing ring.

(3) If the crane manufacturer specifies the location of the operator's cabin to be on the boom of a tower crane, the crane manufacturer shall provide to the owner of the crane a report for the specific model and specific configuration of a crane on a project.

(4) The crane manufacturer's report shall include,

(a) the crane load restrictions, reductions or modifications resulting from the effect of the cabin weight and its offset from the boom centreline;

(b) the crane configuration and operating restrictions resulting from the effect of the cabin location and attachment method; and

(c) engineering design drawings that include,

(i) the structural and ergonomic design of the cabin,

(ii) the location of the cabin on the boom,

(iii) the attachment method including all fittings and hardware, and

(iv) all means of access.

164. A load block of an unattended tower crane shall be left empty, at the top position and located at minimum radius.

165. (1) The track bed of a rail-mounted tower crane shall have a sound and rigid base capable of carrying all loads to which it is likely to be subjected without deformation or settlement which affects the stability of the crane.

(2) The undercarriage of a rail-mounted tower crane shall be fitted with rail clamps that can be firmly attached to the rails to lock the crane in position.

(3) A rail-mounted tower crane shall be locked in position on the rails when not in use.

(4) A rail-mounted tower crane shall have rail stops or bumpers that extend at least as high as the centre of the undercarriage wheels and that are securely attached to the rail at both ends.

Derricks, Stiff-leg Derricks and Similar Hoisting Devices

166. (1) No derrick, stiff-leg derrick or similar hoisting device shall be attached to a building or structure unless this section is complied with.

(2) A professional engineer shall prepare design drawings and specifications for the attachment of a derrick, stiff-leg derrick or similar hoisting device to a building or structure.

(3) The design drawings and specifications shall include,

    (a) the location of the derrick, stiff-leg derrick or similar hoisting device on the building or structure;

    (b) the location of anchor bolts, guy wires, supports and shoring for it;

    (c) particulars of the weight of the loads and the radius at which the loads are to be lifted; and

    (d) particulars of the loads and forces on the building or structure imposed by the derrick, stiff-leg derrick or similar hoisting device.

(4) The constructor shall ensure that the structural engineer responsible for the structural integrity of a building or structure reviews and approves in writing the design drawings and specifications for a derrick, stiff-leg derrick or similar hoisting device before it is installed.

(5) A professional engineer shall inspect a derrick, stiff-leg derrick or similar hoisting device before it is first used on a building or structure to ensure that it is installed in accordance with the design drawings and specifications.

(6) The professional engineer conducting the inspection shall prepare a written report of the inspection.

(7) The constructor shall keep a copy of the design drawings and specifications for a derrick, stiff-leg derrick or similar hoisting device and the report prepared under subsection (6) at a project while the derrick, stiff-leg derrick or similar hoisting device is on the project.

O. Reg. 85/04 s. 19

167. (1) The pilot of a helicopter that is hoisting materials shall be competent to fly an externally-loaded helicopter.

(2) The pilot shall be in charge of the hoisting operation and shall determine the size and weight of loads to be hoisted and the method by which they are attached to the helicopter.

(3) Ground personnel including signallers for a helicopter being used to hoist materials shall be competent workers.

(4) The constructor shall take precautions against hazards caused by helicopter rotor downwash.

213/91

Cables, Slings, Rigging

168. (1) A cable used by a crane or similar hoisting device.

(a) shall be steel wire rope of the type, size, grade and construction recommended by the manufacturer of the crane or similar hoisting device;

(b) shall be compatible with the sheaves and the drum of the crane or similar hoisting device;

(c) shall be lubricated to prevent corrosion and wear;

(d) shall not be spliced; and

(e) shall have its end connections securely fastened and shall be kept with at least three full turns on the drum.

(2) No cable used by a crane or similar hoisting device,

(a) subject to subsection (3), shall contain six randomly-distributed wires that are broken in one rope lay or three or more wires that are broken in one strand in a rope lay;

(b) shall be smaller than its nominal rope diameter by more than,

(i) one millimetre for a diameter up to and including nineteen millimetres,

(ii) two millimetres for a diameter greater than nineteen millimetres up to and including twenty-nine millimetres, and

(iii) three millimetres for a diameter greater than twenty-nine millimetres;

(c) shall be worn by more than one-third of the original diameter of its outside individual wires;

(d) shall show evidence of kinking, bird-caging, corrosion or other damage resulting in distortion of the rope structure; or

(e) shall show evidence of possible rope failure including rope damage caused by contact with electricity.

(3) No cable that is static or is used for pendants,

(a) shall contain three or more broken wires in one lay or in a section between end connectors; or

(b) shall have more than one broken wire at an end connector.

(4) Rotation-resistant wire rope shall not be used for a cable for boom hoist reeving and pendants.

(5) Rotation-resistant wire rope shall not be used where an inner wire or strand for a cable is damaged or broken.

169. A cable used by a crane or similar hoisting device shall be capable of supporting at least,

(a) three and one-half times the maximum load to which it is likely to be subjected if it is used on a device other than a tower crane and it winds on a drum or passes over a sheave;

(b) five times the maximum load to which it is likely to be subjected if it is used on a tower crane and it winds on a drum or passes over a sheave;

(c) three times the maximum load to which it is likely to be subjected if it is a pendant or is not subject to winding or bending; and

(d) ten times the maximum load to which it is likely to be subjected if the crane or similar hoisting device is used for supporting persons.

170. (1) All cable used by a crane or similar hoisting device shall be visually inspected by a competent worker at least once a week when the crane or similar hoisting device is being used.

(2) The worker performing an inspection shall record the condition of the rope or cable inspected in the log book for the crane or similar hoisting device.

171. (1) A cable used by a crane or similar hoisting device shall be securely attached,

(a) by binding and fastening the cable around an oval thimble in a way that is strong enough to prevent the cable thimble from separating; or

(b) by fastening the cable within either a tapered socket by means of virgin zinc or a wedge-type socket fitted with a wire rope clip at the dead end to prevent the accidental release or loosening of the wedge.

(2) The dead end cable of a wedge socket assembly on a hoisting line shall extend between 100 millimetres and 300 millimetres out of the socket.

172. (1) A container, sling or similar device for rigging or hoisting an object, including its fittings and attachments,

    (a) shall be suitable for its intended use;

    (b) shall be suitable for and capable of supporting the object being rigged or hoisted;

    (c) shall be so arranged as to prevent the object or any part of the object from slipping or falling;

    (d) shall be capable of supporting at least five times the maximum load to which it may be subjected; and

    (e) shall be capable of supporting at least ten times the load to which it may be subjected if it is to be used to support a person.

213/91

(2) A sling or similar device made of web-type fabric or nylon shall be labelled to indicate its load rating capacity.

(3) No sling or similar device for rigging or hoisting made of web-type fabric or nylon shall be used if it may be cut.

173. (1) Every hoisting hook shall be equipped with a safety catch.

(2) No safety catch is required on a hoisting hook used in placing structural members if the method of placing protects workers to the same standard as a safety catch does.

(3) A hoisting hook shall have its load rating legibly cast or stamped on it in a location where the person using the hook can readily see it.

(4) A hoisting hook shall not be used if it is cracked, has a throat opening that is greater than as manufactured or is twisted from the plan of the unbent hook.

174. A hook block shall have its load rating and weight legibly cast or stamped on it in a conspicuous location.

175. (1) An overhauling weight used on the cable of a crane or similar hoisting device,

    (a) shall be prevented from sliding up or down the cable; and

    (b) shall be securely attached to the load hook and the cable.

(2) No overhauling weight used on the cable of a crane or similar hoisting device shall be split.

176. (1) Only an alloy steel chain or a chain manufactured for the purpose shall be used for hoisting.

(2) No alloy steel chain shall be annealed or welded.

(3) A chain used for hoisting shall,

(a) be labelled to indicate its load rating capacity;

(b) be repaired and reconditioned in accordance with the specifications of its manufacturer;

(c) after being repaired or reconditioned, be proof tested in accordance with the specifications of its manufacturer; and

(d) be visually inspected by a competent worker as frequently as recommended by its manufacturer and, in any case, at least once a week when the chain is in service.

O. Reg. 345/15 s. 20

177. [Repealed O. Reg. 345/15, s. 21.]

178. A friction-type clamp used in hoisting materials shall be constructed so that an accidental slackening of the hoisting cable does not release the clamp.

179. (1) If a worker may be endangered by the rotation or uncontrolled motion of a load being hoisted by a crane or similar hoisting device, one or more guide ropes or tag lines shall be used to prevent the rotation or uncontrolled motion.

(2) No guide rope or tag line shall be removed from a load referred to in subsection (1) until the load is landed and there is no danger of it tipping, collapsing or rolling.

180. (1) Piles and sheet-piling shall be adequately supported to prevent their uncontrolled movement while they are being hoisted, placed, removed or withdrawn.

(2) No worker shall be in an area where piles or sheet-piling are being hoisted, placed, removed or withdrawn unless the worker is directly engaged in the operation.

Electrical Hazards

181. (1) Except where otherwise required by this Regulation, electrical work performed on or near electrical transmission or distribution systems shall be performed in accordance with the document entitled "Electrical Utility Safety Rules" published by the Infrastructure Health and Safety Association and revised 2014.

(2) Sections 182, 187, 188, 189, 190, 191 and 193 do not apply to electrical work that is performed on or near electrical transmission or distribution systems if the work is performed in accordance with the document referred to in subsection (1).

(3) [Repealed O. Reg. 627/05, s. 4.]

O. Reg. 631/94 s. 6; 627/05 s. 4; 443/09 s. 5; 345/15 s. 22

182. (1) No worker shall connect, maintain or modify electrical equipment or installations unless,

(a) the worker holds a certificate of qualification issued under the *Ontario College of Trades and Apprenticeship Act, 2009*, that is not suspended, in the trade of,

(i) electrician—construction and maintenance, or

(ii) electrician—domestic and rural, if the worker is performing work that is limited to the scope of practice for that trade; or

(b) the worker is otherwise permitted to connect, maintain or modify electrical equipment or installations under the *Ontario College of Trades and Apprenticeship Act, 2009* or the *Technical Standards and Safety Act, 2000*.

(2) A worker who does not meet the requirements of clause (1)(a) or (b) may insert an attachment plug cap on the cord of electrical equipment or an electrical tool into, or remove it from, a convenience receptacle.

O. Reg. 627/05 s. 4; 88/13 s. 2

183. Every reasonable precaution shall be taken to prevent hazards to workers from energized electrical equipment, installations and conductors.

O. Reg. 143/99 s. 1; 627/05 ss. 5, 6

184. (1) No person, other than a person authorized to do so by the supervisor in charge of the project, shall enter or be permitted to enter a room or other enclosure containing exposed energized electrical parts.

(2) The entrance to a room or other enclosure containing exposed energized electrical parts shall be marked by conspicuous warning signs stating that entry by unauthorized persons is prohibited.

O. Reg. 627/05 s. 7

185. (1) Electrical equipment, installations, conductors and insulating materials shall be suitable for their intended use and shall be installed, maintained, modified and operated so as not to pose a hazard to a worker.

(2) For greater certainty, the regulations made under section 113 of the *Electricity Act, 1998* apply to electrical equipment, installations, conductors and insulating materials and to temporary wiring installations on projects.

O. Reg. 627/05 s. 7

186. Electrical equipment, installations and conductors that are not to be used for the purpose for which they were designed shall be,

    (a) removed; or

    (b) left in an electrically non-hazardous condition by being disconnected, de-energized, tagged and,

        (i) grounded, in the case of power lines,

        (ii) locked out, in the case of electrical equipment.

O. Reg. 627/05 s. 7

187. Tools, ladders, scaffolding and other equipment or materials capable of conducting electricity shall not be stored or used so close to energized electrical equipment, installations or conductors that they can make electrical contact.

O. Reg. 627/05 s. 7

188. (1) This section applies unless the conditions set out in clauses 189(a) and (b) are satisfied.

(2) No object shall be brought closer to an energized overhead electrical conductor with a nominal phase-to-phase voltage rating set out in Column 1 of the Table to this subsection than the distance specified opposite to it in Column 2.

TABLE

Item	Column 1 Nominal phase-to-phase voltage rating	Column 2 Minimum distance
1.	750 or more volts, but no more than 150,000 volts	3 m
2.	more than 150,000 volts, but no more than 250,000 volts	4.5 m
3.	more than 250,000 volts	6 m

(3) Subsections (4) to (9) apply if a crane, similar hoisting device, backhoe, power shovel or other vehicle or equipment is operated near an energized overhead electrical conductor and it is possible for a part of the vehicle or equipment or its load to encroach on the minimum distance permitted under subsection (2).

(4) A constructor shall,

(a) establish and implement written measures and procedures adequate to ensure that no part of a vehicle or equipment or its load encroaches on the minimum distance permitted by subsection (2); and

(b) make a copy of the written measures and procedures available to every employer on the project.

(5) The written measures and procedures shall include taking the following precautions to protect workers:

1. Adequate warning devices, visible to the operator and warning of the electrical hazard, shall be positioned in the vicinity of the hazard.

2. The operator shall be provided with written notification of the electrical hazard before beginning the work.

3. A legible sign, visible to the operator and warning of the potential electrical hazard, shall be posted at the operator's station.

(6) Before a worker begins work that includes an activity described in subsection (3), the employer shall provide a copy of the written measures and procedures to the worker and explain them to him or her.

(7) The worker shall follow the written measures and procedures.

(8) A competent worker, designated as a signaller, shall be stationed so that he or she is in full view of the operator and has a clear view of the electrical conductor and of the vehicle or equipment, and shall warn the operator each time any part of the vehicle or equipment or its load may approach the minimum distance.

(9) Section 106 also applies with respect to the signaller designated under subsection (8).

O. Reg. 627/05 s. 7; 345/15 s. 23

189. Section 188 does not apply if,

(a) under the authority of the owner of the electrical conductor, protective devices and equipment are installed, and written measures and procedures are established and implemented, that are adequate to protect workers from electrical shock and burn; and

(b) the workers involved in the work use protective devices and equipment, including personal protective equipment, and follow written measures and procedures that are adequate to protect workers from electrical shock and burn.

O. Reg. 627/05 s. 7

190. (1) This section applies if work is to be done on or near energized exposed parts of electrical equipment or of an electrical installation or conductor.

(2) An employer shall,

(a) establish and implement written measures and procedures for complying with this section to ensure that workers are adequately protected from electrical shock and burn; and

(b) make a copy of the written measures and procedures available to every worker on the project.

(3) The worker shall follow the written measures and procedures.

(4) Subject to subsection (9), the power supply to the electrical equipment, installation or conductor shall be disconnected, locked out of service and tagged in accordance with subsection (6) before the work begins, and kept disconnected, locked out of service and tagged while the work continues.

(5) Hazardous stored electrical energy shall be adequately discharged or contained before the work begins and shall be kept discharged or contained while the work continues.

(6) The following rules apply to the tagging of the power supply under subsection (4):

1. The tag shall be made of non-conducting material and shall be installed so as not to become energized.

2. The tag shall be placed in a conspicuous location and shall be secured to prevent its inadvertent removal.

3. The tag shall indicate,

i. why the equipment, installation or conductor is disconnected,

ii. the name of the person who disconnected the equipment, installation or conductor,

iii. the name of the person's employer, and

iv. the date on which the equipment, installation or conductor
was disconnected.

4. The tag shall not be removed unless it is safe to do so.

(7) A worker, before beginning work to which this section applies, shall verify that subsections (4) and (5) have been complied with.

(8) If more than one worker is involved in work to which this section applies, a means shall be provided to communicate the purpose and status of,

(a) the disconnecting, locking out and tagging of the electrical equipment, installation or conductor; and

(b) the discharging and containment of any hazardous stored electrical energy.

(9) Locking out is not required under subsection (4) if,

(a) in the case of a conductor, it is adequately grounded with a visible grounding mechanism;

(b) in the case of equipment or an installation,

(i) the power supply is less than 300 volts, the equipment or installation was not manufactured with provision for a locking device for the circuit breakers or fuses, and a written procedure has been implemented that is adequate to ensure that the circuit is not inadvertently energized, or

(ii) the power supply is 300 or more volts but not more than 600 volts, the equipment or installation was not manufactured with provision for a locking device for the circuit breakers or fuses, a written procedure as to how work is to be done has been implemented and the work is supervised by a competent worker to ensure that the circuit is not inadvertently energized.

O. Reg. 627/05 s. 7

191. (1) This section applies instead of section 190 if work is to be done on or near energized exposed parts of electrical equipment or of an electrical installation or conductor and,

(a) it is not reasonably possible to disconnect the equipment, installation or conductor from the power supply before working on or near the energized exposed parts;

(b) the equipment, installation or conductor is rated at a nominal voltage of 600 volts or less, and disconnecting the equipment, installation or conductor would create a greater hazard to a worker than proceeding without disconnecting it; or

(c) the work consists only of diagnostic testing of the equipment, installation or conductor.

(2) Subsection (10) applies, in addition to subsections (3) to (9), if the equipment, installation or conductor is nominally rated at,

(a) greater than 400 amperes and greater than 200 volts; or

(b) greater than 200 amperes and greater than 300 volts.

(3) Only a worker who meets the requirements of clause 182(1)(a) or (b) shall perform the work.

(4) The constructor shall,

(a) ensure that written measures and procedures for complying with this section are established and implemented, so that workers are adequately protected from electrical shock and burn; and

(b) make a copy of the written measures and procedures available to every employer on the project.

(5) Before a worker begins work to which this section applies, the employer shall provide a copy of the written measures and procedures to the worker and explain them to him or her.

(6) The worker shall follow the written procedures.

(7) A worker shall use mats, shields or other protective devices or equipment, including personal protective equipment, adequate to protect the worker from electrical shock and burn.

(8) If the electrical equipment, installation or conductor is rated at a nominal voltage of 300 volts or more, an adequately equipped competent worker who can perform rescue operations, including cardiopulmonary resuscitation, shall be stationed so that he or she can see the worker who is performing the work.

(9) Subsection (8) does not apply if the work consists only of diagnostic testing of the equipment, installation or conductors.

(10) In the case of equipment or of an installation or conductor described in subsection (2), a worker shall not perform the work unless the following additional conditions are satisfied:

1. The owner of the equipment, installation or conductor has provided the employer and the constructor with a record showing that

it has been maintained according to the manufacturer's specifications.

2. A copy of the maintenance record is readily available at the project.

3. The employer has determined from the maintenance record that the work on the equipment, installation or conductor can be performed safely without disconnecting it.

4. Before beginning the work, the worker has verified that paragraphs 1, 2 and 3 have been complied with.

O. Reg. 627/05 s. 7

192. All tools, devices and equipment, including personal protective equipment, that are used for working on or near energized exposed parts of electrical equipment, installations or conductors shall be designed, tested, maintained and used so as to provide adequate protection to workers.

O. Reg. 627/05 s. 7

193. (1) A worker who may be exposed to the hazard of electrical shock or burn while performing work shall use rubber gloves,

(a) that are adequate to protect him or her against electrical shock and burn;

(b) that have been tested and certified in accordance with subsection (2), if applicable; and

(c) that have been air tested and visually inspected for damage and adequacy immediately before each use.

(2) Rubber gloves rated for use with voltages above 5,000 volts AC shall be tested and certified to ensure that they can withstand the voltages for which they are rated,

(a) at least once every three months, if they are in service;

(b) at least once every six months, if they are not in service.

(3) Rubber gloves shall be worn with adequate leather protectors and shall not be worn inside out.

(4) Leather protectors shall be visually inspected for damage and adequacy immediately before each use.

(5) Rubber gloves or leather protectors that are damaged or not adequate to protect workers from electrical shock and burn shall not be used.

(6) Workers shall be trained in the proper use, care and storage of rubber gloves and leather protectors.

O. Reg. 627/05 s. 7

194. (1) A switch and panel board controlling a service entrance, service feeder or branch circuit shall meet the requirements of this section.

(2) A switch and panel board shall be securely mounted on a soundly constructed vertical surface and shall have a cover over uninsulated parts carrying current.

(3) A switch and panel board shall be located,
    (a) in an area where water will not accumulate; and
    (b) within easy reach of workers and readily accessible to them.

(4) The area in front of a panel board shall be kept clear of obstructions.

(5) A switch that controls a service entrance, service feeder or branch circuit providing temporary power,
    (a) shall not be locked in the energized position; and
    (b) shall be housed in an enclosure that can be locked and is provided with a locking device.

O. Reg. 627/05 s. 7

195. All electrical extension cords used at a project shall have a grounding conductor and at least two other conductors.

O. Reg. 627/05 s. 7

195.1(1) Cord-connected electrical equipment or tools shall have a casing that is adequately grounded.

(2) All cord connections to electrical equipment or tools shall be polarized.

(3) Subsections (1) and (2) do not apply to cord-connected electrical equipment or tools that are adequately double-insulated and whose insulated casing shows no evidence of cracks or defects.

(4) Subsection (1) does not apply to a portable electrical generator in which the electrical equipment or tools are not exposed to an external electric power source if the casing of portable electrical equipment or tools connected to the generator is bonded to a non-current-carrying part of the generator.

O. Reg. 627/05 s. 7

195.2 When a portable electrical tool is used outdoors or in a wet location,

(a) if the source of power is an ungrounded portable generator having a maximum output of 1.8 kilowatts or less, a ground fault circuit interrupter of the Class A type shall be located in the cord feeding the tool, as close to the tool as possible;

(b) in all other cases, the tool shall be plugged into a receptacle protected by a ground fault circuit interrupter of the Class A type.

O. Reg. 627/05 s. 7

195.3(1) Defective electrical equipment and tools that may pose a hazard shall be immediately disconnected, removed from service and tagged as being defective.

(2) The cause of a ground fault or the tripping of a ground fault circuit interrupter shall be immediately investigated to determine the hazard and corrective action shall be taken immediately.

O. Reg. 627/05 s. 7

Explosives

196. (1) If explosives are to be used on a project, the employer responsible for blasting shall designate a competent worker to be in charge of blasting operations.

(2) The employer shall post the name of the worker in charge of blasting operations for a project in a conspicuous place on the project and in every magazine.

(3) The worker in charge of blasting operations for a project shall personally supervise blasting operations at the project, including the loading, priming and initiating of all charges.

(4) The worker in charge of blasting operations for a project,

(a) shall inspect for hazardous conditions explosives and the magazines in which they are stored,

(i) at least once a month, and

(ii) on the day they are to be used;

(b) shall promptly report the results of inspections under clause (a) to the supervisor in charge of the project;

(c) shall take immediate steps to correct any hazardous condition; and

(d) shall dispose of all deteriorated explosives.

(5) If an act of careless placing or handling of explosives on the project is discovered by, or reported to the worker in charge of blasting operations, the worker shall promptly investigate the circumstances and report the results of the investigation to the supervisor in charge of the project.

197. Only a competent worker or a worker who is working under the direct personal supervision of a competent worker shall handle, transport, prepare and use explosives on a project.

198. (1) A magazine containing an explosive shall be securely locked at all times when the competent worker described in section 197 is not present.

(2) No explosive shall be outside a magazine unless the explosive is required for immediate use.

(3) An explosive outside a magazine shall be attended at all times.

199. An explosive shall remain in its original wrapper unless it is manufactured and intended for use other than in its original wrapper.

200. (1) No fire or other naked flame shall be located in a magazine or eight metres or less from any explosive.

(2) No person shall smoke in a magazine or eight metres or less from any explosive.

O. Reg. 142/17, s. 22

201. Blasting mats shall be used to prevent flying objects caused by blasting operations from endangering persons and property located on or adjacent to a project.

202. (1) This section applies if electric blasting caps are used on a project.

(2) The protective shunt shall not be removed from the leg wire until connections are made.

(3) The firing circuit shall be short-circuited while the leads from the blasting caps are being connected to each other and to the firing cables.

(4) The short circuit shall not be removed until immediately before blasting and until all workers have left the area affected by the blasting operations.

(5) The source of energy for a blasting operation shall be disconnected from the firing circuit immediately after firing.

203. (1) Before blasting begins, the worker in charge of blasting operations shall post workers at the approaches to the affected area in order to prevent access to it.

(2) Before blasting begins, the worker in charge of blasting operations shall ensure,

(a) that only workers required to carry out the blasting are located in the affected area;

(b) that no workers remain in an area whose means of egress passes the affected area; and

(c) that a warning that is clearly audible within a radius of one kilometre of the blast is given by siren.

204. (1) Before a drill hole for loading explosives is drilled, the exposed surface shall be examined for drill holes or remnants of drill holes that may contain explosives and any explosive found shall be removed if practicable.

(2) No drill hole shall be drilled,

(a) 7.5 metres or less from of another hole that is being loaded with or contains explosives; and

(b) 150 millimetres or less from another hole or remnant of a hole that has been charged or blasted unless adequate precautions have been taken to ensure that the other hole is free from explosives.

(3) Clause (2)(a) does not apply to a hole being drilled adjacent to another hole that is being loaded with explosives,

(a) if a professional engineer prepares a specification showing the location of the drill hole and the adjacent hole and describing the precautions to be taken to prevent the accidental detonation by the drilling operation of the explosives in the adjacent hole; and

(b) if the drilling is done as described in the specification referred to in clause (a).

(4) No drill hole permitted under subsection (3) shall be drilled one metre or less from another hole containing explosives.

(5) The professional engineer's specification shall be in writing.

(6) The employer responsible for blasting shall keep a copy of the specification at the project until the blasting to which the specification refers is completed.

O. Reg. 85/04 s. 20; 142/17, s. 23

205. (1) If cartridges of explosives are to be used in a drill hole, the hole shall be made large enough that a cartridge can be inserted easily to the bottom of the hole.

(2) No drill hole shall be charged with explosives unless a properly prepared detonation agent is placed in the charge.

(3) Drill holes charged with explosives in one loading operation shall be fired in one operation.

(4) No drill hole that is charged with explosives shall be left unfired for any longer than is required in a continuing operation to complete the charging and blasting of adjacent holes.

206. Only a non-sparking tool or rod shall be used in the charging of a drill hole or in a drill hole containing explosives.

Roofing

207. (1) If a built-up roof is being constructed, repaired or resurfaced, a barrier shall be placed in the immediate work area at least two metres from the perimeter of the roof.

(2) The barrier shall consist of portable weighted posts supporting a taut chain, cable or rope that is located 1.1 metres above the roof level.

208. (1) A pipe that supplies hot tar or bitumen to a roof shall be securely fixed and supported to prevent its deflection.

(2) If a pipe discharges hot tar or bitumen two metres or less from of the edge of a roof, a guardrail shall be provided at the edge of the roof.

O. Reg. 142/17, s. 24

209. (1) A hoist used on a roof,
  (a) shall have a guardrail installed on both sides of the frame at the edge of the roof; and
  (b) shall be positioned in such a way that the hoist cable is vertical at all times while a load is being hoisted.

(2) Only a competent worker shall operate a hoist used on a roof.

210. The counterweights on a roofer's hoist,
  (a) shall be suitable for the purpose;
  (b) shall not consist of roofing or other construction material;
  (c) shall be securely attached to the hoist; and

(d) shall provide a safety factor against overturning of not less than three.

Hot Tar or Bitumen Roadtankers

211. (1) Only a competent worker shall operate a hot tar or bitumen roadtanker or kettle.

(2) If a hot tar or bitumen roadtanker or kettle is fitted with a propane-fuelled heater,

(a) the storage cylinder for propane shall not be placed closer than three metres to a source of fire or ignition;

(b) the lines connecting the storage cylinder for propane to the heating device shall be located so that they do not come into contact with the hot tar or bitumen in the case of a spill or a failure of a component of the system; and

(c) a fire extinguisher with an Underwriters' Laboratories of Canada rating of at least 4A40BC shall be provided with the road-tanker or kettle.

(3) A propane burner used on a bitumen roadtanker or kettle,

(a) shall have a thermal rating no greater than that recommended by the manufacturer of the roadtanker or kettle; and

(b) shall consist of components that are adequate for their intended use.

(4) Hot tar or bitumen shall be transferred from a roadtanker to a kettle through enclosed piping.

Demolition and Damaged Structures

212. (1) If a structure is so damaged that a worker is likely to be endangered by its partial or complete collapse,

(a) the structure shall be braced and shored; and

(b) safeguards appropriate in the circumstances shall be provided to prevent injury to a worker.

(2) Safeguards shall be installed progressively from a safe area towards the hazard so that the workers installing the safeguards are not endangered.

213. (1) Only a worker who is directly engaged in the demolition, dismantling or moving of a building or structure shall be in, on or near it.

(2) If the demolition or dismantling of a building or structure is discontinued, barriers shall be erected to prevent access by people to the remaining part of the building or structure.

(3) A worker shall enter only the part of a building or structure being demolished that will safely support the worker.

214. (1) No building or structure shall be demolished, dismantled or moved until this section is complied with.

(2) Precautions shall be taken to prevent injury to a person on or near the project or the adjoining property that may result from the demolition, dismantling or moving of a building or structure.

(3) All gas, electrical and other services that may endanger persons who have access to a building or structure shall be shut off and disconnected before, and shall remain shut off and disconnected during, the demolition, dismantling or moving of the building or structure.

(4) All toxic, flammable or explosive substances shall be removed from a building or structure that is to be demolished, dismantled or moved.

215. (1) Sections 216, 217, 218 and 220 do not apply with respect to a building or structure that is being demolished by,

    (a) a heavy weight suspended by cable from a crane or similar hoisting device;

    (b) a power shovel, bulldozer or other vehicle;

    (c) the use of explosives; or

    (d) a combination of methods described in clauses (a) to (c).

(2) The controls of a mechanical device used to demolish a building or structure shall be operated from a location that is as remote as is practicable from the building or structure.

(3) If a swinging weight is used to demolish a building or structure, the supporting cable of the weight shall be short enough or shall be so restrained that the weight does not swing against another building or structure.

216. (1) Demolition and dismantling of a building or structure shall proceed systematically and continuously from the highest to the lowest point unless a worker is endangered by this procedure.

(2) Despite subsection (1), the skeleton structural frame in a skeleton structural frame building may be left in place during the demolition or dismantling of the masonry if the masonry and any loose material are removed from the frame systematically and continuously from the highest to the lowest point.

(3) The work above a tier or floor of a building or structure shall be completed before the support of the tier or floor is affected by demolition or dismantling operations.

217. No exterior wall of a building or structure shall be demolished until all glass is removed from windows, doors, interior partitions and components containing glass or is protected to prevent the glass from breaking during the demolition.

218. (1) Masonry walls of a building or structure being demolished or dismantled shall be removed in reasonably level courses.

(2) No materials in a masonry wall of a building or structure being demolished or dismantled shall be loosened or permitted to fall in masses that are likely to endanger,

    (a) a person; or

    (b) the structural stability of a scaffold or of a floor or other support of the building or structure.

219. No worker shall stand on top of a wall, pier or chimney to remove material from it unless flooring, scaffolding or staging is provided on all sides of it not more than 2.4 metres below the place where the worker is working.

220. No truss, girder or other structural member of a building or structure being demolished or dismantled shall be disconnected until,

    (a) it is relieved of all loads other than its own weight; and

    (b) it has temporary support.

221. (1) A basement, cellar or excavation left after a building or structure is demolished, dismantled or moved,

    (a) shall be backfilled to grade level; or

    (b) shall have fencing along its open sides.

(2) Subsection (1) does not apply to a basement or cellar that is enclosed by a roof, floor or other solid covering if all openings in the roof, floor or covering are covered with securely fastened planks.

Part II.1

[Heading repealed O. Reg. 96/11, s. 1.]

221.1 to 221.19 [Repealed O. Reg. 96/11, s. 1.]

Part III — Excavations

Interpretation and Application

222. In this Part,

"engineered support system" means an excavation or trench shoring system, designed for a specific project or location, assembled in place and which cannot be moved as a unit;

"hydraulic support system" means a system capable of being moved as a unit, designed to resist the pressure from the walls of an excavation by applying a hydraulic counterpressure through the struts;

"prefabricated support system" means a trench box, trench shield or similar structure, composed of members connected to each other and capable of being moved as a unit, and designed to resist the pressure from the walls of an excavation but does not include a hydraulic support system;

"pressure", in relation to a wall of an excavation, means the lateral pressure of the earth on the wall calculated in accordance with generally accepted engineering principles and includes hydrostatic pressure and pressure due to surcharge.

O. Reg. 142/17, s. 25

223. This Part applies to all excavating and trenching operations.

Entry and Working Alone

224. No person shall enter or be permitted to enter an excavation that does not comply with this Part.

225. Work shall not be performed in a trench unless another worker is working above ground in close proximity to the trench or to the means of access to it.

Soil Types

226. (1) For the purposes of this Part, soil shall be classified as Type 1, 2, 3 or 4 in accordance with the descriptions set out in this section.

(2) Type 1 soil,

(a) is hard, very dense and only able to be penetrated with difficulty by a small sharp object;

(b) has a low natural moisture content and a high degree of internal strength;

(c) has no signs of water seepage; and

(d) can be excavated only by mechanical equipment.

(3) Type 2 soil,

(a) is very stiff, dense and can be penetrated with moderate difficulty by a small sharp object;

(b) has a low to medium natural moisture content and a medium degree of internal strength; and

(c) has a damp appearance after it is excavated.

(4) Type 3 soil is,

(a) previously excavated soil; or

(b) soil that is stiff to firm or compact to loose in consistency and has one or more of the following characteristics:

    (i) It exhibits signs of surface cracking.

    (ii) It exhibits signs of water seepage.

    (iii) If it is dry, it may run easily into a well-defined conical pile.

    (iv) It has a low degree of internal strength.

(5) Type 4 soil,

(a) is soft to very soft and very loose in consistency, very sensitive and upon disturbance is significantly reduced in natural strength;

(b) runs easily or flows, unless it is completely supported before excavating procedures;

(c) has almost no internal strength;

(d) is wet or muddy; and

(e) exerts substantial fluid pressure on its supporting system.

O. Reg. 345/15 s. 24

227. (1) The type of soil in which an excavation is made shall be determined by visual and physical examination of the soil,

(a) at the walls of the excavation; and

(b) within a horizontal distance from each wall equal to the depth of the excavation measured away from the excavation.

(2) The soil in which an excavation is made shall be classified as the type described in section 226 that the soil most closely resembles.

(3) If an excavation contains more than one type of soil, the soil shall be classified as the type with the highest number as described in section 226 among the types present.

Precautions Concerning Services

228. Precautions Concerning Services —

(1) Before an excavation is begun,

　(a) the employer excavating shall ensure that all gas, electrical and other services in and near the area to be excavated are located and marked;

　(b) the employer and worker locating and marking the services described in clause (a) shall ensure that they are accurately located and marked; and

　(c) if a service may pose a hazard, the service shall be shut off and disconnected.

(2) If a service may pose a hazard and it cannot be shut off or disconnected, the owner of the service shall be requested to supervise the uncovering of the service during the excavation.

(3) Pipes, conduits and cables for gas, electrical and other services in an excavation shall be supported to prevent their failure or breakage.

(4) [Repealed O. Reg. 443/09, s. 6.]

O. Reg. 443/09 s. 6

Protection of Adjacent Structures

229. (1) If an excavation may affect the stability of an adjacent building or structure, the constructor shall take precautions to prevent damage to the adjacent building or structure.

(2) A professional engineer shall specify in writing the precautions required under subsection (1).

(3) Such precautions as the professional engineer specifies shall be taken.

General Requirements

230. Every excavation that a worker may be required to enter shall be kept reasonably free of water.

231. An excavation in which a worker may work shall have a clear work space of at least 450 millimetres between the wall of the excavation and any formwork or masonry or similar wall.

232. (1) The walls of an excavation shall be stripped of loose rock or other material that may slide, roll or fall upon a worker.

(2) The walls of an excavation cut in rock shall be supported by rock anchors or wire mesh if support is necessary to prevent the spalling of loose rock.

233. (1) A level area extending at least one metre from the upper edge of each wall of an excavation shall be kept clear of equipment, excavated soil, rock and construction material.

(2) The stability of a wall of an excavation shall be maintained where it may be affected by stockpiling excavated soil or rock or construction materials.

(3) No person shall operate a vehicle or other machine and no vehicle or other machine shall be located in such a way as to affect the stability of a wall of an excavation.

(4) If a person could fall into an excavation that is more than 2.4 metres deep, a barrier at least 1.1 metres high shall be provided at the top of every wall of the excavation that is not sloped as described in clauses 234(2)(e), (f) and (g).

Support Systems

234. (1) The walls of an excavation shall be supported by a support system that complies with sections 235, 236, 237, 238, 239 and 241.

(2) Subsection (1) does not apply with respect to an excavation,

    (a) that is less than 1.2 metres deep;

    (b) that no worker is required to enter;

    (c) that is not a trench and with respect to which no worker is required to be closer to a wall than the height of the wall;

    (d) that is cut in sound and stable rock;

    (e) made in Type 1 or Type 2 soil and whose walls are sloped to 1.2 metres or less from its bottom with a slope having a minimum gradient of one vertical to one horizontal;

(f) made in Type 3 soil and whose walls are sloped from its bottom with a slope having a minimum gradient of one one vertical to one horizontal;

(g) made in Type 4 soil and whose walls are sloped from its bottom with a slope having a minimum gradient of one vertical to three horizontal; or

(h) that is not a trench and is not made in Type 4 soil and with respect to which a professional engineer has given a written opinion that the walls of the excavation are sufficiently stable that no worker will be endangered if no support system is used.

(3) The opinion in clause (2)(h) shall include details of,

(a) the specific project and the location thereon;

(b) any specific condition for which the opinion applies; and

(c) the frequency of inspections.

(4) The constructor shall keep on the project a copy of every opinion given by a professional engineer for the purpose of clause (2)(h) while the project is in progress.

(5) The professional engineer who gives an opinion described in clause (2)(h), or a competent worker designated by him or her, shall inspect the excavation to which the opinion relates as frequently as the opinion specifies.

O. Reg. 142/17, s. 26

235. (1) Subject to subsection (2), a support system shall consist of,

(a) timbering and shoring that meet the requirements of subsection 238(2), if no hydrostatic pressure is present in the soil, and if the width and depth of the excavation are equal to or less than the width and depth indicated in the Table to section 238;

(b) a prefabricated support system that complies with sections 236 and 237;

(c) a hydraulic support system that complies with sections 236 and 237; or

(d) an engineered support system that complies with section 236.

(2) Where the excavation is a trench and the depth exceeds six metres or the width exceeds 3.6 metres, the support system shall consist of an engineered support system designed for the specific location and project.

O. Reg. 631/94 s. 7

236. (1) Every prefabricated, hydraulic or engineered support system shall be designed by a professional engineer.

(2) Every prefabricated, hydraulic or engineered support system shall be constructed, installed, used and maintained in accordance with its design drawings and specifications.

(3) The design drawings and specifications for a prefabricated, hydraulic or an engineered support system,

    (a) shall indicate the size of the system and the type and grade of materials of which it is to be made;

    (b) shall indicate the maximum depth and the types of soil for which it is designed;

    (c) shall indicate the proper positioning of the system in the excavation, including the maximum allowable clearance between the walls of the support system and the walls of the excavation; and

    (d) shall indicate how to install and remove the system.

    (e) [Revoked O. Reg. 85/04, s. 21.]

(4) In addition to the requirements of subsection (3), the design drawings and specifications for a hydraulic support system,

    (a) shall indicate the minimum working pressure required for the system; and

    (b) shall require the use of a device to ensure the protection of workers if a loss of hydraulic pressure occurs in the system.

(5) Before a variation from the design drawings and specifications for a prefabricated, hydraulic or an engineered support system is permitted, the variation shall be approved in writing by a professional engineer.

(6) If the soil conditions on a project differ from those assumed by the professional engineer in designing a prefabricated, hydraulic or an engineered support system, a professional engineer shall modify the design drawings and specifications for the actual soil conditions or shall approve the support system for use in the actual soil conditions.

(7) The constructor shall keep the design drawings and specifications for a prefabricated, hydraulic or an engineered support system at a project while the system is on the project.

(8) [Repealed O. Reg. 443/09, s. 7.]

              O. Reg. 145/00 s. 32; 85/04 s. 21; 443/09 s. 7

237. (1) Subject to subsection (2),

(a) no prefabricated or hydraulic support system shall be used in type 4 soil;

(b) the space between the walls of a prefabricated support system and the walls of the excavation shall be restricted to the minimum clearance required for the forward progression of the support system; and

(c) the walls of a hydraulic support system shall touch the walls of the excavation.

(2) A prefabricated or hydraulic support system may be used for repairing underground pipe breaks if the system,

(a) meets the requirements of section 236;

(b) has four side walls;

(c) is designed for a maximum depth of 3.6 metres;

(d) is not used at a greater depth than 3.6 metres;

(e) is designed to resist all hydrostatic and earth pressures found in type 3 and type 4 soils;

(f) is installed so as to extend to the bottom of the excavation;

(g) is installed so that the walls of the system touch the walls of the excavation; and

(h) is not pulled forward after being installed in the excavation.

(3) Before a support system is used as described in subsection (2), the constructor shall submit two copies of its design drawings and specifications to the office of the Ministry of Labour nearest to the project.

O. Reg. 631/94 s. 8

238. (1) In this section,

"cleat" means a member of shoring that directly resists the downward movement of a wale or strut;

"o/c" means the maximum distance measured from the centre of one member of sheathing, wale or strut to the centre of the adjacent member of sheathing, wale or strut;

"post" means a vertical member of shoring that acts as a spacer between the wales;

"10 millimetres gap" means that the space between two adjacent members of sheathing is a maximum of ten millimetres.

(2) Timbering and shoring referred to in clause 235(1)(a) for the walls of an excavation with a depth described in Column 2 of the Table to this section shall meet the corresponding specifications set out in Columns 3 to 8 of the Table.

(3) Every piece of sheathing referred to in the Table to this section shall be made of sound Number 1 Grade spruce and,

    (a) shall be placed against the side of the excavation so that it is vertical;

    (b) shall be secured in place by wales; and

    (c) shall be driven into the soil and firmly secured in place if the excavation is made in Type 3 or 4 soil.

(4) Every strut referred to in the Table to this section shall be made of sound number 1 structural grade spruce and,

    (a) shall be placed in the excavation so that it is horizontal and at right angles to the wales;

    (b) shall be cut to the proper length and held in place by at least two wedges driven between the strut and the wales; and

    (c) shall be cleated with cleats that extend over the top of the strut and rest on the wales or that are attached securely to the wales by spikes or bolts.

(5) Every wale referred to in the Table to this section shall be made of sound number 1 structural grade spruce and,

    (a) shall be placed in the excavation so that it is parallel to the bottom, or proposed bottom, of the excavation; and

    (b) shall be supported by either cleats secured to the sheathing or posts set on the wale next below it or, if it is the lowest wale, on the bottom of the excavation.

TABLE
EXCAVATION SHORING AND TIMBERING

Item	Column 1 Excavation Depth	Column 2 Soil Type	Column 3 Sheathing	Column 4 Strut width where width of excavation at strut location is 1.8 to 3.6 metres	Column 5 Strut width where width of excavation at strut location is up to 1.8 metres	Column 6 Vertical strut spacing	Column 7 Horizontal strut spacing	Column 8 Wales
1.	3.0 m or less	1	50 mm × 200 mm at 1.2 m o/c	200 mm × 200 mm	150 mm × 150 mm	1.2 m	* 2.4 m	*200 mm × 200 mm
2.	3.0 m or less	2	50 mm × 200 mm at 1.2 m o/c	200 mm × 200 mm	150 mm × 150 mm	1.2 m	* 2.4 m	*200 mm × 200 mm
3.	3.0 m or less	3	50 mm × 200 mm at 10 mm gap	200 mm × 200 mm	200 mm × 200 mm	1.2 m	2.4 m	250 mm × 250 mm
4.	3.0 m or less	4	75 mm × 200 mm at 10 mm gap	250 mm × 250 mm	200 mm × 200 mm	1.2 m	2.4 m	300 mm × 300 mm
5.	Over 3.0 m to 4.5 m	1	50 mm × 200 mm with 10 mm gap	200 mm × 200 mm	150 mm × 150 mm	1.2 m	2.4 m	200 mm × 200 mm
6.	Over 3.0 m to 4.5 m	2	50 mm × 200 mm with 10 mm gap	200 mm × 200 mm	200 mm × 200 mm	1.2 m	2.4 m	250 mm × 250 mm
7.	Over 3.0 m to 4.5 m	3	50 mm × 200 mm with 10 mm gap	250 mm × 250 mm	250 mm × 250 mm	1.2 m	2.4 m	250 mm × 250 mm
8.	Over 3.0 m to 4.0 m	4	75 mm × 200 mm with 10 mm gap	300 mm × 300 mm	300 mm × 300 mm	1.2 m	2.4 m	300 mm × 300 mm
9.	Over 4.5 m to 6.0 m	1	50 mm × 200 mm with 10 mm gap	200 mm × 200 mm	200 mm × 200 mm	1.2 m	2.4 m	200 mm × 200 mm
10.	Over 4.5 m to 6.0 m	2	50 mm × 200 mm with 10 mm gap	250 mm × 250 mm	250 mm × 250 mm	1.2 m	2.4 m	250 mm × 250 mm
11.	Over 4.5 m to 6.0 m	3	50 mm × 200 mm with 10 mm gap	300 mm × 300 mm	300 mm × 300 mm	1.2 m	2.4 m	300 mm × 300 mm

*Note: For excavations to 3 m deep in soil types 1 and 2, the wales can be omitted if the struts are used at 1.2 m horizontal spacings.

O. Reg. 631/94 s. 9; 345/15 s. 25

239. (1) A support system for the walls of an excavation shall be installed,

(a) progressively in an excavation in Type 1, 2 or 3 soil; and

(b) in advance of an excavation in Type 4 soil, if practicable.

(2) A support system for the walls of an excavation shall provide continuous support for it.

(3) No support system for the walls of an excavation shall be removed until immediately before the excavation is backfilled.

(4) A competent person shall supervise the removal of a support system for the walls of an excavation.

240. If a support system is used for the walls of an excavation, a ladder for access to or egress from the excavation shall be placed within the area protected by the support system.

241. (1) A support system for the walls of an excavation shall extend at least 0.3 metres above the top of the excavation unless otherwise permitted or required by this section.

213/91

(2) If an excavation is located where there is vehicular or pedestrian traffic and if the excavation will be covered when work on or in it is not in progress, the support system for the walls of the excavation shall extend at least to the top of the excavation.

(3) If the upper portion of the walls of an excavation are sloped for the soil types as described in clauses 234 (2)(e), (f) and (g) and the lower portion of the walls are vertical or near vertical, the walls shall be supported by a support system which extends at least 0.5 metres above the vertical walls.

242. (1) A metal trench-jack or trench-brace may be used in place of a timber strut; and

> (a) if the allowable working load of the trench-jack or trench-brace is equal to or greater than that of the timber strut; and
>
> (b) if the size of the replaced timber strut is shown on the trench-jack or trench-brace.

(2) The allowable working load of a metal trench-jack or trench-brace shall be determined by a professional engineer in accordance with good engineering practice and shall be legibly cast or stamped on the trench-jack or trench-brace.

(3) No metal trench-jack or trench-brace shall be extended beyond the length used to establish its maximum allowable working load.

(4) Every metal trench-jack or trench-brace, when it is used,

> (a) shall be placed against the wales in such a way that the load from the wales is applied axially to the trench-jack or trench-brace; and
>
> (b) shall be adequately supported so that it does not move out of position.

Part IV — Tunnels, Shafts, Caissons and Cofferdams

Application

243. This Part applies with respect to,

(a) tunnels and shafts other than those located at or used in connection with a mine; and

(b) caissons and cofferdams.

Land Requirements

244. A tunnel or shaft shall be commenced or started only where sufficient land space is available to permit compliance with Parts IV and V of this Regulation.

Notice

245. (1) An employer who will be constructing a tunnel, shaft, caisson or cofferdam shall file a notice with a Director before beginning work on a tunnel, shaft, caisson or cofferdam.

(2) The notice shall,

(a) describe the work;

(b) provide specifications and drawings showing profiles, transverse sections and plans for the tunnel, shaft, caisson or cofferdam signed and sealed by the professional engineer who designed the support system for the tunnel, shaft, caisson or cofferdam;

(c) provide complete details of all temporary and permanent ground support;

(d) state the name, mailing address, address for service and telephone number of the constructor, of the owner and of the employer in charge of the work;

(e) state the name of the supervisor in charge of the work and the supervisor's mailing address, address for service and telephone number;

(f) provide the municipal address of the work or include a description of its location relative to the nearest highway such that the Director is able to locate the work;

(g) state the starting date and the anticipated duration of the work;

(h) state the estimated total cost for labour and materials for the work; and

(i) list all designated substances that may be used, handled or disturbed by the work.

O. Reg. 145/00 s. 33

Working Alone and Entry

246. Work shall not be performed in a shaft, tunnel, caisson or cofferdam unless another worker is working above ground in close proximity to the shaft, tunnel, caisson or cofferdam or to the means of access to it.

247. (1) No worker shall enter a well or augered caisson where the excavation is deeper than 1.2 metres unless,

(a) a steel liner of adequate capacity is installed in the well or caisson;

(b) the requirements of Ontario Regulation 632/05 (*Confined Spaces*) made under the Act are complied with; and

(c) the worker is inside the steel liner and is wearing a fall arrest system with a full body harness secured to a fixed support.

(2) A steel liner,

(a) shall extend sixty centimetres above ground level and to a point that is 1.2 metres or closer to the point in the well or caisson where work is being done;

(b) shall be supported on two sides by steel wire rope and steel beams; and

(c) shall have a diameter which is not less than 100 millimetres less than the diameter of the excavation.

O. Reg. 628/05 s. 4; 96/11 s. 2; 142/17, s. 27

Fire Protection

248. Notices describing how to sound a fire alarm shall be posted in conspicuous places on a project to which this Part applies.

249. (1) A means of extinguishing fire shall be provided,

(a) at the top and bottom of every shaft;

(b) if a project consists of or includes a tunnel, at each panel board for electricity, on each electric-powered locomotive and at each battery charging station; and

(c) 30 metres or less from each work face of a tunnel and of each location where a fire hazard exists.

(2) The means of extinguishing fire shall be inspected at least once a week to ensure that it is in working order.

O. Reg. 142/17, s. 28

250. (1) A fire suppression system for equipment that contains flammable hydraulic fluids shall be provided while the equipment is underground.

(2) A fire suppression system shall include a dry chemical fire extinguisher with an Underwriters' Laboratories of Canada rating of at least 4A40BC.

O. Reg. 345/15 s. 26

251. (1) If the diameter of a tunnel will be equal to or greater than 1.5 metres when it is completed, a standpipe, a fire line and a hose shall be provided in the tunnel.

(2) A siamese connection shall be provided on the fire line at the surface of the shaft.

252. (1) Every standpipe in a shaft or tunnel,

(a) shall be made of metal pipe that has at least a fifty-one milli-metres inside diameter; and

(b) shall have a connection for the use of the local fire department outside the shaft or tunnel to which there is clear and ready access at all times.

(2) Every standpipe in a shaft shall be installed progressively as the shaft is excavated.

O. Reg. 142/17, s. 29

253. (1) Every fire line in a tunnel,

(a) shall be made of metal pipe that has at least a fifty-one milli-metres inside diameter; and

(b) shall have, at intervals of not more than forty-five metres along it, an outlet with a valve.

(2) Every fire line in a tunnel shall be installed progressively as the tunnel is excavated.

254. (1) Every hose in a tunnel,

(a) shall have at least a thirty millimetres inside diameter;

(b) shall have a combination straight stream and fog nozzle; and

(c) shall be at least twenty-three metres long.

(2) A hose shall be provided in a tunnel at forty-six metre intervals horizontally along it.

(3) Every hose shall be stored on a rack when it is not in use so as to be readily available.

255. (1) No flammable liquid or gas shall be brought underground except as permitted by this section.

(2) A compressed gas storage cylinder to which gas welding or flame-cutting equipment is attached may be brought underground.

(3) Fuel may be brought underground if,
    (a) it is in a tank that is supplied with and that forms a part of an engine or heating device; or
    (b) it is in a container and is intended for transfer into a tank described in clause (a).

(4) The maximum amount of fuel that may be brought underground in a container referred to in clause (3)(b) is the amount required for eight hours use of the engine or heating device.

256. (1) A flammable liquid or gas shall be stored,
    (a) as far as is practicable from a shaft; and
    (b) in a place from which it is impossible for spilled liquid to flow underground.

(2) Lubricating oil shall be stored in a suitable building or storage tank located in a place from which spilled liquid cannot run toward any shaft or tunnel.

257. Oil for use in hydraulic-powered equipment underground shall be of the type that,
    (a) is not readily flammable; and
    (b) does not readily support combustion.

258. (1) No combustible equipment, including welding cable and air-hoses, shall be stored underground unless the equipment is required for immediate use.

(2) No electrical cable or gas hose shall be taken or used underground unless,
    (a) it has an armoured casing or jacket made of a material that is not readily flammable and that does not readily support combustion; and

213/91

(b) it is marked to indicate that it has the casing or jacket required by clause (a).

259. (1) No combustible rubbish, used or decayed timber, scrap wood or paper shall be accumulated underground.

(2) Material described in subsection (1) shall be promptly removed from underground.

Facilities for Workers

260. (1) A heated room shall be provided for the use of underground workers.

(2) The wet clothes of workers employed underground shall be dried using sanitary means in a change room on the project.

(3) A change room,
      (a) shall have an open floor area no smaller than the greater of,
          (i) ten square metres, and
          (ii) one square metre per worker on a shift;
      (b) shall be equipped with mechanical ventilation that provides no less than six air changes per hour;
      (c) shall have suitable drainage facilities;
      (d) shall be kept at a temperature of at least 27 degrees celsius; and
      (e) shall have, for every worker employed underground, a locker that locks.

(4) Every change room shall be scrubbed once every twenty-four hours.

(5) If workers are employed underground, a change room shall be provided with one shower and one washbasin for each group of ten or fewer workers.

(6) Showers and washbasins provided in a change room shall be supplied with hot and cold water, soap or hand cleaner and paper towels or individual hand towels.

First Aid

261. The supervisor in charge of a project shall appoint at least one competent worker to be available to give first aid at a shaft or tunnel.

262. (1) A first aid kit shall be kept in the immediate vicinity of the above-ground entrance to every shaft, tunnel, caisson or cofferdam.

(2) At least one first aid kit shall be kept underground in every shaft and tunnel.

263. (1) At least one stretcher for each group of twenty-five or fewer workers who are underground shall be kept at every tunnel, shaft or cofferdam.

(2) Every stretcher shall be a wire-basket type and shall be designed and equipped to permit the safe hoisting and transport of a worker.

Rescue of Workers

264. (1) Before a project begins, an employer shall establish in writing emergency procedures for the rescue of underground workers.

(2) Copies of the rescue procedures signed by the employer and supervisor of the underground workers shall be posted in conspicuous places on the project.

(3) The emergency procedures shall be practised in preparation for an emergency and shall be followed in an emergency.

265. (1) At least four workers at a project or, if fewer than four workers work at the project, all workers shall be trained in and readily available to perform rescues of underground workers.

(2) Rescue workers shall be provided with suitable equipment to perform rescues.

(3) Rescue workers shall be trained by a competent person appointed by a Director.

(4) A Director who makes an appointment described in subsection (3) shall, in doing so, consider any recommendations of the representatives of labour and of management.

(5) Rescue workers shall be trained within thirty days before tunnelling operations begin and retrained at least every thirty days after the initial training.

(6) Before a project begins, the supervisor of the construction of a tunnel shall designate a rescue worker who shall inspect and test all rescue equipment every thirty days.

O. Reg. 145/00 s. 34

266. (1) This section applies if, on a project, there is a tunnel and shaft whose combined length exceeds forty-five metres.

(2) Every rescue worker shall be provided with a self-contained breathing apparatus that meets the requirements of subsection (5) and subsection (6), (7) or (8), as is appropriate to the length of the underground work place.

(3) A competent person referred to in subsection 265(3) shall train rescue workers in the proper operation of the self-contained breathing apparatus.

(4) The training required by subsection (3) shall be repeated at least every thirty days.

(5) The self-contained breathing apparatus shall have a full face mask.

(6) For use in an underground work place that is less than 100 metres long, the minimum rated duration of use for a self-contained breathing apparatus shall be one-half hour.

(7) For use in an underground work place that is 100 metres or more but less than 150 metres long, the minimum rated duration of use for a self-contained breathing apparatus shall be one hour.

(8) For use in an underground work place that is 150 metres or more long, the minimum rated duration of use for a self-contained breathing apparatus shall be one and one-half hours.

(9) All self-contained breathing apparatuses intended for rescue work on a project shall be the same model and made by the same manufacturer.

(10) All self-contained breathing apparatuses shall be kept in close proximity to the means of access to an underground work place and shall be readily available.

(11) A sufficient number, four as a minimum, of self-contained breathing apparatuses shall be available on the project to provide for all rescue work that may be required.

(12) A competent person shall inspect every self-contained breathing apparatus at least once a month or as often as is required by the manufacturer to ensure it is in proper condition.

267. Every worker who is in, or may be required to enter, a tunnel or a shaft leading to it shall be provided with a self-rescue respirator for the worker's exclusive use which is suitable for protection against hazardous gases.

O. Reg. 631/94 s. 10

268. (1) A worker's self-rescue respirator shall be kept in the vicinity of the worker while he or she is in a tunnel or shaft.

(2) All workers on a tunnel project shall be instructed in the proper use, care, maintenance and limitations of the self-rescue respirator in accordance with the manufacturer's specifications.

Communications

269. (1) Subject to subsection (2), a telephone connected to a public telephone system shall be installed at a project that is to be over fourteen days duration.

(2) If it is not practicable to install at a project a telephone connected to a public telephone system, a radio telephone shall be available that permits communication with an office of the constructor that has a telephone connected to a public telephone system.

(3) At a project of fourteen or fewer days duration, before work is begun, a public telephone or a radio telephone shall be installed or shall be arranged for nearby if,

    (a) the services of a police or fire department or ambulance are reasonably available; and

    (b) prompt direct telephone communication is possible with the police or fire department or ambulance.

270. (1) A telephone system shall be provided at a tunnel if the work at the face of the tunnel is or will be done twenty-three metres or more from,

    (a) the top of the service shaft; or

    (b) the opening into the tunnel, if the tunnel is not constructed from a service shaft.

(2) A telephone system shall be installed before work on the tunnel is begun.

(3) A telephone system shall consist of telephones that are located,

    (a) in the office of the supervisor in charge of the project;

    (b) at the top and bottom of the service shaft or at the opening into the tunnel, if the tunnel is not constructed from a service shaft;

    (c) at all other means of access to the service shaft, if any; and

    (d) at intervals not exceeding thirty metres in every area of the tunnel where work is being performed.

(4) A notice shall be posted by each telephone,

(a) indicating how to call every other telephone in the system;

(b) describing the emergency signal to be used; and

(c) stating that a worker who hears the emergency signal shall answer the telephone.

(5) A telephone system shall be installed in such a way that a conversation can be carried on between any two telephones in the system.

(6) The voice communication circuits used in a telephone system shall be independent from the circuits used to signal from one telephone to another.

271. During the construction of a shaft, an effective means of communicating between the lowest point of the shaft and the surface shall be provided.

272. A completed service shaft more than six metres deep shall have a means, other than a telephone, of exchanging distinct and definite signals between the top and bottom of the shaft.

273. (1) If a person is about to be conveyed by a hoist in a shaft, the pit bottom worker shall notify the hoist operator before the person enters the conveyance.

(2) A hoist operator shall acknowledge every signal received by repeating the signal.

(3) A signal to a hoist operator to move a conveyance shall be given only from the landing from which the conveyance is being moved.

(4) A signal set out in Column 1 of the Table shall be used to communicate the meaning set out opposite to it in Column 2 between a hoist operator, the top or bottom of a shaft and all landings in the shaft:

Item	Column 1 Code of signals	Column 2 Meaning
1.	1 signal	When no people are in the air lock, MATERIAL IS COMING OUT.
2.	2 signals	When people are in the air lock, STOP COMPRESSING.
3.	3 signals	PEOPLE ARE COMING OUT OF THE AIR

		LOCK.

(5) The supervisor in charge of a project may establish signals in addition to those set out in subsection (4) if required for the operation of a hoist on the project.

(6) A notice setting out the signals used for a hoist shall be securely posted,

      (a) where it is readily visible to the hoist operator; and

      (b) at each landing of the hoistway.

(7) The notice shall be on a board or a metal plate that is not less than 450 millimetres by 450 millimetres and shall be written in letters that are at least thirteen millimetres high.

O. Reg. 345/15 s. 27

Lighting and Electricity Supply

274. All electrical circuits of 100 volts or more shall be in an insulated cable that consists of at least two conductors and a grounding conductor.

O. Reg. 627/05 s. 8

275. All electrical pumps and electrical tools shall be either adequately grounded or double-insulated.

276. (1) An area of a tunnel or shaft that is not adequately lit by natural light shall be electrically illuminated.

(2) Flashlights shall be readily available at the top and bottom of every shaft and near the work face of a tunnel.

(3) If electric lighting is used in a tunnel or shaft, an emergency lighting system shall be installed in the tunnel or shaft.

(4) An emergency lighting system,

      (a) shall be connected to the electrical supply so that in the event of the failure of the electrical supply, the system will automatically turn on;

      (b) shall be provided with a testing switch, if the system is battery-powered; and

      (c) shall be tested at least as frequently as is recommended by its manufacturer to ensure that the system will function in an emergency.

277. [Repealed O. Reg. 627/05, s. 9.]

Shafts

278. (1) Every shaft shall be large enough that its walls can be adequately shored and shall have enough clear space for work to be done.

(2) In a service shaft that is more than six metres deep or that serves a tunnel more than fifteen metres long,

(a) the minimum inside dimension of the shaft, measured between the wales or other wall supports, shall be 2.4 metres for a cylindrical shaft and 1.5 metres for a shaft that is not cylindrical; and

(b) the minimum transverse cross-sectional area of a shaft that is not cylindrical shall be 5.7 square metres.

279. (1) The walls of a shaft shall be supported by shoring and bracing adequate to prevent their collapse.

(2) Subsection (1) does not apply to the walls of a shaft that is less than 1.2 metres deep or is cut in sound rock.

(3) If a shaft is to be cut in sound rock, the constructor shall obtain a written opinion from a professional engineer as to whether the walls of the shaft need to be supported by rock bolts or wire mesh to prevent the spalling of loose rock.

(4) The walls of a shaft cut in sound rock shall be supported by rock bolts or wire mesh where necessary in the opinion of the professional engineer.

280. (1) Shoring and bracing for a shaft that is more than 1.2 metres deep shall be capable of withstanding all loads likely to be applied to them.

(2) The shoring and bracing,

(a) shall be designed by a professional engineer in accordance with good engineering practice; and

(b) shall be constructed in accordance with the professional engineer's design.

(3) Design drawings by a professional engineer for the shoring and bracing shall show the size and specifications of the shoring and bracing including the type and grade of all materials to be used in their construction.

(4) [Repealed O. Reg. 443/09, s. 8.]

(5) The constructor shall keep a copy of design drawings for the shoring and bracing at the project while the shoring and bracing are in use.

O. Reg. 145/00 s. 35; 85/04 s. 22; 443/09 s. 8

281. (1) If a square or rectangular shaft is not more than six metres deep and has walls that are not more than 3.6 metres wide, the walls,

(a) shall be fully sheathed with Number 1 Grade spruce planks that are at least fifty-one millimetres thick by 152 millimetres wide and are placed side by side; and

(b) shall be supported by wales and struts.

(2) Wales and struts,

(a) shall be made of number 1 structural grade spruce planks that are,

(i) at least 152 millimetres by 152 millimetres, for a shaft that is not more than 2.7 metres deep,

(ii) at least 203 millimetres by 203 millimetres, for a shaft that is more than 2.7 metres but not more than 4.3 metres deep, and

(iii) at least 254 millimetres by 254 millimetres, for a shaft that is more than 4.3 metres but not more than six metres deep;

(b) shall be spaced not more than 1.2 metres apart vertically; and

(c) shall be adequately supported by vertical posts that extend to the bottom of the shaft.

O. Reg. 631/94 s. 11

282. (1) An adequate barrier that is at least 1.1 metres high shall be provided around the top of an uncovered shaft.

(2) A barrier around the top of an uncovered shaft that is more than 2.4 metres deep,

(a) shall consist of a top rail, an intermediate rail and a toe-board; and

(b) shall be made of thirty-eight by 140 millimetres lumber securely fastened to vertical supports that are spaced at intervals of not more than 2.4 metres.

(3) A barrier shall be kept free of splinters and protruding nails.

(4) A gate in a barrier around the top of an uncovered shaft shall be kept closed and latched.

(5) The ground adjacent to a barrier around the top of a shaft shall be sloped away from the barrier.

283. A shaft shall be kept clear of ice and loose objects that may endanger a worker.

284. A shaft shall be kept reasonably free of water when a worker is required to be in the shaft.

285. Every shaft shall have a means of access and egress by stairway, ladder or ladderway for its full depth during its construction and when it is completed.

286. (1) A stairway, ladder or ladderway for a shaft that is more than six metres deep,

(a) shall have landings or rest platforms spaced at intervals not greater than 4.5 metres;

(b) shall be off-set at each landing or rest platform; and

(c) shall be located in a sheathed compartment that is constructed in such a way that a worker who falls while on the stairway, ladder or ladderway will land on the landing or rest platform below.

(2) Every landing and rest platform shall be wide enough to permit at least two workers to pass on it safely.

(3) Every opening and ladderway shall be wide enough to permit the passage of a worker wearing rescue equipment and shall be at least 750 mm by 750 mm.

O. Reg. 631/94 s. 12; 345/15 s. 28

287. (1) Every conveyance located in a service shaft that is more than six metres deep shall be separated from a stairway, ladder or ladderway in the shaft by a lining described in subsection (3).

(2) Subsection (1) does not apply with respect to a conveyance located in a service shaft if the hoisting area is so remote from the stairway, ladder or ladderway that is not possible for a load, bucket or device being hoisted or lowered to come into contact with the stairway, ladder or ladderway.

(3) A lining shall consist of solid planks at least fifty-one millimetres thick and spaced not more than ten millimetres apart.

Hoistways

288. (1) This section applies with respect to a hoistway that is more than six metres deep in which hoisting is carried out by mechanical power.

(2) Every landing on a hoistway shall have a gate located 200 millimetres or less from the hoistway that,

(a) extends the full width of the hoistway from 50 millimetres or less from the floor level to a height of at least 1.8 metres;

(b) is constructed without any gaps that would permit the entry of a ball no more than thirty-eight millimetres in diameter; and

(c) is equipped with a light readily visible to the hoist operator indicating when the gate is closed.

(3) Subsection (2) does not apply to a landing at the bottom of a hoistway if the landing has one or more red lights that,

(a) are located where a person approaching the hoistway from a tunnel or from the lower end of a stair or ladder can see at least one of them; and

(b) are controlled by a switch readily accessible to a shaft attendant.

(4) A gate required by subsection (2) shall be kept closed unless a conveyance is stopped at the landing.

(5) The red lights referred to in subsection (3) shall be continuously flashed off and on during a hoisting operation.

O. Reg. 142/17, s. 30

289. (1) All parts of a hoisting apparatus used in a hoistway or shaft shall be able to be conveniently inspected.

(2) Every hoist drum shall have a flange at each end to keep the hoist rope on the drum.

290. (1) A hoist operator shall operate and watch over a hoist and all machinery associated with the hoist to detect any hazardous conditions.

(2) A hoist operator shall report immediately to the supervisor in charge of the project any defects in the hoisting machinery and safety devices.

(3) The hoist operator shall test all safety devices on a hoisting apparatus to ensure that they function and shall perform the tests,

(a) before a conveyance is first put into service on a project;

(b) at least once every three months after being put into service on the project; and

(c) daily, if the hoisting apparatus is used to hoist persons.

(4) The hoist operator shall make a record of tests performed under subsection (3).

(5) The hoist operator shall keep available for inspection at the project the record of tests performed under subsection (3).

O. Reg. 142/17, s. 31

291. (1) No person other than a competent worker appointed by the supervisor in charge of a project shall operate a hoist in a hoistway or shaft.

(2) No person, other than a worker required to do so as part of the worker's job, shall enter or attend the machine room of a hoist.

292. A hoist operator shall inspect the hoisting machinery and safety devices connected to it at least once a day and shall make a record of the inspection in a log book.

O. Reg. 142/17, s. 32

293. (1) A hoist operator and all shaft attendants shall understand the signal code established for the hoist.

(2) No hoist operator shall converse with another person while the hoist is in motion or signals are being given.

(3) No hoist operator shall turn over the controls of a hoist to another person while a conveyance is in motion.

(4) No hoist operator shall operate a hoist,

    (a) unless it is equipped with,

        (i) indicators showing the position of the conveyance on the hoist, and

        (ii) brakes and distance markers on the hoisting ropes and cables;

    (b) in a compartment of a shaft in which work is being done unless the hoist is being operated for the purpose of work in the compartment.

(5) After a hoist has been stopped for repairs, a hoist operator shall run an empty conveyance up and down the shaft at least once and shall determine that the hoist is in good working order before carrying a load in it.

294. (1) The supervisor in charge of a project,

    (a) shall establish the maximum speed for a conveyance transporting persons in a hoistway; and

    (b) shall determine the maximum number of persons and the maximum weight of material that may be carried safely on a conveyance in a hoistway.

(2) A notice setting out the maximums referred to in subsection (1) shall be conspicuously posted near each hoistway entrance.

(3) No person shall load a conveyance in a hoistway beyond the maximum limits established under clause (1)(b).

(4) A hoist operator shall operate a hoist in accordance with the notice posted under subsection (2).

295. (1) The supervisor in charge of a project shall appoint shaft attendants for a shaft where a hoist is being used.

(2) No shaft attendant shall be less than nineteen years of age.

(3) At least one shaft attendant shall be on duty at the top of a shaft if a hoist, crane or similar hoisting device is being used or if a worker is present in the shaft or in a tunnel connected to the shaft.

(4) A shaft attendant,

    (a) shall give the hoist operator the signals for starting and stopping the hoist;
    (b) shall warn workers of hazards in or near the shaft; and
    (c) as far as is practicable, shall remove known hazards.

296. (1) The supervisor in charge of a project shall, before a hoist is used on the project, establish a communication system of signals to be used between a hoist operator, shaft attendants and any other attendants working at a hoist.

(2) The supervisor in charge of a project shall ensure that all hoist operators, shaft attendants and other attendants working at a hoist know and understand the signals.

297. (1) The supervisor in charge of a project shall appoint workers to control the movement of materials to and from a conveyance on a hoist at every landing and at the bottom of a shaft.

(2) A worker appointed under subsection (1) shall control and direct the movement of materials to and from a conveyance.

298. No worker shall be transported in a conveyance or a hoist while it is being used to carry materials or equipment other than hand tools or similar small objects.

299. The path of travel of an object being hoisted from or lowered into a shaft by a crane shall not pass over a manway unless the manway has adequate overhead protection.

300. (1) A service shaft that will be over thirty metres deep when completed shall have a hoist with a conveyance consisting of a cage or car suitable for transporting workers.

(2) A hoist shall be installed in the service shaft as soon as is practicable.

(3) A hoist,

  (a) shall have a headframe that is grounded for protection against lightning and is designed by a professional engineer;

  (b) shall have guides to control the movement of the conveyance;

  (c) shall have a device that automatically stops the conveyance when it runs beyond the normal limit of its travel; and

  (d) shall have a brake on the hoisting machine that automatically stops and holds the conveyance if the hoist fails or the power to the hoist is interrupted.

(4) A shaft in sound rock may be excavated to a depth of not more than thirty metres before the headframe and guides are installed on the hoist.

O. Reg. 142/17, s. 33

301. (1) Every conveyance on a hoist used for transporting workers in a shaft shall have a suitable device that, if the cable breaks or becomes slack,

  (a) automatically prevents the conveyance from falling; and

  (b) is capable of holding the conveyance stationary when it contains the maximum number of passengers it is permitted to carry.

(2) Subsection (1) does not apply with respect to a bucket or a skip operated in accordance with sections 303 and 305.

(3) A device shall be installed to warn the hoist operator when a conveyance transporting workers in a shaft has reached the normal limit of its travel.

302. (1) A cage or car on a hoist used for transporting workers in a shaft,

  (a) shall be at least 1.8 metres high;

  (b) shall be solidly enclosed, except for openings for access and egress;

  (c) shall have a maximum of two openings for access and egress;

  (d) shall have a gate at each opening for access and egress; and

  (e) shall have a protective cover suitable to protect passengers from falling objects.

(2) A gate for access and egress,

(a) shall be constructed without any gaps that would permit the entry of a ball no more than thirty-eight millimetres in diameter;

(b) shall extend the full width of the opening and 50 millimetres or less from of the floor of the cage or car to a height of at least 1.8 metres; and

(c) shall not open outward.

(3) A protective cover referred to in clause (1)(e) shall have a trap door for emergency access which measures not less than 600 millimetres by 600 millimetres.

O. Reg. 142/17,   s. 34

213/91

303. (1) Subject to subsection (2), a bucket or similar conveyance shall not be used to transport a worker in a shaft.

(2) A bucket or similar conveyance may be used to transport a worker in a shaft for the purpose of inspecting the hoistway if no other method of access to the parts of the hoistway is available.

(3) A bucket referred to in subsection (2),

(a) shall be at least 1.2 metres deep;

(b) shall have smoothly-contoured outer surfaces to prevent it from tipping or becoming snagged by an obstacle during hoisting or lowering; and

(c) shall not be self-opening.

(4) If a pivoted bucket that is manually-dumped and is not self-guided is being used to transport a worker, the bucket,

(a) shall be equipped with a lock to prevent tipping; and

(b) shall be pivoted in such a way that it does not automatically invert when the lock is released.

(5) A bucket that is not controlled by a cross head running in vertical guides shall not be hoisted or lowered at a speed greater than 0.5 metres per second when it is transporting a worker.

304. (1) A hinged door that opens upward shall be provided over the opening at the top of a shaft.

(2) The door shall be closed while a worker is entering or leaving a bucket over the opening at the top of the shaft.

305. A skip shall not be used to transport a worker unless,

(a) the worker is inspecting guiderails or shaft supports; and

(b) the skip is protected by an overwind device to prevent the skip from being hoisted to the dump position.

Tunnels

306. (1) A tunnel shall have enough clear space for the passage of vehicles and the movement of workers.

(2) The diameter of a circular or elliptical tunnel and the width and height of a square or rectangular tunnel shall be at least 760 millimetres.

(3) A clear space of at least 450 millimetres shall be left between the side of a tunnel and the nearer side of,

(a) all trackless haulage equipment being used; and

(b) all locomotives, haulage cars and machines operating on a track.

(4) A circular or elliptical tunnel shall have safety platforms at sixty metre intervals along it.

(5) A safety platform shall be long enough for a crew of workers to stand on, shall be constructed above the tunnel invert and shall be clear of passing equipment.

307. (1) Except for a tunnel cut in sound rock, the sides and roof of a tunnel shall be supported by timbers set on ribs or beams or by an equivalent system of lining.

(2) If a tunnel is to be cut in sound rock, the constructor shall obtain a written opinion from a professional engineer as to whether the sides and roof of the tunnel need to be supported by rock bolts or wire mesh to prevent the spalling of loose rock.

(3) The sides and roof of a tunnel cut in sound rock,

(a) shall be supported, where necessary in the opinion of the professional engineer, by rock bolts or wire mesh;

(b) shall be inspected daily by a competent worker; and

(c) shall have all loose pieces of rock removed.

(4) If the permanent lining of a tunnel will, when completed, consist of a primary lining and a secondary lining, the primary lining shall be strong enough to support the sides and roof of the tunnel until the secondary lining is installed.

(5) If the permanent lining of a tunnel consists only of a concrete cast-in-place lining, the tunnel shall not be excavated beyond the leading edge of

the permanent lining unless adequate temporary shoring is installed as soon as is practicable.

(6) The primary supports of a tunnel,

> (a) shall be designed by a professional engineer in accordance with good engineering practice to withstand all loads likely to be applied to them; and
>
> (b) shall be constructed in accordance with the design.

(7) The constructor shall keep available for inspection at a project the design drawings for the primary supports.

O. Reg. 85/04 s. 23

308. A tunnel shall be kept reasonably free of water when a worker is required to be in the tunnel.

Tunnel Equipment

309. When a haulage locomotive, trackless haulage equipment or a hoist in a shaft or tunnel is left unattended,

> (a) its controls shall be left in the neutral position; and
>
> (b) its brakes shall be set or other measures, such as blocking, shall be taken to prevent its moving.

310. (1) A haulage locomotive shall have suitable brakes, an audible bell and controls that can be operated only by a worker at the driver's station.

(2) A haulage locomotive shall be designed so that power for its driving mechanism is cut off unless the control regulating the power is continuously operated by a worker at the driver's station.

(3) The driver of a haulage locomotive shall sound the bell when the locomotive is set in motion or is approaching someone.

(4) No person other than the driver shall ride on a haulage locomotive.

311. No worker shall ride on a haulage train except in a car provided to carry passengers.

312. A haulage car shall have a device to prevent uncontrolled travel by the car.

313. (1) Track for haulage equipment shall be securely fastened to the ties on which it is laid.

213/91

(2) If the ties interfere with the use of the bottom of the tunnel as a walkway, a solid walkway that is at least 300 millimetres wide shall be provided.

314. **(1)** The air inlet to an air compressor shall be located in such a position that fumes or noxious contaminants are not drawn in with the air to be compressed.

(2) A valve connected to a vessel used for storing compressed air,

    (a) shall be connected at the lowest point of the vessel to permit the discharge of the compressed air; and

    (b) shall be opened at least once each shift for the purpose of ejecting oil, water and other matter from the vessel.

315. **(1)** A project shall have pumping equipment of sufficient capacity to handle the pumping requirements of the project.

(2) Pumping equipment shall be connected to an adequate source of energy.

(3) Sufficient spare pumping equipment and an alternative source of energy for it shall be readily available at the project in case of emergency.

316. No internal combustion engine shall be used in a tunnel on a project without the prior written consent of a Director.

O. Reg. 145/00 s. 36

Explosives

317. Before blasting begins in a shaft, tunnel, caisson or cofferdam that is located within the greater of 4.5 metres and twice the length of the longest drill rod used away from another shaft, tunnel, caisson or cofferdam, the worker in charge of the blasting operations shall determine whether work in the adjacent shaft, tunnel, caisson or cofferdam can safely continue during blasting operations.

318. **(1)** No vehicle or conveyance being used to transport explosives or blasting agents shall carry any other cargo or any person other than the vehicle operator.

(2) No detonator shall be transported in a vehicle or conveyance while it is carrying explosives or blasting agents.

(3) Where mechanical track haulage is used in a tunnel, explosives or blasting agents shall not be transported on the locomotive or in the same car as the detonators.

O. Reg. 142/17, s. 35

319. (1) A vehicle or conveyance, including trackless equipment, that is transporting explosives or blasting agents in a tunnel by mechanical haulage,

(a) shall be given an uninterrupted and a clear passage of travel;

(b) shall be conspicuously marked by signs or red flags that are easily visible from the front and the rear;

(c) shall not travel at a speed greater than six kilometres per hour; and

(d) shall not be left unattended.

(2) Explosives and blasting agents referred to in subsection (1),

(a) shall be in a box made of wood or be separated from every metal part of the vehicle or conveyance in which they are being transported by a lining made of wood; and

(b) shall be arranged or secured so as to prevent any part of an explosive or blasting agent from being dislodged.

320. If explosives or blasting agents are to be transported in a shaft, the worker in charge of blasting operations shall notify the hoist operator and shaft attendants before the explosives or blasting agents are put in the conveyance.

321. A flashlight shall be provided to every worker who is engaged in blasting operations in a tunnel or is in an area from which the means of egress passes a place where blasting is to be done.

322. Drilling or charging operations in a shaft or tunnel shall not be done simultaneously,

(a) above or below one another on the same face; or

(b) 7.5 metres or less, measured horizontally, from one another.

O. Reg. 142/17, s. 36

323. (1) Explosives and blasting agents shall be fired electrically.

(2) Despite subsection (1), tape fuse may be used to fire explosives and blasting agents if block holing is to be done.

324. (1) If a portable direct current battery or a blasting machine is the source of current for blasting, the firing cables or wires,

(a) shall not be connected to the source of current until immediately before the charges are fired; and

(b) shall be disconnected immediately after the charges are fired.

(2) All firing cables or wires leading to a face shall be short-circuited while the leads from the blasting caps are being connected to one another and to the firing cables.

(3) No short-circuit of a firing cable or wire shall be removed until all workers have retreated from the face and are so located that, should a premature explosion occur, the workers are not endangered.

(4) A short-circuit shall be replaced immediately after the firing cables or wires are disconnected from the blasting machine or the blasting switch is opened.

(5) Separate firing cables or wires for firing charges shall be used for each work location.

(6) Firing cables or wires,

(a) shall be located as far as is practicable from every other electrical circuit; and

(b) shall not be permitted to come in contact with power, lighting or communication cables, or pipes, rails or other continuous metal grounded surfaces.

325. (1) Every device, other than a portable hand-operated device, used for firing a charge shall meet the requirements of this section.

(2) No person other than a competent worker shall use a device used for firing a charge.

(3) A device used for firing a charge shall have a switch mechanism that automatically returns by gravity to the open position.

(4) The live side of a device used for firing a charge shall be installed in a fixed locked box which is accessible only to the worker doing the blasting.

(5) The lock on the box referred to in subsection (4) shall be able to be closed only when the contacts of the device are open and a short-circuiting device is in place.

(6) The leads to the face shall be short-circuited when the contacts of the device are in the open position.

326. (1) A circuit used for blasting shall originate from an isolated un-grounded power source and shall be used only for blasting.

(2) Subsection (1) does not apply with respect to blasting done with a portable hand-operated device.

327. (1) When a charge is fired and after a shot is heard, every worker in a place of refuge from a blast shall remain there and not return to the blast area for at least ten minutes.

(2) If a charge is fired and no shot is heard, before the circuit is repaired,

    (a) the blasting circuit shall be locked in the open position; and

    (b) the lead wires shall be short-circuited.

(3) A worker who suspects a misfire of an explosive or a blasting agent shall report it to the supervisor in charge of the project.

(4) A charge of an explosive or a blasting agent that has misfired shall be left in place and blasted as soon as it is discovered.

328. When a blasting operation is completed, the blasting switch shall be locked in the open position, the lead wires short-circuited and the blasting box locked.

Ventilation

329. An adequate supply of fresh air shall be provided and circulated throughout an underground work place.

330. (1) An underground work place shall be tested regularly for noxious or toxic gases, fumes or dust.

(2) A competent worker shall regularly test the air and the mechanical ventilation for an underground work place to ensure that the mechanical ventilation is adequate.

(3) When the results of the tests referred to in subsection (2) indicate there is a need for respiratory protective equipment, the employer shall provide respiratory protective equipment.

331. (1) Mechanical ventilation shall be provided in a shaft in which an internal combustion engine or other device which emits a noxious gas or fume operates.

(2) Subsection (1) does not apply if the noxious gas or fume is discharged outside the shaft in such a way that its return to the shaft is prevented.

Part V — Work in Compressed Air

Interpretation and Application

332. In this Part,

"air lock" means a chamber designed for the passage of persons or materials from one place to another place that has a different air pressure from the first;

"compressed air" means air whose pressure is mechanically raised to more than atmospheric pressure;

"decompression sickness", in relation to a worker, means a condition of bodily malfunction caused by a change from a higher to a lower air pressure and includes the condition commonly known as **"the bends"**;

"kilopascals", except in section 376, means kilopascals relative to atmospheric pressure;

"maximum air pressure", in relation to a worker, means the greatest level of air pressure to which a worker is subjected for a period of more than five minutes;

"medical lock" means a chamber in which workers may be subjected to changes in air pressure for medical purposes;

"superintendent" means the person appointed by a constructor to be supervisor over and in charge of work done in compressed air;

"work chamber" means a part of a project that is used for work in compressed air but does not include an air lock or a medical lock.

333. This Part applies with respect to work done in compressed air, other than work done in diving bells or work done by divers.

General Requirements

334. (1) No constructor or employer shall begin work at a project where a worker may be subjected to compressed air until the requirements of this section are met.

(2) The employer of workers who may be subjected to compressed air at a project shall give a Director written notice of the intended use of compressed air on the project at least fourteen days before beginning work on the project.

(3) Before work is begun in compressed air, the employer shall obtain written permission from a Director.

O. Reg. 145/00 s. 37

335. (1) Before work is begun in compressed air at a project, a constructor shall give written notice,

    (a) to the local police department and the fire department and public hospital nearest to the project; and

    (b) to a Director, together with the names and addresses of those to whom notice is given under clause (a).

(2) A notice shall set out,

    (a) the location of the project;

    (b) the name, address and telephone number of the project physician and the superintendent; and

    (c) the location of a medical lock for the project and of every other readily-available medical lock.

(3) The employer shall give notice of the completion of work in compressed air at the project to those who were given notice under clause (1)(a).

O. Reg. 145/00 s. 38

336. (1) The employer shall appoint a competent person as superintendent of all work in compressed air at a project.

(2) The superintendent, before a worker is first subjected to compressed air,

    (a) shall ensure that the worker is fully instructed,

        (i) in the hazards of working in compressed air, and

        (ii) in the measures to be taken to safeguard the health and safety of the worker and other workers on the project; and

    (b) shall obtain an acknowledgement signed by the worker who is receiving the instruction stating that the worker has been so instructed.

337. (1) A superintendent at a project shall designate for each shift at least one competent worker as lock tender who shall attend to the controls of an air lock.

(2) A lock tender must be able to speak, read and write English competently.

(3) A superintendent at a project shall ensure that at least one competent worker in addition to the lock tender is available in an emergency to perform the duties of the lock tender while a worker is working in compressed air.

338. (1) The superintendent shall keep available at a project for inspection by an inspector,

    (a) all Form 1 reports by a project by a project physician;

    (b) all records required under section 373 of air pressure in air locks on the project; and

    (c) all records required under section 394 to be kept by a lock tender.

(2) The superintendent shall send all Form 1 reports to a Director promptly when work in compressed air at the project is finished.

O. Reg. 145/00 s. 39

339. (1) A worker who works in compressed air shall wear for at least twenty-four hours after working in compressed air a sturdy metal or plastic badge that meets the requirements of subsection (2).

(2) A badge shall measure at least fifty millimetres in diameter and shall set out,

    (a) the name of the constructor of the project;

    (b) the name and telephone number of the project physician;

    (c) the location of a medical lock at the project; and

    (d) the words, "compressed air worker—in case of decompression sickness take immediately to a medical lock".

(3) The constructor at a project shall provide workers with the badge required under subsection (1).

Communications

340. (1) A telephone system for work in compressed air shall be provided at a project.

(2) A telephone system shall consist of telephones located,

    (a) at a location as close as is practicable to the work face;

    (b) in every work chamber near a door that leads to an air lock;

    (c) in every air lock;

    (d) near every lock tender's work position;

    (e) adjacent to every compressor plant; and

(f) in the superintendent's office.

341. **(1)** An electric buzzer or bell system for work in compressed air shall be provided at a project.

(2) An electric buzzer or bell system shall consist of a switch and a buzzer or bell located,

    (a) in every work chamber near a door that leads to an air lock;

    (b) in every air lock; and

    (c) near every lock tender's work position.

(3) A signal set out in Column 1 of the Table shall be used to communicate the meaning set out opposite to it in Column 2 between a work chamber, an air lock and the lock tender's work position:

Item	Column 1 Code of signals	Column 2 Meaning
1.	1 signal	When no people are in the air lock, MATERIAL IS COMING OUT.
2.	2 signals	When people are in the air lock, STOP COMPRESSING.
3.	3 signals	PEOPLE ARE COMING OUT OF THE AIR LOCK.

(4) A copy of the signal code shall be posted near every switch of an electric buzzer or bell system.

(5) A lock tender shall acknowledge every signal received on an electric buzzer or bell system by returning the same signal.

O. Reg. 345/15 s. 29

Fire Prevention

342. **(1)** No person shall use acetylene while working in compressed air.

(2) No person shall smoke or be permitted to smoke in an air lock or work chamber, other than in an area designated as a smoking area by the superintendent.

343. Before a flame-cutting, gas-welding or similar source of ignition is introduced into a work chamber that is in the vicinity of a combustible material,

(a) a firewatch shall be established and maintained;

(b) a fire hose shall be prepared for use;

(c) the fire hose shall be tested to ensure there is an adequate supply of water and water pressure to extinguish a fire; and

(d) a fire extinguisher suitable for the hazard shall be provided nearby.

344. As far as practicable, no combustible material shall be installed in or stored in an air lock or work chamber.

345. (1) A standpipe connected to a source of water or connected to other pipes above ground shall be installed in every air lock and work chamber at a project.

(2) A standpipe shall have,

(a) valves that isolate the standpipe from the rest of the fire prevention system;

(b) a fitting that is controlled by a valve installed on the standpipe on the work chamber side of the bulkhead and by a valve inside the material lock;

(c) a fitting and valve similar to that described in clause (b) installed at the end of the standpipe nearest to the work face; and

(d) the location of the fittings and valves clearly marked.

(3) A fitting described in clause (2)(b) shall be such that a fire hose of the local fire department can be connected to it.

Lighting and Electrical Supply

346. Electrical wiring passing through an air lock or the bulkheads adjacent to an air lock, other than telephone and signal system wiring, shall be installed in a rigid metal conduit.

347. (1) A lighting system shall be provided in each work chamber.

(2) Electric light bulbs used in an air lock shall be enclosed in a glass and metal protective screen cover.

(3) Flashlights shall be readily available at the entrance to an air lock, on the atmospheric side in an air lock and at every telephone required by section 340.

348. An auxiliary source of supply of electricity that is not a portable emergency source of supply shall be provided for the lighting system.

349. (1) An emergency electrical lighting system shall be provided and maintained in each air lock and work chamber.

(2) An emergency electrical lighting system,

    (a) shall be connected to the electrical supply so that it automatically turns on in the event of the failure of the electrical supply; and

    (b) shall have a testing switch, if the system is battery-powered.

(3) An emergency electrical lighting system shall be tested at intervals that are at least as frequent as recommended by the manufacturer and that are adequate to ensure that it will function in an emergency.

O. Reg. 142/17, s. 37

Sanitation

350. A work chamber shall be provided with a reasonable supply of drinking water and at least one chemical toilet.

Medical Requirements

351. (1) An employer who is constructing a tunnel or caisson in which a worker works or will work in compressed air shall employ as project physician at least one legally qualified medical practitioner.

(2) The project physician shall conduct such medical examinations of workers as in his or her opinion are necessary and shall establish a medical treatment program for the workers.

(3) A project physician shall be reasonably available to render medical treatment or advice on the treatment of decompression sickness while a worker is working in compressed air.

(4) The employer shall ensure that the project physician instruct workers on the hazards of working in compressed air and the necessary precautions to be taken to avoid decompression sickness.

(5) If the pressure in a work chamber at a project may exceed 350 kilopascals for a period of more than five minutes, a project physician shall establish procedures to control decompression sickness including,

(a) the maximum length of work periods for the workers in the chamber;

(b) the minimum length of rest periods for workers in the chamber; and

(c) compression and decompression procedures.

352. (1) No worker shall work or be permitted to work in compressed air on a project unless,

(a) the project physician has complied with subsection (4); and

(b) the project physician indicates on Form 1 that the worker is physically fit to work in compressed air.

(2) Subsection (1) does not apply with respect to an inspector or with respect to a worker accompanying an inspector at the inspector's request.

(3) Every worker working in compressed air at a project shall have a medical examination performed by the project physician before beginning work in compressed air and every two months thereafter while the worker is working in compressed air to determine the worker's fitness for working in compressed air.

(4) The project physician shall complete Form 1 for the worker, stating whether the worker is physically fit to work in compressed air and ensure that the superintendent receives a copy.

(5) The medical examination shall include,

(a) a physical examination;

(b) a test under compressed air, if the worker has not previously worked in compressed air; and

(c) such clinical tests as the project physician may require.

(6) The clinical tests referred to in clause (5)(c) shall include x-rays of the chest and shoulders, and hip and knee joints taken at least once every five years.

(7) If a worker undergoes a medical examination, the employer shall pay,

(a) the worker's costs for any medical examinations and tests; and

(b) the worker's reasonable travel costs respecting any medical examinations and tests.

(8) The time the worker spends to undergo medical examinations and tests, including travel time, shall be deemed to be work time for which the worker shall be paid by the employer at the worker's regular or premium rate, as may be proper.

(9) The project physician conducting the physical examination or clinical tests or under whose supervision the examination or tests are made shall advise the employer whether the worker is fit or is fit with limitations or unfit for work in compressed air, without giving or disclosing to the employer the records or results of the examination or tests.

(10) The employer shall act on the advice given by the physician under subsection (9).

(11) Where a project physician advises the employer that a worker, because of a condition resulting from work in compressed air, is fit with limitations or is unfit, the project physician shall forthwith communicate such advice to the Chief Physician of the Ministry.

(12) The records of medical examinations, tests, medical treatment and worker exposure to compressed air made or obtained by the project physician under section 351 and this section shall be kept in a secure place by the project physician who has conducted the examinations and tests or under whose supervision the examinations and tests have been made, for at least six years.

(13) After six years, the project physician may forward the records to the Chief Physician of the Ministry, or a physician designated by the Chief Physician, and, in any event, the records shall not be destroyed for a period the greater of forty years from the time such records were first made or twenty years from the time the last of such records were made.

O. Reg. 142/17, s. 38

353. (1) A worker who is about to work in compressed air and who does not feel well for any reason shall report the fact as soon as is practicable to the superintendent or a project physician before working in compressed air.

(2) A worker who is working in compressed air and who does not feel well for any reason shall report the fact as soon as practicable to the superintendent or a project physician.

354. A worker who is absent for a period of ten or more days from working in compressed air shall not resume work in compressed air until a project physician indicates on Form 1 that the worker is physically fit to resume work in compressed air.

Medical Locks

355. (1) A first aid room shall be provided in close proximity to each medical lock at a project.

(2) A first aid room shall contain all equipment necessary for first aid for workers working in compressed air and facilities adequate for conducting medical examinations.

356. (1) A constructor shall supply at least one medical lock at a project where work in compressed air is done and shall maintain it ready for operation while work in compressed air is being done.

(2) A certificate of inspection issued under Ontario Regulation 220/01 (Boilers and Pressure Vessels) made under the *Technical Standards and Safety Act, 2000* for a working pressure of at least 520 kilopascals is required for every medical lock on a project.

O. Reg. 142/17, s. 39

357. (1) A medical lock shall not be less than 1.8 metres high at its centre line.

(2) A medical lock shall be divided into two pressure compartments.

(3) Each compartment of a medical lock shall have all valves that are arranged so that the compartment can be pressurized and depressurized from inside and outside the lock.

(4) An observation window shall be installed in each door and in the rear wall of the medical lock.

(5) A medical lock shall be equipped with,
    (a) a pressure release valve which will automatically blow-off at a pressure not greater than seventy kilopascals more than the operating pressure of the work chamber;
    (b) a pressure gauge, a thermometer, a telephone, a cot, seating and a radiant heater; and
    (c) a cot mattress, mattress cover and blankets all of which are made of material that is not readily flammable.

(6) The pressure release valve shall be tested and calibrated before the medical lock is used.

(7) A medical lock shall be maintained at a temperature of at least 18 degrees celsius, well-lit and well-ventilated and kept clean and sanitary.

358. (1) A project physician shall control the medical treatment of workers in a medical lock at a project.

(2) While a worker is working in compressed air and for twenty-four hours afterwards, at least one worker experienced in the decompression of persons suffering from decompression sickness,

(a) shall be present on the project, if the work in compressed air was done at a pressure greater than 100 kilopascals; or

(b) shall be readily available, if the work in compressed air was done at a pressure of 100 kilopascals or less.

Air Compressors

359. (1) The superintendent shall designate at least one competent worker to be in charge of the compressors compressing air for a work chamber and air lock.

(2) [Repealed O. Reg. 88/13, s. 3.]

(3) A competent worker designated under subsection (1) shall attend to the compressors,

(a) while a person is in compressed air in the work chamber or air lock; and

(b) for twenty-four hours after a person has been in compressed air with a pressure exceeding 100 kilopascals in the work chamber or air lock.

(4) [Repealed O. Reg. 88/13, s. 3.]

O. Reg. 631/94 s. 13; 571/99 s. 1; 88/13 s. 3

360. (1) At least two air compressors shall be provided for every work chamber and air lock at a project.

(2) The air compressors for a work chamber or an air lock shall have capacity enough to ensure that, if one compressor is not operating, the remaining compressors are capable of supplying the air required for the work chamber or air lock.

361. (1) The energy required to furnish compressed air to a work chamber or an air lock shall be readily available at a project from at least two independent sources.

(2) The two sources of energy shall be arranged so that, should the principal energy source fail, an auxiliary source automatically energizes the compressor.

(3) An auxiliary source of energy shall be inspected and tested by being operated at regular intervals of not more than seven days to ensure that it works.

362. (1) A compressor for a work chamber or an air lock shall be constructed so as to ensure that lubricating oil is not discharged with the air that the compressor supplies.

(2) The air intake for a compressor shall be located so as to prevent the entry of exhaust gases from internal combustion engines or other contaminants.

363. Air supplied for use in a work chamber or an air lock,
   (a) shall be clean and free from excessive moisture, oil or other contaminants; and
   (b) shall be kept between 10 degrees and 27 degrees celsius, as far as is practicable.

Air Locks and Work Chambers

364. One air lock shall be provided for each work chamber at a project.

365. (1) An air lock, including the bulkheads and doors, shall be designed by a professional engineer in accordance with good engineering practice to withstand the pressures to be used in the work chamber and in the air lock.

(2) An air lock shall be constructed in accordance with the professional engineer's design drawings for it.

(3) An air lock used for people,
   (a) shall measure at least two metres laterally and vertically;
   (b) shall be large enough to accommodate the maximum number of people expected to be in the work chamber without them being in cramped positions;
   (c) other than an ancillary air lock that complies with section 367, shall contain a functional and accurate electric time piece, thermometer and pressure gauge.

(4) The constructor shall send to a Director before construction of an air lock begins a copy of the design drawings, for the air lock.

(5) The constructor shall keep at a project a copy of the design drawings for an air lock while the air lock is at the project.

O. Reg. 145/00 s. 40; 85/04 s. 24

366. Separate air locks shall be used for people and for materials,

(a) if the air lock is in a shaft; or

(b) where practicable, if the air locks are installed in a tunnel and if the air pressure is likely to exceed 100 kilopascals.

367. (1) Every air lock shall have an ancillary air lock that,

(a) can be pressurized independently of the primary air lock;

(b) has a door into the primary air lock or into the work chamber; and

(c) has a door into air at atmospheric pressure.

(2) Except in an emergency, a door in an ancillary air lock into air at atmospheric pressure shall be kept open.

(3) A vertical air lock in a shaft or pneumatic caisson shall not be used to decompress workers unless a separate worker-lock with its own controls for compression and decompression is provided.

(4) An ancillary air lock shall be used to enter the work chamber only,

(a) when the door between the chamber and the primary air lock is open; and

(b) when it is impossible or impracticable for the door to be closed.

(5) Except in an emergency, an ancillary air lock shall not be used to decompress people.

368. (1) At least two pipes shall supply air to each work chamber and each air lock.

(2) Each of the pipes shall have a valve installed in the vicinity of the compressors to enable one pipe to be disconnected while another pipe remains in service at the work chamber or air lock.

(3) The outlet end of a pipe supplying air to a work chamber or an air lock shall have a hinged flap valve.

369. (1) Each work chamber and each air lock, including an ancillary air lock, shall have a means of controlling and of automatically limiting the maximum air pressure in it.

(2) The air pressure control mechanism shall be set at a level not greater than,

(a) for an air lock, the pressure for which the air lock, bulkheads and doors are designed; and

(b) for a work chamber, seventy kilopascals more than the maximum air pressure to be used in the chamber.

370. At each set of valves controlling the air supply to and discharge from an air lock, there shall be,

(a) a pressure gauge showing the air pressure in the air lock;

(b) a pressure gauge showing the air pressure in the work chamber;

(c) an electric time piece;

(d) a thermometer showing the temperature in the air lock; and

(e) a legible copy of the procedures governing maximum work periods and minimum decompression times for the air lock.

371. (1) Separate valves controlling the air supply to and discharge from an air lock shall be provided inside and outside the lock.

(2) The valves shall be arranged so that a person can enter or leave the air lock or work chamber if not lock tender is attending the air lock.

372. If an automatic compression and decompression device is installed in an air lock used for people, the air lock shall have a manual means of controlling the air pressure in the lock.

373. (1) An air lock, other than an ancillary air lock, used for people shall have an automatic recording gauge to permanently record the air pressure in the lock.

(2) The gauge shall be a rotating dial or strip-chart rectilinear type.

(3) The gauge,

(a) shall be installed so that the lock tender cannot see it when at the controls of the air lock;

(b) shall indicate the change in air pressure at intervals of not more than five minutes; and

(c) shall be kept locked except when the recording paper is being changed.

(4) Despite subsection (2) and clause (3)(b), the gauge for an air lock at a work chamber whose air pressure exceeds 100 kilopascals shall be the strip-chart rectilinear type and shall indicate the change in air pressure at intervals of not more than one minute.

(5) The recording paper used in a gauge shall be changed every seven days and shall be marked to identify the period of time to which it relates.

213/91

374. (1) An air lock shall have a pressure gauge that can be read from the work chamber and that shows the air pressure in the lock.

(2) A pressure gauge, other than a portable pressure gauge, shall have fittings for attaching test gauges to it and shall be tested daily for accuracy.

375. A work chamber shall contain, in a protective container less than 15 metres from the work face, a portable pressure gauge and a thermometer.

O. Reg. 142/17, s. 40

376. (1) Only one unit of measuring pressure (either kilopascals or pounds per square inch) shall be used on a project.

(2) Pressure gauges for decompression equipment and decompression procedures established for a project shall be calibrated using the unit of pressure for the project.

377. (1) The door between an air lock and a work chamber shall be kept open,

(a) unless the air lock is being used to compress or decompress people or to move materials; or

(b) when people are in the work chamber.

(2) Clause (1)(a) does not apply with respect to an ancillary air lock.

378. Every air lock door shall have a transparent observation window.

379. If practicable, an air lock used for people, other than an ancillary air lock, shall have one seat for each person being decompressed at one time.

380. (1) An air lock in which people are decompressed shall have a means of radiant heat if the air pressure in the lock exceeds 100 kilopascals.

(2) The temperature in an air lock used for people shall not exceed 27 degrees celsius.

381. (1) A smoke line shall be provided from each work face of a work chamber if an air lock or bulkhead is located between the chamber and the surface.

(2) Each smoke line shall extend to a point less than 15 metres from a work face.

(3) Each smoke line shall have two quick opening valves at least 100 millimetres in diameter,

(a) one located less than 17 metres from the work face; and

(b) one located between the air lock closest to the work chamber and the work chamber and less than two metres from the air lock.

(4) Each smoke line shall be at least 100 millimetres in diameter and shall have a readily-accessible outlet above ground,

(a) that has a quick opening valve at least 100 millimetres in diameter;

(b) that is clearly marked with a sign stating "SMOKELINE—TO BE USED ONLY IN CASE OF EMERGENCY"; and

(c) that is sealed to prevent the inadvertent opening of the valve.

(5) Each smoke line shall extend from inside the work chamber to above ground and shall pass vertically through either the air lock or the bulkhead between the work chamber and air at atmospheric pressure.

O. Reg. 142/17, s. 41

382. (1) No bulkhead in a work chamber shall interfere with the free passage from the work face to an air lock of people in a tunnel or shaft.

(2) Subsection (1) does not apply with respect to a partial bulkhead in a sub-aqueous tunnel if the bulkhead is designed and placed to trap air so that workers can escape from the tunnel if it is flooded.

383. (1) Except when it is necessary to protect people during an emergency, the pressure in a work chamber shall not exceed 350 kilopascals for more than five minutes.

(2) If the pressure in a work chamber exceeds 350 kilopascals for more than five minutes,

(a) the superintendent shall promptly notify an inspector by telephone, two-way radio or in person; and

(b) the pressure maintained in the work chamber shall be the least possible pressure required to meet the emergency.

384. (1) Subject to subsection (2), no worker shall work or be permitted to work in a work chamber in which the temperature exceeds the greater of,

(a) 27 degrees celsius; and

(b) the temperature at the entrance to the service shaft above ground.

(2) No worker shall work or be permitted to work in a work chamber in which the temperature exceeds 38 degrees celsius.

385. (1) Water on the floor of a work chamber or an air lock shall be drained by a pipe or mop line and, if necessary, a pump.

213/91

(2) A pipe or mop line shall have an inside diameter of at least fifty-one millimetres.

(3) At least one inlet with a valve to a pipe or mop line for an air lock and work chamber shall be located,

(a) in the air lock;

(b) less than 15 metres from the work face; and

(c) at intervals of not more than thirty metres along the length of the work chamber.

(4) An inlet shall be diverted downward.

(5) An outlet from an air lock shall discharge downward under atmospheric air pressure.

O. Reg. 142/17, s. 42

Work Periods and Rest Periods

386. (1) Subject to subsection (2), no worker shall,

(a) work for more than two working periods in any consecutive twenty-four hour period where the maximum air pressure is not greater than 100 kilopascals; or

(b) work for more than one working period in any consecutive twenty-four hour period where the maximum air pressure is more than 100 kilopascals.

(2) No worker shall work or be permitted to work more than eight hours in a period of twenty-four hours.

(3) No lock tender shall work or be permitted to work more than nine hours in a period of twenty-four hours.

(4) The period between the end of one work period and the beginning of the next for a worker doing manual work under compressed air where the maximum air pressure exceeds 100 kilopascals shall be at least twelve hours.

387. (1) A worker who is working in compressed air shall have a rest period of at least,

(a) 1/4 hour, if the worker was working in pressure of 100 kilopascals or less;

(b) 3/4 hour, if the worker was working in pressure greater than 100 kilopascals up to and including 140 kilopascals;

(c) 1 1/2 hours, if the worker was working in pressure greater than 140 kilopascals up to and including 220 kilopascals; or

(d) two hours, if the worker was working in pressure greater than 220 kilopascals.

(2) No worker shall be permitted to perform manual work or engage in physical exertion during a rest period.

(3) No worker shall be permitted to leave a project during a rest period.

388. (1) The employer shall provide, free of charge, sugar and hot beverages for workers working in compressed air to consume during their rest periods.

(2) An employer shall keep containers and cups for beverages in a sanitary condition and shall store them in a closed container.

Lock Tenders

389. (1) A lock tender shall supervise the controls of an air lock when a worker is about to be, or is being, subjected to compressed air in the air lock or work chamber.

(2) Subject to subsection (3), a lock tender shall tend only one air lock at a time.

(3) A lock tender may tend two locks if,

(a) they are in close proximity;

(b) the pressure in each work chamber does not exceed 100 kilopascals; and

(c) only one of the locks is being used to compress or decompress a worker.

390. (1) A lock tender shall ensure that the requirements of this section are met before a worker enters an air lock.

(2) A worker shall be examined by a project physician before the worker enters an air lock in preparation for working in compressed air.

(3) A lock tender shall ensure that any worker who enters the air lock in preparation for working in compressed air has been examined by a physician in accordance with subsection (2).

(4) The means of air supply, air pressure gauges and controls, lock equipment and other devices necessary for the safe operation of an air lock and the protection of workers shall be in working order.

391. (1) A lock tender shall increase the air pressure on a worker in an air lock in accordance with this section.

(2) Air pressure shall be increased uniformly and to no more than thirty-five kilopascals in the first two minutes of application of compressed air.

(3) Air pressure shall not be increased to more than thirty-five kilopascals until the lock tender ensures that every worker in the air lock is free from discomfort due to air pressure.

(4) Air pressure shall be increased above thirty-five kilopascals at a uniform rate of not greater than thirty-five kilopascals per minute.

(5) A lock tender shall observe a worker in an air lock while increasing the air pressure on the worker and, if the worker shows signs of discomfort and the discomfort does not quickly disappear, the lock tender shall gradually decrease the air pressure until the worker reports that the discomfort has ceased or until the air pressure reaches atmospheric pressure.

392. (1) A lock tender shall decrease the air pressure on a worker in an air lock in accordance with this section and section 395.

(2) Air pressure shall be decreased uniformly in each of the stages of decompression referred to in section 395.

(3) A lock tender shall constantly observe a worker in an air lock while decreasing the air pressure on the worker and, if the worker shows signs of discomfort and the discomfort does not quickly disappear, the lock tender shall gradually increase the air pressure until the worker reports that the discomfort has ceased or until the air pressure equals the pressure in the work chamber.

393. (1) If a worker in an air lock appears to be suffering from decompression sickness, a lock tender shall notify, and follow the instructions of, a project physician, the superintendent or a person designated by the superintendent.

(2) If a worker in an air lock appears to be injured or to be unwell from a cause unrelated to air pressure, a lock tender shall notify, and follow the instructions of, a project physician.

(3) In the circumstances described in subsection (2), a lock tender shall decompress the worker unless otherwise instructed by the project physician.

213/91

394. (1) A lock tender shall record information about the compression and decompression of a worker in an air lock.

(2) A separate record shall be kept for each air lock and each compression and decompression of a worker.

(3) The information to be recorded is,

    (a) the description of the air lock;

    (b) the worker's name;

    (c) the time of the beginning and end of each compression or decompression to which the worker is subjected;

    (d) the pressure and temperature in the air lock before and after each compression or decompression to which the worker is subjected; and

    (e) a description of any unusual occurrence respecting the worker, the air lock or any related matter.

(4) A lock tender shall give the record to the superintendent.

Decompression Procedures

395. (1) A worker who has been in air pressure greater than atmospheric air pressure for more than five minutes shall be decompressed down to atmospheric pressure in accordance with this section.

(2) Subject to subsection (3), decompression shall be done in accordance with the Tables to this Regulation.

(3) The rate of decompression required by subsection (2) may be doubled with respect to a worker if, while performing the work in compressed air, the worker,

    (a) has not been exposed to air pressure greater than 200 kilopascals;

    (b) has remained under compressed air for a maximum of thirty minutes; and

    (c) has not done manual work.

(4) Subsection (3) applies only if every worker who is in the air lock,

    (a) meets the requirements of clauses 3(a), (b) and (c); and

    (b) has previously experienced decompression.

(5) A copy of the Tables to this Regulation shall be kept posted at a project,

    (a) in each air lock;

(b) at the control outside each air lock; and

(c) in each change room.

396. A worker who believes he or she has decompression sickness shall promptly notify,

(a) the superintendent or a project physician; or

(b) the lock tender, if the worker is under compressed air.

397. (1) The superintendent shall make a report at least once a week to a Director concerning every case of decompression sickness at a project occurring since the previous report, if any.

(2) The superintendent shall promptly make a report by telephone, two-way radio or other direct means to a Director concerning a case of decompression sickness that does not respond to first-aid treatment.

(3) A report under this section shall indicate, for each case of decompression sickness,

(a) the air pressure to which the worker was subjected;

(b) the length of time the worker was subjected to the air pressure;

(c) the nature of the medical treatment given to the worker; and

(d) the extent of the worker's recovery.

O. Reg. 145/00 s. 41

Transition and Commencement

398. Regulation 691 of Revised Regulations of Ontario, 1980 and Ontario Regulations 156/84, 635/86 and 528/88 are revoked.

399. This Regulation comes into force on the 1st day of August, 1991.

Table 1

Work-ing pres-sure, kPa	Total decompression time, min									
	Working period, h									
	0.5	1	1.5	2	3	4	5	6	7	8
10						1	1	1	1	1
20						1	1	1	1	1

Working pressure, kPa	Total decompression time, min									
	Working period, h									
	0.5	1	1.5	2	3	4	5	6	7	8
30						1	1	1	1	1
40						2	2	2	2	2
50						2	2	2	2	2
60						2	2	2	2	2
70						2	2	2	2	2
80						8	8	8	8	8
90						10	10	10	15	20
100						10	10	20	30	40
110					12	13	30	44		
120					16	28	47	73		
130					25	46	73	108		
140					37	65	105	140		
150				27	61	103				
160				36	77	131				
170				45	93	152				
180			34	55	110	175				
190		28	42	65	132					
200		29	47	77	154					
210		33	56	88	175					
220		36	64	101	197					
230		39	72	114						

Work-ing pressure, kPa	Total decompression time, min									
	Working period, h									
	0.5	1	1.5	2	3	4	5	6	7	8
240		44	80	131						
250	30	51	90	148						
260	32	56	101	164						
270	34	62	111							
280	35	67	125							
290	37	73	139							
300	40	78	155							
310	42	90								
320	43	95								
330	46	103								
340	48	113								
350	50	122								

213/91

Table 2
Pressure reduction, kPa

Working pressure, kPa	Working period, h	Stage No.	From	To	Time in stage, min	Pressure reduction rate, min/10 kPa	Total time decompress., min
10	4-8	1	10	0	1.0		1.0
20	4-8	1	20	0	1.0		1.0
30	4-8	1	30	0	1.0		1.0
40	4-8	1	40	0	2.0		2.0
50	4-8	1	50	0	2.0		2.0
60	4-8	1	60	0	2.0		2.0
70	4-8	1	70	0	2.0		2.0
80	4-8	1	80	40	1.0	0.33	
		2	40	30	1.0	1	
		3	30	30	5.0		
		4	30	0	1.0		8.0
90	5	1	90	45	1.5	0.33	
		2	45	30	1.5	1	
		3	30	30	6.0		

213/91

Working pressure, kPa	Working period, h	Stage No.	Pressure reduction, kPa		Time in stage, min	Pressure reduction rate, min/10 kPa	Total time decompress., min
			From	To			
		4	30	0	1.0		10
	6	1	90	45	1.5	0.33	
		2	45	30	1.5	1	
		3	30	30	6.0		
		4	30	0	1.0		10
	7	1	90	45	1.5	0.33	
		2	45	30	1.5	1	
		3	30	30	11.0		
		4	30	0	1.0		15
	8	1	90	45	1.5	0.33	
		2	45	30	1.5	1	
		3	30	30	16.0		
		4	30	0	1.0		20
100	4	1	100	50	2	0.33	
		2	50	30	2	1	
		3	30	30	5		

299

Working pressure, kPa	Working period, h	Stage No.	Pressure reduction, kPa		Time in stage, min	Pressure reduction rate, min/10 kPa	Total time decompress., min
			From	To			
		4	30	0	1		10
	5	1	100	50	2	0.33	
		2	50	30	2	1	
		3	30	30	5		
		4	30	0	1		10
	6	1	100	50	2	0.33	
		2	50	30	2	1	
		3	30	30	15		
		4	30	0	1		20
	7	1	100	50	2	0.33	
		2	50	30	2	1	
		3	30	30	25		
		4	30	0	1		30
	8	1	100	50	2	0.33	
		2	50	30	2	1	
		3	30	30	35		

Working pressure, kPa	Working period, h	Stage No.	Pressure reduction, kPa From	To	Time in stage, min	Pressure reduction rate, min/10 kPa	Total time decompress., min
		4	30	0	1		40
110	3	1	110	55	2	0.33	
		2	55	30	3	1	
		3	30	30	6		
		4	30	0	1		12
	4	1	110	55	2	0.33	
		2	55	30	3	1	
		3	30	30	7		
		4	30	0	1		13
	5	1	110	55	2	0.33	
		2	55	30	3	1	
		3	30	30	24		
		4	30	0	1		30
	6	1	110	55	2	0.33	
		2	55	30	3	1	
		3	30	30	38		

Working pressure, kPa	Working period, h	Stage No.	Pressure reduction, kPa		Time in stage, min	Pressure reduction rate, min/10 kPa	Total time decompress., min
			From	To			
		4	30	0	1		44
120	3	1	120	60	2	0.33	
		2	60	30	3	1	
		3	30	30	10		
		4	30	0	1		16
	4	1	120	60	2	0.33	
		2	60	30	3	1	
		3	30	30	22		
		4	30	0	1	28	28
	5	1	120	60	2	0.33	
		2	60	30	3	1	
		3	30	30	41		
		4	30	0	1		47
	6	1	120	60	2	0.33	
		2	60	30	6	2	
		3	30	30	64		

Working pressure, kPa	Working period, h	Stage No.	Pressure reduction, kPa		Time in stage, min	Pressure reduction rate, min/10 kPa	Total time decompress., min
			From	To			
		4	30	0	1		73
130	3	1	130	65	3	0.33	
		2	65	30	4	1	
		3	30	30	17		
		4	30	0	1		25
	4	1	130	65	3	0.33	
		2	65	30	4	1	
		3	30	30	38		
		4	30	0	1		46
	5	1	130	65	3	0.33	
		2	65	30	7	2	
		3	30	30	62		
		4	30	0	1		73
	6	1	130	65	3	0.33	
		2	65	30	14	4	
		3	30	30	90		

Working pressure, kPa	Working period, h	Stage No.	Pressure reduction, kPa		Time in stage, min	Pressure reduction rate, min/10 kPa	Total time decompress., min
			From	To			
		4	30	0	1		108
140	3	1	140	70	3	0.33	
		2	70	30	4	1	
		3	30	30	29		
		4	30	0	1		37
	4	1	140	70	3	0.33	
		2	70	30	6	1.5	
		3	30	30	55		
		4	30	0	1		65
	5	1	140	70	3	0.33	
		2	70	30	12	3	
		3	30	30	89		
		4	30	0	1		105
	6	1	140	70	3	0.33	
		2	70	30	20	5	
		3	30	30	116		

Working pressure, kPa	Working period, h	Stage No.	Pressure reduction, kPa From	To	Time in stage, min	Pressure reduction rate, min/10 kPa	Total time decompress., min
		4	30	0	1		140
150	2	1	150	75	3	0.33	
		2	75	30	5	1	
		3	30	30	18		
		4	30	0	1		27
	3	1	150	75	3	0.33	
		2	75	30	7	1.5	
		3	30	30	50		
		4	30	0	1		61
	4	1	150	75	3	0.33	
		2	75	30	9	2	
		3	30	30	90		
		4	30	0	1		103
160	2	1	160	80	3	0.33	
		2	80	30	5	1	
		3	30	30	27		

305

Working pressure, kPa	Working period, h	Stage No.	Pressure reduction, kPa		Time in stage, min	Pressure reduction rate, min/10 kPa	Total time decompress., min
			From	To			
		4	30	0	1		36
	3	1	160	80	3	0.33	
		2	80	30	10	2	
		3	30	30	63		
		4	30	0	1		77
	4	1	160	80	3	0.33	
		2	80	30	25	5	
		3	30	30	102		
		4	30	0	1		131
170	2	1	170	85	3	0.33	
		2	85	45	4	1	
		3	45	30	5	3	
		4	30	30	32		
		5	30	0	1		45
	3	1	170	85	3	0.33	
		2	85	45	6	1.5	

Working pressure, kPa	Working period, h	Stage No.	Pressure reduction, kPa		Time in stage, min	Pressure reduction rate, min/10 kPa	Total time decompress., min
			From	To			
		3	45	30	6	4	
		4	30	30	77		
		5	30	0	1		93
	4	1	170	85	3	0.33	
		2	85	45	12	3	
		3	45	30	18	12	
		4	30	30	118		
		5	30	0	1		152
180	1.5	1	180	90	3	0.33	
		2	90	45	5	1	
		3	45	30	5	3	
		4	30	30	20		
		5	30	0	1		34
	2	1	180	90	3	0.33	
		2	90	45	5	1	
		3	45	30	5	3	

Working pressure, kPa	Working period, h	Stage No.	Pressure reduction, kPa		Time in stage, min	Pressure reduction rate, min/10 kPa	Total time decompress., min
			From	To			
		4	30	30	41		
		5	30	0	1		55
	3	1	180	90	3	0.33	
		2	90	45	7	1.5	
		3	45	30	9	6	
		4	30	30	90		
		5	30	0	1		110
	4	1	180	90	3	0.33	
		2	90	45	14	3	
		3	45	30	23	15	
		4	30	30	134		
		5	30	0	1		175
190	1	1	190	95	4	0.33	
		2	95	50	5	1	
		3	50	30	6	3	
		4	30	30	12		

Working pressure, kPa	Working period, h	Stage No.	Pressure reduction, kPa		Time in stage, min	Pressure reduction rate, min/10 kPa	Total time decompress., min
			From	To			
		5	30	0	1		28
	1.5	1	190	95	4	0.33	
		2	95	50	5	1	
		3	50	30	6	3	
		4	30	30	26		
		5	30	0	1		42
	2	1	190	95	4	0.33	
		2	95	50	7	1.5	
		3	50	30	6	3	
		4	30	30	47		
		5	30	0	1		65
	3	1	190	95	4	0.33	
		2	95	50	9	2	
		3	50	30	16	8	
		4	30	30	102		
		5	30	0	1		132

Working pressure, kPa	Working period, h	Stage No.	Pressure reduction, kPa From	To	Time in stage, min	Pressure reduction rate, min/10 kPa	Total time decompress., min
200	1	1	200	100	4	0.33	
		2	100	50	5	1	
		3	50	30	6	3	
		4	30	30	13		
		5	30	0	1		29
	1.5	1	200	100	4	0.33	
		2	100	50	5	1	
		3	50	30	6	3	
		4	30	30	31		
		5	30	0	1		47
	2	1	200	100	4	0.33	
		2	100	50	8	1.5	
		3	50	30	8	4	
		4	30	30	56		
		5	30	0	1		77
	3	1	200	100	4	0.33	

213/91

Working pressure, kPa	Working period, h	Stage No.	Pressure reduction, kPa From	Pressure reduction, kPa To	Time in stage, min	Pressure reduction rate, min/10 kPa	Total time decompress., min
		2	100	50	15	3	
		3	50	30	20	10	
		4	30	30	114		
		5	30	0	1		154
210	1	1	210	105	4	0.33	
		2	105	55	5	1	
		3	55	30	8	3	
		4	30	30	15		
		5	30	0	1		33
	1.5	1	210	105	4	0.33	
		2	105	55	5	1	
		3	55	30	8	3	
		4	30	30	38		
		5	30	0	1		56
	2	1	210	105	4	0.33	
		2	105	55	8	1.5	

311

Working pressure, kPa	Working period, h	Stage No.	Pressure reduction, kPa From	To	Time in stage, min	Pressure reduction rate, min/10 kPa	Total time decompress., min
		3	55	30	10	4	
		4	30	30	65		
		5	30	0	1		88
	3	1	210	105	4	0.33	
		2	105	55	15	3	
		3	55	30	30	12	
		4	30	30	125		
		5	30	0	1		175
220	1	1	220	110	4	0.33	
		2	110	55	6	1	
		3	55	30	8	3	
		4	30	30	17		
		5	30	0	1		36
	1.5	1	220	110	4	0.33	
		2	110	55	9	1.5	
		3	55	30	10	4	

Working pressure, kPa	Working period, h	Stage No.	Pressure reduction, kPa		Time in stage, min	Pressure reduction rate, min/10 kPa	Total time decompress., min
			From	To			
		4	30	30	40		
		5	30	0	1		64
	2	1	220	110	4	0.33	
		2	110	55	9	1.5	
		3	55	30	13	5	
		4	30	30	74		
		5	30	0	1		101
	3	1	220	110	4	0.33	
		2	110	55	17	3	
		3	55	30	38	15	
		4	30	30	137		
		5	30	0	1		197
230	1	1	230	115	4	0.33	
		2	115	60	6	1	
		3	60	30	9	3	
		4	30	30	19		

313

Working pressure, kPa	Working period, h	Stage No.	Pressure reduction, kPa From	To	Time in stage, min	Pressure reduction rate, min/10 kPa	Total time decompress., min
		5	30	0	1		39
	1.5	1	230	115	4	0.33	
		2	115	60	9	1.5	
		3	60	30	9	3	
		4	30	30	49		
		5	30	0	1		72
	2	1	230	115	4	0.33	
		2	115	60	9	1.5	
		3	60	30	18	6	
		4	30	30	82		
		5	30	0			114
240	1	1	240	120	4	0.33	
		2	120	60	6	1	
		3	60	30	9	3	
		4	30	30	24		
		5	30	0	1		44

Working pressure, kPa	Working period, h	Stage No.	Pressure reduction, kPa		Time in stage, min	Pressure reduction rate, min/10 kPa	Total time decompress., min
			From	To			
	1.5	1	240	120	4	0.33	
		2	120	60	9	1.5	
		3	60	30	12	4	
		4	30	30	54		
		5	30	0	1		80
	2	1	240	120	4	0.33	
		2	120	60	12	2	
		3	60	30	24	8	
		4	30	30	90		
		5	30	0	1		11
250	0.5	1	250	125	5	0.33	
		2	125	65	6	1	
		3	65	30	11	3	
		4	30	30	7		
		5	30	0	1		30
	1	1	250	125	5	0.33	

315

Working pressure, kPa	Working period, h	Stage No.	Pressure reduction, kPa		Time in stage, min	Pressure reduction rate, min/10 kPa	Total time decompress., min
			From	To			
		2	125	65	6	1	
		3	65	30	11	3	
		4	30	30	28		
		5	30	0	1		51
	1.5	1	250	125	5	0.33	
		2	125	65	9	1.5	
		3	65	30	14	4	
		4	30	30	61		
		5	30	0	1		90
	2	1	250	125	5	0.33	
		2	125	65	12	2	
		3	65	30	28	8	
		4	30	30	102		
		5	30	0	1		148
260	0.5	1	260	130	5	0.33	
		2	130	65	7	1	

Working pressure, kPa	Working period, h	Stage No.	Pressure reduction, kPa		Time in stage, min	Pressure reduction rate, min/10 kPa	Total time decompress., min
			From	To			
		3	65	30	11	3	
		4	30	30	8		
		5	30	0	1		32
	1	1	260	130	5	0.33	
		2	130	65	7	1	
		3	65	30	11	3	
		4	30	30	32		
		5	30	0	1		56
	1.5	1	260	130	5	0.33	
		2	130	65	10	1.5	
		3	65	30	18	5	
		4	30	30	67		
		5	30	0	1		101
	2	1	260	130	5	0.33	
		2	130	65	13	2	
		3	65	30	35	10	

317

Working pressure, kPa	Working period, h	Stage No.	Pressure reduction, kPa		Time in stage, min	Pressure reduction rate, min/10 kPa	Total time decompress., min
			From	To			
		4	30	30	110		
		5	30	0	1		164
270	0.5	1	270	135	5	0.33	
		2	135	70	7	1	
		3	70	30	12	3	
		4	30	30	9		
		5	30	0	1		34
	1	1	270	135	5	0.33	
		2	135	70	7	1	
		3	70	30	16	4	
		4	30	30	33		
		5	30	0	1		62
	1.5	1	270	135	5	0.33	
		2	135	70	10	1.5	
		3	70	30	20	5	
		4	30	30	75		

213/91

Working pressure, kPa	Working period, h	Stage No.	Pressure reduction, kPa		Time in stage, min	Pressure reduction rate, min/10 kPa	Total time decompress., min
			From	To			
		5	30	0	1		111
280	0.5	1	280	140	5	0.33	
		2	140	70	7	1	
		3	70	30	12	3	
		4	30	30	10		
		5	30	0	1		35
	1	1	280	140	5	0.33	
		2	140	70	7	1	
		3	70	30	16	4	
		4	30	30	38		
		5	30	0	1		67
	1.5	1	280	140	5	0.33	
		2	140	70	11	1.5	
		3	70	30	32	8	
		4	30	30	76		
		5	30	0	1		125

Working pressure, kPa	Working period, h	Stage No.	Pressure reduction, kPa		Time in stage, min	Pressure reduction rate, min/10 kPa	Total time decompress., min
			From	To			
290	0.5	1	290	145	5	0.33	
		2	145	75	7	1	
		3	75	30	14	3	
		4	30	30	10		
		5	30	0	1		37
	1	1	290	145	5	0.33	
		2	145	75	7	1	
		3	75	30	18	4	
		4	30	30	42		
		5	30	0	1		73
	1.5	1	290	145	5	0.33	
		2	145	75	11	1.5	
		3	75	30	36	8	
		4	30	30	86		
		5	30	0	1		139
300	0.5	1	300	150	5	0.33	

Working pressure, kPa	Working period, h	Stage No.	Pressure reduction, kPa		Time in stage, min	Pressure reduction rate, min/10 kPa	Total time decompress., min
			From	To			
		2	150	75	8	1	
		3	75	30	14	3	
		4	30	30	12		
		5	30	0	1		40
	1	1	300	150	5	0.33	
		2	150	75	8	1	
		3	75	30	18	4	
		4	30	30	46		
		5	30	0	1		78
	1.5	1	300	150	5	0.33	
		2	150	75	15	2	
		3	75	30	36	8	
		4	30	30	98		
		5	30	0	1		155
310	0.5	1	310	155	6	0.33	
		2		155	80	8	1

321

Working pressure, kPa	Working period, h	Stage No.	Pressure reduction, kPa		Time in stage, min	Pressure reduction rate, min/10 kPa	Total time decompress., min
			From	To			
		3	80	30	15	3	
		4	30	30	12		
		5	30	0	1		42
	1	1	310	155	6	0.33	
		2	155	80	12	1.5	
		3	80	30	20	4	
		4	30	30	51		
		5	30	0	1		90
320	0.5	1	320	160	6	0.33	
		2	160	80	8	1	
		3	80	30	15	3	
		4	30	30	13		
		5	30	0	1		43
	1	1	320	160	6	0.33	
		2	160	80	12	1.5	
		3	80	30	20	4	

Working pressure, kPa	Working period, h	Stage No.	Pressure reduction, kPa From	To	Time in stage, min	Pressure reduction rate, min/10 kPa	Total time decompress., min
		4	30	30	56		
		5	30	0	1		95
330	0.5	1	330	165	6	0.33	
		2	165	85	8	1	
		3	85	30	17	3	
		4	30	30	14		
		5	30	0	1		46
	1	1	330	165	6	0.33	
		2	165	85	12	1.5	
		3	85	30	22	4	
		4	30	30	62		
		5	30	0	1		103
340	0.5	1	340	170	6	0.33	
		2	170	85	9	1	
		3	85	30	17	3	
		4	30	30	15		

| Working pressure, kPa | Working period, h | Stage No. | Pressure reduction, kPa | | Time in stage, min | Pressure reduction rate, min/10 kPa | Total time decompress., min |
			From	To			
		5	30	0	1		48
	1	1	340	170	6	0.33	
		2	170	85	13	1.5	
		3	85	30	28	5	
		4	30	30	65		
		5	30	0	1		113
350	0.5	1	350	175	6	0.33	
		2	175	90	9	1	
		3	90	30	18	3	
		4	30	30	16		
		5	30	0	1		50
	1	1	350	175	6	0.33	
		2	175	90	13	1.5	
		3	90	30	30	5	
		4	30	30	72		
		5	30	0	1		122

Form 1 — Record of Compressed Air Worker
Occupational Health and Safety Act

Name .... Age ....

Address ....

Social Insurance Number ....

File No. .... Location (Municipality)

....

Project ....

Constructor ....

Employer ....

Previous Compressed Air Experience ....

Pre-Employment Medical Examination ....

Date .... Accept .... Reject ....

Signature .... M.D.

213/91

Subsequent Medical Examinations

	Date	Accept	Reject	Signature
1				M.D.
2				M.D.
3				M.D.
4				M.D.
5				M.D.
6				M.D.
7				M.D.
8				M.D.
9				M.D.
10				M.D.
11				M.D.
12				M.D.

Schedule 67

Occupational Health and Safety Act (as it relates to Ontario Regulation 213/91)			
ITEM	COLUMN 1	COLUMN 2 SECTION	SET FINE (INCL COSTS)
1.	Worker failing to work in compliance with subsection 26.1(2) of Ontario Regulation 213/91 by not being adequately protected by fall protection	28 (1) (a)	$300.00
2.	Worker failing to work in compliance with section	28 (l) (a)	$200.00

Occupational Health and Safety Act (as it relates to Ontario Regulation 213/91)			
ITEM	COLUMN 1	COLUMN 2 SECTION	SET FINE (INCL COSTS)
	115 of Ontario Regulation 213/91 by using loose object as workplace or as support for object		
3.	Worker having or using stilts or leg extension devices contrary to section 116 of Ontario Regulation 213/91	28 (l) (a)	$200.00
4.	Employer failing to ensure compliance with stilts and leg extension devices re-	28 (l) (c)	$300.00

Occupational Health and Safety Act (as it relates to Ontario Regulation 213/91)			
ITEM	COLUMN 1	COLUMN 2 SECTION	SET FINE (INCL COSTS)
	quirements in section 116 of Ontario Regulation 213/91		
5.	Supervisor failing to ensure worker working in compliance with stilts and leg extension devices requirements in section 116 of Ontario Regulation 213/91	27 (l) (a)	$300.00
6.	Worker failing to work in compliance with subsection 195.1(1) of Ontario Regula-	28 (l) (a)	$200.00

Occupational Health and Safety Act (as it relates to Ontario Regulation 213/91)			
ITEM	COLUMN 1	COLUMN 2 SECTION	SET FINE (INCL COSTS)
	tion 213/91 by using inadequately grounded cord-connected equipment or tools		

Schedule 67.1

| | | | 213/91 |

Ontario Regulation 213/91-Construction Projects under the Occupational Health and Safety Act

ITEM	COLUMN 1	COLUMN 2 SECTION	SET FINE (INCL COSTS)
1.	Worker failing to wear protective headwear	22	$200.00
2.	Worker failing to wear protective footwear	23	$200.00
3.	Worker failing to wear eye protection	24	$200.00
4.	Worker failing to use provided protective respiratory	46 (2)	$200.00

Ontario Regulation 213/91-Construction Projects under the Occupational Health and Safety Act			
ITEM	**COLUMN 1**	**COLUMN 2 SECTION**	**SET FINE (INCL COSTS)**
	equipment		
5.	Worker who may be endangered by vehicular traffic failing to wear prescribed garment	69.1	$200.00
6.	Operator leaving the controls of machine unattended	102	$200.00
7.	Signaller failing to wear prescribed garment	106 (1.1)-(1.4)	$200.00

Ontario Regulation 213/91-Construction Projects under the Occupational Health and Safety Act			
ITEM	**COLUMN 1**	**COLUMN 2 SECTION**	**SET FINE (INCL COSTS)**
8.	Worker failing to wear adequate personal protective equipment while using fastening tool	117 (3) (a)	$200.00
9.	Worker failing to wear adequate eye protection while using fastening tool	117 (3) (b)	$200.00
10.	Worker failing to wear full	141 (1)	$300.00

213/91

Ontario Regulation 213/91-Construction Projects under the Occupational Health and Safety Act			
ITEM	COLUMN 1	COLUMN 2 SECTION	SET FINE (INCL COSTS)
	body harness connected to fall arrest system while on suspended equipment		

ONT. REG. 833 — CONTROL OF EXPOSURE TO BIOLOGICAL OR CHEMICAL AGENTS

made under the *Occupational Health and Safety Act*

R.R.O. 1990, Reg. 833, as am. O. Reg. 513/92; 597/94; 388/00; 100/04; 16/05; 77/05; 177/05; 607/05; 83/07; 248/08; 491/09; 419/10, ss. 1, 2 (Fr.); 149/12; CTR 16 MA 14 - 2; 274/ 14; 347/15; 287/17.

1. In this Regulation,

"ACGIH" means the American Conference of Governmental Industrial Hygienists;

"ACGIH Table" means the table entitled "Adopted Values" shown at pages 11 to 61 of the publication entitled *2015 Threshold Limit Values for Chemical Substances and Physical Agents & Biological Exposure Indices* published by ACGIH and identified by International Standard Book Number 978-1-607260-77-6;

"C" or **"ceiling limit"** means the maximum airborne concentration of a biological or chemical agent to which a worker may be exposed at any time;

"chemical agent" includes a chemical substance;

"exposure" means exposure by inhalation, ingestion, skin absorption or skin contact;

"Ontario Table" means Table 1 to this Regulation;

"STEL" or **"short-term exposure limit"** means the maximum airborne concentration of a biological or chemical agent to which a worker may be exposed in any 15-minute period;

"TWA" or **"time-weighted average limit"** means the time-weighted average airborne concentration of a biological or chemical agent to which a worker may be exposed in a work day or work week.

491/09 s. 1; 149/12 s. 1; 274/14 s. 1; 287/17, s. 1

2. (1) [Repealed O. Reg. 347/15, s. 1.]

(2) This Regulation does not apply,

    (a) to a chemical agent listed in Table 1 of Ontario Regulation 490/09 (*Designated Substances*) made under the Act, in a workplace that is subject to that regulation with respect to that agent; or

    (b) with respect to asbestos, in a workplace that is subject to Ontario Regulation 278/05 (*Designated Substance—Asbestos on Construction Projects and in Buildings and Repair Operations*) made under the Act.

O. Reg. 654/86 s. 2; 491/09 s. 2; 347/15, s. 1

2.1 Codes of practice relating to exposure of workers to biological or chemical agents that have been approved by the Minister for the purposes of subsection 32.2(1) of the Act are available on the Ministry's or the Government of Ontario's website.

O. Reg. 347/15 s. 2

3. (1) Every employer shall take all measures reasonably necessary in the circumstances to protect workers from exposure to a hazardous biological or chemical agent because of the storage, handling, processing or use of such agent in the work place.

(2) The measures to be taken shall include the provision and use of,

    (a) engineering controls;

    (b) work practices;

    (c) hygiene facilities and practices; and

    (d) if section 7.2 applies, personal protective equipment.

491/09 s. 3

4. Without limiting the generality of section 3, every employer shall take the measures required by that section to limit the exposure of workers to a hazardous biological or chemical agent in accordance with the following rules:

    1. If the agent is listed in the Ontario Table, exposure shall not exceed the TWA, STEL, or C set out in the Ontario Table.

    2. If the agent is not listed in the Ontario Table but is listed in the ACGIH Table, exposure shall not exceed the TWA, STEL, or C set out in the ACGIH Table.

    3. If the Table that applies under paragraph 1 or 2 sets out a TWA for an agent but sets out neither a STEL nor a C for that agent, exposure shall not exceed the following excursion limits:

i. Three times the TWA for any period of 30 minutes.

ii. Five times the TWA at any time.

4. Paragraph 3 does not apply with respect to an agent that is prescribed as a designated substance under Ontario Regulation 490/09 (*Designated Substances*) made under the Act.

100/04 s. 1; 607/05 s. 1; 491/09 s. 4

5. In determining the exposure of workers to a hazardous biological or chemical agent under section 3 or 4, no regard shall be had to the wearing and use of personal protective equipment.

6. Airborne concentrations of hazardous biological or chemical agents and daily and weekly time-weighted average exposures shall be calculated in accordance with the rules set out in Schedule 1.

607/05 s. 2; 491/09 s. 5

7. If the listing for an agent in the Ontario Table or in the ACGIH Table includes the notation "Skin" and the agent is present at the workplace, the employer shall take all measures reasonably necessary in the circumstances to protect workers from skin absorption of the agent.

491/09 s. 5

7.1 If the listing for an agent in the ACGIH Table includes the reference "Simple asphyxiant"? or "see Appendix F: Minimal Oxygen Content"? and the agent is present in the air at the workplace, the employer shall take all measures reasonably necessary in the circumstances to protect workers from,

(a) exposure to an atmospheric oxygen level that is less than 19.5 per cent by volume; and

(b) related hazards such as fire and explosion.

O. Reg. 491/09 s. 5; 287/17, s. 2

7.2(1) An employer shall protect workers from exposure to a hazardous biological or chemical agent without requiring them to wear and use personal protective equipment, unless subsection (2) applies or the employer complies with an applicable code of practice.

(2) The employer shall provide, and workers shall wear and use, personal protective equipment appropriate in the circumstances to protect the workers from exposure to the agent, if engineering controls required by this Regulation,

(a) are not in existence or are not obtainable;

(b) are not reasonable or not practical to adopt, install or provide because of the duration or frequency of the exposures or because of the nature of the process, operation or work;

(c) are rendered ineffective because of a temporary breakdown of the controls; or

(d) are ineffective to prevent, control or limit exposure because of an emergency.

O. Reg. 491/09 s. 5; 347/15, s. 3

8. (1) If a worker has been exposed to a hazardous biological or chemical agent and,

(a) the worker or the worker's physician has reason to believe that the worker's health has been affected by exposure to the agent and the worker or the worker's physician has so notified the employer in writing; or

(b) the employer has reason to believe that the worker's health is likely to be affected by the exposure and the employer has so notified the worker in writing,

(c) [Repealed O. Reg. 491/09, s. 6.]

the worker, if he or she agrees, shall undergo medical examinations and clinical tests, at the employer's expense, to determine whether the worker has an occupational illness because of exposure to the agent and whether the worker is fit, fit with limitations or unfit to continue working in exposure to the agent.

(2) [Repealed O. Reg. 491/09, s. 6.]

(3) [Repealed O. Reg. 491/09, s. 6.]

(4) The employer shall provide the physician who examines the worker or under whose supervision clinical tests are performed with a copy of the records, if any, of the exposure of the worker to the hazardous biological or chemical agent.

513/92 s. 1; 491/09 s. 6

9. [Repealed O. Reg. 607/05, s. 3(2).]

SCHEDULE [Repealed O. Reg. 491/09, s. 8.]

[Repealed O. Reg. 491/09, s. 8.]

Table 1 — Exposure Limits   S. 9

TABLE 1
Ontario Table of Occupational Exposure Limits
[Heading added O. Reg. 491/09, s. 7.]

List-ing	French Listing Equiva-lent	Agent [CAS No.]	Time-Weigh-ted Aver-age Limit (TWA)	Short-Term Ex-posure Limit (STEL) or Ceiling Limit (C)	No-ta-tions
1.	4.	*Acrylonitrile [107-13-1]	2 ppm	C 10 ppm	Skin
2a.		[Repealed O. Reg. 287/17, s. 3(1).]			
2b.		[Repealed O. Reg. 287/17, s. 3(1).]			
3.	7.	*Arsenic, ele-mental arsenic and inorganic compounds [7440-38-2], and organic compounds (only where both inorganic and organic compounds are present), as As.	0.01 mg/m^3	0.05 mg/m^3	

833

List-ing	French Listing Equiva-lent	Agent [CAS No.]	Time-Weigh-ted Aver-age Limit (TWA)	Short-Term Ex-posure Limit (STEL) or Ceiling Limit (C)	No-ta-tions
4a.	5a.	*Asbestos - All forms [1332-21-4]	0.1 f/cc (F)		
4b.	5b.	*Asbestos - Actinolite [77536-21-4]	0.1 f/cc (F)		
4c.	5c.	*Asbestos - Amosite [12172-73-5]	0.1 f/cc (F)		
4d.	5d.	*Asbestos - Anthophyllite [77536-67-5]	0.1 f/cc (F)		
4e.	5e.	*Asbestos - Chrysotile [132207-32-0]	0.1 f/cc (F)		
4f.	5f.	*Asbestos - Crocidolite [12001-28-4]	0.1 f/cc (F)		
4g.	5g.	*Asbestos - Tremolite [77536-68-6]	0.1 f/cc (F)		
5.	10.	Benzaldehyde [100-52-7]		4 ppm, or 17 mg/m^3	

Table 1 — Exposure Limits **S. 9**

List-ing	French Listing Equiva-lent	Agent [CAS No.]	Time-Weigh-ted Aver-age Limit (TWA)	Short-Term Ex-posure Limit (STEL) or Ceiling Limit (C)	No-ta-tions
6.	11.	*Benzene [71-43-2]	0.5 ppm	2.5 ppm	Skin
7.		[Repealed O. Reg. 287/17, s. 3(1).]			
8.	19.	Calcium chloride [10043-52-4]	5 mg/m^3		
9.	15.	Carbon tetra-chloride [56-23-5]	2 ppm	3 ppm	Skin
10.	16.	Charcoal, except activated [16291-96-6]	10 mg/m^3		
11.	66.	Chlorinated di-phenyl oxides [55720-99-5]	0.5 mg/m^3	2 mg/m^3	
12.	17.	o-Chlorobenzal-dehyde [89-98-5]		4 ppm, or 23 mg/m^3	

833

List-ing	French Listing Equiva-lent	Agent [CAS No.]	Time-Weigh-ted Aver-age Limit (TWA)	Short-Term Ex-posure Limit (STEL) or Ceiling Limit (C)	No-ta-tions
13a.	14a.	Chlorodiphenyl (42 per cent chlorine) [53469-21-9]	See list-ing for Poly-chlori-nated Biphe-nyls (PCBs)		
13b.	14b.	Chlorodiphenyl (54 per cent chlorine) [11097-69-1]	See list-ing for Poly-chlori-nated Biphe-nyls (PCBs)		
14.	22.	N-Cocomorpho-line [1541-81-7]	5 ppm, or 52 mg/m³		Skin
15.	46.	*Coke Oven Emissions[1]	0.15 mg/m³		

Table 1 — Exposure Limits   **S. 9**

List-ing	French Listing Equiva-lent	Agent [CAS No.]	Time-Weigh-ted Aver-age Limit (TWA)	Short-Term Ex-posure Limit (STEL) or Ceiling Limit (C)	No-ta-tions
16.	87.	Coumarone-In-dene Resins (to-tal dust) [63393-89-5]	5 mg/m^3		
17.	24.	Cymene (sum of o-, m- and p-iso-mers) [25155-15-1]	50 ppm, or 274 mg/m^3		Skin
18.	28.	1,1-Dichlor-oethene [75-35-4]	1 ppm, or 4 mg/m^3	20 ppm, or 80 mg/m^3	
19.	29.	1,3-Dichloro-2-Propanol [96-23-1]		1 ppm, or 5 mg/m^3	Skin
20.	40.	Diethylene gly-col monoethyl ether [111-90-0]	30 ppm, or 165 mg/m^3		
21.	74.	Di(2-ethylhex-yl)phthalate (DEHP) [117-81-7]	3 mg/m^3	5 mg/m^3	

833

343

List-ing	French Listing Equiva-lent	Agent [CAS No.]	Time-Weigh-ted Aver-age Limit (TWA)	Short-Term Ex-posure Limit (STEL) or Ceiling Limit (C)	No-ta-tions
22.	73.	Diisodecyl phthalate [26761-40-0]	5 mg/m³		
23.	30.	3-(Dimethylami-no) propylamine [109-55-7]	0.5 ppm, or 2 mg/m³		Skin
24.	31.	N, N-Dimethyl-cyclohexylamine [98-94-2]		5 ppm, or 26 mg/m³	
25.	32.	N, N-Dimethyl-ethanolamine [108-01-0]	3 ppm, or 11 mg/m³	6 ppm, or 22 mg/m³	
26.	103.	Dimethyl ter-ephthalate [120-61-6]	5 mg/m³		
27.	18.	Dimethyl 2,3,5,6-tetracho-loroterephtha-late [1861-32-1]	5 mg/m³		
28.	59.	Dipropylene gly-col monomethyl ether acetate [88917-22-0]	100 ppm, or 776 mg/m³	150 ppm, or 1,164 mg/m³	

Table 1 — Exposure Limits   S. 9

List-ing	French Listing Equiva-lent	Agent [CAS No.]	Time-Weigh-ted Aver-age Limit (TWA)	Short-Term Ex-posure Limit (STEL) or Ceiling Limit (C)	No-ta-tions
29.	34.	Diquat [2764-72-9; 85-00-7; 6385-62-2]	0.5 mg/m^3, or 0.1 mg/m^3(R)		Skin
30.	35.	Enflurane [13838-16-9]	2 ppm, or 16 mg/m^3		
31.	42.	Ethyl-3-ethoxy propionate [763-69-9]	50 ppm, or 300 mg/m^3		
32.	26.	Ethylene dibro-mide [106-93-4]	(L)		Skin
33.	39.	Ethylene glycol dimethyl ether [110-71-4]	5 ppm, or 18 mg/m^3		Skin
34.	41.	Ethylene glycol mono-n-propyl ether [2807-30-9]	25 ppm, or 110 mg/m^3		Skin
35.	63.	Ethylene glycol mononitrate [16051-48-2]	0.05 ppm, or 0.22 mg/m^3		Skin

List-ing	French Listing Equiva-lent	Agent [CAS No.]	Time-Weigh-ted Aver-age Limit (TWA)	Short-Term Ex-posure Limit (STEL) or Ceiling Limit (C)	No-ta-tions
36.	67.	*Ethylene oxide [75-21-8]	1 ppm, or 1.8 mg/m^3	10 ppm, or 18 mg/m^3	
37.	57.	Ethyl methacry-late [97-63-2]	50 ppm	100 ppm	
38.	79.	Flour dust	See list-ing for Wheat Flour Dust (total dust)		
39.	44.	Forane [26675-46-7]	2 ppm, or 15 mg/m^3		
40.	45.	Formaldehyde [50-00-0]		STEL 1 ppm, or C 1.5 ppm	
41.	47.	Halothane [151-67-7]	2 ppm, or 16 mg/m^3		

Table 1 — Exposure Limits   S. 9

Listing	French Listing Equivalent	Agent [CAS No.]	Time-Weighted Average Limit (TWA)	Short-Term Exposure Limit (STEL) or Ceiling Limit (C)	Notations
42.	1.	Heptyl acetate [112-06-1]	50 ppm, or 320 mg/m^3		
43.	48.	Hexamethylene-tetramine (HMT) [100-97-0]		0.35 ppm, or 2 mg/m^3	
44.	49.	Hexamethyl phosphoramide [680-31-9]	(L)		Skin
45.	2.	Hexyl acetate (isomeric mixture) [88230-35-7]	50 ppm, or 294 mg/m^3		
46.	97.	Hydrogen sulfide [7783-06-4]	10 ppm	15 ppm	
47.	104.	Hydrogenated terphenyls[2] [61788-32-7]	0.5 ppm		

833

347

List-ing	French Listing Equiva-lent	Agent [CAS No.]	Time-Weigh-ted Aver-age Limit (TWA)	Short-Term Ex-posure Limit (STEL) or Ceiling Limit (C)	No-ta-tions
48a.	52a.	*Isocyanates, organic compounds - Toluene diiso-cyanate (TDI) [584-84-9] [91-08-7] ppm	0.005 ppm	C 0.02 ppm	
48b.	52b.	*Isocyanates, organic compounds - Methylene bi-sphenyl isocya-nate (MDI) [101-68-8]	0.005 ppm	C 0.02 ppm	
48c.	52c.	*Isocyanates, organic compounds - Hexamethylene diisocyanate (HDI) [822-06-0]	0.005 ppm	C 0.02 ppm	

Table 1 — Exposure Limits   S. 9

List-ing	French Listing Equiva-lent	Agent [CAS No.]	Time-Weigh-ted Aver-age Limit (TWA)	Short-Term Ex-posure Limit (STEL) or Ceiling Limit (C)	No-ta-tions
48d.	52d.	*Isocyanates, organic compounds - Isophorone dii-socyanate (IPDI) [4098-71-9]	0.005 ppm	C 0.02 ppm	
48e.	52e.	*Isocyanates, organic compounds - Methylene bis (4-cyclohexyliso-cyanate) [5124-30-1]	0.005 ppm	C 0.02 ppm	
48f.	52f.	*Isocyanates, organic compounds - Methyl Isocya-nate [624-83-9]	0.02 ppm	0.06 ppm	Skin
48g.	52g.	*Isocyanates, organic compounds - Ethyl isocya-nate [109-90-0]	0.02 ppm	0.06 ppm	Skin

833

349

List-ing	French Listing Equivalent	Agent [CAS No.]	Time-Weighted Average Limit (TWA)	Short-Term Exposure Limit (STEL) or Ceiling Limit (C)	No-ta-tions
48h.	52h.	*Isocyanates, organic compounds - Phenyl isocyanate [103-71-9]	0.005 ppm	0.015 ppm	Skin
49.	53.	Isopropylami-noethanols [109-56-8] [121-93-7]		400 ppm, or 1,900 mg/m^3	
50.	33.	Isosorbide dinitrate [87-33-2]	0.2 mg/m^3		Skin
51a.	77a.	*Lead [7439-92-1], elemental lead, inorganic and organic compounds of lead, as Pb - except tetraethyl lead [78-00-2]	0.05 mg/m^3		Skin (organic compounds)
51b.	77b.	*Lead [7439-92-1] - Tetraethyl lead, as Pb [78-00-2]	0.10 mg/m^3	0.30 mg/m^3	

Table 1 — Exposure Limits   S. 9

List-ing	French Listing Equiva-lent	Agent [CAS No.]	Time-Weigh-ted Aver-age Limit (TWA)	Short-Term Ex-posure Limit (STEL) or Ceiling Limit (C)	No-ta-tions
52a.	21a.	*Lead chromate [7758-97-6] - as Pb (see listing for lead) [7439-92-1]	0.05 mg/m^3		
52b.	21b.	*Lead chromate [7758-97-6] - as Cr	0.012 mg/m^3		
53.	54.	Lincomycin [154-21-2]	0.1 mg/m^3		
54a.	51a.	Lithium hydroxide - Anhydrous [1310-65-2]		1 mg/m^3	
54b.	51b.	Lithium hydroxide - Monohydrate [1310-66-3]		1 mg/m^3	
55.	55.	Manganese [7439-96-5]	0.2 mg/m^3		

833

List-ing	French Listing Equiva-lent	Agent [CAS No.]	Time-Weigh-ted Aver-age Limit (TWA)	Short-Term Ex-posure Limit (STEL) or Ceiling Limit (C)	No-ta-tions
56a.	56a.	*Mercury [7439-97-6], elemental mercury, inor-ganic and organ-ic compounds of mercury, as Hg - All forms of except alkyl, as Hg	0.2 mg/m^3		
56.b	56b.	*Mercury [7439-97-6] - Alkyl com-pounds of, as Hg	0.01 mg/m^3	0.03	Skin
57.	58.	Methoxyflurane [76-38-0]	2 ppm, or 13 mg/m^3		
58.	60.	Methyl n-amyl ketone [110-43-0]	25 ppm, or 115 mg/m^3		
59.	38.	Methyl tert-bu-tyl ether (MTBE) [1634-04-4]	40 ppm		

Table 1 — Exposure Limits   S. 9

Listing	French Listing Equivalent	Agent [CAS No.]	Time-Weighted Average Limit (TWA)	Short-Term Exposure Limit (STEL) or Ceiling Limit (C)	Notations
59.	38.	Methyl tert-butyl ether (MTBE) [1634-04-4]	40 ppm		
60.	61.	Methyl n-butyl ketone [591-78-6]	1 ppm, or 4 mg/m^3		Skin
61.	27.	4,4'-Methylene bis(2-chloroaniline) (MBOCA; MOCAÛ) [101-14-4]	0.0005 ppm, or 0.005 mg/m^3		Skin
62.	25.	4,4'-Methylene dianiline [101-77-9]	0.04 mg/m^3		Skin
63.	62.	N-Methyl-2-pyrrolidone [872-50-4]	400 mg/m^3		
65.	98.	Nepheline syenite (total dust) [37244-96-5]	10 mg/m^3		
66a.	64a.	Nickel - Elemental/metal [7440-02-0]	1 mg/m^3(I)		

833

Listing	French Listing Equivalent	Agent [CAS No.]	Time-Weighted Average Limit (TWA)	Short-Term Exposure Limit (STEL) or Ceiling Limit (C)	Notations
66b.	64b.	Nickel - Insoluble compounds, as Ni [7440-02-0]	0.2 mg/m^3(I)		
66c.	64c.	Nickel - Soluble compounds, as Ni [7440-02-0]	0.1 mg/m^3(I)		
66d.	64d.	Nickel - Nickel subsulfide, as Ni [12035-72-2]	0.1 mg/m^3(I)		
67.	8.	Nitrogen dioxide [10102-44-0]	3 ppm	5 ppm	
68.	65.	N-Nitrosamines, including n-Nitrosodimethylamine [62-75-9]	(L)		Skin
69.	9.	Nitrous oxide [10024-97-2]	25 ppm, or 45 mg/m^3		

Table 1 — Exposure Limits S. 9

Listing	French Listing Equivalent	Agent [CAS No.]	Time-Weighted Average Limit (TWA)	Short-Term Exposure Limit (STEL) or Ceiling Limit (C)	Notations
70.	68.	Ozone [10028-15-6]	0.1 ppm, or 0.2 mg/m^3	0.3 ppm, or 0.6 mg/m^3	
71.	69.	Paraquat [4685-14-7]	0.1 mg/m^3		
72.	70.	Particles (Insoluble or Poorly Soluble) Not Otherwise Specified (PNOS)	10 mg/m^3(I), or 3 mg/m^3(R)		
73.	71.	Penicillin (total dust) [1406-05-9]	0.1 mg/m^3		
74.	101.	Pentaerythritol tetrabenzoate [4196-86-5]		2 mg/m^3	
75.	23.	Petroleum coke (total dust) [64741-79-3]	3.5 mg/m^3(a)		
76.	72.	2-Phenoxyethanol [122-99-6]	25 ppm, or 141 mg/m^3		Skin

833

List-ing	French Listing Equiva-lent	Agent [CAS No.]	Time-Weigh-ted Aver-age Limit (TWA)	Short-Term Ex-posure Limit (STEL) or Ceiling Limit (C)	No-ta-tions
77a.	76a.	Platinum [7440-06-4] - Metal	1 mg/m^3		
77b.	76b.	Platinum [7440-06-4] - Water-soluble compounds of, including chlor-oplatinates (as Pt)	0.002 mg/m^3		
78.	13.	Polychlorinated biphenyls (PCBs)[2]	0.05 mg/m^3		
79.	84.	Poultry dust (to-tal dust)	5 mg/m^3		
80.	85.	1,2-Propylene glycol [57-55-6]	50 ppm (V), or 155 mg/m^3(V), or 10 mg/m^3(-H)(b)		

Table 1 — Exposure Limits   S. 9

List-ing	French Listing Equiva-lent	Agent [CAS No.]	Time-Weigh-ted Aver-age Limit (TWA)	Short-Term Ex-posure Limit (STEL) or Ceiling Limit (C)	No-ta-tions
81.	3.	Propylene glycol monomethyl ether acetate [108-65-6]	50 ppm, or 270 mg/ m^3		
82.	88.	Selenium hexa-fluoride, as Se [7783-79-1]	0.025 ppm, or 0.1 mg/ m^3		
83.	82.	Shellac dust (to-tal dust) [9000-59-3]	10 mg/ m^3		
84a.	91.	*Silica, Crystalline - Quartz/Tripoli [14808-60-7; 1317-95-9]	0.10 mg/ m^3(R)		
84b.	91b.	*Silica, Crystalline - Cristobalite [14464-46-1]	0.05 mg/ m^3(R)		
85.	90.	Silica fume [69012-64-2]	2 mg/ m^3(R)		
86.	89.	Silica fused [60676-86-0]	0.1 mg/ m^3(R)		

List-ing	French Listing Equiva-lent	Agent [CAS No.]	Time-Weigh-ted Aver-age Limit (TWA)	Short-Term Ex-posure Limit (STEL) or Ceiling Limit (C)	No-ta-tions
87a.	92a.	Silicon carbide [409-21-2] - Non-fibrous	10 mg/ m^3(I)(-E), or 3 mg/ m^3(R)(-E)		
87b.	92b.	Silicon carbide [409-21-2] - Fibrous (in-cluding whis-kers)	0.1 f/cc (R)(F)		
88.	83.	Sisal dust (total dust)	2 mg/ m^3		
89.	81.	Soap dust [68918-36-5]	5 mg/ m^3		
90.	95.	Spectinomycin [1695-77-8]	2 mg/ m^3		
91.	93.	Stoddard Sol-vent - 140F Flash Aliphatic Sol-vent, Type of Stoddard Sol-vent	525 mg/ m^3		

Table 1 — Exposure Limits   S. 9

List-ing	French Listing Equiva-lent	Agent [CAS No.]	Time-Weigh-ted Aver-age Limit (TWA)	Short-Term Ex-posure Limit (STEL) or Ceiling Limit (C)	No-ta-tions
92.	96.	Styrene - mono-mer [100-42-5]	35 ppm	100 ppm	
93.	94.	Sulfur dioxide [7446-09-5]	2 ppm, or 5.2 mg/m^3	5 ppm, or 10.4 mg/m^3	
94a.	93a.	Synthetic Vitr-eous Fibres (Man Made Mineral Fibres) - Continuous fi-lament glass fi-bres	5 mg/m^3(I), or 1 f/cc (F)		
94b.	43b.	Synthetic Vitr-eous Fibres (Man Made Mineral Fibres) - Glass wool fi-bres	1 f/cc (F)		
94c.	43c.	Synthetic Vitr-eous Fibres (Man Made Mineral Fibres) - Refractory ceramic fibres	0.5 f/cc (F)		

833

Listing	French Listing Equivalent	Agent [CAS No.]	Time-Weighted Average Limit (TWA)	Short-Term Exposure Limit (STEL) or Ceiling Limit (C)	Notations
94d.	43d.	Synthetic Vitreous Fibres (Man Made Mineral Fibres) - Rock wool fibres	1 f/cc (F)		
94e.	43e.	Synthetic Vitreous Fibres (Man Made Mineral Fibres) - Slag wool fibres	1 f/cc (F)		
94f.	43f.	Synthetic Vitreous Fibres (Man Made Mineral Fibres) - Special purpose glass fibres	1 f/cc (F)		

Table 1 — Exposure Limits   S. 9

List-ing	French Listing Equiva-lent	Agent [CAS No.]	Time-Weigh-ted Aver-age Limit (TWA)	Short-Term Ex-posure Limit (STEL) or Ceiling Limit (C)	No-ta-tions
94g.	43g.	Synthetic Vitr-eous Fibres (Man Made Mineral Fibres) - Synthetic Vitr-eous Fibres, not otherwise classi-fied (excluding fibrous glass dust and mineral wool fibre)	1 f/cc (F)(c)		
95.	99.	Talc [14807-96-6],containing no asbestos	2 mg/m^3(R)(-E), or 2 f/cc (K)		
96.	100.	Tellurium hexa-fluoride, as Te [7783-80-4]	0.01 ppm, or 0.1 mg/m^3		
97.	6.	Tetrachloropha-thalic anhydride [117-08-8]	0.1 mg/m^3		
98.	102.	Tetrachlorophe-nol [25167-83-3]	0.5 mg/m^3		Skin

List-ing	French Listing Equiva-lent	Agent [CAS No.]	Time-Weigh-ted Aver-age Limit (TWA)	Short-Term Ex-posure Limit (STEL) or Ceiling Limit (C)	No-ta-tions
99.	86.	Tetrasodium pyrophosphate [7722-88-5]	5 mg/m^3		
100-a.	37a.	Tin, as Sn [7440-31-5] - Metal	2 mg/m^3		
100-b.	37b.	Tin, as Sn [7440-31-5] - Oxide and in-organic com-pounds, as Sn, except tin hy-dride	2 mg/m^3		
100-c.	37c.	Tin, as Sn [7440-31-5] - Organic com-pounds, as Sn	0.1 mg/m^3		Skin (or-ga-nic com-pou-nds)
101.	105.	o-Tolidine [119-93-7]	(L)		Skin

Table 1 — Exposure Limits **S. 9**

Listing	French Listing Equivalent	Agent [CAS No.]	Time-Weighted Average Limit (TWA)	Short-Term Exposure Limit (STEL) or Ceiling Limit (C)	Notations
102.	106.	Triethanolamine [102-71-6]	0.5 ppm, or 3.1 mg/m^3		
103.	107.	Triethylenediamine [280-57-9]	1 ppm, or 4.6 mg/m^3		Skin
104.	108.	Triethylenetetramine [112-24-3]	0.5 ppm, or 3 mg/m^3		Skin
105.	109.	Trimethoxyvinylsilane [2768-02-7]		10 ppm, or 60 mg/m^3	
106.	75.	Trixylylphosphate [25155-23-1]	0.1 mg/m^3		
107.	20.	*Vinyl chloride [75-01-04]	1 ppm		
108.	80.	Wheat flour dust (total dust)	3 mg/m^3		

833

List-ing	French Listing Equiva-lent	Agent [CAS No.]	Time-Weigh-ted Aver-age Limit (TWA)	Short-Term Ex-posure Limit (STEL) or Ceiling Limit (C)	No-ta-tions
109-a.	78.	Wood dust - Certain hard-woods as beech and oak	1 mg/m^3		
109-b.	79b.	Wood dust - Softwood	5 mg/m^3	10 mg/m^3	

Endnotes and Abbreviations:

* Denotes a chemical agent listed in Table 1 of Ontario Regulation 490/09 (*Designated Substances*) made under the Act. See clause 2(2)(a) of this Regulation.

[1] Means the benzene soluble fraction of total particulate matter of the substances emitted into the atmosphere from metallurgical coke ovens including condensed vapours and solid particulates.

[2] As sum of components assayed by chromatographic procedure with reference to the bulk sample.

[CAS No.] - CAS Registry Number.

f/cc - Fibres per cubic centimetre of air.

mg/m^3 - Milligrams of the agent per cubic metre of air.

ppm - Parts of the agent per million parts of air by volume.

Skin - Danger of cutaneous absorption. (E) The value is for particulate matter containing no asbestos and < 1 per cent crystalline silica. (F) Respirable fibres: length > 5 μm; aspect ratio ≥ 3:1, as determined by the membrane filter method at 400-450 times magnification (4-mm objective), using phase-contrast illumination. (H) Aerosol only. (I) Inhalable frac-tion: means that size fraction of the airborne particulate deposited any-where in the respiratory tract and collected during air sampling with a particle size-selective device that, (a) meets the ACGIH particle size-selective sampling criteria for airborne particulate matter; and (b) has the cut point of 100 μm at 50 per cent collection efficiency. (K) Should not exceed 2 mg/m^3 respirable particulate mass. (L) Exposure by all routes should be carefully controlled to levels as low as possible. (R) Respirable fraction: means that size fraction of the airborne particulate deposited in the gas-exchange region of the respiratory tract and collected during air sampling with a particle size-selective device that, (a) meets the ACGIH particle size-selective sampling criteria for airborne particulate matter; and (b) has the cut point of 4 μm at 50 per cent collection efficiency. (V) Vapour and aerosol. (a) Provided that the total dust contains less than 0.7 per cent vanadium. (b) For assessing the visibility in a work environment where 1,2-propylene glycol aerosol is present. (c) A secondary limit of 5 mg/m^3 (total dust) is recommended to deal with dusty operations where fibre counts are usually difficult to determine. Where both types of measurements are made simultaneously, the more restrictive limit should be used to assess the exposures.

O. Reg. 491/09 s. 7; 419/10 s. 1; 149/12 s. 2; 274/14 s. 2; 287/17, s. 3

SCHEDULE 1

Airborne Measurement and Calculation of Exposure

[Heading added O. Reg. 491/09, s. 9.]

1. Airborne concentrations of a biological or chemical agent are expressed as,

(a) parts of the agent per million parts of air by volume (ppm);

(b) milligrams of the agent per cubic metre of air (mg/m^3); or

(c) fibres per cubic centimetre of air (f/cc).

O. Reg. 491/09 s. 9

2. Air sampling of the airborne concentrations of the biological or chemical agent is not required for the full period of a work day or a work week if the air sampling is representative of airborne concentrations of the agent likely to be present during the full period.

O. Reg. 491/09 s. 9

3. The method of air sampling, the number and volume of the samples and the method of analysis of the samples shall be determined,

(a) according to the nature of the operations or processes and the characteristics of the biological or chemical agent; and

(b) in accordance with recognized industrial hygiene practice.

O. Reg. 491/09 s. 9

4. In determining exposure to airborne concentrations of the biological or chemical agent, no regard shall be had to the wearing or use of personal protective equipment.

O. Reg. 491/09 s. 9

5. The time-weighted average exposure to an airborne biological or chemical agent in a work day or work week shall be calculated as follows:

1. The cumulative daily or weekly exposure shall be calculated using the following formula:

$$C_1T_1 + C_2T_2 + \ldots + C_nT_n$$

where,

C_1 is the concentration found in an air sample, and

T_1 is the total time in hours to which the worker is taken to be exposed to concentration C_1 in a work day or a work week.

2. The time-weighted average exposure shall be calculated by dividing the cumulative daily exposure by eight and the cumulative weekly exposure by 40 respectively.

O. Reg. 491/09 s. 9

6. Short-term exposures to the biological or chemical agent in any 15-minute period are determined from a single sample or from a time-weighted average of sequential samples taken during that period.

O. Reg. 491/09 s. 9

7. For mixtures of airborne chemical agents that exert an additive health effect, if analytical results of individual airborne agents are available, the following formula shall be used, subject to section 8 of this Schedule:

$$\frac{C_1}{L_1} + \frac{C_2}{L_2} + \ldots + \frac{C_n}{L_n} = E$$

where,

$C_1, C_2, \ldots, C_n$ are the concentrations of the individual agents found in the air sample,

$L_1, L_2, \ldots, L_n$ are the respective exposure limits for the agents determined in accordance with the rules set out in section 4 of the Regulation,

and the sum of these ratios, E, shall not exceed 1.

O. Reg. 491/09 s. 9

8. If the agents in a mixture of airborne chemical agents have substantially different health effects,

    i. section 7 of this Schedule does not apply, and

    ii. exposure to each agent shall be calculated independently.

O. Reg. 491/09 s. 9

833

Ont. Reg. 243/95 — Criteria to be Used and Other Matters to be Considered by the Board under Subsection 46(6) of Act

made under the *Occupational Health and Safety Act*

O. Reg. 243/95, as am. O. Reg. 22/09, ss. 1-3, 4 (Fr.).

[*Note: The title of this Regulation was changed from Criteria to be Used and Other Matters to be Considered by Adjudicators under Subsection 46(6) of Act to Criteria to be Used and Other Matters to be Considered by the Board under Subsection 46(6) of Act by O. Reg. 22/09, s. 1.*]

1. For the purpose of subsection 46(6) of the Act, the following criteria are prescribed for determining whether the constructor or employer has demonstrated a failure to protect the health and safety of workers;

1. The record of accidents, deaths, injuries and work-related illnesses in the workplace.

2. The constructor's or employer's occupational health and safety policies and the length of time they have been in place.

3. The training, communications and programs established to implement the policies under paragraph 2, and the length of time they have been in place.

4. The constructor's or employer's health and safety record under the Act, including,

    i. complaints made to the Ministry of Labour against the constructor or employer,

    ii. work refusals under section 43 of the Act,

    iii. the Board's or adjudicators' decisions under section 46 of the Act,

    iv. work stoppages under sections 45 and 47 of the Act,

    v. the results of inspections conducted by the Ministry,

    vi. convictions for contraventions of the Act or the regulations made under it,

    vii. the record of compliance with inspectors' orders.

5. Any other factors that it is reasonable to consider in the circumstances.

O. Reg. 22/09 s. 2

2. The following matters are prescribed as matters to be considered by the Board in deciding upon an application under section 46:

1. Any previous occasion on which the Board or an adjudicator found under that section that the procedure for stopping work set out in section 45 of the Act would not be sufficient to protect the constructor's or employer's workers.
2. The constructor's or employer's course of conduct with respect to the establishment and operation of the committee and the appointment and certification of its members.
3. A pattern, if any, of the constructor or employer dealing in bad faith with the committee.
4. The nature and extent of the health and safety hazards at the workplace, including the risks they pose and whether adequate measures have been established to respond to them.
5. If the measure established to respond to the health and safety hazards are not adequate, the length of time that would be required to establish adequate measures and the degree of intervention by an inspector that would be necessary.
6. Any other matters that it is reasonable to consider in the circumstances.

O. Reg. 22/09 s. 3

3. This Regulation comes into force on May 20, 1995.

ONT. REG. 834 — CRITICAL INJURY — DEFINED

made under the *Occupational Health and Safety Act*

R.R.O. 1990, Reg. 834, as am. O. Reg. 351/91 (Fr.).

1. For the purposes of the Act and the Regulations, "**critically injured**" means an injury of a serious nature that,

(a) places life in jeopardy;

(b) produces unconsciousness;

(c) results in substantial loss of blood;

(d) involves the fracture of a leg or arm but not a finger or toe;

(e) involves the amputation of a leg, arm, hand or foot but not a finger or toe;

(f) consists of burns to a major portion of the body; or

(g) causes the loss of sight in an eye.

O. Reg. 714/82 s. 1.

834

ONT. REG. 490/09 — DESIGNATED SUBSTANCES

made under the *Occupational Health and Safety Act*

O. Reg. 490/09, as am. O. Reg. 259/10, ss. 1, 2 (Fr.); 148/12; 288/17.

General

1. Definitions — In this Regulation,

"arsenic" means,

(a) arsenic in its elemental form,

(b) arsenic in inorganic compounds, except arsine, and

(c) arsenic in organic form only where both inorganic and organic compounds of arsenic are present;

"asbestos" means any of the following fibrous silicates:

1. Actinolite.
2. Amosite.
3. Anthophyllite.
4. Chrysotile.
5. Crocidolite.
6. Tremolite;

"C" or **"ceiling limit"** means the maximum airborne concentration of a biological or chemical agent to which a worker may be exposed at any time;

"code for measuring an airborne substance" means, with respect to acrylonitrile, arsenic, coke oven emissions, ethylene oxide or isocyanates, the Code listed in Part I of Schedule 2 that pertains to that substance;

"code for medical surveillance" means, with respect to a designated substance other than arsenic or ethylene oxide, the Code listed in Part II of Schedule 2 that pertains to that substance;

"code for respiratory equipment" means, with respect to a designated substance, the Code listed in Part III of Schedule 2 that pertains to that substance;

"coke oven emissions" means the benzene soluble fraction of total particulate matter of the substances emitted into the atmosphere from metallurgical coke ovens including condensed vapours and solid particulates;

"exposure" means exposure by inhalation, ingestion, skin absorption or skin contact;

"isocyanates" means organic isocyanates;

"joint health and safety committee" includes, in addition to a joint health and safety committee established under the Act,

(a) a committee of like nature described in subsection 9(4) of the Act,

(b) an arrangement, program or system described in subsection 9(4) of the Act in which workers or their representatives participate;

"lead" means elemental lead, inorganic compounds of lead and organic compounds of lead;

"mercury" means elemental mercury, inorganic compounds of mercury and organic compounds of mercury;

"metallurgical coke ovens" means a coke oven battery, including topside and its machinery, coke side and its machinery, pusher side and its machinery, the battery ends, the wharf and the screening station;

"Provincial Physician" means the person employed in the Ministry as the Provincial Physician;

"silica" means crystalline silica in a respirable form;

"STEL" or **"short-term exposure limit"** means the maximum airborne concentration of a biological or chemical agent to which a worker may be exposed in any 15-minute period;

"TWA" or **"time-weighted average limit"** means the time-weighted average airborne concentration of a biological or chemical agent to which a worker may be exposed in a work day or work week.

2. Designated substances — The following chemical agents are prescribed as designated substances:

1. Acrylonitrile.
2. Arsenic.

3. Asbestos.
4. Benzene.
5. Coke oven emissions.
6. Ethylene oxide.
7. Isocyanates.
8. Lead.
9. Mercury.
10. Silica.
11. Vinyl chloride.

Application

3. Acrylonitrile —

(1) Subject to subsection (2), this Regulation applies, with respect to acrylonitrile, to every employer and worker at a workplace where acrylonitrile is present, produced, processed, used, handled or stored and at which a worker is likely to be exposed to acrylonitrile.

(2) With respect to acrylonitrile, this Regulation does not apply to an employer or the workers of an employer at a workplace where acrylonitrile is not produced, processed or used, if a worker's exposure to acrylonitrile results only from the presence, use, handling or storage of goods made in the last stage of a process using polymers made from acrylonitrile.

4. Arsenic —

(1) Subject to subsection (2), this Regulation applies, with respect to arsenic, to every employer and worker at a workplace at which arsenic is produced, processed, used, handled or stored or is a waste product or by-product of a process and at which a worker is likely to be exposed to arsenic.

(2) With respect to arsenic, this Regulation does not apply to mining operations, including concentrating, milling, washing, crushing, grinding, sifting or conveying of a metallic or non-metallic mineral or mineral-bearing substance or rock, unless the operations are carried on,

(a) in a plant where smelting, roasting or refining is carried on; or
(b) in or at a place that is contiguous with a plant where smelting, roasting or refining is carried on.

5. Asbestos —

(1) This Regulation applies, with respect to asbestos, to,

490/09

(a) every employer operating a mine or mining plant for the purpose of mining, crushing, grinding or sifting asbestos and to those workers of such an employer who are likely to be exposed to asbestos;

(b) every employer processing, adapting or using asbestos in connection with the manufacturing or assembling of goods or products and to those workers of such an employer who are likely to be exposed to asbestos;

(c) every employer engaged in the activities set out in subsection (2), and to those workers of such an employer who are engaged in those activities and are likely to be exposed to asbestos, if,

　　(i) on or before December 16, 1985, the employer,

　　　　(A) put into effect and maintained measures and procedures to control the exposure of workers to asbestos, and

　　　　(B) incorporated the measures and procedures into an asbestos control program in accordance with the regulations, and

　　(ii) the employer has maintained the control program referred to in sub-subclause (i)(B) in accordance with the regulations

(2) The activities mentioned in clause (1)(c) are:

　　1. The repair, alteration or maintenance of machinery, equipment, aircraft, ships, locomotives, railway cars and vehicles.

　　2. Work on a building that is necessarily incidental to the repair, alteration or maintenance of machinery or equipment.

6. Benzene —

(1) Subject to subsection (2), this Regulation applies, with respect to benzene, to every employer and worker at a workplace where a worker is likely to be exposed to benzene or a product containing benzene,

　　(a) during its transportation or transfer; or

　　(b) during its manufacture, processing, use, handling or storage.

(2) With respect to benzene, this Regulation does not apply to the delivery of gasoline by a gasoline pump into the fuel tank of a motor vehicle, motor boat or other water craft or into a portable container at a service station or other premises.

7. Coke oven emissions — This Regulation applies, with respect to coke oven emissions, to every employer and worker who works at a metallurgical coke oven and is likely to be exposed to coke oven emissions.

8. Ethylene oxide — This Regulation applies, with respect to ethylene oxide, to every employer and worker at a workplace where ethylene oxide is present.

9. Isocyanates — This Regulation applies, with respect to isocyanates, to every employer and worker at a workplace where isocyanates are produced, used, handled or stored and at which a worker is likely to be exposed to isocyanates.

10. Lead — This Regulation applies, with respect to lead, to every employer and worker at a workplace where lead is present, produced, processed, used, handled or stored and at which a worker is likely to be exposed to lead.

11. Mercury —

(1) Subject to subsection (2), this Regulation applies, with respect to mercury, to every employer and worker at a workplace where mercury is present, produced, processed, used, handled or stored and at which a worker is likely to be exposed to mercury.

(2) With respect to mercury, this Regulation does not apply to,

    (a) an employer,

        (i) who is engaged in the practice of dentistry, within the meaning of the *Dentistry Act, 1991*, or

        (ii) who has one or more workers who engage in the practice of dentistry, within the meaning of the *Dentistry Act, 1991*;

    (b) a worker who works in the office of an employer described in clause (a).

12. Silica — This Regulation applies, with respect to silica, to every employer and worker at a workplace where silica is present, produced, processed, used, handled or stored and at which a worker is likely to be exposed to silica.

13. Vinyl chloride — This Regulation applies, with respect to vinyl chloride, to every employer and worker at a workplace where vinyl chloride is present, produced, processed, used, handled or stored and at which a worker is likely to be exposed to vinyl chloride.

490/09

14. Exception—construction — Despite sections 3 to 13, this Regulation does not apply, at a project,

    (a) to an employer who engages in construction; or

    (b) to the workers of an employer described in clause (a) who are engaged in construction.

Employer Duties

15. Duty to third party workers —

(1) Subject to clause 14(b), an employer to whom this Regulation applies with respect to a designated substance shall take every precaution reasonable in the circumstances to ensure the protection of a worker who,

    (a) is not a worker of the employer; and

    (b) is working in the workplace of the employer, is exposed to the designated substance and his or her health is likely to be affected by that exposure.

(2) A worker shall comply with the requirements an employer imposes for the protection of the worker in accordance with subsection (1).

16. Duty to limit airborne exposure —

(1) Every employer shall take all necessary measures and procedures by means of engineering controls, work practices and hygiene facilities and practices to ensure that a worker's airborne exposure to each of the following designated substances and forms of designated substances does not exceed the TWA, STEL or C set out for the substance or form of substance in Table 1:

    1. Benzene.

    2. Coke oven emissions.

    3. The forms of lead listed in Table 1.

    4. The forms of mercury listed in Table 1.

(2) Every employer shall take all necessary measures and procedures by means of engineering controls, work practices and hygiene facilities and practices to ensure that a worker's airborne exposure to each of the following designated substances and forms of designated substances is reduced to the lowest practical level and, in any event, does not exceed the TWA, STEL or C set out for the substance or form of substance in Table 1:

    1. Acrylonitrile.

    2. Arsenic.

3. The forms of asbestos listed in Table 1.

4. Ethylene oxide.

5. The forms of isocyanates listed in Table 1.

6. The forms of silica listed in Table 1.

7. Vinyl chloride.

(3) Subject to section 18, an employer shall comply with this section without requiring a worker to wear and use respiratory equipment.

(4) An employer shall calculate the airborne exposure of a worker to a designated substance in accordance with Part I of Schedule 1 to this Regulation.

17. Duty re other isocyanates —

(1) With respect to isocyanates other than those listed in Table 1, an employer shall,

(a) adopt and implement all such engineering controls, work practices and hygiene practices as are reasonable and practical; and

(b) provide a worker who handles, dispenses, mixes, applies, uses, transfers, disposes of, or deals with isocyanates and is likely to inhale isocyanates or come into contact with isocyanates, with appropriate personal protective equipment.

(2) A worker shall wear and use the personal protective equipment provided by his or her employer when working with isocyanates other than those listed in Table 1.

18. When respiratory equipment permitted —

(1) An employer shall provide a worker with respiratory equipment if the employer cannot comply with the strict duty imposed by subsection 16(1) or (2) because,

(a) an emergency exists; or

(b) the measures and procedures necessary to control the exposure of a worker to the airborne designated substance,

(i) do not exist or are not available,

(ii) are not reasonable or practical for the length of time or frequency of exposure or the nature of the process, operation or work, or

(iii) are not effective because of a temporary breakdown of equipment.

490/09

(2) A worker who is exposed to any level of an airborne designated substance may request respiratory equipment from his or her employer, and the employer shall provide respiratory equipment in response to the request.

(3) An employer who provides a worker with respiratory equipment shall ensure that the equipment,

(a) is appropriate in the circumstances for the form and concentration of airborne designated substance in respect of which the equipment is to be used;

(b) meets or exceeds the requirements set out in the applicable code for respiratory equipment; and

(c) is used in accordance with the requirements of the applicable code for respiratory equipment.

(4) An employer who provides a worker with respiratory equipment shall provide training and instruction to the worker in the care and use of the equipment.

Assessment and Control Program

19. Assessment —

(1) An employer shall carry out an assessment of the exposure or likelihood of exposure of a worker to a designated substance in the workplace and record it in writing.

(2) In carrying out the assessment, the employer shall consider and take into account,

(a) in the case of acrylonitrile, benzene, ethylene oxide, isocyanates or vinyl chloride, the methods and procedures used or to be used in the production, processing, use, handling and storage of the acrylonitrile, benzene, ethylene oxide, isocyanates or vinyl chloride;

(b) in the case of arsenic, lead, mercury or silica, the methods and procedures used or to be used in the processing, use, handling and storage of the arsenic, lead, mercury or silica;

(c) in the case of asbestos, the methods and procedures used or to be used in the processing, mining, use, handling and storage of the asbestos;

(d) in the case of coke oven emissions, the methods and procedures used or to be used in the metallurgical coking operation;

(e) the extent and potential extent of a worker's exposure to the designated substance; and

(f) the measures and procedures that are necessary to control exposure to the designated substance by means of engineering controls, work practices and hygiene facilities and practices.

(3) The employer shall carry out the assessment in consultation with the joint health and safety committee and the committee may make recommendations respecting the assessment.

(4) The employer shall provide a copy of the assessment to every member of the joint health and safety committee.

20. Control program —

(1) Subject to section 21, if an assessment discloses or would disclose, if carried out in accordance with section 19, that a worker is likely to be exposed to a designated substance and that the health of a worker may be affected by that exposure, the employer shall,

(a) develop, establish, put into effect and maintain measures and procedures to control the worker's exposure to the designated substance; and

(b) incorporate the measures and procedures described in clause (a) into a control program that satisfies the requirements of this section.

(2) All control programs must provide for the following:

1. Engineering controls, work practices and hygiene facilities and practices to control the exposure of a worker to the designated substance.

2. Methods and procedures to monitor,

    i. airborne concentrations of the designated substance in the workplace, and

    ii. worker exposure to airborne concentrations of the designated substance.

3. The personal records described in subsection (6).

4. A training program for supervisors and workers on the health effects of the designated substance and the measures and procedures required under the control program.

(3) In the case of a control program respecting coke oven emissions, the control program must provide for engineering controls, work practices

490/09

and hygiene facilities and practices set out in Part II of Schedule 1, in addition to those provided for under paragraph 1 of subsection (2).

(4) In the case of a control program respecting a designated substance other than arsenic or ethylene oxide, the control program for the substance must provide for pre-employment, pre-placement and periodic medical examinations of workers that include,

(a) a medical history that satisfies the requirements of the applicable code for medical surveillance;

(b) a physical examination that satisfies the requirements of the applicable code for medical surveillance; and

(c) clinical tests that are required by the examining physician and satisfy the requirements of the applicable code for medical surveillance.

(5) The employer shall pay the expenses for the medical examinations and clinical tests described in subsection (4).

(6) The records mentioned in paragraph 3 of subsection (2) are:

1. Personal records, maintained by the employer, of the exposure of a worker to a designated substance at the workplace, which must include,

   i. an identification of the worker, including the worker's date of birth,

   ii. the worker's jobs or occupations at the workplace,

   iii. results of monitoring the worker's exposure to airborne concentrations of the designated substance,

   iv. the time-weighted average exposure of the worker to the designated substance, and

   v. the use of respiratory equipment by the worker and its type.

2. Personal records, maintained by the employer, of the length of time a worker is taken to be exposed to isocyanates other than those listed in Table 1, which must include the information listed in subparagraphs 1 i, ii and v.

3. Personal records, maintained by physicians who have examined a worker under the control program, or under whose supervision clinical tests have been performed on a worker, of those medical examinations and clinical tests.

(7) An employer shall develop the measures and procedures described in clause (1)(a) and the control program respecting a designated substance in consultation with the joint health and safety committee at the workplace, and the committee may make recommendations respecting them.

(8) An employer shall,

(a) provide a copy of the control program to every member of the joint health and safety committee;

(b) acquaint every worker affected by the control program with its provisions; and

(c) make a copy of the control program available to workers both in English and the majority language of the workplace.

21. Ethylene oxide, emergency program —

(1) An employer is not required to develop a control program under section 20 with respect to ethylene oxide for a workplace if,

(a) ethylene oxide is handled or stored only in closed cylinders and is not otherwise present in the workplace; and

(b) the assessment discloses or would disclose, if carried out in accordance with section 19,

(i) that a worker is likely to be exposed to ethylene oxide only in the case of an accident or leak, and

(ii) that the health of the worker may be affected.

(2) If subsection (1) applies, the employer shall,

(a) develop, establish, put into effect and maintain measures and procedures to protect workers in the event of an accident or leak of ethylene oxide; and

(b) incorporate the measures and procedures described in clause (a) into an emergency program that satisfies the requirements of subsection (3).

(3) An emergency program respecting ethylene oxide shall include provisions for,

(a) identifying, by means of easily visible warning signs, each area where an ethylene oxide cylinder is present;

(b) an effective evacuation system;

(c) the location and supply of respiratory equipment to be used during an emergency;

490/09

(d) the testing and evaluation, where practical, of the atmosphere to determine the presence or absence of ethylene oxide during and following an emergency; and

(e) a training program to familiarize supervisors and workers with the health effects of ethylene oxide and the measures and procedures to be taken in case of an emergency.

(4) The employer shall develop the measures and procedures described in clause (2)(a) and the emergency program respecting ethylene oxide in consultation with the joint health and safety committee at the workplace, and the committee may make recommendations respecting the measures and procedures or program.

(5) The employer shall,

(a) provide a copy of the emergency program to every member of the joint health and safety committee;

(b) acquaint every worker affected by the emergency program with its provisions; and

(c) make a copy of the emergency program available to workers both in English and the majority language of the workplace.

22. Change requiring further assessment —

(1) For the purposes of this section, a "change" means,

(a) a change in a process involving a designated substance or in the methods and procedures in which the substance is produced, mined, processed, used, handled or stored, as the case may be; and

(b) in the case of coke oven emissions, a change in metallurgical coking operations.

(2) If there is a change in a workplace that could result in a significant difference in the exposure of a worker to a designated substance, the employer shall promptly carry out a further assessment of the exposure or likelihood of exposure of a worker to the designated substance.

(3) Subsections 19(2), (3) and (4) apply to a further assessment under this section.

(4) Sections 20 and 21 apply with respect to the results of a further assessment under this section.

23. Disputes —

(1) An employer, a joint health and safety committee or a member of a joint health and safety committee may notify an inspector when a dispute arises between an employer and the joint health and safety committee as to,

(a) an assessment or further assessment required under section 19 or 22;

(b) measures and procedures mentioned in clause 20(1)(a) or 21(2)(a);

(c) a control program respecting a designated substance, or any of its provisions required under section 20 or 22; or

(d) an emergency program for ethylene oxide, or any of its provisions required under section 21 or 22.

(2) An inspector who receives a notice under subsection (1) shall investigate the dispute and shall give a decision in writing to,

(a) the employer; and

(b) the joint health and safety committee.

(3) Nothing in subsection (2) applies so as to affect the power of an inspector to issue an order for a contravention of this Regulation.

24. Measuring airborne concentrations — An employer shall ensure that procedures for monitoring, sampling and determining airborne concentrations of a designated substance and worker exposure to airborne concentrations of a designated substance,

(a) in the case of acrylonitrile, arsenic, coke oven emissions, ethylene oxide or isocyanates, satisfy the requirements of the applicable code for measuring an airborne substance, subject to section 32; or

(b) in the case of asbestos, benzene, lead, mercury, silica or vinyl chloride, are in accordance with standard methods for workplace air sampling and analysis.

25. Posting of monitoring results — Whenever results become available under a control program that relate to the monitoring of airborne concentrations of a designated substance and worker exposure to airborne concentrations of a designated substance, the employer shall,

(a) promptly post the results in a conspicuous place or places where they are most likely to come to the attention of workers who would be affected by them and leave them posted for no less than 14 days;

(b) provide a copy of the results to the joint health and safety committee; and

(c) keep the results for no less than five years.

490/09

26. Worker's duty re control program — Every worker shall work in compliance with the work practices and hygiene practices in accordance with every control program respecting a designated substance that applies to the workplace.

Medical Examinations and Clinical Tests

27. Physician to receive records —

(1) The employer shall provide a copy of a worker's personal exposure record to a physician who examines the worker or supervises clinical tests on a worker,

    (a) in accordance with a control program to which subsection 20(4) applies respecting a designated substance to which the worker may be or has been exposed; or

    (b) under section 28, where the worker has been exposed to arsenic or ethylene oxide.

(2) If subsection (1) requires an employer to provide a physician with a copy of a worker's personal exposure record, the worker may request the physician to provide the worker or the worker's physician with a copy of,

    (a) the worker's personal exposure record;

    (b) the results of the examination or clinical test.

(3) In the case of a deceased worker, subsection (2) applies, with necessary modifications, to the next of kin or personal representative of the worker.

(4) A physician who receives a request under subsection (2) or (3) shall comply with the request.

28. Medical examination after exposure to arsenic or ethylene oxide —

(1) A worker who has been exposed to arsenic or ethylene oxide shall, if he or she agrees, undergo a medical examination and any clinical tests, if,

    (a) the worker or the worker's physician has reason to believe that the worker's health may be affected by the exposure and the worker or physician has so notified the employer in writing; or

    (b) the employer has reason to believe that the worker's health may be affected by the exposure and the employer has so notified the worker in writing.

(2) The employer shall pay the expenses of the medical examination and clinical tests.

(3) The purpose of the medical examination and clinical tests is to determine whether the worker has an occupational illness because of the exposure to arsenic or ethylene oxide and whether the worker is fit, fit with limitations or unfit to continue working in exposure to arsenic or ethylene oxide.

29. Results of examinations and tests —

(1) This section applies when a physician conducts a medical examination of a worker or supervises clinical tests of a worker,

   (a) in accordance with a control program to which subsection 20(4) applies respecting a designated substance to which the worker may be or has been exposed; or

   (b) under section 28, where the worker has been exposed to arsenic or ethylene oxide.

(2) The physician who conducts the medical examination or supervises the clinical tests shall advise the worker and the worker's employer whether the worker has an occupational illness because of exposure to a designated substance and whether the worker is fit, fit with limitations or unfit to continue working in exposure to the designated substance.

(3) In advising the worker and the worker's employer that the worker is fit with limitations or unfit to continue working in exposure to a designated substance, the physician shall,

   (a) be governed by the applicable code for medical surveillance, if any; and

   (b) provide the advice without giving or disclosing to the employer the records or results of the examination or tests.

(4) The worker's employer shall act in accordance with the advice provided by a physician under subsection (2).

(5) If a worker is removed from working in exposure to a designated substance because a medical examination or clinical test discloses that the worker has or may have a condition resulting from exposure to the substance and the worker suffers a loss of earnings occasioned thereby, the worker is entitled to compensation for the loss in the manner and to the extent provided by the *Workplace Safety and Insurance Act, 1997*.

(6) On advising the worker and the worker's employer that the worker is fit with limitations or unfit to continue working in exposure to a designated substance, the physician shall also advise the joint health and safety

490/09

committee, in writing and on a confidential basis, and in giving the advice shall indicate his or her opinion as to the interpretation to be placed on the advice.

(7) On advising the worker and the worker's employer that a worker is fit with limitations or unfit to continue working in exposure to a designated substance, the physician shall promptly communicate that advice to the Provincial Physician.

30. Retention: personal exposure records —

(1) A physician who is provided with a copy of a worker's personal exposure record under clause 27(1)(a) shall keep the copy in a secure place until the later of the following dates:

    1. The 40th anniversary of the date the first record was created in the personal exposure record.

    2. The 20th anniversary of the date the last record was added to the personal exposure record.

(2) If the physician is no longer able to keep the copy of the personal exposure record, he or she shall forward it to the Provincial Physician or to a physician designated by the Provincial Physician, who shall keep the copy until the later of the dates specified in subsection (1).

(3) If a physician is not required by subsection (1) to keep a copy of a worker's personal exposure record, the employer shall keep the record in a secure place until the later of the dates specified in subsection (1).

(4) If the employer is unable to keep the personal exposure record, the employer shall forward it to the Provincial Physician, who shall keep it until the later of the dates specified in subsection (1).

O. Reg. 148/12 s. 1

31. Retention: records of medical examinations —

(1) A physician who conducted medical examinations of a worker or supervised clinical tests of a worker shall, if section 29 applies, keep the records of the examinations and tests in a secure place until the later of the following dates:

    1. The 40th anniversary of the date the first record was made.

    2. The 20th anniversary of the date the last record was made.

(2) If the physician is no longer able to keep the records of the medical examinations and clinical tests, he or she shall forward them to the Provincial Physician or to a physician designated by the Provincial Physician, who shall keep the records until the later of the dates specified in sub-section (1).

O. Reg. 148/12 s. 2

Variance from a Code

32. Variance from a code — For the purposes of this Regulation, the methods and procedures that may be used or adopted may vary from the Codes issued by the Ministry if the protection afforded thereby or the factors of accuracy and precision used or adopted are equal to or exceed the protection or the factors of accuracy and precision in the Codes issued by the Ministry.

Revocations and Commencement

33. Revocations — The following Regulations are revoked:

1. Regulation 835 of the Revised Regulations of Ontario, 1990.
2. Regulation 836 of the Revised Regulations of Ontario, 1990.
3. Regulation 837 of the Revised Regulations of Ontario, 1990.
4. Regulation 839 of the Revised Regulations of Ontario, 1990.
5. Regulation 840 of the Revised Regulations of Ontario, 1990.
6. Regulation 841 of the Revised Regulations of Ontario, 1990.
7. Regulation 842 of the Revised Regulations of Ontario, 1990.
8. Regulation 843 of the Revised Regulations of Ontario, 1990.
9. Regulation 844 of the Revised Regulations of Ontario, 1990.
10. Regulation 845 of the Revised Regulations of Ontario, 1990.
11. Regulation 846 of the Revised Regulations of Ontario, 1990.

34. Commencement — This Regulation comes into force on the later of July 1, 2010 and the day this Regulation is filed.

490/09

TABLE 1 Exposure Limits

Agent [CAS No.]	Time-Weighted Average Limit (TWA), Short-Term Exposure Limit (STEL), Ceiling Limit (C) and Notations		
	TWA	STEL / C	Notations
Acrylonitrile [107-13-1]	2 ppm	C 10 ppm	Skin
Arsenic, elemental arsenic and inorganic compounds [7440-38-2], and organic compounds (only where both inorganic and organic compounds are present), as As.	0.01 mg/m^3	0.05 mg/m^3	
Asbestos—All forms [1332-21-4]	0.1 f/cc (F)		
Actinolite [77536-66-4]	0.1 f/cc (F)		
Amosite [12172-73-5]	0.1 f/cc (F)		
Anthophyllite [77536-67-5]	0.1 f/cc (F)		
Chrysotile [132207-32-0]	0.1 f/cc (F)		
Crocidolite [12001-28-4]	0.1 f/cc (F)		
Tremolite [77536-68-6]	0.1 f/cc (F)		

Table 1 — Exposure Limits   **S. 34**

Agent [CAS No.]	Time-Weighted Average Limit (TWA), Short-Term Exposure Limit (STEL), Ceiling Limit (C) and Notations		
	TWA	STEL / C	Notations
Benzene [71-43-2]	0.5 ppm	2.5 ppm	Skin
Coke Oven Emissions[1]	0.15 mg/m^3		
Ethylene oxide [75-21-8]	1 ppm	10 ppm	
	1.8 mg/m^3	18 mg/m^3	
Isocyanates, organic compounds			
Toluene diisocyanate (TDI) [584-84-9] [91-08-7]	0.005 ppm	C 0.02 ppm	
Methylene bisphenyl isocyanate (MDI) [101-68-8]	0.005 ppm	C 0.02 ppm	
Hexamethylene diisocyanate (HDI) [822-06-0]	0.005 ppm	C 0.02 ppm	
Isophorone diisocyanate (IPDI) [4098-71-9]	0.005 ppm	C 0.02 ppm	
Methylene bis (4-cyclohexyliso-cyanate) [5124-30-1]	0.005 ppm	C 0.02 ppm	

490/09

Agent [CAS No.]	Time-Weighted Average Limit (TWA), Short-Term Exposure Limit (STEL), Ceiling Limit (C) and Notations		
	TWA	STEL / C	Notations
Methyl Isocyanate [624-83-9]	0.02 ppm	0.06 ppm	Skin
Ethyl isocyanate [109-90-0]	0.02 ppm	0.06 ppm	Skin
Phenyl isocyanate [103-71-9]	0.005 ppm	0.015 ppm	Skin
Lead [7439-92-1], elemental lead, inorganic and organic compounds of lead, as Pb			
Elemental lead, inorganic and organic compounds of lead, as Pb except tetraethyl lead [78-00-2]	0.05 mg/m³		Skin (organic compounds)
Tetraethyl lead, as Pb [78-00-2]	0.10 mg/m³	0.30 mg/m³	
Mercury [7439-97-6], elemental mercury, inorganic and organic compounds of mercury, as Hg			
All forms of except alkyl, as Hg	0.025 mg/m³		Skin
Alkyl compounds of, as Hg	0.01 mg/m³	0.03 mg/m³	Skin
Silica, Crystalline			

Table 1 — Exposure Limits **S. 34**

Agent [CAS No.]	Time-Weighted Average Limit (TWA), Short-Term Exposure Limit (STEL), Ceiling Limit (C) and Notations		
	TWA	STEL / C	Notations
Quartz /Tripoli [14808-60-7; 1317-95-9]	0.10 mg/m^3 (R)		
Cristobalite [14464-46-1]	0.05 mg/m^3 (R)		
Vinyl chloride [75-01-04]	1 ppm		

1 Means the benzene soluble fraction of total particulate matter of the substances emitted into the atmosphere from metallurgical coke ovens including condensed vapours and solid particulates.

[CAS No.]—CAS Registry Number.

f/cc—Fibres per cubic centimetre of air.

mg/m^3—Milligrams of the agent per cubic metre of air.

ppm—Parts of the agent per million parts of air by volume.

Skin—Danger of cutaneous absorption.

(F) Respirable fibres: length > 5 μm; aspect ratio ⩾ 3:1, as determined by the membrane filter method at 400-450 times magnification (4-mm objective), using phase-contrast illumination.

(R) Respirable fraction: means that size fraction of the airborne particulate deposited in the gas-exchange region of the respiratory tract and collected during air sampling with a particle size-selective device that, (a) meets the ACGIH particle size-selective sampling criteria for airborne particulate matter; and (b) has the cut point of 4 μm at 50 per cent collection efficiency.

O. Reg. 259/10 s. 1; 148/12 s. 3; 288/17, s. 1

490/09

SCHEDULE 1

Part I — Airborne Measurement and Calculation of Exposure

1. Airborne concentrations of a designated substance are expressed as,
    (a) parts of the agent per million parts of air by volume (ppm);
    (b) milligrams of the agent per cubic metre of air (mg/m^3); or
    (c) fibres per cubic centimetre of air (f/cc).

2. In determining exposure to airborne concentrations of a designated substance, no regard shall be had to the wearing or use of personal protective equipment.

3. The average concentrations of a designated substance to which a worker is exposed shall be determined from analysis of air samples taken as being representative of the exposure of the worker to the designated substance during work operations in accordance with section 24 of the Regulation.

4. The time-weighted average exposure to an airborne designated substance in a work day or work week shall be calculated as follows:
    1. The cumulative daily or weekly exposure shall be calculated using the following formula:

$$C_1T_1 + C_2T_2 + ... + C_nT_n$$

where,

C$_1$ is the concentration found in an air sample, and
T$_1$ is the total time in hours to which the worker is taken to be exposed to concentration C$_1$ in a work day or a work week.

    2. The time-weighted average exposure shall be calculated by dividing the cumulative daily exposure by eight and the weekly exposure by 40 respectively.

5. Short-term exposures to the designated substance in any 15-minute period are determined from a single sample or from a time-weighted average of sequential samples taken during that period.

Part II
— Coke Oven Emissions Control Program —
Additional Elements

A.
— Engineering Controls

1. — Charging

1. The charging operation shall be conducted in one of the following ways:
   1. Stage charging.
   2. Sequential charging.
   3. Pipeline charging of preheated coal.
   4. Chain conveyor charging of preheated coal.
2. During the charging operation, provision shall be made for the following engineering controls:
   1. Drafting from two or more points of the oven chamber by,
      i. a double collecting main,
      ii. a jumper pipe on the larry car or oven top, or
      iii. a separate charging main attached to the larry car.
   2. A functional steam aspiration system.
   3. Adjustable volumetric controls on the larry car hoppers to provide the appropriate quantity of coal to be charged so as to ensure an adequate free space for gas evacuation.
   4. Stainless steel hopper liners, mechanical vibrators or pneumatic stimulators to allow the proper flow of coal into the oven chamber.
   5. Gooseneck and standpipe cleaners as is appropriate in the circumstances.
   6. A leveller bar seal to the chuck door opening.
   7. Carbon cutter or compressed air roof decarbonization on the pusher ram.

2. — Coking

1. During the coking operation, provision shall be made for the following engineering controls:

1. Backpressure control on each battery to ensure uniform collector main pressure.

2. An adequate number of spare doors readily available and in good condition for the replacement of leaking doors when such replacement is appropriate in the circumstances.

3. Chuck door gaskets or sealing material to be used when such use is appropriate in the circumstances.

B. — Work Practices

1. — Charging

1. During the charging operation, provision shall be made for the following work practices:

    1. Inspection and cleaning of goosenecks and standpipes prior to each charge to provide an appropriate open area for the passage of gases from the oven to the collecting main.

    2. Inspection and, when appropriate in the circumstances, the removal of roof carbon so as to ensure an adequate free space above the coal charge to allow for the passage of gases to the off-take system.

    3. Routine inspection of the steam aspiration system.

    4. Routine inspection of the flushing liquor sprays.

    5. Cleaning and sealing of standpipe caps as is appropriate in the circumstances.

    6. Filling of the larry car hoppers with an appropriate quantity of coal.

    7. Alignment of the larry car at the oven so that the drop sleeves fit tightly over the charging holes.

    8. Charging of the coal into the oven using the proper sequence for the type of charging operation utilized.

    9. The aspiration system to be turned off only when the charging holes have been closed.

2. — Coking

1. During the coking operation, provision shall be made for the following work practices:

1. Repair, replacement or adjustment of oven doors and chuck doors, as well as maintenance of door jambs, as is appropriate in the circumstances, to provide a gas tight fit.

2. Clean oven doors, chuck doors and door jambs between each coking cycle to provide a gas tight fit.

3. An inspection system and a corrective action program to control door and top side emissions.

3. — Pushing

1. During the pushing operation, provision shall be made for the following work practices:

    1. Coke spillage to be cleaned up after each push.

    2. Coal spillage on the bench to be collected in the bin on the pusher machine.

    3. Coal charge to be heated as uniformly as possible for the set time period before pushing.

    4. Heating maintenance to be performed to provide heating which is as uniform as possible.

4. — Maintenance and Repair

1. In order to ensure adequate maintenance and repair, provision shall be made for the following work practices:

    1. Regular inspection of all engineering controls which have been installed to decrease coke oven emissions and effective implementation of all necessary repairs thereto.

    2. Regular inspection of battery function and prompt and effective implementation of necessary repairs thereto.

C. — Hygiene Facilities

1. Provision shall be made for the following hygiene facilities:

    1. Positive pressure, temperature controlled, filtered air for the larry car, pusher machine, door machine and quench car cabs.

    2. Positive pressure, temperature controlled, filtered air rest areas for workers.

490/09

SCHEDULE 2

Part I — Codes for Measuring Airborne Substances

1. *Code for Measuring Airborne Acrylonitrile* dated October 30, 1984, and issued by the Ministry.

2. *Code for Measuring Airborne Arsenic* dated March 22, 1986, and issued by the Ministry.

3. *Code for Measuring Coke Oven Emissions* dated June 30, 1982, and issued by the Ministry.

4. *Code for Measuring Airborne Ethylene Oxide* dated February 28, 1986 and issued by the Ministry.

5. *Code for Measuring Airborne Isocyanates* dated June 17, 1983, and issued by the Ministry.

Part II — Codes for Medical Surveillance

1. *Code for Medical Surveillance of Acrylonitrile Exposed Workers* dated October 30, 1984, and issued by the Ministry.

2. *Code for Medical Surveillance of Asbestos Exposed Workers* dated July 19, 1982 and issued by the Ministry.

3. *Code for Medical Surveillance of Benzene Exposed Workers* dated October 29, 1984, and issued by the Ministry.

4. *Code for Medical Surveillance of Workers Exposed to Coke Oven Emissions* dated June 30, 1982, and issued by the Ministry.

5. *Code for Medical Surveillance of Isocyanates Exposed Workers* dated June 17, 1983, and issued by the Ministry.

6. *Code for Medical Surveillance of Silica Exposed Workers* dated October 17, 1983, and issued by the Ministry.

7. *Code for Medical Surveillance for Lead* dated May 28, 1981 and issued by the Ministry.

8. *Code for Medical Surveillance for Mercury* dated November 16, 1981, and issued by the Ministry.

9. *Code for Medical Surveillance for Vinyl Chloride* dated January 11, 1982, and issued by the Ministry.

Part III — Code for Respiratory Equipment

1. *Code for Respiratory Equipment for Acrylonitrile* dated October 30, 1984, and issued by the Ministry.

2. *Code for Respiratory Equipment for Arsenic* dated March 22, 1986, and issued by the Ministry.

3. *Code for Respiratory Equipment for Asbestos* dated June 30, 2000 and issued by the Ministry.

4. *Code for Respiratory Equipment for Benzene* dated June 30, 2000 and issued by the Ministry.

5. *Code for Respiratory Equipment for Coke Oven Emissions* dated June 30, 1982, and issued by the Ministry.

6. *Code for Respiratory Equipment for Ethylene Oxide* dated February 28, 1986 and issued by the Ministry.

7. *Code for Respiratory Equipment for Isocyanates* dated June 17, 1983, and issued by the Ministry.

8. *Code for Respiratory Equipment for Lead* dated June 30, 2000, and issued by the Ministry.

9. *Code for Respiratory Equipment for Mercury* dated June 30, 2000, and issued by the Ministry.

10. *Code for Respiratory Equipment for Silica* dated June 30, 2000 and issued by the Ministry.

11. *Code for Respiratory Equipment for Vinyl Chloride* dated June 30, 2000, and issued by the Ministry.

490/09

Ont. Reg. 278/05 — Designated Substance — Asbestos on Construction Projects and in Buildings and Repair Operations

made under the *Occupational Health and Safety Act*

O. Reg. 278/05, as am. O. Reg. 493/09; 422/10, ss. 1, 2 (Fr.); 479/10.

1. Definitions —

(1) In this Regulation,

"asbestos" means any of the fibrous silicates listed in subsection (2);

"asbestos-containing material" means material that contains 0.5 per cent or more asbestos by dry weight;

"building" means any structure, vault, chamber or tunnel including, without limitation, the electrical, plumbing, heating and air handling equipment (including rigid duct work) of the structure, vault, chamber or tunnel;

"competent worker", in relation to specific work, means a worker who,

    (a) is qualified because of knowledge, training and experience to perform the work,

    (b) is familiar with the Act and with the provisions of the regulations that apply to the work, and

    (c) has knowledge of all potential or actual danger to health or safety in the work;

"demolition" includes dismantling and breaking up;

"examine", when used with reference to material, means to carry out procedures in accordance with section 3 to establish its asbestos content and to establish the type of asbestos, and **"examination"** has a corresponding meaning;

"friable material" means material that,

401

(a) when dry, can be crumbled, pulverized or powdered by hand pressure, or

(b) is crumbled, pulverized or powdered;

"HEPA filter" means a high efficiency particulate aerosol filter that is at least 99.97 per cent efficient in collecting a 0.3 micrometre aerosol;

"homogeneous material" means material that is uniform in colour and texture;

"joint health and safety committee" means,

(a) a joint health and safety committee established under section 9 of the Act,

(b) a similar committee described in subsection 9(4) of the Act, or

(c) the workers or their representatives who participate in an arrangement, program or system described in subsection 9(4) of the Act;

"occupier" has the same meaning as in the *Occupiers' Liability Act*;

"Type 1 operation" means an operation described in subsection 12(2);

"Type 2 operation" means an operation described in subsection 12(3);

"Type 3 operation" means an operation described in subsection 12(4).

(2) The fibrous silicates referred to in the definition of "asbestos" in subsection (1) are:

1. Actinolite.
2. Amosite.
3. Anthophyllite.
4. Chrysotile.
5. Crocidolite.
6. Tremolite.

2. Application —

(1) This Regulation applies to,

(a) every project, its owner, and every constructor, employer and worker engaged in or on the project;

(b) the repair, alteration or maintenance of a building, the owner of the building, and every employer and worker engaged in the repair, alteration or maintenance;

(c) every building in which material that may be asbestos-containing material has been used, and the owner of the building;

(d) the demolition of machinery, equipment, aircraft, ships, locomotives, railway cars and vehicles, and every employer and worker
engaged in the demolition; and
(e) subject to subsection (3),
  (i) work described in subsection (2) in which asbestos-containing material is likely to be handled, dealt with, disturbed
  or removed, and
  (ii) every employer and worker engaged in the work.

(2) Clause (1)(e) applies to,
(a) the repair, alteration or maintenance of machinery, equipment,
aircraft, ships, locomotives, railway cars and vehicles; and
(b) work on a building that is necessarily incidental to the repair,
alteration or maintenance of machinery or equipment.

(3) This Regulation does not apply to an employer in respect of those
workers who are employed by the employer and engaged in the activities
described in clause (1)(e) if, pursuant to clause 5(1)(c) of Ontario Regulation 490/09 (*Designated Substances*) made under the Act, that regulation applies to the employer and those workers with respect to asbestos.

(4) This Regulation does not apply to an owner of a private residence
occupied by the owner or the owner's family or to an owner of a residential building that contains not more than four dwelling units, one of
which is occupied by the registered owner or family of the registered
owner.

(5) This Regulation does not apply to workers and their employers when
the workers are engaged in the following work under the authority of the
Fire Protection and Prevention Act, 1997:
  1. Fire suppression.
  2. Rescue and emergency services.
  3. The investigation of the cause, origin and circumstances of a fire
  or explosion or condition that might have caused a fire, explosion,
  loss of life or damage to property.

(6) While the work described in subsection (5) is being performed at a
workplace, this Regulation does not apply to that workplace in respect of
the workers engaged in the work and their employers, and Regulation 833
of the Revised Regulations of Ontario, 1990 (*Control of Exposure to
Biological or Chemical Agents*) made under the Act applies.

O. Reg. 493/09 s. 1; 479/10 s. 1

3. Adoption of standard —

(1) For the purposes of this Regulation, the method and procedures for establishing whether material is asbestos-containing material and for establishing its asbestos content and the type of asbestos shall be in accordance with the following standard:

    1. U.S. Environmental Protection Agency. Test Method EPA/600/R-93/116: Method for the Determination of Asbestos in Bulk Building Materials. June 1993.

(2) The procedures required by subsection (1) shall be carried out on bulk material samples that are randomly collected by a competent worker and are representative of each area of homogeneous material.

(3) The minimum number of bulk material samples to be collected from an area of homogeneous material is set out in Table 1.

(4) If analysis establishes that a bulk material sample contains 0.5 per cent or more asbestos by dry weight,

    (a) it is not necessary to analyze other bulk material samples taken from the same area of homogeneous material; and

    (b) the entire area of homogeneous material from which the bulk material sample was taken is deemed to be asbestos-containing material.

4. Restrictions re sprayed material, insulation, sealants —

(1) No person shall apply or install or cause to be applied or installed, by spraying, material containing 0.1 per cent or more asbestos by dry weight that can become friable.

(2) No person shall apply or install or cause to be applied or installed, as thermal insulation, material containing 0.1 per cent or more asbestos by dry weight that can become friable.

(3) A liquid sealant shall not be applied to friable asbestos-containing material if,

    (a) the material has visibly deteriorated; or

    (b) the material's strength and its adhesion to the underlying materials and surfaces are insufficient to support its weight and the weight of the sealant.

5. Information for workers —

(1) This section applies whenever a worker is to do work that,

(a) involves material that,
  (i) is asbestos-containing material,
  (ii) is being treated as if it were asbestos-containing material,
  (iii) is the subject of advice under section 9 or a notice under subsection 10(8); or
(b) is to be carried on in close proximity to material described in clause (a) and may disturb it.

(2) The constructor or employer shall advise the worker and provide him or her with the following information:
  1. The location of all material described in clause (1)(a).
  2. For each location, whether the material is friable or non-friable.
  3. In the case of sprayed-on friable material, for each location,
    i. if the material is known to be asbestos-containing material, the type of asbestos, if known, or
    ii. in any other case, a statement that the material will be treated as though it contained a type of asbestos other than chrysotile.

6. Demolition —

(1) The demolition of all or part of machinery, equipment, a building, aircraft, locomotive, railway car, vehicle or ship shall be carried out or continued only when any asbestos-containing material that may be disturbed during the work has been removed to the extent practicable.

(2) Subsection (1) does not apply so as to prevent work necessary to gain access to the asbestos-containing material that is to be removed, if the workers doing the work are protected from the hazard.

7. [Repealed O. Reg. 422/10, s. 1.]

8. Ongoing asbestos management in buildings after transitional period —

(1) This section applies on and after November 1, 2007.

(2) Subsection (3) applies if,
  (a) the owner of a building treats material that has been used in the building for any purpose related to it, including insulation, fireproofing and ceiling tiles, as if it were asbestos-containing material;
  (b) the owner of a building has been advised under section 9 of the discovery of material that may be asbestos-containing material;

278/05

(c) the owner of a building knows or ought reasonably to know that asbestos-containing material has been used in a building for any purpose related to the building, including insulation, fireproofing and ceiling tiles;

(d) an examination under subsection (8) or section 10 establishes, or would have established if carried out as required, that asbestos-containing material has been used in a building for any purpose related to the building, including insulation, fireproofing and ceiling tiles; or

(e) a constructor or employer advises the owner of a building, in accordance with subsection 10(8), of the discovery of material that may be asbestos-containing material and that was not referred to in a report prepared under subsection 10(4).

(3) If this subsection applies, the owner shall,

(a) prepare and keep on the premises a record containing the information set out in subsection (4);

(b) give any other person who is an occupier of the building written notice of any information in the record that relates to the area occupied by the person;

(c) give any employer with whom the owner arranges or contracts for work that is not described in clause 10(1)(a) written notice of the information in the record, if the work,

(i) may involve material mentioned in the record, or

(ii) may be carried on in close proximity to such material and may disturb it;

(d) advise the workers employed by the owner who work in the building of the information in the record, if the workers may do work that,

(i) involves material mentioned in the record, or

(ii) is to be carried on in close proximity to such material and may disturb it;

(e) establish and maintain, for the training and instruction of every worker employed by the owner who works in the building and may do work described in clause (d), a program dealing with,

(i) the hazards of asbestos exposure,

(ii) the use, care and disposal of protective equipment and clothing to be used and worn when doing the work,

(iii) personal hygiene to be observed when doing the work, and

(iv) the measures and procedures prescribed by this Regulation; and

(f) inspect the material mentioned in the record at reasonable intervals in order to determine its condition.

(4) The record shall contain the following information:

1. The location of all material described in clauses (2)(a), (b), (c), (d) and (e).

2. For each location, whether the material is friable or non-friable.

3. In the case of friable sprayed-on material, for each location,

i. if the material is known to be asbestos-containing material, the type of asbestos, if known, or

ii. in any other case, a statement that the material will be treated as though it contained a type of asbestos other than chrysotile.

(5) The owner shall update the record described in clause (3)(a),

(a) at least once in each 12-month period; and

(b) whenever the owner becomes aware of new information relating to the matters the record deals with.

(6) If updating under subsection (5) results in any change to the record, clauses (3)(b), (c) and (d) apply with necessary modifications.

(7) An occupier who receives a notice under clause (3)(b) is responsible for performing the duties set out in clauses (3)(d) and (e) with respect to the occupier's own workers.

(8) If it is readily apparent that friable material used in a building as fireproofing or acoustical or thermal insulation has fallen and is being disturbed so that exposure to the material is likely to occur,

(a) the owner shall cause the material to be examined to establish whether it is asbestos-containing material; and

(b) until it has been established whether the material is asbestos-containing material, no further work involving the material shall be done.

(9) Subsection (8) does not apply if the work is carried out in accordance with this Regulation as though the material were asbestos-containing material and, in the case of friable sprayed-on material, as though it contained a type of asbestos other than chrysotile.

(10) If the examination mentioned in subsection (8) establishes that the material is asbestos-containing material, or if the material is treated as though it were asbestos-containing material as described in subsection (9),

(a) the owner shall cause the fallen material to be cleaned up and removed; and

(b) if it is readily apparent that material will continue to fall because of the deterioration of the fireproofing or insulation, the owner shall repair, seal, remove or permanently enclose the fireproofing or insulation.

(11) Subsection (10) does not apply if the fallen material is confined to an area that is,

(a) above a closed false ceiling; and

(b) not part of a return air plenum.

9. Responsibility of employer other than owner —
An employer whose workers work in a building of which the employer is not the owner shall advise the owner if the workers discover material that may be asbestos-containing material in the building.

10. Owner's responsibilities before requesting tender or arranging work —

(1) An owner shall comply with subsections (2), (3), (4), (5) and (6) before,

(a) requesting tenders for the demolition, alteration or repair of all or part of machinery, equipment, or a building, aircraft, locomotive, railway car, vehicle or ship; or

(b) arranging or contracting for any work described in clause (a), if no tenders are requested.

(2) Unless clause (3)(a) or (b) applies, the owner shall have an examination carried out in accordance with section 3 to establish whether any material that is likely to be handled, dealt with, disturbed or removed, whether friable or non-friable, is asbestos-containing material.

(3) An examination under subsection (2) is not required if,

(a) the owner,

(i) already knows that the material is not asbestos-containing material, or

(ii) already knows that the material is asbestos-containing material and, in the case of sprayed-on friable material, knows the type of asbestos; or

(b) the work is being arranged or contracted for in accordance with this Regulation as though the material were asbestos-containing material and, in the case of sprayed-on friable material, as though it contained a type of asbestos other than chrysotile.

(4) Whether an examination is required under subsection (2) or not, the owner shall have a report prepared,

    (a) stating whether,

        (i) the material is or is not asbestos-containing material, or

        (ii) the work is to be performed in accordance with this Regulation as though the material were asbestos-containing material and, in the case of sprayed-on friable material, as though it contained a type of asbestos other than chrysotile;

    (b) describing the condition of the material and stating whether it is friable or non-friable; and

    (c) containing drawings, plans and specifications, as appropriate, to show the location of the material identified under clause (a).

(5) An owner shall give any prospective constructor a copy of the complete report prepared under subsection (4).

(6) Subsection (5) applies, with necessary modifications, with respect to,

    (a) a constructor and a prospective contractor; and

    (b) a contractor and a prospective subcontractor.

(7) Subsections (8), (9) and (10) apply if, during work described in clause (1)(a), material is discovered that,

    (a) was not referred to in the report prepared under subsection (4); and

    (b) may be asbestos-containing material.

(8) The constructor or employer shall immediately notify, orally and in writing,

    (a) an inspector at the office of the Ministry of Labour nearest the workplace;

    (b) the owner;

    (c) the contractor; and

    (d) the joint health and safety committee or the health and safety representative, if any, for the workplace.

(9) The written notice referred to in subsection (8) shall include the information referred to in clauses 11(3)(a) to (f).

278/05

(10) No work that is likely to involve handling, dealing with, disturbing or removing the material referred to in subsection (7) shall be done unless,

    (a) it has been determined under section 3 whether the material is asbestos-containing material; or

    (b) the work is performed in accordance with this Regulation as though the material were asbestos-containing material and, in the case of sprayed-on friable material, as though it contained a type of asbestos other than chrysotile.

(11) Subsection (10) does not prohibit handling, dealing with, disturbing or removing material for the sole purpose of determining whether it is asbestos-containing material.

11. Advance notice re Type 3 operations and certain Type 2 operations —

(1) Before commencing a Type 3 operation, the constructor, in the case of a project, and the employer, in any other case, shall notify, orally and in writing, an inspector at the office of the Ministry of Labour nearest the workplace of the operation.

(2) Subsection (1) also applies with respect to a Type 2 operation described in paragraph 9 of subsection 12(3) in which one square metre or more of insulation is to be removed.

(3) The written notice required by subsection (1) shall set out,

    (a) the name and address of the person giving the notice;

    (b) the name and address of the owner of the place where the work will be carried out;

    (c) the municipal address or other description of the place where the work will be carried out sufficient to permit the inspector to locate the place, including the location with respect to the nearest public highway;

    (d) a description of the work that will be carried out;

    (e) the starting date and expected duration of the work; and

    (f) the name and address of the supervisor in charge of the work.

12. Type 1, Type 2 and Type 3 operations —

(1) For the purposes of this Regulation, operations that may expose a worker to asbestos are classified as Type 1, Type 2 and Type 3 operations.

(2) The following are Type 1 operations:

1. Installing or removing ceiling tiles that are asbestos-containing material, if the tiles cover an area less than 7.5 square metres and are installed or removed without being broken, cut, drilled, abraded, ground, sanded or vibrated.

2. Installing or removing non-friable asbestos-containing material, other than ceiling tiles, if the material is installed or removed without being broken, cut, drilled, abraded, ground, sanded or vibrated.

3. Breaking, cutting, drilling, abrading, grinding, sanding or vibrating non-friable asbestos-containing material if,

    i. the material is wetted to control the spread of dust or fibres, and

    ii. the work is done only by means of non-powered hand-held tools.

4. Removing less than one square metre of drywall in which joint-filling compounds that are asbestos-containing material have been used.

(3) The following are Type 2 operations:

1. Removing all or part of a false ceiling to obtain access to a work area, if asbestos-containing material is likely to be lying on the surface of the false ceiling.

2. The removal or disturbance of one square metre or less of friable asbestos-containing material during the repair, maintenance or demolition of all or part of machinery or equipment or a building, aircraft, locomotive, railway car, vehicle or ship.

3. Enclosing friable asbestos-containing material.

4. Applying tape or a sealant or other covering to pipe or boiler insulation that is asbestos-containing material.

5. Installing or removing ceiling tiles that are asbestos-containing material, if the tiles cover an area of 7.5 square metres or more and are installed or removed without being broken, cut, drilled, abraded, ground, sanded or vibrated.

6. Breaking, cutting, drilling, abrading, grinding, sanding or vibrating non-friable asbestos-containing material if,

    i. the material is not wetted to control the spread of dust or fibres, and

    ii. the work is done only by means of non-powered hand-held tools.

7. Removing one square metre or more of drywall in which joint filling compounds that are asbestos-containing material have been used.

8. Breaking, cutting, drilling, abrading, grinding, sanding or vibrating non-friable asbestos-containing material if the work is done by means of power tools that are attached to dust-collecting devices equipped with HEPA filters.

9. Removing insulation that is asbestos-containing material from a pipe, duct or similar structure using a glove bag.

10. Cleaning or removing filters used in air handling equipment in a building that has sprayed fireproofing that is asbestos-containing material.

11. An operation that,

    i. is not mentioned in any of paragraphs 1 to 10,

    ii. may expose a worker to asbestos, and

    iii. is not classified as a Type 1 or Type 3 operation.

(4) The following are Type 3 operations:

1. The removal or disturbance of more than one square metre of friable asbestos-containing material during the repair, alteration, maintenance or demolition of all or part of a building, aircraft, ship, locomotive, railway car or vehicle or any machinery or equipment.

2. The spray application of a sealant to friable asbestos-containing material.

3. Cleaning or removing air handling equipment, including rigid ducting but not including filters, in a building that has sprayed fireproofing that is asbestos-containing material.

4. Repairing, altering or demolishing all or part of a kiln, metallurgical furnace or similar structure that is made in part of refractory materials that are asbestos-containing materials.

5. Breaking, cutting, drilling, abrading, grinding, sanding or vibrating non-friable asbestos-containing material, if the work is done by means of power tools that are not attached to dust-collecting devices equipped with HEPA filters.

6. Repairing, altering or demolishing all or part of any building in which asbestos is or was used in the manufacture of products, unless the asbestos was cleaned up and removed before March 16, 1986.

(5) Work on ceiling tiles, drywall or friable asbestos-containing material is classified according to the total area on which work is done consecutively in a room or enclosed area, even if the work is divided into smaller jobs.

(6) The following provisions apply if a dispute arises as to the classification of an operation under this section:

1. A party to the dispute may notify an inspector at the office of the Ministry of Labour nearest the workplace of the dispute.

2. The party who notifies the inspector shall promptly inform the other parties that the inspector has been notified.

3. Work on the operation shall cease until the inspector has given a decision under paragraph 4.

4. The inspector shall, as soon as possible, investigate the matter and give the parties a decision in writing.

(7) Nothing in subsection (6) affects an inspector's power to issue an order for a contravention of this Regulation.

13. Respirators —

(1) A respirator provided by an employer and used by a worker in a Type 1, Type 2 or Type 3 operation,

(a) shall be fitted so that there is an effective seal between the respirator and the worker's face, unless the respirator is equipped with a hood or helmet;

(b) shall be assigned to a worker for his or her exclusive use, if practicable;

(c) shall be used and maintained in accordance with written procedures that are established by the employer and are consistent with the manufacturer's specifications;

(d) shall be cleaned, disinfected and inspected after use on each shift, or more often if necessary, when issued for the exclusive use of one worker, or after each use when used by more than one worker;

(e) shall have damaged or deteriorated parts replaced prior to being used by a worker; and

(f) when not in use, shall be stored in a convenient, clean and sanitary location.

(2) The following additional requirements apply to a respirator of the supplied air type:

278/05

1. The compressed air used for breathing shall meet the standards set out in Table 1 of CSA Standard Z180.1-00, Compressed Breathing Air and Systems (March, 2000).

2. If an oil-lubricated compressor is used to supply breathing air, a continuous carbon monoxide monitor equipped with an alarm shall be provided.

3. If an ambient breathing air system is used, the air intake shall be located in accordance with Appendix B of the standard referred to in paragraph 1.

(3) If respirators are used in the workplace,

    (a) the employer shall establish written procedures regarding the selection, use and care of respirators; and

    (b) a copy of the procedures shall be provided to and reviewed with each worker who is required to wear a respirator.

(4) A worker shall not be assigned to an operation requiring the use of a respirator unless he or she is physically able to perform the operation while using the respirator.

14. Measures and procedures, Type 1 operations —

The following measures and procedures apply to Type 1 operations:

1. Before beginning work, visible dust shall be removed with a damp cloth or a vacuum equipped with a HEPA filter from any surface in the work area, including the thing to be worked on, if the dust on that surface is likely to be disturbed.

2. The spread of dust from the work area shall be controlled by measures appropriate to the work to be done including the use of drop sheets of polyethylene or other suitable material that is impervious to asbestos.

3. In the case of an operation mentioned in paragraph 4 of subsection 12(2), the material shall be wetted before and kept wet during the work to control the spread of dust or fibres, unless wetting would create a hazard or cause damage.

4. A wetting agent shall be added to water that is to be used to control the spread of dust and fibres.

5. Frequently and at regular intervals during the doing of the work and immediately on completion of the work,

    i. dust and waste shall be cleaned up and removed using a vacuum equipped with a HEPA filter, or by damp mopping or wet sweeping, and placed in a container as described in paragraph 5 of section 15, and

ii. drop sheets shall be wetted and placed in a container as described in paragraph 5 of section 15, as soon as practicable after subparagraph i has been complied with.

6. Drop sheets shall not be reused.

7. After the work is completed, polyethylene sheeting and similar materials used for barriers and enclosures shall not be reused, but shall be wetted and placed in a container as described in paragraph 5 of section 15 as soon as practicable after paragraph 5 of this section has been complied with.

8. After the work is completed, barriers and portable enclosures that will be reused shall be cleaned, by using a vacuum equipped with a HEPA filter or by damp wiping, as soon as practicable after paragraphs 5 and 7 have been complied with.

9. Barriers and portable enclosures shall not be reused unless they are rigid and can be cleaned thoroughly.

10. Compressed air shall not be used to clean up and remove dust from any surface.

11. Eating, drinking, chewing or smoking shall not be permitted in the work area.

12. If a worker requests that the employer provide a respirator to be used by the worker, the employer shall provide the worker with a NIOSH approved respirator in accordance with Table 2, and the worker shall wear and use the respirator.

13. If a worker requests that the employer provide protective clothing to be used by the worker, the employer shall provide the worker with protective clothing as described in paragraph 12 of section 15, and the worker shall wear the protective clothing.

14. A worker who is provided with protective clothing shall, before leaving the work area,

i. decontaminate his or her protective clothing by using a vacuum equipped with a HEPA filter, or by damp wiping, before removing the protective clothing,

ii. if the protective clothing will not be reused, place it in a container as described in paragraph 5 of section 15.

15. Facilities for the washing of hands and face shall be made available to workers and shall be used by every worker when leaving the work area.

278/05

15. Measures and procedures, Type 2 and Type 3 operations —
The following measures and procedures apply to Type 2 operations and to
Type 3 operations:

1. The work area shall be identified by clearly visible signs warning
of an asbestos dust hazard.

2. Signs required by paragraph 1 shall be posted in sufficient
numbers to warn of the hazard and shall state in large clearly visible
letters that,

    i. there is an asbestos dust hazard, and

    ii. access to the work area is restricted to persons wearing
    protective clothing and equipment.

3. A wetting agent shall be added to water that is to be used to
control the spread of dust and fibres.

4. Eating, drinking, chewing or smoking shall not be permitted in
the work area.

5. Containers for dust and waste shall be,

    i. dust tight,

    ii. suitable for the type of waste,

    iii. impervious to asbestos,

    iv. identified as asbestos waste,

    v. cleaned with a damp cloth or a vacuum equipped with a
    HEPA filter immediately before being removed from the
    work area, and

    vi. removed from the workplace frequently and at regular
    intervals.

6. Frequently and at regular intervals during the doing of the work
and immediately on completion of the work,

    i. dust and waste shall be cleaned up and removed using a
    vacuum equipped with a HEPA filter, or by damp mopping
    or wet sweeping, and placed in a container as described in
    paragraph 5, and

    ii. drop sheets shall be wetted and placed in a container as
    described in paragraph 5, as soon as practicable after sub-
    paragraph i has been complied with.

7. Drop sheets shall not be reused.

8. After the work is completed, polyethylene sheeting and similar
materials used for barriers and enclosures shall not be reused, but
shall be wetted and placed in a container as described in paragraph
5 as soon as practicable after paragraph 6 has been complied with.

9. After the work is completed, barriers and portable enclosures that will be reused shall be cleaned, by using a vacuum equipped with a HEPA filter or by damp wiping, as soon as practicable after paragraphs 6 and 8 have been complied with.

10. Barriers and portable enclosures shall not be reused unless they are rigid and can be cleaned thoroughly.

11. The employer shall provide every worker who will enter the work area with a NIOSH approved respirator in accordance with Table 2 and the worker shall wear and use the respirator.

12. Protective clothing shall be provided by the employer and worn by every worker who enters the work area, and the protective clothing,

    i. shall be made of a material that does not readily retain nor permit penetration of asbestos fibres,

    ii. shall consist of head covering and full body covering that fits snugly at the ankles, wrists and neck, in order to prevent asbestos fibres from reaching the garments and skin under the protective clothing,

    iii. shall include suitable footwear, and

    iv. shall be repaired or replaced if torn.

13. Compressed air shall not be used to clean up and remove dust from any surface.

14. Only persons wearing protective clothing and equipment shall enter a work area where there is an asbestos dust hazard.

16. Additional measures and procedures, Type 2 operations —

In addition to the measures and procedures prescribed by section 15, the following measures and procedures apply to Type 2 operations:

1. If the operation is one mentioned in paragraph 1 of subsection 12(3), the friable material that is likely to be disturbed shall be cleaned up and removed by using a vacuum equipped with a HEPA filter when access to the work area is obtained.

2. Before commencing work that is likely to disturb friable asbestos-containing material that is crumbled, pulverized or powdered and that is lying on any surface, the friable material shall be cleaned up and removed by damp wiping or by using a vacuum equipped with a HEPA filter.

3. Friable asbestos-containing material that is not crumbled, pulverized or powdered and that may be disturbed or removed during

278/05

the work shall be thoroughly wetted before the work and kept wet during the work, unless wetting would create a hazard or cause damage.

4. Subject to paragraph 5, the spread of dust from a work area shall be controlled by measures appropriate to the work to be done, including the use of drop sheets of polyethylene or other suitable material that is impervious to asbestos.

5. If the operation is one mentioned in paragraph 1 or 2 of subsection 12(3) and is carried on indoors, the spread of dust from the work area shall be prevented, if practicable, by,

    i. using an enclosure of polyethylene or other suitable material that is impervious to asbestos (including, if the enclosure is opaque, one or more transparent window areas to allow observation of the entire work area from outside the enclosure), if the work area is not enclosed by walls,

    ii. disabling the mechanical ventilation system serving the work area, and

    iii. sealing the ventilation ducts to and from the work area.

6. Before leaving the work area, a worker shall,

    i. decontaminate his or her protective clothing by using a vacuum equipped with a HEPA filter, or by damp wiping, before removing the protective clothing, and

    ii. if the protective clothing will not be reused, place it in a container as described in paragraph 5 of section 15.

7. Facilities for the washing of hands and face shall be made available to workers and shall be used by every worker when leaving the work area.

17. Additional measures and procedures, glove bag operations — In addition to the measures and procedures prescribed by sections 15 and 16, the following measures and procedures apply to Type 2 operations referred to in paragraph 9 of subsection 12(3):

1. The work area shall be separated from the rest of the workplace by walls, barricades, fencing or other suitable means.

2. The spread of asbestos-containing material from the work area shall be prevented by disabling the mechanical ventilation system serving the work area and sealing all openings or voids, including ventilation ducts to and from the working area.

3. Surfaces below the work area shall be covered with drop sheets of polyethylene or other suitable material that is impervious to asbestos.

4. The glove bag shall be made of material that is impervious to asbestos and sufficiently strong to support the weight of material the bag will hold.

5. The glove bag shall be equipped with,

    i. sleeves and gloves that are permanently sealed to the body of the bag to allow the worker to access and deal with the insulation and maintain a sealed enclosure throughout the work period,

    ii. valves or openings to allow insertion of a vacuum hose and the nozzle of a water sprayer while maintaining the seal to the pipe, duct or similar structure,

    iii. a tool pouch with a drain,

    iv. a seamless bottom and a means of sealing off the lower portion of the bag, and

    v. a high strength double throw zipper and removable straps, if the bag is to be moved during the removal operation.

6. A glove bag shall not be used to remove insulation from a pipe, duct or similar structure if,

    i. it may not be possible to maintain a proper seal for any reason including, without limitation,

        A. the condition of the insulation, or

        B. the temperature of the pipe, duct or similar structure, or

    ii. the bag could become damaged for any reason including, without limitation,

        A. the type of jacketing, or

        B. the temperature of the pipe, duct or similar structure.

7. Immediately before the glove bag is attached, the insulation jacketing or coating shall be inspected for damage or defects, and if any damage or defect is present, it shall be repaired.

8. The glove bag shall be inspected for damage or defects,

    i. immediately before it is attached to the pipe, duct or other similar structure, and

    ii. at regular intervals during its use.

9. If damage or defects are observed when the glove bag is inspected under subparagraph 8 i, the glove bag shall not be used and shall be disposed of.

10. If damage or defects are observed when the glove bag is inspected under subparagraph 8 ii or at any other time,

  i. the use of the glove bag shall be discontinued,

  ii. the inner surface of the glove bag and the contents, if any, shall be thoroughly wetted,

  iii. the glove bag and the contents, if any, shall be removed and placed in a container as described in paragraph 5 of section 15, and

  iv. the work area shall be cleaned by vacuuming with a vacuum equipped with a HEPA filter before removal work is resumed.

11. When the removal work is completed,

  i. the inner surface of the glove bag and the waste inside shall be thoroughly wetted and the air inside the bag shall be removed through an elasticized valve, by means of a vacuum equipped with a HEPA filter,

  ii. the pipe, duct or similar structure shall be wiped down and sealed with a suitable encapsulant,

  iii. the glove bag, with the waste inside, shall be placed in a container as described in paragraph 5 of section 15, and

  iv. the work area shall be cleaned by damp wiping or by cleaning with a vacuum equipped with a HEPA filter.

18. Additional measures and procedures, Type 3 operations —

(1) In addition to the measures and procedures prescribed by section 15, the following measures and procedures apply to Type 3 operations:

1. The work area shall be separated from the rest of the workplace by walls, the placing of barricades or fencing or other suitable means.

2. Subsection (2) applies to an operation mentioned in paragraph 5 of subsection 12(4).

3. Subsection (3) applies to an operation mentioned in paragraph 1, 2, 3 or 4 of subsection 12(4) that is carried on outdoors.

4. Subsection (4) applies to an operation mentioned in paragraph 1, 2, 3, 4 or 6 of subsection 12(4) that is carried on indoors.

(2) In the case of an operation mentioned in paragraph 5 of subsection 12(4), the following measures and procedures also apply:

1. The spread of dust from the work area shall be prevented by,

    i. using enclosures of polyethylene or other suitable material that is impervious to asbestos (including, if the enclosure material is opaque, one or more transparent window areas to allow observation of the entire work area from outside the enclosure), if the work area is not enclosed by walls, and

    ii. using curtains of polyethylene sheeting or other suitable material that is impervious to asbestos, fitted on each side of each entrance or exit from the work area.

2. Unless the operation is carried on outdoors, or inside a building that is to be demolished and will not be entered by any person except the workers involved in the operation and the workers involved in the demolition, the spread of dust from the work area shall also be prevented by,

    i. creating and maintaining within the enclosed area, by installing a ventilation system equipped with a HEPA filtered exhaust unit, a negative air pressure of 0.02 inches of water, relative to the area outside the enclosed area,

    ii. ensuring that replacement air is taken from outside the enclosed area and is free from contamination with any hazardous dust, vapour, smoke, fume, mist or gas, and

    iii. using a device, at regular intervals, to measure the difference in air pressure between the enclosed area and the area outside it.

3. The ventilation system referred to in subparagraph 2 i shall be inspected and maintained by a competent worker before each use to ensure that there is no air leakage, and if the filter is found to be damaged or defective, it shall be replaced before the ventilation system is used.

4. Before leaving the work area, a worker shall,

    i. decontaminate his or her protective clothing by using a vacuum equipped with a HEPA filter, or by damp wiping, before removing the protective clothing, and

    ii. if the protective clothing will not be reused, place it in a container as described in paragraph 5 of section 15.

5. Facilities for the washing of hands and face shall be made available to workers and shall be used by every worker when leaving the work area.

(3) In the case of an operation mentioned in paragraph 1, 2, 3 or 4 of subsection 12(4) that is carried on outdoors, the following measures and procedures also apply:

1. If practicable, any asbestos-containing material to be removed shall be thoroughly wetted before and during removal, unless wetting would create a hazard or cause damage.

2. Dust and waste shall not be permitted to fall freely from one work level to another.

3. If practicable, the work area shall be washed down with water after completion of the clean-up and removal described in paragraph 6 of section 15.

4. Temporary electrical power distribution systems for tools and equipment involved in wet removal operations shall be equipped with ground fault circuit interrupters.

5. A decontamination facility shall be located as close as practicable to the work area and shall consist of,

     i. a room suitable for changing into protective clothing and for storing contaminated protective clothing and equipment,

     ii. a shower room as described in paragraph 7 of subsection (4), and

     iii. a room suitable for changing into street clothes and for storing clean clothing and equipment.

6. The rooms described in subparagraphs 5 i, ii and iii shall be arranged in sequence and constructed so that any person entering or leaving the work area must pass through each room.

7. When leaving the work area, a worker shall enter the decontamination facility and shall, in the following order,

     i. decontaminate his or her protective clothing by using a vacuum equipped with a HEPA filter, or by damp wiping, before removing the protective clothing,

     ii. if the protective clothing will not be reused, place it in a container as described in paragraph 5 of section 15,

     iii. shower, and

     iv. remove and clean the respirator.

(4) In the case of an operation mentioned in paragraph 1, 2, 3, 4 or 6 of subsection 12(4) that is carried on indoors, the following measures and procedures also apply:

1. Friable asbestos-containing material that is crumbled, pulverized or powdered and that is lying on any surface in the work area shall be cleaned up and removed using a vacuum equipped with a HEPA filter or by damp wiping and everything shall be removed from the work area or covered with polyethylene sheeting or other suitable material that is impervious to asbestos.

2. The spread of dust from the work area shall be prevented by an enclosure of polyethylene or other suitable material that is impervious to asbestos, if the work area is not enclosed by walls, and by a decontamination facility consisting of a series of interconnecting rooms including,

    i. a room suitable for changing into protective clothing and for storing contaminated protective clothing and equipment,

    ii. a shower room as described in paragraph 7,

    iii. a room suitable for changing into street clothes and for storing clean clothing and equipment, and

    iv. curtains of polyethylene sheeting or other suitable material that is impervious to asbestos, fitted to each side of the entrance or exit to each room.

3. The rooms described in subparagraphs 2 i, ii and iii shall be arranged in sequence and constructed so that any person entering or leaving the work area must pass through each room.

4. The mechanical ventilation system serving the work area shall be disabled and all openings or voids, including ventilation ducts to or from the work area, shall be sealed by tape or other appropriate means.

5. Unless the operation is carried on inside a building that is to be demolished and will not be entered by any person except the workers involved in the operation and the workers involved in the demolition, the spread of dust from the work area shall also be prevented by,

    i. creating and maintaining within the enclosed area, by installing a ventilation system equipped with a HEPA filtered exhaust unit, a negative air pressure of 0.02 inches of water, relative to the area outside the enclosed area,

278/05

ii. ensuring that replacement air is taken from outside the enclosed area and is free from contamination with any hazardous dust, vapour, smoke, fume, mist or gas, and

iii. using a device, at regular intervals, to measure the difference in air pressure between the enclosed area and the area outside it.

6. The ventilation system referred to in subparagraph 5 i shall be inspected and maintained by a competent worker before each use to ensure that there is no air leakage, and if the filter is found to be damaged or defective, it shall be replaced before the ventilation system is used.

7. The shower room in the decontamination facility shall,

i. be provided with hot and cold water or water of a constant temperature that is not less than 40° Celsius or more than 50° Celsius,

ii. have individual controls inside the room to regulate water flow and, if there is hot and cold water, individual controls inside the room to regulate temperature,

iii. be capable of providing adequate supplies of hot water to maintain a water temperature of at least 40° Celsius, and

iv. be provided with clean towels.

8. When leaving the work area, a worker shall enter the decontamination facility and shall, in the following order,

i. decontaminate his or her protective clothing by using a vacuum equipped with a HEPA filter, or by damp wiping, before removing the protective clothing,

ii. if the protective clothing will not be reused, place it in a container as described in paragraph 5 of section 15,

iii. shower, and

iv. remove and clean the respirator.

9. If practicable, existing electrical power distribution systems that are not water-tight shall be de-energized and locked out where wet removal operations are to be carried out.

10. Temporary electrical power distribution systems for tools and equipment involved in wet removal operations shall be equipped with ground fault circuit interrupters.

11. Friable asbestos-containing material shall be thoroughly wetted before and during removal, unless wetting would create a hazard or cause damage.

12. The work area shall be inspected by a competent worker for defects in the enclosure, barriers and decontamination facility,

    i. at the beginning of each shift,

    ii. at the end of a shift if there is no shift that begins immediately after the first-named shift, and

    iii. at least once each day on days when there are no shifts.

13. Defects observed during an inspection under paragraph 12 shall be repaired immediately and no other work shall be carried out in the work area until the repair work is completed.

14. If practicable, dust and waste shall be kept wet.

15. On completion of the work,

    i. negative air pressure shall be maintained if required by subparagraph 5 i,

    ii. the inner surface of the enclosure and the work area inside the enclosure shall be cleaned by a thorough washing or by vacuuming with a vacuum equipped with a HEPA filter,

    iii. equipment, tools and other items used in the work shall be cleaned with a damp cloth or by vacuuming with a vacuum equipped with a HEPA filter or they shall be placed in a container as described in paragraph 5 of section 15 before being removed from the enclosure, and

    iv. a visual inspection shall be conducted by a competent worker to ensure that the enclosure and the work area inside the enclosure are free from visible dust, debris or residue that may contain asbestos.

16. Once the work area inside the enclosure is dry after the steps set out in subparagraphs 15 ii, iii and iv have been completed, clearance air testing shall be conducted by a competent worker in accordance with subsection (5), unless the operation is carried on inside a building that is to be demolished and will not be entered by any person except the workers involved in the operation and the workers involved in the demolition.

17. The barriers, enclosure and decontamination facility shall not be removed or dismantled until,

    i. cleaning has been done as described in paragraph 15, and

    ii. if clearance air testing is required, it has been completed and the work area inside the enclosure has passed the clearance air test.

278/05

(5) The following rules apply to clearance air testing:

    1. Sample collection and analysis shall be done,

        i. using the phase contrast microscopy method, in accordance with subsection (6), or

        ii. using the transmission electron microscopy method, in accordance with subsection (7).

    2. If the work area inside the enclosure fails the clearance air test, the steps set out in subparagraphs 15 ii, iii and iv of subsection (4) shall be repeated and the work area shall be allowed to dry before a further test is carried out, unless paragraph 6 of subsection (6) applies.

(6) Clearance air testing using the phase contrast microscopy method shall be carried out in accordance with U.S. National Institute of Occupational Safety and Health Manual of Analytical Methods, Method 7400, Issue 2: Asbestos and other Fibres by PCM (August 15, 1994), using the asbestos fibre counting rules, and shall comply with the following requirements:

    1. Testing shall be based on samples taken inside the enclosure.

    2. Forced air shall be used, both before and during the sampling process, to ensure that fibres are dislodged from all surfaces inside the enclosure before sampling begins and are kept airborne throughout the sampling process.

    3. At least 2,400 litres of air shall be drawn through each sample filter, even though the standard mentioned above provides for a different amount.

    4. The number of air samples to be collected shall be in accordance with Table 3.

    5. The work area inside the enclosure passes the clearance air test only if every air sample collected has a concentration of fibres that does not exceed 0.01 fibres per cubic centimetres of air.

    6. If the work area inside the enclosure fails a first test that is done using the phase contrast microscopy method, the samples may be subjected to a second analysis using transmission electron microscopy in accordance with the standard mentioned in subsection (7).

    7. When a second analysis is done as described in paragraph 6, the work area inside the enclosure passes the clearance air test only if every air sample collected has a concentration of asbestos fibres that does not exceed 0.01 fibres per cubic centimetre of air.

(7) Clearance air testing using the transmission electron microscopy method shall be carried out in accordance with U.S. National Institute of Occupational Safety and Health Manual of Analytical Methods, Method 7402, Issue 2: Asbestos by TEM (August 15, 1994), and shall comply with the following requirements:

    1. Testing shall be based on samples taken inside the enclosure and samples taken outside the enclosure but inside the building.

    2. Forced air shall be used inside the enclosure, both before and during the sampling process, to ensure that fibres are dislodged from all surfaces before sampling begins and are kept airborne throughout the sampling process.

    3. At least 2,400 litres of air shall be drawn through each sample filter, even though the standard mentioned above provides for a different amount.

    4. At least five air samples shall be taken inside each enclosure and at least five air samples shall be taken outside the enclosure but inside the building.

    5. Sampling inside and outside the enclosure shall be conducted concurrently.

    6. The work area inside the enclosure passes the clearance air test if the average concentration of asbestos fibres in the samples collected inside the enclosure is statistically less than the average concentration of asbestos fibres in the samples collected outside the enclosure, or if there is no statistical difference between the two average concentrations.

(8) Within 24 hours after the clearance air testing results are received,

    (a) the owner and the employer shall post a copy of the results in a conspicuous place or places,

        (i) at the workplace, and

        (ii) if the building contains other workplaces, in a common area of the building; and

    (b) a copy shall be provided to the joint health and safety committee or the health and safety representative, if any, for the workplace and for the building.

(9) The owner of the building shall keep a copy of the clearance air testing results for at least one year after receiving them.

19. Instruction and training —

278/05

(1) The employer shall ensure that instruction and training in the following subjects are provided by a competent person to every worker working in a Type 1, Type 2 or Type 3 operation:

1. The hazards of asbestos exposure.

2. Personal hygiene and work practices.

3. The use, cleaning and disposal of respirators and protective clothing.

(2) The joint health and safety committee or the health and safety representative, if any, for the workplace shall be advised of the time and place where the instruction and training prescribed by subsection (1) are to be carried out.

(3) Without restricting the generality of paragraph 3 of subsection (1), the instruction and training related to respirators shall include instruction and training related to,

(a) the limitations of the equipment;

(b) inspection and maintenance of the equipment;

(c) proper fitting of a respirator; and

(d) respirator cleaning and disinfection.

20. Asbestos abatement training programs —

(1) The employer shall ensure that,

(a) every worker involved in a Type 3 operation has successfully completed the Asbestos Abatement Worker Training Program approved by the Ministry of Training, Colleges and Universities; and

(b) every supervisor of a worker involved in a Type 3 operation has successfully completed the Asbestos Abatement Supervisor Training Program approved by the Ministry of Training, Colleges and Universities.

(2) The employer shall ensure that every worker and supervisor successfully completes the appropriate program required under subsection (1) before performing or supervising the work to which the program relates.

(3) A document issued by the Ministry of Training, Colleges and Universities, showing that a worker has successfully completed a program mentioned in subsection (1), is conclusive proof, for the purposes of this section, of his or her successful completion of the program.

(4) In accordance with the *Agreement on Internal Trade, 1995* and the *Protocols of Amendment*, a worker shall be deemed to hold a document showing successful completion referred to in subsection (3) if he or she has successfully completed equivalent training in another province or territory of Canada, as determined by the Director.

21. Asbestos work report —

(1) The employer of a worker working in a Type 2 operation or a Type 3 operation shall complete an asbestos work report in a form obtained from the Ministry for each such worker,

    (a) at least once in each 12-month period; and

    (b) immediately on the termination of the employment of the worker.

(2) As soon as the asbestos work report is completed, the employer shall,

    (a) forward it to the Provincial Physician, Ministry of Labour, and

    (b) give a copy to the worker.

(3) For the purposes of clause (2)(a), the employer may deliver the report to the Provincial Physician in person or send it by ordinary mail, by courier or by fax.

22. Asbestos Workers Register —

(1) The Provincial Physician, Ministry of Labour, shall establish and maintain an Asbestos Workers Register listing the name of each worker for whom an employer submits an asbestos work report under section 21.

(2) On the recommendation of the Provincial Physician, a worker who is listed in the Register may volunteer to undergo the prescribed medical examination described in paragraph 1 of subsection (4).

(3) A worker who has undergone the prescribed medical examination described in paragraph 1 of subsection (4) may volunteer to undergo subsequent examinations of the same type if they are recommended by his or her physician.

(4) The following medical examinations are prescribed for the purposes of subsection 26(3) of the Act:

    1. An examination consisting of a medical questionnaire, chest x-rays and pulmonary function tests.

    2. A subsequent examination that consists of the components described in paragraph 1, is recommended by the worker's physician and takes place at least two years after the most recent examination.

278/05

(5) A worker who is removed from exposure to asbestos because an examination discloses that he or she may have or has a condition resulting from exposure to asbestos and suffers a loss of earnings as a result of the removal from exposure to asbestos is entitled to compensation for the loss in the manner and to the extent provided by the *Workplace Safety and Insurance Act, 1997*.

23. Use of equivalent measure or procedure —

A constructor, in the case of a project, or the employer, in any other case, may vary a measure or procedure required by this Regulation if the following conditions are satisfied:

  1. The measure or procedure, as varied, affords protection for the health and safety of workers that is at least equal to the protection that would be provided by complying with this Regulation.

  2. The constructor or employer gives written notice of the varied measure or procedure, in advance, to the joint health and safety committee or the health and safety representative, if any, for the workplace.

24. Notice to inspector —

(1) When this Regulation requires written notice to an inspector at an office of the Ministry of Labour, the notice shall be given,

  (a) by delivering it to the office in person;

  (b) by sending it by ordinary mail, by courier or by fax, or

  (c) by sending the notice to the inspector by electronic means that are acceptable to the Ministry.

(2) When this Regulation requires oral notice to an inspector at an office of the Ministry of Labour, the notice shall be given,

  (a) in person;

  (b) by telephoning the inspector; or

  (c) by sending the notice to the inspector by electronic means that are acceptable to the Ministry.

25. Revocation —

Regulation 838 of the Revised Regulations of Ontario, 1990 is revoked.

26. Commencement —

(1) Subject to subsection (2), this Regulation comes into force on November 1, 2005.

(2) Section 20 comes into force on November 1, 2007.

TABLE 1 Bulk Material Samples

Subsection 3(3)

Item	Type of material	Size of area of homogeneous material	Minimum number of bulk material samples to be collected
1.	Surfacing material, including without limitation material that is applied to surfaces by spraying, by troweling or otherwise, such as acoustical plaster on ceilings and fireproofing materials on structural members	Less than 90 square metres	3
		90 or more square metres, but less than 450 square metres	5
		450 or more square metres	7
2.	Thermal insulation, except as described in item 3	Any size	3
3.	Thermal insulation patch	Less than 2 linear metres or 0.5 square metres	1
4.	Other material	Any size	3

TABLE 2 Respirators

Paragraph 12 of section 14 and paragraph 11 of section 15

Column 1	Column 2

278/05

Work Category	Required respirator
Type 1 Operations	
Worker requests that the employer provide a respirator to be used by the worker, as described in paragraph 12 of section 14	Air purifying half-mask respirator with N-100, R-100 or P-100 particulate filter
Type 2 Operations	
Work described in paragraph 1 of subsection 12(3)	One of the following: - Air purifying full-face-piece respirator with N-100, R-100 or P-100 particulate filter - Powered air purifying respirator equipped with a tight-fitting facepiece (half or full-facepiece) and a high efficiency filter or N-100, P-100 or R-100 particulate filter - Negative pressure (demand) supplied air respirator equipped with a full-facepiece - Continuous flow supplied air respirator equipped with a tight fitting facepiece (half or full-facepiece)

Work described in paragraphs 2 to 7 and 9 to 11 of subsection 12(3)		Air purifying half-mask respirator with N-100, R-100 or P-100 particulate filter
Breaking, cutting, drilling, abrading, grinding, sanding or vibrating non-friable material containing asbestos by means of power tools, if the tool is attached to a dust collecting device equipped with a HEPA filter as described in paragraph 8 of subsection 12(3)	Material is not wetted	One of the following: - Air purifying full-facepiece respirator with N-100, R-100 or P-100 particulate filter - Powered air purifying respirator equipped with a tight-fitting facepiece (half or full-facepiece) and a high efficiency filter or N-100, P-100 or R-100 particulate filter - Negative pressure (demand) supplied air respirator equipped with a full-facepiece - Continuous flow supplied air respirator equipped with a tight fitting facepiece (half or full-facepiece)

278/05

	Material is wetted to control spread of fibre	Air purifying half-mask respirator with N-100, R-100 or P-100 particulate filter
Type 3 Operations		

Breaking, cutting, drilling, abrading, grinding, sanding or vibrating non-friable material containing asbestos by means of power tools, if the tool is not attached to a dust collecting device equipped with a HEPA filter as described in paragraph 5 of subsection 12(4)	Material is not wetted	Pressure demand supplied air respirator equipped with a half mask
	Material is wetted to control spread of fibre	One of the following: - Air purifying full-face-piece respirator with N-100, R-100 or P-100 particulate filter - Powered air purifying respirator equipped with a tight-fitting facepiece (half or full-facepiece) and a high efficiency filter or N-100, P-100 or R-100 particulate filter - Negative pressure (demand) supplied air respirator equipped with a full-facepiece - Continuous flow supplied air respirator equipped with a tight fitting facepiece (half or full-facepiece)
Work with friable material containing asbestos, as described in paragraphs 1 to 4 and 6 of subsection 12(4)	Material is not wetted	Pressure demand supplied air respirator equipped with a full facepiece

278/05

Work with friable material, as described in paragraphs 1 to 4 and 6 of subsection 12(4), that contains a type of asbestos other than chrysotile	Material was applied or installed by spraying, and is wetted to control spread of fibre	Pressure demand supplied air respirator equipped with a half mask
Work with friable material, as described in paragraphs 1 to 4 and 6 of subsection 12(4), that contains only chrysotile asbestos		One of the following: - Air purifying full-face-piece respirator with N-100, R-100 or P-100 particulate filter - Powered air purifying respirator equipped with a tight-fitting facepiece (half or full-facepiece) and a high efficiency filter or N-100, P-100 or R-100 particulate filter - Negative pressure (demand) supplied air respirator equipped with a full-facepiece - Continuous flow supplied air respirator equipped with a tight fitting facepiece (half or full-facepiece)

Work with friable material containing asbestos, as described in paragraphs 1 to 4 and 6 of subsection 12(4)	Material was not applied or installed by spraying, and is wetted to control spread of fibre	One of the following: - Air purifying full-face-piece respirator with N-100, R-100 or P-100 particulate filter - Powered air purifying respirator equipped with a tight-fitting facepiece (half or full-facepiece) and a high efficiency filter or N-100, P-100 or R-100 particulate filter - Negative pressure (demand) supplied air respirator equipped with a full-facepiece - Continuous flow supplied air respirator equipped with a tight fitting facepiece (half or full-facepiece)

TABLE 3 Air Samples

Paragraph 4 of subsection 18(6)

Minimum number of air samples to be taken from each enclosure	Area of enclosure
2	10 square metres or less
3	More than 10 but less than 500 square

278/05

	metres
5	500 square metres or more

ONT. REG. 629/94 — DIVING OPERATIONS

made under the *Occupational Health and Safety Act*

O. Reg. 629/94, as am. O. Reg. 155/04; 32/14, ss. 1-53, 54 (Fr.).

Part I — Interpretation

1. In this Regulation,

"**adequate**", in relation to a procedure, material, device, object or any other thing, means sufficient for its intended and actual use and sufficient to protect a worker from damage to the worker's body or health, and "**adequately**" has a corresponding meaning;

"**aquarium exhibit diver**" means a diver who, at an aquarium facility, maintains underwater exhibits, conducts public presentations or monitors animal husbandry;

"**atmospheric diving**" means diving where the diver is always at one atmosphere;

"**atmospheric diving system**" means a diving system designed to withstand external pressures greater than one atmosphere while the internal pressure remains at one atmosphere and includes a one-person submarine;

"**bail-out system**" means an emergency breathing mixture supply worn by a diver;

"**bottom time**" means the total elapsed time measured in minutes, from the time a descending diver leaves the surface to the time the diver begins final ascent, rounded to the next whole minute;

"**breathing mixture**" means a mixture of gases for human respiration and includes pure oxygen;

"**CSA Standard**" means a standard published by the Canadian Standards Association;

"decompression" means the procedure that a diver follows during the ascent from depth in order to minimize the risk of decompression sickness;

"deep diving" means diving to depths greater than 165 feet;

"dive site" means a surface location at which diving personnel and equipment are located in support of the underwater work site;

"diver" means,

 (a) an atmospheric diving system operator, and

 (b) a worker who performs work underwater at any pressure greater than one atmosphere, and includes a standby diver who dives in the event of a health or safety emergency;

"diver's tender" means a competent person who assists a diver at the dive site;

"diving operation" means work performed underwater by divers or work performed on the surface in support of divers, and includes underwater inspection, investigation, excavation, construction, alteration, repair or maintenance of equipment, machinery, structures or ships and the salvage of sunken property;

"employer associated with a diving operation" means an employer of,

 (a) a diver who participates in the diving operation,

 (b) a standby diver who participates in the diving operation,

 (c) a diver's tender who participates in the diving operation,

 (d) a diving supervisor for the diving operation,

 (e) a hyperbaric chamber operator who participates in the diving operation,

 (f) a life support technician who participates in the diving operation, or

 (g) any other worker who participates in the diving operation at or near the dive site or underwater work site;

"hyperbaric chamber" means a pressure vessel and associated equipment designed for subjecting humans to pressures greater than one atmosphere;

"lifeline" means a safety rope used to tether a diver;

"liveboating" means a diving operation conducted from a vessel the propeller of which is turning, whether the vessel is stationary or moving;

"lock-out submersible" [Repealed O. Reg. 32/14, s. 1(6).]

"**lock-out**" means made inoperable by means that are under the direct control of the diving supervisor or a person authorized by the diving supervisor;

"**man basket**" means a device used to transport a diver from a height above the water surface to the surface of the water for safe entry and exit to and from the water;

"**mixed gas**" means a breathing mixture other than air;

"**non-saturation diving**" means diving in which decompression occurs during ascent from the underwater work site;

"**open (wet) bell**" means a diving bell designed to be operated without a differential pressure across its hull;

"**saturation chamber**" means a hyperbaric chamber that is equipped to permit divers to remain under pressure for an unlimited period of time;

"**saturation diving**" means diving in which the decompression procedure used allows a bottom time of unlimited duration;

"**scientific diving**" means diving performed on behalf of an educational or research institution for the purpose of collecting specimens or data for scientific use;

"**S.C.U.B.A.**" means a self-contained underwater breathing apparatus;

"**sledding**" means a diving technique in which a diver who uses S.C.U.B.A. and a dive sled is pulled through water by a vessel;

"**stage**" means a device used to lower or raise a diver to or from an underwater work site but does not include an open (wet) bell, a submersible compression chamber, an atmospheric diving system or a man basket;

"**standby diver**" means a diver who is present at the dive site or in a submersible compression chamber and is prepared to rescue a submerged diver should rescue become necessary;

"**submersible compression chamber**" means a hyperbaric chamber that has the capacity to transport divers at pressures greater than one atmosphere from the surface to an underwater work site and back;

"**submersible compression chamber attendant**" [Repealed O. Reg. 32/14, s. 1(10).]

629/94

"surface-supplied diving" means diving where the diver is supplied with a breathing mixture through an umbilical bundle, whether or not an open (wet) bell or a submersible compression chamber is used;

"umbilical bundle" means a composite of hoses, wires and cables designed to supply services, such as breathing mixtures, power, heat and communications, from the surface to a diver, to an open (wet) bell or to a submersible compression chamber;

"underwater work site" means the underwater location where work is performed;

"UXO diving operation" means a diving operation involving searching for, locating, accessing, identifying, diagnosing, limiting damage from, recovering, or finally disposing of underwater unexploded explosive ordnance or munitions;

"water control structure" includes dams, head gates, stop logs, turbine intake gates and pump intake gates.

"wet bell" [Repealed O. Reg. 32/14, s. 1(14).]

O. Reg. 32/14 s. 1

Part II — General

Application

2. (1) This Regulation applies in relation to,

(a) any diving operation: and

(b) any function in support of a diving operation.

(2) Despite subsection (1), this Regulation does not apply in relation to,

(a) recreational diving, including any diving operation whose purpose is to train people for recreational diving;

(b) any diving operation in which the only underwater breathing equipment used is snorkelling equipment;

(c) a dive the sole purpose of which is to respond to an unforeseen emergency situation involving imminent danger to the life, health or safety of any person, if the dive is undertaken voluntarily; or

(d) any function in support of a diving operation described in clause (a) or (b) or any dive described in clause (c).

O. Reg. 155/04 s. 1

Method of Giving Notice to Ministry

3. (1) In this section,

"Form" means the form available from the Ministry entitled **"Notice of Diving Operation"**.

(2) Written notice required by this Regulation shall be given by completing the Form and,

    (a) delivering it to the address specified on the Form;

    (b) faxing it to the number specified on the Form; or

    (c) sending it as otherwise specified on the Form.

(3) Oral notice required by this Regulation shall be given by telephoning the number specified on the Form.

O. Reg. 155/04 s. 2; 32/14 s. 2

Equivalency

4. (1) An employer, owner, constructor or diving supervisor may vary a procedure required by this Regulation or a composition, design, size or arrangement of a material, object, device or thing required by this Regulation if,

    (a) the varied procedure, composition, design, size or arrangement affords protection for the health and safety of workers that is at least equal to the protection that would otherwise be afforded; and

    (b) written notice of the variance has been given to the joint health and safety committee or the health and safety representative, if any, and to the Ministry.

(2) Subsection (1) does not apply in respect of any requirement in the Act or this Regulation to give notice.

O. Reg. 32/14 s. 3

Duties of Employers, Constructors and Owners

4.1(1) In this section,

"Standard" means CSA Standard Z275.4-12, **"Competency Standard for diving, hyperbaric chamber, and remotely operated vehicle operations"**.

(2) An employer shall ensure that every person who participates in a diving operation meets the competency requirement applicable to the type of diving operation being participated in as set out in the Standard.

(3) For the purposes of subsection (2) and despite Clause 1.5 of the Standard, the Standard applies to scientific diving as defined in section 1 of this Regulation.

(4) For the purposes of subsection (2) and despite Clause 5.1 of the Standard, Clause 5 of the Standard applies to aquarium exhibit divers using S.C.U.B.A. to the maximum depth of the aquarium facility.

(5) For the purposes of subsection (2), Clause 5.8.1 of the Standard applies to aquarium exhibit divers for work performed at an aquarium facility.

(6) For the purposes of subsection (2) and despite Clause 5.8.2 of the Standard, an aquarium exhibit diver shall complete 25 dives and 15 hours of bottom time at an aquarium facility to fulfil the in-water training requirement.

(7) For the purposes of subsection (2), Clauses 32 and 33 of the Standard do not apply.

O. Reg. 155/04 s. 3; 32/14 s. 4

5. (1) Each constructor of a project where a diving operation is to take place, each employer associated with a diving operation and each owner associated with a diving operation shall ensure that the Ministry is given notice of the diving operation.

(2) Except as provided in subsections (3) and (3.1), notice under subsection (1) shall be given,

    (a) in writing at least 24 hours before the diving operation begins; or

    (b) orally at least 24 hours before the diving operation begins and in writing within five days after the day on which the diving operation begins.

(3) If a mixed gas is expected to be used in the diving operation other than in a diving operation involving emergency recovery, inspection or repair, notice shall be given in writing at least 24 hours before the diving operation begins.

(3.1) In the event of an emergency recovery, inspection or repair,

    (a) oral notice shall be given to the Ministry before any diving equipment is moved to the dive site; and

(b) written notice shall be given to the Ministry within five days after the day on which the diving operation begins.

(4) Written notice under subsection (1) shall include the following:

1. Information sufficient to permit an inspector to locate the dive site.

2. The expected starting date and duration of the diving operation.

3. The dates when and times of day during which the diving operation is expected to be carried out.

4. The name, mailing address and telephone number of an owner, constructor or employer who is associated with the diving operation.

5. The names of all diving supervisors for the diving operation appointed under section 6.

6. The expected maximum depth of any dive in the diving operation.

7. A description of the tasks expected to be performed in the diving operation.

8. The breathing mixtures expected to be used in the diving operation.

9. A statement whether the diving operation is to be offshore or onshore.

10. A statement whether recirculating S.C.U.B.A. is to be used in the diving operation.

11. A statement whether the diving operation is one to which Part XI applies.

(5) Oral notice under subsection (1) shall include the following:

1. Information sufficient to permit an inspector to locate the dive site.

2. The expected starting date and duration of the diving operation.

3. The dates when and times of day during which the diving operation is expected to be carried out.

4. The name, mailing address and telephone number of an owner, constructor or employer who is associated with the diving operation.

5. A statement whether the diving operation is to be offshore or onshore.

(6) Each person responsible for ensuring that notice of a diving operation is given under subsection (1) shall also ensure that prior oral notice is given to the Ministry of any departure from the plans described in the notice under subsection (1).

(7) Notice under subsection (6) shall be given as soon as reasonably possible.

O. Reg. 32/14 s. 5

6. Each person responsible for ensuring that notice of a diving operation is given under subsection 5(1) shall also ensure,

> (a) that one or more competent persons are appointed as diving supervisors for the diving operation; and
>
> (b) that one of the persons appointed under clause (a) is present at the dive site, and is acting as diving supervisor whenever the diving operation is being carried out.

O. Reg. 32/14 s. 6

7. (1) Each person responsible for ensuring that notice of a diving operation is given under subsection 5(1) shall also ensure that a written operational plan and a written contingency plan for the diving operation are prepared, with input from one or more of the diving supervisors appointed for the diving operation under section 6.

(2) An operational plan shall,

> (a) describe the tasks to be performed in the diving operation;
>
> (b) state how the tasks referred to in clause (a) are to be performed;
>
> (c) state how the hazards that could be encountered in the diving operation are to be identified and handled; and
>
> (d) state which agencies, plants and facilities will be given notice under section 9.

(3) A contingency plan shall,

> (a) include instructions for communicating with medical assistance in the event of an emergency;
>
> (b) outline emergency procedures for the evacuation of an injured diver from the dive site;
>
> (c) outline emergency procedures for responding to any significant failure of a component of any diving equipment;
>
> (d) outline emergency procedures for responding to a loss of communications with a diver;
>
> (e) outline emergency procedures for responding to hazardous weather or ice conditions;
>
> (f) outline emergency procedures for aborting a dive; and

(g) outline emergency procedures for responding to any inability of an offshore dive site to maintain station.

8. Each person responsible for ensuring that notice of a diving operation is given under subsection 5(1) shall also ensure that each of the following is available for inspection by an inspector at the dive site whenever the diving operation is being carried out:

1. A copy of any written notice that has been given in respect of the diving operation under subsection 5(1).

2. Where written notice has not yet been given in respect of the diving operation under subsection 5(1), a written statement including the date of the oral notice given in respect of the diving operation and the name of the person to whom the oral notice was given.

3. A copy of the operational plan prepared for the diving operation under section 7.

4. A copy of the contingency plan prepared for the diving operation under section 7.

5. A copy of this Regulation.

6. A copy of any CSA Standard referred to in this Regulation that may apply to the diving operation.

O. Reg. 32/14 s. 7

9. (1) Each person responsible for ensuring that notice of a diving operation is given under subsection 5(1) shall also ensure that notice of the diving operation is given to,

(a) each law enforcement agency that,

(i) has responsibilities in relation to the area in which the dive site is located, and

(ii) would need to know about the diving operation in order to ensure that it is carried out safely and in a manner that takes into account other activities and events in the area;

(b) each industrial plant that is within two kilometres of the dive site and might discharge effluent that would be harmful to the health or safety of a worker associated with the diving operation; and

(c) each water control facility, such as a hydro-electric authority, or water intake plant that is within one kilometre of the dive site.

(2) For the purposes of clause (1)(a), examples of law enforcement agencies include harbour commissions, harbour masters, navigable water authorities and police departments.

629/94

(3) For the purposes of subsection (1), notice is given to an agency, plant or facility when it is given to a person with control over or responsibility for the agency, plant or facility.

(4) Notice under subsection (1) shall include the following:

1. Information sufficient to permit the person receiving the notice to locate the dive site.
2. The expected starting date and duration of the diving operation.
3. The dates when and times of day during which the diving operation is expected to be carried out.
4. The name, mailing address and telephone number of an owner, constructor or employer who is associated with the diving operation.

(5) Notice under subsection (1) shall be given at least 24 hours before the diving operation begins and may be given orally or in writing.

(6) Despite subsection (5), notice may be given less than 24 hours before the diving operation begins in the case of an emergency.

O. Reg. 32/14 s. 8

10. (1) Each person responsible for ensuring that notice of a diving operation is given under subsection 5(1) shall also ensure that the Ministry is given written notice if any of the following incidents occur in connection with the diving operation;

    1. A diver becoming trapped underwater.

    2. A diver failing to comply with the decompression requirements of this Regulation.

    3. Failure of any diving equipment posing a risk to the health or safety of a diver.

    4. Emergency rescue of a diver in a submersible compression chamber or atmospheric diving system.

    5. Emergency use of a recompression chamber.

    6. A person becoming unconscious.

    7. A diver suffering from decompression sickness.

(2) A notice under subsection (1) shall be given within two days of the incident and shall include the following:

    1. The name, mailing address and telephone number of an owner, constructor or employer associated with the diving operation.

    2. The nature and the circumstances of the incident.

    2.1 The injury or illness, if any, sustained by any person as a result of the incident.

3. The time and place of the incident.

4. The name and address of any person who sustained injury or illness as a result of the incident.

5. The steps taken to prevent a recurrence.

O. Reg. 32/14 s. 9

Notices and Reports

11. (1) A written report under subsection 51(1) of the Act respecting an occurrence in which a person is killed or critically injured shall set out,

(a) the name and address of the person submitting the report;

(b) the nature and the circumstances of the occurrence;

(b.1) the bodily injury sustained by the person;

(c) a description of any machinery, equipment or procedure involved;

(d) the time and place of the occurrence;

(e) the name and address of the person who was killed or critically injured;

(f) the names and addresses of all witnesses to the occurrence;

(g) the name and address of the physician or surgeon, if any, by whom the person was or is being attended for the injury; and

(h) the steps taken to prevent a recurrence.

(2) A written notice under subsection 52(1) of the Act respecting an occurrence shall set out,

(a) the nature and the circumstances of the occurrence and the injury or illness sustained by any person as a result of the occurrence;

(b) the nature and the circumstances of the occurrence;

(b.1) the injury or illness sustained by any person as a result of the occurrence;

(c) a description of any machinery, equipment or procedure involved;

(d) the time and place of the occurrence;

(e) the name and address of any person who sustained injury or illness as a result of the occurrence;

(f) the names and addresses of all witnesses to the occurrence;

(g) the name and address of the physician or surgeon, if any, by whom the person was or is being attended for the injury or illness; and

(h) the steps taken to prevent a recurrence.

(3) A written notice under subsection 52(2) of the Act respecting an illness shall set out,

(a) the name and address of the person submitting the notice;

(b) the nature of the occupational illness;

(c) the name and address of the worker involved;

(d) the name and address of the physician or surgeon, if any, by whom the worker was or is being attended for the illness; and

(e) the steps taken to prevent a recurrence.

O. Reg. 32/14 s. 10

Duties of Diving Supervisors

12. (1) The diving supervisor for a diving operation shall have proof of his or her training and his or her diving log book or equivalent statement of diving experience at the dive site and available for inspection by an inspector.

(2) The diving supervisor for a diving operation shall be present at the dive site and shall be in direct control of the diving operation whenever the diving operation is being carried out.

(3) The diving supervisor for a diving operation shall,

(a) ensure that the operational plan and the contingency plan for the diving operation are followed;

(b) brief the workers associated with the diving operation on the operational plan, the contingency plan and the procedures to be followed during the diving operation;

(c) ensure that each diver participating in the diving operation is competent and fit to perform the work;

(d) ensure that each diver has his or her diving log book at the dive site and available for inspection by an inspector;

(e) immediately before each dive, review the nature of the hazards that could be encountered in the underwater work site and brief divers on those hazards;

(f) ensure that any diving equipment to be used in the diving operation is examined by a competent person at least once on each day on which it is to used, before the use, and is tested and repaired as appropriate;

(g) ensure that, whenever the diving operation is being carried out, adequate warning devices are displayed to indicate the area around the dive site that is to be kept clear of any equipment other than that associated with the diving operation;

(h) except in the case of a health or safety emergency, ensure that a diver is not permitted to remain at any depth longer than the maximum time planned for the depth of the dive;

(i) supervise all decompression and therapeutic recompression in strict accordance with adequate decompression procedures and tables;

(j) terminate or interrupt the diving operation if continuing the operation may endanger the health or safety of any worker.

(4) The diving supervisor for a diving operation shall supervise the standby divers associated with the diving operation and, in particular, shall,

(a) ensure that an adequate number of standby divers are present and properly positioned at the dive site or submersible compression chamber so that each submerged diver can be reached as quickly as possible in the event that he or she needs to be rescued;

(b) ensure that no person is permitted to act as a standby diver unless he or she is adequately trained, having regard to the depths and circumstances in which the standby diver would have to operate should a rescue become necessary;

(c) ensure that each standby diver is adequately dressed and has adequate diving and communication equipment checked, ready and at hand, having regard to the depths and circumstances in which the standby diver would have to operate should a rescue become necessary;

(d) ensure that each standby diver is equipped with a lifeline or umbilical bundle that is at least 10 feet longer than the lifeline of any submerged diver the standby diver might need to rescue;

(e) ensure that no standby diver is assigned any duties other than,

(i) duties of standby diver,

(ii) where the standby diver is also acting as diving supervisor, duties of diving supervisor, and

(iii) duties of communicating with a submerged diver; and

629/94

451

(f) ensure that no standby diver dives or leaves the submersible compression chamber except in the event of a health or safety emergency.

(g) [Repealed O. Reg. 32/14, s. 11(5).]

(h) [Repealed O. Reg. 32/14, s. 11(5).]

(i) [Repealed O. Reg. 32/14, s. 11(5).]

(5) The diving supervisor for a diving operation shall supervise the divers' tenders associated with the diving operation and, in particular, shall,

(a) ensure that a diver's tender is acceptable to each diver to be tended by him or her;

(b) ensure that no diver's tender is assigned to any duties other than,

(i) duties of diver's tender, and

(ii) where the diver's tender is also acting as diving supervisor, duties of diving supervisor,

(iii) [Repealed O. Reg. 32/14, s. 11(6).]

(c) ensure that no person is permitted to act as a diver's tender unless he or she meets the competency requirement applicable to the type of diving operation being participated in as set out in Clause 7 of CSA Standard Z275.4-12, "Competency Standard for diving, hyperbaric chamber, and remotely operated vehicle operations"

(6) Except in the event of a health or safety emergency, a person acting as a diving supervisor for a diving operation shall not dive.

(7) [Repealed O. Reg. 32/14, s. 11(8).]

O. Reg. 32/14 s. 11

Duties of Divers and Standby Divers

13. (1) Before participating in a diving operation, a diver or standby diver shall ensure that he or she,

(a) understands the operational plan and the contingency plan for the diving operation;

(b) is aware of the hazards that could be encountered in the underwater work site;

(c) has his or her diving log book at the dive site and available for inspection by an inspector;

(d) has undergone a medical examination in accordance with section 32;

(e) has a physician's statement, obtained in accordance with section 32, at the dive site and available for inspection by an inspector;

(f) is not fatigued; and

(g) is not impaired in his or her diving ability because of consumption of alcohol or drugs.

(h) [Repealed O. Reg. 32/14, s. 12(1).]

(2) A diver or standby diver who is unfit to dive shall promptly inform the diving supervisor of that fact and shall refrain from diving or from acting as standby diver.

(3) Immediately before diving, while at the dive site, a diver or standby diver shall check that he or she has all the necessary personal diving equipment and that it is all functioning properly.

(4) At the onset of any sign of equipment malfunction or distress on the part of any submerged diver, a diver shall, if possible, notify the diver's tender, the diving supervisor and any diving partner and terminate the dive.

(5) On completion of any dive for which this Regulation does not require decompression, a diver, other than an atmospheric diving system operator, shall remain under observation in the presence of the diving supervisor for a period set by the diving supervisor.

(6) On completion of any dive for which this Regulation requires decompression, a diver, other than an atmospheric diving system operator, shall remain under observation at the dive site for at least one hour.

(7) Where the diving supervisor is of the opinion that, because of the nature of a dive to which subsection (6) applies, a diver should remain under observation for a period longer than one hour, the diver shall remain under observation at the dive site for such longer period as the diving supervisor sets.

(8) A diver, other than an atmospheric diving system operator, shall not fly at an altitude greater than 1,000 feet above the dive site during,

(a) the 12-hour period following a no-decompression dive;

(b) the 24-hour period following an air dive requiring decompression;

(c) the 24-hour period following a mixed gas dive requiring decompression with a bottom time of less than two hours;

629/94

(d) the 48-hour period following a mixed gas dive requiring decompression with a bottom time of two hours or longer;

(e) the 72-hour period following a saturation dive; and

(f) any period set by an attending physician following treatment for decompression sickness.

(9) A standby diver shall ensure that he or she,

(a) does not dive or leave a submersible compression chamber except in the event of a health or safety emergency;

(b) does not perform any duties other than,

(i) duties of standby diver,

(ii) where he or she is also acting as diving supervisor, duties of diving supervisor, and

(iii) duties of communicating with a submerged diver; and

(c) is adequately dressed and has adequate diving and communication equipment checked, ready and at hand, having regard to the depths and circumstances in which the standby would have to operate should a rescue become necessary.

(10) [Repealed O. Reg. 32/14, s. 12(3).]

O. Reg. 32/14 s. 12

Duties of Diver's Tenders

14. A diver's tender shall ensure that he or she does not perform any duties other than,

(a) tending a diver's lifeline;

(b) providing tools and equipment to a diver;

(c) operating a compressor and associated equipment; and

(d) where he or she is also acting as a diving supervisor, performing the duties of diving supervisor.

O. Reg. 32/14 s. 13

Part III — Equipment

Diving Equipment — General

15. (1) Each employer associated with a diving operation and the diving supervisor for a diving operation shall ensure that all diving equipment to be used in the diving operation is adequate.

(2) Without limiting the generality of subsection (1), each employer associated with a diving operation and the diving supervisor for a diving operation shall ensure that all diving equipment to be used in the diving operation,

(a) is of sound construction and adequate strength and is free from patent defects;

(b) is adequately maintained;

(c) is tested and repaired by a competent person in accordance with the manufacturer's recommended procedures; and

(d) is constructed in a way that ensures against malfunctions caused by low air or water temperatures or by the expansion of air or gas.

(3) Each employer associated with a diving operation and the diving supervisor for a diving operation shall ensure that all written material necessary for adequate dive site maintenance and operation of all diving equipment to be used in the diving operation is available at the dive site.

(4) For the purposes of subsection (3), examples of written material include operation manuals, field manuals, maintenance manuals, alerts and safety checklists.

(5) Each employer associated with a diving operation and the diving supervisor for a diving operation shall ensure that any compressed gas cylinder to be used in the diving operation is hydrostatically tested and visually inspected in accordance with CSA Standard Z275.2-11, "Occupational Safety Code for Diving Operations".

O. Reg. 32/14 s. 14

Personal Diving Equipment

16. (1) A diver participating in a diving operation and the diving supervisor for the diving operation shall ensure that the diver is adequately equipped.

(2) A standby diver participating in a diving operation and the diving supervisor for the diving operation shall ensure that the standby diver is adequately equipped.

(3) Without limiting the generality of subsection (1), a diver, other than an atmospheric diving system operator, participating in a diving operation and the diving supervisor for the diving operation shall ensure that the diver is equipped with,

(a) a knife that is adequately strong and sharp;

629/94

455

(b) adequate weights;

(c) an adequate diving suit or, where a diving suit is not necessary because of the circumstances of the dive, other adequate protective clothing; and

(d) a five-point diving harness that meets the requirements of Clause 8.3.5 of CSA Standard Z275.2-11, "Occupational Safety Code for "Diving Operations".

(4) Clauses (3)(a) and (d) do not apply to an aquarium exhibit diver.

O. Reg. 32/14 s. 15

17. (1) The diving supervisor for a diving operation shall ensure that, whenever diving is in progress, the dive site is adequately equipped.

(2) Without limiting the generality of subsection (1), the diving supervisor for a diving operation shall ensure, whenever diving is in progress, that the dive site is equipped with,

(a) an oxygen system capable of administering an adequate quantity of 100 per cent pure oxygen to an injured diver until the diver is under the care of a paramedic, physician or other person who,

(i) is qualified to determine whether the diver requires continued oxygen,

(ii) has a source of 100 per cent pure oxygen, and

(iii) is capable of continuing to administer oxygen if required;

(b) a first-aid kit that is adequate having regard to the nature and circumstances of the diving operation;

(c) a set of adequate decompression tables;

(d) where appropriate because of temperature conditions, an adequate climate-controlled facility for the use of workers that is located at or adequately near to the dive site;

(e) an adequate two-way communication system connecting the dive site with medical assistance;

(f) adequate means to facilitate the entry and exit of divers to and from the water;

(g) adequate means to facilitate the immediate exit from the water of an unconscious diver; and

(h) any other equipment that may be required to protect the health and safety of workers, having regard to the nature and circumstances of the diving operation.

(2.1) For the purposes of clause (2)(f), a ladder is not an adequate means to facilitate the entry and exit of divers to and from the water if the dive site is located more than five metres above the water.

(3) Each employer associated with a diving operation and the diving supervisor for a diving operation shall ensure that the dive site is of sufficient size to accommodate all workers and equipment needed for the diving operation without overcrowding.

(4) Where a diving operation is to be conducted from an offshore dive site, each employer associated with the diving operation and the diving supervisor for the diving operation shall ensure that, whenever there are workers present at the dive site,

    (a) there are at least two adequate means of evacuating workers from the dive site; or

    (b) a vessel equipped with an adequate primary motor and an adequate back-up motor is available at the dive site as a means of evacuating workers from the dive site.

(5) Each employer associated with a diving operation and the diving supervisor for a diving operation shall ensure that any vessel used in the diving operation is capable of maintaining station or of being anchored or moored without risk to any diver.

O. Reg. 32/14 s. 16

Lifelines

18. (1) The diving supervisor for a diving operation shall ensure that an adequate lifeline or strength member is attached to each diver participating in the diving operation when the diver is in the water.

(2) Subsection (1) does not apply to an atmospheric diving system operator or an aquarium exhibit diver.

(3) Without limiting the generality of subsection (1), the diving supervisor for a diving operation shall ensure that any lifeline or strength member used in the diving operation,

    (a) is free of knots or splices, other than knots or splices necessary to attach the lifeline or strength member to the diver and to the dive site or submersible compression chamber;

    (b) has a breaking strength of not less than 907 kilograms;

    (c) is securely attached to the diver's harness by a device that has a breaking strength of not less than 907 kilograms;

629/94

(d) is no longer than is required to perform the work;

(e) is securely attached to the dive site or submersible compression chamber, if the diver is using surface-supplied diving techniques;

(f) is securely attached to the dive site or to a float visible to the diver's tender, if the diver is using S.C.U.B.A;

(g) is tended at all times by a diver's tender continuously holding the umbilical bundle, if the diver is working at a location where,

    (i) differential pressure hazards may exist,

    (ii) strong currents exist,

    (iii) the diver may fall into deeper depth, or

    (iv) liveboating is in progress;

(h) is tended by an in-water diver's tender during penetration dives, if line pull signals are not effective or if the diver cannot be pulled to the surface without danger of entanglement;

(i) is tended at all times by a diver's tender continuously holding the lifeline or, in the case of a lifeline attached to a float, continuously observing the float, if the diver is using S.C.U.B.A.;

(j) is tended at all times by a standby diver continuously holding the umbilical bundle, if the diver is operating from a submersible compression chamber; and

(k) is incorporated in the umbilical bundle, if the diver is using an umbilical bundle.

(4) Despite subsection (1), a diving supervisor may permit a diver to operate untethered if,

(a) the diver is a police diver searching for and disposing of explosives;

(b) the diver is working in accordance with the requirements of Clause 4.5 of CSA Standard Z275.6-11, "Unexploded Explosive Ordnance (UXO) and Munitions Diving"; or

(c) the diver is a police diver using a dive sled that is outfitted with an adequate diver locating device.

O. Reg. 32/14 s. 17

Communications

19. (1) Each employer associated with a diving operation and the diving supervisor for a diving operation shall ensure that each submerged diver, other than an aquarium exhibit diver, is connected to the dive site by a two-way communication system that is adequate and that meets the requirements of subsections (2) to (5).

(2) Subject to subsection (3), the two-way communication system may be by voice or by pre-arranged line signals.

(3) The two-way communication system must be by voice where,

    (a) the depth of the dive exceeds 100 feet;

    (b) a diver uses any power tool, explosive, burning equipment or welding equipment;

    (c) a diver directs the use of any hoisting device to place any materials underwater while the diver is underwater;

    (d) a diver works in or near a pipe, tunnel, duct, underwater intake or other confined space or in or near a water control structure;

    (e) a diver places any materials underwater in a way that poses a risk to the health or safety of the diver;

    (f) an atmospheric diving system is used;

    (g) an open (wet) bell is used;

    (h) a submersible compression chamber is used;

    (i) the diving operation is one to which Part XI applies; or

    (j) during sledding, nothing underwater interferes with through-water voice communication.

(4) For the purposes of clause (3)(d), a diver works near a thing where the proximity of the thing to the diver poses a health or safety risk to the diver.

(5) The two-way voice communication system must,

    (a) afford sound reproduction that enables the diver's breathing to be heard clearly; and

    (b) where a breathing mixture containing helium or any other gas that significantly distorts voice transmission is used, unscramble voices effectively.

(6) Each employer associated with a diving operation and the diving supervisor for a diving operation shall ensure that,

    (a) all communication through a two-way voice communication system used for a dive to a depth greater than 165 feet or for a dive using an atmospheric diving system is continuously recorded; and

    (b) the recordings referred to in clause (a) are saved for at least 48 hours after they are made.

(7) Each employer associated with a diving operation and the diving supervisor for a diving operation shall ensure that each submerged diver operating at a depth greater than 100 feet is connected to the dive site by an adequate back-up two-way communications system that is independent of the primary communications system required by subsection (1).

(8) Each employer associated with a diving operation and the diving supervisor for a diving operation shall ensure that any atmospheric diving system or submersible compression chamber used in a diving operation is provided with an adequate back-up two-way communications system that is independent of the primary communications system required by subsection (1).

O. Reg. 32/14 s. 18

Cranes and Hoisting Devices

20. (1) Where a crane or other hoisting device is used to lower a stage or man basket carrying a diver into the water, each employer associated with the diving operation and the diving supervisor for the diving operation shall ensure that,

    (a) the crane or other hoisting device remains available throughout the dive for the immediate recovery of the diver if required in the event of an emergency; and

    (b) except in the event of an emergency, all directions to the operator of the crane or other hoisting device are given, throughout the dive, by the diver, the diver's tender or the diving supervisor.

(2) Each employer associated with a diving operation and the diving supervisor for a diving operation shall ensure that a diver who is being lowered in a stage or man basket into the water by means of a crane or other hoisting device is continuously able to communicate with the diving supervisor by using pre-arranged visual or line signals or a two-way voice communication system.

(3) Each employer associated with a diving operation shall ensure that any crane or other hoisting device used in a diving operation is adequate.

(4) Without limiting the generality of subsection (3), each employer associated with a diving operation shall ensure that any crane or other hoisting device used in a diving operation,

    (a) is of sound construction and adequate strength and is free from patent defects;

(b) is equipped with a failsafe mechanism that will prevent the boom from descending or telescoping in the event of a power source failure or hoisting system failure;

(c) is equipped with a brake or mechanical locking device that is applied automatically when the control lever, handle or switch is not held in the operating position;

(d) is equipped with brakes that can stop and hold 100 per cent of the maximum working load with the outermost layer of wire on the drum;

(e) is so constructed that any brakes that are power released will be applied automatically on loss of power;

(f) is so constructed that the lowering and rising of loads is controlled by power drives that are independent of the brake mechanism;

(g) is not fitted with a pawl-and-ratchet gear on which the pawl has to be disengaged before commencing the lowering or raising of the load; and

(h) is constructed in a way that ensures against malfunctions at low temperatures.

(5) Each employer associated with a diving operation and the diving supervisor for a diving operation shall ensure that any crane or other hoisting device to be used in the diving operation is adequately maintained and is examined by a competent person at least once on each day on which it is to be used.

(6) Each employer associated with a diving operation and the diving supervisor for a diving operation shall ensure that any cable used with a crane or other hoisting device in the diving operation is used in accordance with the Code for Cable, Slings and Rigging, dated July 4, 1994 and issued by the Ministry.

(7) Where a crane or other hoisting device is used to lower a submersible compression chamber or atmospheric diving system into the water, each employer associated with the diving operation and the diving supervisor for the diving operation shall ensure that, except in the event of an emergency, all directions to the operator of the crane or other hoisting device are given, throughout the dive by the diving supervisor.

(8) Where a crane or other hoisting device is used to lower an open (wet) bell, a submersible compression chamber or atmospheric diving system

629/94

461

into the water, each employer associated with the diving operation and the diving supervisor for the diving operation shall ensure that the crane or other hoisting device is equipped with,

> (a) a primary lifting cable that permits the chamber or system to be lowered safely to the maximum depth of the dive and to be returned safely to the surface, without undue lateral, vertical or rotational movement;
>
> (b) a secondary lifting cable that is,
>
>> (i) readily available at the dive site, and
>>
>> (ii) compatible with the secondary lifting eye or similar device.

(9) Where a crane or other hoisting device is used to lower an open (wet) bell or submersible compression chamber into the water, each employer associated with the diving operation and the diving supervisor for the diving operation shall ensure that, during any air-water interface transfer, the crane or other hoisting device is equipped with a safety rope that will, in the event of the primary cable breaking, cause the open (wet) bell or chamber to stop directly below the turbulent wave zone.

O. Reg. 32/14 s. 19

Fall Arrest Systems

21. (1) Each employer associated with a diving operation and the diving supervisor for a diving operation shall ensure that an adequate system to arrest the fall of a stage or man basket is used whenever a diver is being lowered into the water and there is a hazard that the stage or man basket might fall,

> (a) a distance of more than 10 feet;
>
> (b) into or onto operating machinery; or
>
> (c) into or onto a hazardous substance or object.

(2) Each employer associated with a diving operation and the diving supervisor for a diving operation shall ensure that the fall arrest system,

> (a) is adequately secured to a fixed support at the dive site or to a line that is securely fastened to a fixed support at the dive site;
>
> (b) is designed so that if the stage or man basket falls, the stage or man basket will be suspended not more than five feet below the location it occupied before the fall; and

(c) is attached to a secondary lifting eye or similar device that is of at least the same strength as the primary lifting eye for the stage or man basket.

(3) Each employer associated with a diving operation and the diving supervisor for a diving operation shall ensure that the fixed support referred to in clause (2)(a) is capable of resisting any arrest forces in the event of a fall and is free of sharp edges that might cut or chafe the connection between the fall arrest system and the fixed support.

O. Reg. 32/14 s. 20

Stages and Open (Wet) Bells
[Heading amended O. Reg. 32/14, s. 21.]

22. Each employer associated with a diving operation and the diving supervisor for a diving operation shall ensure that any stage or open (wet) bell used in the diving operation is designed in accordance with good engineering practice and, in the case of a stage, meets the requirements of Clause 6.12 of CSA Standard Z275.2-11, "Occupational Safety Code for Diving Operations", and in the case of an open (wet) bell, meets the requirements of Clause 6.13 of the same Standard.

O. Reg. 32/14 s. 21

Hyperbaric Chambers

23. (1) Each employer associated with a diving operation and the diving supervisor for a diving operation shall ensure that a hyperbaric chamber is at the dive site during any dive that exceeds,

(a) the no-decompression limit given by the decompression tables used for the dive; or

(b) a depth of 100 feet.

(2) Subsection (1) does not apply in relation to a dive where the diver is always at one atmosphere.

(3) Each employer associated with a diving operation and the diving supervisor for a diving operation shall ensure that hyperbaric chamber is at the dive site during any dive where that would be reasonable in the circumstances for the protection of the diver.

629/94

(3.1) Despite subsections (1) and (3), where the dive site is located on an ice surface, the hyperbaric chamber may be located on land as close as possible to the dive site.

(4) Each employer associated with a diving operation shall ensure that any hyperbaric chamber used on land in the diving operation has been registered with the Technical Standards and Safety Authority, for use in Ontario.

(5) Each employer associated with a diving operation and the diving supervisor for a diving operation shall ensure that any hyperbaric chamber used in the diving operation, other than as a submersible compression chamber or saturation chamber, meets and is operated in accordance with the requirements specified in Clauses 1 to 9 of CSA Standard Z275.1-05, "Hyperbaric Facilities".

(6) Each employer associated with a diving operation and the diving supervisor for a diving operation shall, in the case of a dive for which a hyperbaric chamber is used other than as a submersible compression chamber or saturation chamber, ensure that a quantity of air or adequate mixed gas is available with the hyperbaric chamber that is twice the quantity required,

    (a) to pressurize the hyperbaric chamber to a pressure equivalent to the pressure at the greatest depth in respect of which the hyperbaric chamber is used in the dive or to the pressure at 165 feet, whichever is greater; and

    (b) to ventilate the hyperbaric chamber at this pressure.

O. Reg. 155/04 s. 4; 32/14 s. 22

Gauges and Metering Equipment

24. Each employer associated with a diving operation and the diving supervisor for a diving operation shall ensure that any gauge or metering equipment to be used in the diving operation meets the requirements of Clause 6.2 of CSA Standard Z275.2-11, "Occupational Safety Code for Diving Operations".

O. Reg. 32/14 s. 23

Part IV — Breathing Mixtures

General Requirements

25. (1) The diving supervisor for a diving operation shall ensure that no diver participating in the diving operation is permitted to dive without a breathing mixture and breathing mixture supply system that are adequate, having regard to the depths and circumstances in which the diver will be operating.

(2) The diving supervisor for a diving operation shall ensure that any breathing mixture used in the diving operation meets the requirements of CSA Standard Z275.2-11, "Occupational Safety Code for Diving Operations".

(3) Except for decompression or therapeutic purposes, the diving supervisor for a diving operation shall ensure that no diver participating in the diving operation is given pure oxygen as a breathing mixture unless notice is given under paragraph 10 of subsection 5(4).

(4) Each employer associated with a diving operation and the diving supervisor for a diving operation shall ensure that any breathing mixture supply system used in the diving operation is designed to ensure that,

  (a) an interruption of the breathing mixture supply to one diver will not affect the supply of breathing mixture to any other diver; and

  (b) an interruption of the primary breathing mixture supply to a diver will not affect the delivery of breathing mixture from,

   (i) any emergency bail-out system worn by the diver,

   (ii) any emergency reserve system worn by the diver, or

   (iii) any secondary breathing mixture supply;

  (c) an interruption of the primary breathing mixture supply to a submersible compression chamber will not affect the delivery of breathing mixture from any emergency reserve system attached to the chamber; and

  (d) an interruption of the primary breathing mixture supply in an atmospheric diving system will not affect delivery of breathing mixture from any secondary breathing mixture supply in the atmospheric diving system.

O. Reg. 32/14 s. 24

Quantities of Primary and Secondary Breathing Mixture Supplies

26. (1) The diving supervisor for a diving operation shall ensure that the total supply of breathing mixture that is available at the dive site at any time during a dive consists of,

(a) an adequate primary supply to complete the dive as planned; and

(b) an adequate secondary supply.

(2) The secondary supply referred to in clause (1)(b) shall at the start of a dive consist of,

(a) in the case of a dive in which S.C.U.B.A. is used, one complete S.C.U.B.A. unit, including regulator and fully charged cylinder, in addition to the sets required for the divers and standby divers;

(b) in the case of a dive in which surface-supplied diving techniques are used, an adequate supply of breathing mixture to allow the diver to return to the surface and undergo any in-water decompression that might be required;

(c) in the case of a dive in which a submersible compression chamber or atmospheric diving system is used, an adequate supply of breathing mixture to enable the occupants of the chamber or system to return to the surface;

(d) in the case of a dive in which an on-line gas blender or diver's gas recovery system is used, an adequate supply of pre-mixed breathing mixture to allow the divers to return to the surface and undergo any in-water decompression that might be required; and

(e) in the case of a dive in which a hyperbaric chamber is used, an adequate supply of breathing mixture to allow the diver to undergo any decompression that might be required and undergo any treatment that might be required for decompression sickness.

Emergency Reserve and Bail-Out Systems

27. The diving supervisor for a diving operation shall ensure that,

(a) each diver wears an adequate bailout system that meets the requirements of Clause 4.7.3 of CSA Standard Z275.2-11, "Occupational Safety Code for Diving Operations";

(b) every submersible compression chamber is equipped with an emergency reserve breathing gas supply that is adequate for all of the chamber's occupants for at least 24 hours;

(c) every submersible compression chamber is equipped with an emergency reserve breathing gas supply that can provide all lock-out divers with at least 30 minutes of breathing gas at a rate of 40 litres per minute; and

(d) every atmospheric diving system is equipped with an emergency reserve breathing gas supply that is adequate for all of the system's occupants for at least 48 hours.

O. Reg. 32/14 s. 25

Breathing Mixtures Containing Nitrogen

28. Each employer associated with a diving operation and the diving supervisor for a diving operation shall ensure that, when nitrogen is a component of any breathing mixture used in the diving operation, the mixture is not used at depths where the nitrogen partial pressure in the breathing mixture exceeds 4.8 bars.

Purity of Breathing Mixtures

29. Each employer associated with a diving operation and the diving supervisor for a diving operation shall ensure that the purity of any breathing mixture used in the diving operation meets the requirements of CSA Standard Z275.2-11, "Occupational Safety Code for Diving Operations".

O. Reg. 32/14 s. 26

Compressor Requirements
[Heading added O. Reg. 32/14, s. 27.]

30. Each employer associated with a diving operation and the diving supervisor for a diving operation shall ensure that,

(a) any compressor and associated equipment used in the diving operation to supply a breathing mixture meets the requirements of CSA Standard Z275.2-11, "Occupational Safety Code for Diving Operations"; and

(b) any compressor and associated equipment used in the diving operation is operated by a competent worker, who may be the diver's tender.

O. Reg. 32/14 s. 27

Oxygen Supply Systems

31. Each employer associated with a diving operation and the diving supervisor for a diving operation shall ensure that any oxygen supply system used in the diving operation meets the requirements of CSA Standard Z275.2-11, "Occupational Safety Code for Diving Operations".

O. Reg. 32/14 s. 28

Part V — Medical Procedures

Medical Examinations

32. (1) No person shall dive, other than as an atmospheric diving system operator, unless he or she,

(a) if under 40 years of age, has undergone a medical examination to determine fitness to dive during the 24-month period preceding the dive or during such shorter period preceding the dive as has been recommended by the person's examining physician;

(b) if 40 years of age or older, has undergone a medical examination to determine fitness to dive during the 12-month period preceding the dive or during such shorter period preceding the dive as has been recommended by the person's examining physician; and

(c) has obtained a written statement from the examining physician who performed the most recent medical examination that indicates the diver is fit to dive or fit to dive with limitations.

(2) A medical examination under subsection (1) shall,

(a) be performed by a physician who is knowledgeable about diving medicine and hyperbaric medicine; and

(b) be performed in accordance with the Code for the Medical Examination of Divers, dated October 2013 and issued by the Ministry.

(3) No person shall dive as an atmospheric diving system operator unless he or she,

(a) if under 40 years of age, has undergone a medical examination to determine fitness to operate an atmospheric diving system during the 24-month period preceding the dive or during such shorter period preceding the dive as has been recommended by the person's examining physician;

(b) if 40 years of age or over, has undergone a medical examination to determine fitness to operate an atmospheric diving system during the 12-month period preceding the dive or during such shorter period preceding the dive as has been recommended by the person's examining physician; and

(c) has obtained a written statement from the examining physician that indicates that the diver is fit to operate an atmospheric diving system or fit to operate an atmospheric diving system with limitations.

(4) A written statement under clauses (1)(c) or (3)(c) shall be signed by the examining physician and shall include,

(a) the physician's name and address;

(b) the date of the examination; and

(c) the recommended date for the next examination.

O. Reg. 32/14 s. 29

Emergency Training

33. (1) Each employer associated with a diving operation shall ensure that up-to-date certification in cardio-pulmonary resuscitation, oxygen administration and first aid is held by,

(a) each person appointed as a diving supervisor for the diving operation;

(b) each diver participating in the diving operation; and

(c) whenever the diving operation is being carried out, at least one diver's tender at the dive site.

(2) For the purposes of subsection (1),

(a) certification for cardio-pulmonary resuscitation and for first aid shall be from St. John Ambulance, the Canadian Red Cross Society or an organization that offers equivalent training; and

(b) certification for oxygen administration for S.C.U.B.A. diving injuries shall be from the Divers Alert Network or an organization that offers equivalent training.

O. Reg. 32/14 s. 30

Medical Assistance

34. Each employer associated with a diving operation shall ensure that arrangements are made with one or more physicians who are knowledgeable about diving medicine and hyperbaric medicine so that any. medical advice or support that may be required is available whenever,

(a) a dive that involves decompression is carried out; or

(b) a dive to a depth greater than 100 feet is carried out using techniques other than those of atmospheric diving.

O. Reg. 32/14 s. 31

Decompression Procedures and Tables

35. The diving supervisor for a diving operation shall ensure that dives that involve decompression are carried out in accordance with adequate decompression procedures and tables.

Part VI — S.C.U.B.A. Diving

Prohibitions on S.C.U.B.A. Use

36. (1) The diving supervisor for a diving operation shall ensure that S.C.U.B.A. is not used by,

(a) a diver working near or in an operating underwater intake;

(b) a diver working near or in a pipe, tunnel, duct or other confined space;

(c) a diver working at a water control structure;

(d) a diver using any power tool, hoisting device, burning equipment or welding equipment;

(e) a diver placing any materials underwater in a way that poses a risk to the health or safety of the diver;

(f) a diver operating at depths in excess of 100 feet;

(g) a diver working in a diving operation to which Part XI applies;

(h) a diver handling an explosive device, unless the diver is a police diver engaged in a diving operation, including a diving operation for training purposes, that involves searching for and disposing of explosives; or

(i) a diver participating in a UXO diving operation, unless the diver meets the requirements of Clause 5 of CSA Standard Z275.6-11, "Unexploded Explosive Ordnance (UXO) and Munitions Diving".

(2) For the purposes of clauses (1)(a) and (b), a diver works near a thing where the proximity of the thing to the diver poses a health or safety risk to the diver.

O. Reg. 32/14 s. 32

Minimum Crew

37. (1) Whenever S.C.U.B.A. is used, each employer associated with a diving operation and the diving supervisor for a diving operation shall ensure that,

(a) an adequate number of diver's tenders, and in any event at least one diver's tender, is present at the dive site;

(b) an adequate number of standby divers, and in any event at least one standby diver, is present at the dive site;

(c) an adequate number of divers, and in any event at least one diver, is present at the dive site; and

(d) one person does not act at the same time both as diver's tender and as standby diver for one or more divers.

(2) Whenever S.C.U.B.A. is used, the diving supervisor may also function either as a standby diver or as a diver's tender.

S.C.U.B.A. Diving Equipment

38. (1) A diving supervisor for a diving operation using open circuit S.C.U.B.A. shall ensure that each diver uses equipment that meets the requirements of Clause 7.8.1. of CSA Standard Z275.2-11, "Occupational Safety Code for Diving Operations".

(2) Despite subsection (1), Subclause (c) of Clause 7.8.1. of CSA Standard Z275.2-11, "Occupational Safety Code for Diving Operations", does not apply to an aquarium diver.

O. Reg. 32/14 s. 33

629/94

Part VII — Surface-Supplied Diving

Minimum Crew

39. (1) Whenever surface-supplied diving is being carried out, each employer associated with a diving operation and the diving supervisor for a diving operation shall ensure that,

  (a) an adequate number of diver's tenders, and in any event at least one diver's tender, is present at the dive site;

  (b) an adequate number of standby divers, and in any event at least one standby diver, is present at the dive site;

  (c) an adequate number of divers, and in any event at least one diver, is present at the dive site;

  (d) except in a health or safety emergency, there is a separate diver's tender for each diver engaged in surface-supplied diving; and

  (e) one person does not act at the same time both as a diver's tender and as a standby diver for one or more divers engaged in surface-supplied diving.

(2) For the purposes of subsection (1), the diving supervisor may also function either as a standby diver or as a diver's tender.

(3) Whenever a hyperbaric chamber is required by subsection 23(1) or (3) and surface-supplied diving is being carried out, each employer associated with a diving operation and the diving supervisor for a diving operation shall ensure that,

  (a) the requirements of subsection (1) are met; and

  (b) a competent worker who does not have any duties that would interfere with his or her adequate operation of the chamber is available to operate the chamber.

(4) For the purposes of subsection (3), the diving supervisor may also function as one of the following:

1. A standby diver.
2. A diver's tender.
3. A chamber operator.

(5) Whenever surface-supplied diving is carried out in a diving operation to which Part X or XI applies, each employer associated with a diving operation and the diving supervisor for a diving operation shall ensure that,

(a) the requirements of subsection (1) or (3), as the case may be, are met; and

(b) the diving supervisor does not perform the duties of a diver's tender or a standby diver.

O. Reg. 32/14 s. 34

Breathing Mixture Supply Lines

40. (1) The diving supervisor for a diving operation shall ensure that any breathing mixture supply line used in surface-supplied diving,

(a) is adequate;

(b) has an internal diameter sufficient to permit adequate flow rates and pressures;

(c) is protected in a way that ensures against damage at the diver site; and

(d) is protected against kinking.

(2) Each employer associated with a diving operation and the diving supervisor for a diving operation shall ensure that each breathing mixture supply line used in surface-supplied diving is fitted with an adequate breathing mixture supply valve.

(3) Each employer associated with a diving operation and the diving supervisor for a diving operation shall ensure that the breathing mixture supply valve of any diver engaged in surface-supplied diving is,

(a) readily accessible to dive site personnel;

(b) protected in a way that ensures against damage at the dive site;

(c) clearly marked to permit dive site personnel to identify the diver whose breathing mixture supply it controls; and

(d) under the care and control of a competent person.

(4) Each employer associated with a diving operation and the diving supervisor for a diving operation shall ensure that each breathing mixture supply line used in surface-supplied diving is fitted with an adequate pressure gauge installed,

(a) downstream of the diver's supply valve, except where the diver's supply valve is a position indicating valve; and

(b) in a way that permits dive site personnel a clear and unobstructed view of its dial and figures.

Helmets, Masks and Hookah

41. (1) Each employer associated with a diving operation and the diving supervisor for a diving operation shall ensure that any diver engaged in surface-supplied diving wears a diving helmet or full face mask or uses a hookah that meets the requirements of subsections (2) to (4).

(2) A helmet, face mask or hookah must be,
> (a) adequate;
> (b) fitted with an adequate non-return valve; and
> (c) attached by a hose to an adequate emergency bail-out system that is,
>> (i) worn by the diver, and
>> (ii) not used for suit-inflation.

(3) A helmet or mask shall be fitted with an adequate locking or fastening device.

(4) A helmet shall be fitted with an adequate and compatible attachment system for securing and sealing the helmet in place.

Part VIII — Deep Diving

General Requirements

42. (1) Each employer associated with a diving operation and the diving supervisor for a diving operation shall ensure that any diver engaged in deep diving, other than atmospheric diving, is provided with an adequate breathing mixture that is mixed gas.

(2) Each employer associated with a diving operation and the diving supervisor for a diving operation shall ensure that deep diving is not carried out unless,
> (a) an adequate stage, downline, structure or other means is available to enable the diver to maintain the decompression stop depths and times specified in the decompression tables used for the dive without undue exertion and movement; and
> (b) the diving supervisor has a means of,
>> (i) monitoring the depth of each diver,
>> (ii) controlling the pressures at which breathing mixtures are being supplied to each diver, and

(iii) analysing the breathing mixtures being supplied to each diver.

(3) Each employer associated with a diving operation and the diving supervisor for a diving operation shall ensure that a submersible compression chamber that meets the requirements of Part IX is used to transfer personnel under pressure greater than one atmosphere to and from the underwater work site during any dive where,

(a) bottom time exceeds 40 minutes and depth is greater than 165 feet;

(b) bottom time exceeds 25 minutes and depth is greater than 195 feet; or

(c) depth exceeds 230 feet.

O. Reg. 32/14 s. 35

Exposure Limits and Rest Periods

43. (1) The diving supervisor for a diving operation shall ensure that a diver who has engaged in deep diving using non-saturation diving techniques does not work at a pressure greater than one atmosphere during the 18-hour period immediately following completion of decompression.

(2) The diving supervisor for a diving operation shall ensure that a diver who has engaged in deep diving using saturation diving techniques does not work at a pressure greater than one atmosphere during the 14-day period immediately following completion of decompression, except as permitted by a physician who is knowledgeable about diving medicine and hyperbaric medicine.

(3) The diving supervisor for a diving operation shall ensure that a diver who has engaged in deep diving using saturation diving techniques observes the following limits:

1. In the case of a dive to a depth of 500 feet or less using a submersible compression chamber, no diver shall spend, seal to seal,

i. more than four hours in the water, or

ii. more than 10 hours in the submersible compression chamber.

2. In the case of a dive to a depth greater than 500 feet using a submersible compression chamber, no diver shall spend, seal to seal,

i. more than three hours in the water, or

ii. more than eight hours in the chamber.

3. A diver shall not work for at least 12 continuous hours immediately after reaching a limit set out in subparagraph i or ii of paragraph 1 or subparagraph i or ii of paragraph 2 and, in any event, a diver shall not work for at least 12 continuous hours in any 24-hour period.

O. Reg. 32/14 s. 36

Part IX — Submersible Compression Chambers, Saturation Chambers, Atmospheric Diving Systems and Remotely-Operated (Underwater) Vehicles

[Heading amended O. Reg. 32/14, s. 37.]

Submersible Compression Chamber Construction and Equipment

44. Each employer associated with a diving operation and the diving supervisor for a diving operation shall ensure that any submersible compression chamber used in the diving operation,

(a) meets and is operated in accordance with the requirements specified in Clauses 1 to 9 and 13 of CSA Standard Z275.1-05, "Hyperbaric Facilities";

(b) is capable of mating to a hyperbaric chamber that meets the requirements specified in Clauses 1 to 9 and, in the case of saturation diving, Clause 12 of CSA Standard Z275.1-05, "Hyperbaric Facilities";

(c) is adequately equipped to permit the transfer of persons under pressure into and out of a hyperbaric chamber;

(d) is of adequate size and design to accommodate the number of occupants that it is to carry during the diving operation without overcrowding;

(e) is designed in a way that permits divers to enter and exit the submersible compression chamber with ease;

(e.1) is equipped with a stage or an adequate standoff;

(f) is designed to permit a diver to disconnect or shear the umbilical bundle of the chamber in the event of a health or safety emergency;
(g) is provided with an adequate mechanism for shedding ballast weights that,

(i) can be operated from within the chamber, and
(ii) is designed in a way that ensures against accidental shedding of the weighs;

(h) is equipped with,

(i) adequate doors and hatches that act as pressure seals and that may be opened from either side,
(ii) adequate valves, gauges and other fittings to control pressure within the chamber and to clearly indicate internal and external pressures,
(iii) adequate pressurization valves and main exhaust valves that are spring-loaded so as to close when not held in the open position,
(iv) adequate primary lighting equipment and emergency back-up lighting equipment,
(v) adequate first aid equipment,
(vi) adequate hoisting equipment to recover an unconscious or injured diver into the chamber,
(vii) adequate heating equipment,
(viii) adequate emergency thermal protection for all occupants,
(ix) an adequate emergency stroboscope light,
(x) an adequate emergency locating device,
(xi) adequate instruments to monitor temperature, oxygen and carbon dioxide levels within the chamber,
(xii) adequate primary and emergency carbon dioxide scrubbers,
(xiii) adequate hull shut-off valves on all gas and water penetrations into the chamber.
(xiv) a secondary lifting eye or similar device that is at least as strong as the primary lifting eye,
(xv) a blind port, and
(xvi) an adequate tool kit;

(i) is designed in a way that ensures against inadvertent operation of the secondary breathing mixture supply system;

629/94

(j) is designed in a way that permits the secondary breathing mixture supply to be brought on-line from within the chamber; and

(k) is provided with an adequate secondary means of retrieving the submersible compression chamber if its primary support cable breaks.

O. Reg. 32/14 s. 38

Saturation Chamber Construction and Equipment

45. Each employer associated with a diving operation and the diving supervisor for a diving operation shall ensure that any saturation chamber used in the diving operation meets and is operated in accordance with the requirements specified in Clauses 1 to 9 and 12 of CSA Standard Z275.1-05, "Hyperbaric Facilities".

O. Reg. 32/14 s. 39

Atmospheric Diving System Construction and Equipment

46. (1) Each employer associated with a diving operation and the diving supervisor for a diving operation shall ensure that any atmospheric diving system used in the diving operation,

(a) is designed to permit a diver to disconnect or shear the umbilical bundle of the system in the event of a health or safety emergency;

(b) is provided with an adequate mechanism for shedding ballast weights that,

(i) can be operated from within the system, and

(ii) is designed in a way that ensures against accidental shedding of the weights;

(c) is designed in a way that ensures against inadvertent operations of the secondary breathing mixture supply system;

(d) is designed in a way that permits the secondary breathing mixture supply to be brought on-line from within the system;

(e) is equipped with the things mentioned in subclauses 44(h)(i), (ii), (iv), (v) and (vii) to (xvi); and

(f) meets the requirements for registration set out in,

(i) Det Norske Veritas, "Rules For Certification of Diving Systems", October 2010,

(ii) Lloyd's Register, "Rules and Regulations For the Construction and Classification of Submersibles and Underwater Systems", 1989, Notice No. 1, July 17, 1991, or

(iii) American Bureau of Shipping, "Rules For Building and Classing Underwater Vehicles, Systems and Hyperbaric Facilities", 2002.

(2) For the purposes of clause (1)(e), a reference in clause 44(h) to "chamber" shall be deemed to be a reference to "system".

O. Reg. 32/14 s. 40

47. [Repealed O. Reg. 32/14, s. 41.]

48. [Repealed O. Reg. 32/14, s. 41.]

49. [Repealed O. Reg. 32/14, s. 41.]

50. [Repealed O. Reg. 32/14, s. 41.]

Back-Up Atmospheric Diving System

51. Each employer associated with a diving operation and the diving supervisor for a diving operation shall ensure that, whenever an atmospheric diving system is used to carry out the diving operation, a back-up atmospheric diving system with adequate depth capability is available and can be deployed quickly enough to effect a rescue within 48 hours of an emergency arising.

Emergency Rescue from Submersible Compression Chamber
[Heading added O. Reg. 32/14, s. 42.]

51.1 Each employer associated with a diving operation and the diving supervisor for a diving operation shall ensure that there are adequate means of rescuing divers from a submersible compression chamber within 24 hours of an emergency arising.

O. Reg. 32/14 s. 42

Minimum Crew

52. (1) Whenever a submersible compression chamber or an atmospheric diving system is used to carry out a diving operation, each employer associated with the diving operation and the diving supervisor for the

629/94

diving operation shall ensure that the number of workers at the dive site meets the number required by Clauses 9.3.4 and 9.3.5 of CSA Standard Z275.2-11, "Occupational Safety Code for Diving Operations".

(2) Whenever a submersible compression chamber or an atmospheric diving system is used to carry out a diving operation, each employer associated with the diving operation and the diving supervisor for the diving operation shall ensure that at least two divers are available at the dive site to render any in-water assistance in the launch or recovery of the chamber or system that may be needed in the event of a health or safety emergency.

(3) [Repealed O. Reg. 32/14, s. 43.]

(4) [Repealed O. Reg. 32/14, s. 43.]

O. Reg. 32/14 s. 43

Remotely-Operated (Underwater) Vehicles
[Heading added O. Reg. 32/14, s. 43.]

52.1(1) In this section,

"ROV" means remotely-operated (underwater) vehicle.

(2) No person shall operate an ROV near a diver unless each employer associated with the diving operation and the diving supervisor for the diving operation ensure that,

> (a) the ROV pilot is under the diving supervisor's authority;
> (b) the ROV pilot is adequately trained to operate an ROV;
> (c) high-voltage electrical connections, terminations and penetrations are clearly marked to warn divers of electrical hazards;
> (d) electrical power to the ROV is disconnected before a diver assists with the recovery of the ROV;
> (e) all thrusters are guarded to prevent contact with any part of a diver or a diver's umbilical bundle;
> (f) an adequate system is provided to permit voice communication between the dive site and the ROV's control station;
> (g) a monitor is available at the dive site showing what the ROV pilot can see; and
> (h) the ROV maintains adequate distance from the diver while the diver ascends to the surface or returns to the submersible compression chamber.

(3) For the purposes of subsection (2), an ROV is near a diver where the ROV's proximity to the diver poses a health or safety risk to the diver.

O. Reg. 32/14 s. 43

Part X — Special Hazards

Liveboating

53. (1) Each employer associated with a diving operation and the diving supervisor for a diving operation shall ensure that liveboating is not conducted,

(a) after sunset and before sunrise;

(b) in sea-state that poses a risk to the health or safety of a diver; or

(c) from vessels without adequate manoeuvrability.

(2) The diving supervisor for a diving operation shall not permit in-water decompression procedures to be used in conjunction with liveboating unless,

(a) a hyperbaric chamber ready for immediate use is available on the vessel used for liveboating;

(b) an independent rope is secured to a weight or structure under-water and is connected to an adequately buoyant flotation device on the surface so that the diver can maintain position during decompression stops;

(c) the vessel's captain has a continuous unobstructed view of the flotation device supporting the diver's decompression line, the diver's umbilical bundle and the diver's tender by means of a remote operating station that allows adequate command of the vessel;

(d) the vessel requires no more than one-third of its power to maintain station; and

(e) the diving supervisor maintains contact with the diver at all times by means of a two-way voice communication system that can be heard adequately by both the captain and the diver's tender.

(3) Each employer associated with a diving operation and the diving supervisor for a diving operation shall ensure that, whenever a diver participates in liveboating, a procedure or device that ensures against the diver's umbilical bundle becoming entangled in the propeller is employed.

629/94

(4) The diving supervisor for a diving operation shall ensure that any diver's tender participating in liveboating has a continuous unobstructed view of the vessel's captain.

(5) Each employer associated with a diving operation shall ensure that any captain of a vessel participating in liveboating is competent to perform the duties of captain during liveboating.

(6) The captain of the vessel and the diving supervisor for a diving operation shall co-operate in carrying out their responsibilities as needed to protect the health and safety of the divers.

O. Reg. 32/14 s. 44

Sledding
[Heading added O. Reg. 32/14, s. 45.]

53.1(1) Each employer associated with a diving operation and the diving supervisor for a diving operation shall ensure that sledding is not conducted,

> (a) after sunset and before sunrise;
> (b) in sea-state that poses a risk to the health or safety of a diver;
> (c) from vessels without adequate manoeuvrability; or
> (d) without either an adequate procedure or an adequate device to prevent the diver's towline from becoming entangled in the propeller.

(2) Each employer associated with a diving operation and the diving supervisor for a diving operation shall ensure that a captain of a vessel participating in sledding is competent to perform the duties of captain during sledding.

O. Reg. 32/14 s. 45

Water Flow Hazards

54. (1) The diving supervisor for a diving operation shall ensure that diving is not conducted in hazardous water flow conditions.

(2) Each employer and each owner associated with a diving operation and the diving supervisor for a diving operation shall ensure before a dive begins that any water flow that may be a hazard to a diver,

> (a) is identified by using the test methods described in the 2011 "Guideline for Diving Operations on Dams and Other Worksites

where Delta-P Hazards May Exist", published by the Canadian Association of Diving Contractors; and

(b) is locked-out or controlled in a manner that,

 (i) is satisfactory to the diver and the diving supervisor, and

 (ii) ensures that the water flow poses no safety hazard to the diver.

(3) [Repealed O. Reg. 32/14, s. 46.]

O. Reg. 32/14 s. 46

Hazardous Mechanisms
[Heading amended O. Reg. 32/14, s. 47.]

55. Each employer and each owner associated with a diving operation and the diving supervisor for a diving operation shall ensure before a dive begins that any mechanism that may be a hazard to a diver is dealt with in accordance with Clause 4.5.4 of CSA Standard Z275.2-11, "Occupational Safety Code for Diving Operations".

O. Reg. 32/14 s. 47

Floating Equipment
[Heading added O. Reg. 32/14, s. 47.]

55.1 A constructor of a project where a diving operation is to take place and each employer associated with a diving operation shall ensure that no barge, scow or vessel is moved into the vicinity of a dive site without permission from the diving supervisor while a diver is in the water.

O. Reg. 32/14 s. 47

Use of Explosives

56. Each employer associated with a diving operation and the diving supervisor for the diving operation shall ensure that,

(a) any transportation, handling, storage or use of explosives is carried out in a manner that does not endanger any worker;

(b) an initiation of explosives is subject to the direct control of the diving supervisor;

(c) the blasting initiator and its operating key or operating mechanism are kept physically separated from each other until initiation of the explosive is to take place; and

629/94

(d) no diver is in the water when an underwater explosive is initiated.

UXO Diving Operations
[Heading added O. Reg. 32/14, s. 48.]

56.1 Each employer associated with a diving operation shall ensure that all persons who participate in a UXO diving operation are trained and work in accordance with CSA Standard Z275.6-11, "Unexploded Explosive Ordnance (UXO) and Munitions Diving", other than Clause 4.1.1 and Clauses 4.7.12.2.3 to 4.7.12.2.6 of the Standard.

O. Reg. 32/14 s. 48

Part XI — Contaminated Environments

Definition

57. In this Part, "contaminant" has the same meaning as in the *Environmental Protection Act*.

Application

58. This Part applies to,

(a) any diving operation that poses a risk to the health or safety of a worker because it is carried out at or near the point of discharge of effluent from an industrial plant, sewage treatment plant or water treatment plant;

(b) any diving operation that poses a risk to the health or safety of a worker because the purpose of the operation is to clean up or contain a contaminant; and

(c) any diving operation that poses a risk to the health or safety of a worker because it is carried out at or near the site of a spill within the meaning of Part X of the *Environmental Protection Act*.

O. Reg. 32/14 s. 49

Identification and Precautions

59. (1) Each constructor of a project where a diving operation is to take place, each employer associated with a diving operation, each owner associated with a diving operation and the diving supervisor for a diving operation shall ensure that, before any dive is begun, a competent person identifies each contaminant that is or is likely to be present during the diving operation, at or near the dive site or underwater work site, at a concentration that would pose a risk to the health or safety of a worker.

(2) Each constructor of a project where a diving operation is to take place, each employer associated with a diving operation and each owner associated with a diving operation shall ensure that a written contaminant management plan is prepared, with input from one or more of the diving supervisors appointed for the diving operation under section 6.

(3) A contaminant management plan shall,

    (a) name the contaminants identified under subsection (1);

    (b) describe the known health or safety risks that the contaminants identified under subsection (1) pose to humans;

    (c) describe the equipment and apparel required to be used by section 60;

    (d) specify the location of the exclusion zone, contaminated reduction zone and support zone required by section 62;

    (e) outline the procedure to be followed by personnel in moving from one zone to another;

    (f) describe the special emergency measures associated with exposure to the contaminants identified under subsection (1), where appropriate; and

    (g) outline procedures for obtaining, within an adequately short-time, information relating to,

        (i) the handling of the contaminants identified under subsection (1), and

        (ii) the administering of any emergency treatment that may become necessary as a result of exposure to a contaminant identified under subsection (1).

(4) The diving supervisor for the diving operation shall ensure that a copy of the plan is prominently posted at the dive site.

O. Reg. 32/14 s. 50

Equipment — General

60. (1) Each employer associated with a diving operation and the diving supervisor for the diving operation shall ensure that,

629/94

(a) adequate precautions are taken to ensure that the breathing mixture supply used is not adversely affected by a contaminant identified under subsection 59(1);

(b) adequate breathing equipment for surface support personnel is provided if there is a risk to their health or safety from inhaling a contaminant identified under subsection 59(1) during the diving operation;

(c) adequate apparel and equipment is worn to prevent exposing surface support personnel to a contaminant identified under subsection 59(1);

(d) an adequate means of decontaminating personnel exposed to a contaminant identified under subsection 59(1) is provided at the dive site;

(e) diving equipment used in the diving operation is not used in any subsequent diving operation unless it is free of all contaminants identified under subsection 59(1); and

(f) diving equipment that is not for reuse is adequately disposed of.

(2) The diving supervisor for the diving operation shall ensure that,

(a) diving equipment that has been or may have been exposed to a contaminant identified under subsection 59(1) is examined before each dive to ensure that it has not deteriorated in a way that would result, if it were used in the dive, in a worker being exposed to a contaminant identified under subsection 59(1); and

(b) diving equipment that has been or may have been exposed to a contaminant identified under subsection 59(1) is not removed from the dive site except as authorized by a competent person.

Surface Supplied Diving

61. Each employer associated with a diving operation and the diving supervisor for the diving operation shall ensure that a diver engaged in surface-supplied diving wears, in addition to the equipment required by section 41.

(a) an adequate diving helmet designed to protect divers from exposure to contaminants; and

(b) an adequate, totally enclosed diving suit that mates to the helmet with a positive seal and locking device and that does not permit contact between the contaminated environment and the diver.

Work Zones

62. (1) Each employer associated with a diving operation and the diving supervisor for the diving operation shall ensure that the dive site has a clearly marked contamination reduction zone that is adequately designed and equipped to permit,

> (a) personnel who have been or may have been exposed to a contaminant identified under subsection 59(1) to dress and undress; and
>
> (b) equipment and personnel that have been or may have been exposed to a contaminant identified under subsection 59(1) to be cleaned.

(2) Each employer associated with a diving operation and the diving supervisor for the diving operation shall ensure that the dive site has a clearly marked support zone that is adequately designed and equipped to permit the further cleaning or the disposal of equipment that has been or may have been exposed to a contaminant identified under subsection 59(1).

(3) Each employer associated with a diving operation and the diving supervisor for the diving operation shall ensure that the dive site has a clearly marked exclusion zone that is adequately designed and equipped for the purpose set out in subsection (4).

(4) Each employer associated with a diving operation and the diving supervisor for the diving operation shall ensure that all handling of contaminants identified under subsection 59(1) that occurs at the dive site and that is not of a sort described in subsection (1) or (2) shall occur in the exclusion zone.

(5) The diving supervisor for the diving operation shall ensure that,

> (a) no person enters the exclusion zone unless he or she is wearing adequate personal protection equipment;
>
> (b) personnel enter and leave the exclusion zone only through the contamination reduction zone or the support zone;
>
> (c) no person cleans contaminated equipment in the contamination reduction zone or the support zone unless he or she is wearing adequate personal protective clothing;

629/94

(d) no food, drink or tobacco is taken into, left or consumed in the contamination reduction zone, the support zone or the exclusion zone; and

(e) no person enters the contamination reduction zone, the support zone or the exclusion zone without the authorization of the diving supervisor.

O. Reg. 32/14 s. 51

Part XII — Diving Records

Diver's Logbook

63. (1) No person shall dive in a diving operation unless he or she has a diving log book that,

(a) is permanently bound;

(b) has numbered pages;

(c) contains the diver's signature and photograph;

(d) has attached to it or entered into it a record of any qualifications obtained by the diver that relate to diving; and

(e) has attached to it or entered into it a record of the certification referred to in section 33.

(2) Each person who dives in a diving operation shall make an entry, in accordance with subsections (4) to (7), in the diving log book in respect of each dive, each medical recompression and each hyperbaric exposure carried out or undergone by the person in connection with the diving operation.

(3) No person shall dive in a diving operation unless he or she has made an entry, in accordance with subsections (6) and (7), in the diving log book in respect of any dive of a type described in clause 2(2)(a), (c) or (d) that the person carried out during the 48 hours preceding the dive that is part of a diving operation.

(4) Entries under subsection (2) shall be made within 48 hours of the dive, medical recompression or hyperbaric exposure and shall appear in the log book in chronological order.

(5) An entry under subsection (2) in respect of a dive shall be signed by the diving supervisor and an entry under subsection (2) in respect of a medical recompression or a hyperbaric exposure shall be signed by the diving supervisor or presiding physician.

(6) An entry under subsection (2) or (3) in respect of a dive shall state,

(a) the type of diving equipment used;

(b) the breathing mixture used;

(c) the time the diver left the surface;

(d) the maximum depth attained;

(e) the time the diver left the bottom;

(f) the time the diver reached the surface;

(g) the time of the surface interval, if a repetitive dive was undertaken;

(h) the decompression table used;

(i) the date;

(j) any unusual incidents; and

(k) the environmental conditions.

(7) In addition, an entry under subsection (2) or (3), in respect of a dive originating from a submersible compression chamber or other submerged base shall state,

(a) the depth at the base;

(b) the maximum and minimum depths attained; and

(c) the duration of the excursions from the base.

(8) A person who is required to have a diving log book shall retain the log book for five years after the date of the last entry in it.

Daily Record

64. (1) The diving supervisor for a diving operation shall make a record in accordance with subsections (2) to (4) in respect of each day of the diving operation.

(2) A daily record shall include an entry in respect of each dive undertaken during the day, stating,

(a) the type of diving equipment used;

(b) whether a hyperbaric chamber was used;

(c) the breathing mixture used;

(d) the time the diver left the surface;

(e) the maximum depth attained;

(f) the time the diver left the bottom;

(g) the time the diver reached the surface;

(h) the time of the surface interval, if a repetitive dive was undertaken;

629/94

(i) the decompression table used;

(j) the name of the diver;

(k) the name of the tenders;

(l) the name of the standby driver;

(m) any unusual incidents;

(n) the location of the dive site;

(o) the environmental conditions;

(p) the purpose of the dive; and

(q) any underwater work site hazards.

(3) A daily record shall also include,

(a) a record of equipment examinations, tests and repairs performed during the day under clause 12(3)(f);

(b) a record of hoisting device maintenance and examinations performed during the day under subsection 20(5);

(c) [Repealed O. Reg. 32/14, s. 52.]

(d) any arrangements for medical advice or support made under section 34 in respect of the day;

(e) a description of any diving vessel used during the day;

(f) a record of any disposal of equipment undertaken during the day under clause 60(1)(f);

(g) the name of any client on whose behalf the diving operation is being carried out on the day; and

(h) a general description of the purpose of the diving operation on the day.

(4) A daily record shall state the date in respect of which it is made and shall include the name and signature of the diving supervisor.

(5) A diving supervisor who makes a daily record under this section shall file the record with his or her employer within a reasonable time.

(6) An employer with whom a daily record is filed shall retain the record for a period of five years from the day in respect of which it is made, together with the attachments described in subsection (7).

(7) An employer shall attach to the daily record a copy of any notice relating to the day that was given under section 10 or 11.

O. Reg. 32/14 s. 52

Part XIII

[Heading repealed O. Reg. 32/14, s. 53.]

65. [Repealed O. Reg. 32/14, s. 53.]
66. [Repealed O. Reg. 32/14, s. 53.]

SCHEDULE 67.2

Ontario Regulation 629/94-Diving Operations under the *Occupational Health and Safety Act*

ITEM	COLUMN 1	COLUMN 2 SECTION	SET FINE (INCL COSTS OF $5.00)
1.	Failing to ensure the Ministry of Labour is given adequate notice of a diving operation	5	$300.00
2.	Failing to have required documents available at the dive site	8	$300.00
3.	Diving supervisor failing to be on site and in direct control of the diving operation	12 (2)	$300.00
4.	Diving supervisor failing to ensure	12 (4) (a)	$300.00

	that an adequate number of standby divers are present and properly positioned		
5.	Diving supervisor failing to ensure that no standby diver dives except in an emergency	12 (4) (g)	$300.00
6.	Diver failing to have log book at dive site	13 (1) (c)	$200.00
7.	Diver failing to undergo medical examination	13 (1) (d)	$200.00
8.	Standby diver unlawfully diving where no emergency	13 (9) (a)	$200.00
9.	Standby diver unlawfully performing other duties	13 (9) (b)	$200.00
10.	Standby diver being inadequately dressed or equipped	13 (9) (c)	$200.00
11.	Failing to ensure adequacy of diving equipment and related materials	15	$300.00

629/94

12.	Diving supervisor failing to ensure that an adequate lifeline is attached to each diver	18	$300.00
13.	Failing to ensure adequate crew for S.C.U.B.A.	37	$300.00
14.	Failing to ensure adequate crew for surface-supplied diving	39	$300.00
15.	Failing to ensure water flow hazards are identified and adequately controlled	54 (2) and (3)	$300.00
16.	Failing to ensure mechanisms hazardous to diving are identified and adequately locked-out	55	$300.00

ONT. REG. 414/05 — FARMING OPERATIONS

made under the *Occupational Health and Safety Act*

O. Reg. 05/05, as am. O. Reg. 90/13; 298/13; 385/15

1. Application of Act to farming operations — Subject to the limitations and conditions set out in this Regulation, the Act applies to farming operations.

2. Exception — Despite section 1, the Act does not apply to a farming operation operated by a self-employed person without any workers.

3. Limitations, joint health and safety committees —

(1) Despite section 1, subsection 9(2) of the Act applies only to farming operations where 20 or more workers are regularly employed and have duties that include performing work related to one or more of the operations specified in subsection (2).

(2) The following are the operations referred to in subsection (1):
1. Mushroom farming.
2. Greenhouse farming.
3. Dairy farming.
4. Hog farming.
5. Cattle farming.
6. Poultry farming.

(3) Despite section 1, where a joint health and safety committee is required at a farming operation, the requirement for certified members set out in subsection 9(12) of the Act applies to that farming operation only if 50 or more workers are regularly employed at it.

4. Application of certain regulations —

(1) Despite section 1 and subject to subsection (2), the regulations made under the Act do not apply to farming operations.

(2) The following regulations apply to farming operations:

414/05

1. Regulation 834 of the Revised Regulations of Ontario, 1990 (*Critical Injury—Defined*) made under the Act.

2. Ontario Regulation 297/13 (*Occupational Health and Safety Awareness and Training*) made under the Act.

3. Ontario Regulation 381/15 made under the Act.

O. Reg. 90/13 s. 1; 298/13 s. 1; 385/15, s. 1

5. Commencement — This Regulation comes into force on June 30, 2006.

ONT. REG. 714/94 — FIREFIGHTERS — PROTECTIVE EQUIPMENT

made under the *Occupational Health and Safety Act*

O. Reg. 714/94, as am. O. Reg. 449/97; 80/02; 24/09, ss. 1, 2, 3 (Fr.); 480/10.

1. In this Regulation,

"firefighter" means a firefighter as defined in subsection 1(1) of the *Fire Protection and Prevention Act, 1997.*

O. Reg. 24/09 s. 1

2. This Regulation applies to every firefighter and to every employer of a firefighter.

3. (1) Anything may vary from a standard prescribed by this Regulation if,

    (a) the variation maintains or increases the protection for the health or safety of workers; and

    (b) at least 60 days before the variation, written notice of the variation is given to a Director and the joint health and safety committee and to the trade union, if any.

(2) The notice under clause (1)(b) is not required if a professional engineer has certified in writing that the variation meets the criteria set out in clause (1)(a).

4. (1) A firefighter who is exposed to the hazard of head injury shall wear head protective equipment that is appropriate in the circumstances.

(2) The employer shall provide training and instruction to every firefighter in the proper care and use of head protective equipment and in the limitations of protection afforded by it.

(3) Head protective equipment shall be kept in good condition and shall be inspected periodically by the employer.

O. Reg. 80/02 s. 1

5. The employer shall provide every firefighter who may be required to perform interior structural fire suppression duties with structural fire-fighting protective garments that meet or exceed the requirements of the following standard:

    1. NFPA 1971 "Standard on Protective Ensembles for Structural Fire Fighting and Proximity Fire Fighting", 2007 edition, in the case of garments manufactured on or after March 1, 2007.

    2. CAN/CGSB-155.1-M88 "Firefighters' Protective Clothing for Protection Against Heat and Flame", in the case of garments manufactured before March 1, 2007.

O. Reg. 480/10 s. 1

6. (1) In this section, "chassis mounted aerial device" means any device, whether extensible, articulating or both, that is mounted on a vehicle's chassis and designed to position persons, handle materials or discharge water, but does not include portable ladders.

(2) Subject to subsection (3), a chassis mounted aerial device shall be visually inspected by a competent person at the times recommended by the manufacturer but in any event at least once every calendar year.

(3) Every chassis mounted aerial device shall be visually inspected by a competent person,

    (a) before being used for the first time;

    (b) after every major repair;

    (c) after being used if it may have been subjected to unusual operating conditions of stress or load; and

    (d) when there is reason to believe that the maximum loads or stresses recommended in the manufacturer's operating specifications have been exceeded.

(4) Every chassis mounted aerial device shall be tested using a method of inspection that does not physically alter or damage material,

    (a) when a visual inspection indicates a potential hazard; and

    (b) not later than December 15, 1999 for the first such testing and subsequently not later than five years from the date of the last non-destructive testing.

(5) The visual inspection and non-destructive tests under this section shall be performed in accordance with NFPA 1914, Standard for Testing Fire Department Aerial Devices, 1991 Edition, excluding section 1-7.

(6) If a visual inspection or any test reveals a hazard to the integrity of the chassis mounted aerial device, the employer shall ensure that,

(a) the chassis mounted aerial device is taken out of service;

(b) the repairs, if any, are undertaken by a competent person; and

(c) if the repairs involve welding, the welds are inspected and approved by an inspector who is a Level III Welding Inspector under CSA Standard W178.2-1990 Certification of Welding Inspectors, and who is employed by an organization certified under CSA Standard W178.1-1990 Certification of Welding Inspection Organizations.

(7) Service records for a chassis mounted aerial device shall be maintained for as long as the device is in service and shall include a record of,

(a) visual inspections;

(b) non-destructive and other tests;

(c) the problems identified;

(d) the repairs made; and

(e) the name and signature of the competent persons who undertook the activities mentioned in clauses (a) to (d).

7. (1) This section applies to:

1. A fire truck first put into service, by the employer or anyone else, on or after December 15, 1995.

2. A fire truck acquired by the employer on or after December 31, 1997.

(2) The cab of the fire truck shall be enclosed and shall have,

(a) one or more driving and crew compartments;

(b) a roof, floor, four sides and positive latching doors which together provide total enclosure of the driver and passengers; and

(c) sufficient seats for the maximum number of persons intended under the manufacturer's specifications to be accommodated in the cab.

(3) The fire truck shall be equipped with sufficient anti-slip handle-holds to allow firefighters to use the position known as the three-point contact method when entering or exiting the cab.

(4) Tools, self-contained breathing apparatus and other fire fighting equipment or paraphernalia carried in the cab of the fire truck shall be secured to fixed positions by positive mechanical means or stowed in compartments with positive latching doors.

O. Reg. 449/97 s. 1

7.1 The cab of a fire truck described in paragraph 1 of subsection 7(1) shall have seats equipped with back and anti-whiplash head supports and seat belts.

O. Reg. 449/97 s. 1

8. (1) No firefighter shall travel on board a fire truck that is moving at more than 8 kilometres an hour unless he or she is seated within a cab or is travelling on the tailboard as allowed under subsection (2).

(2) Until December 15, 1999, a firefighter may travel on the tailboard of a fire truck that was first put into service by the employer before February 15, 1995 if,

    (a) adequate handles and suitable safety belts or harnesses are provided by the employer and are approved by the joint health and safety committee or the trade union, if any;

    (b) the surface of the tailboard has safe footing;

    (c) no person is standing on any other side of the truck while it is moving;

    (d) each firefighter has a minimum standing space on the tailboard of 56 cm x 56 cm;

    (e) the tailboard is strong enough to carry the number of firefighters who are standing on it; and

    (f) the employer provides an electrical signal system or a voice communication system between the driver and the persons on the tailboard.

O. Reg. 449/97 s. 1; 24/09 s. 2

9. Regulation 849 of the Revised Regulations of Ontario, 1990 and Ontario Regulations 249/91 and 289/91 are revoked.

Ont. Reg. 67/93 — Health Care and Residential Facilities

made under the *Occupational Health and Safety Act*

O. Reg. 67/93, as am. O. Reg. 142/99; 631/05; 25/09, ss. 1-9,
10 (Fr.); 495/09; 94/10; 97/11; 169/11; 89/13.

Interpretation and Application

1. In this Regulation,

"adequate", when used in relation to a procedure, plan, material, device, object or thing, means that it is,

(a) sufficient for both its intended and its actual use, and

(b) sufficient to protect a worker from occupational illness or occupational injury;

"adequately" has a meaning that corresponds to the meaning of **"adequate"**;

"patient or resident" means a person, including an out-patient, who is received, lodged in, admitted or registered at a facility for the purposes of being observed, examined, diagnosed or rehabilitated or for the purposes of receiving care or treatment;

"work surface" means a floor, platform or other surface used by a worker to stand or walk on in performing work and includes a surface on the premises of a facility used by a worker in performing work or in travelling to or from a work area.

O. Reg. 631/05 s. 1

2. (1) This Regulation applies to the following types of facilities:

1. A hospital as defined in the *Public Hospitals Act*.

2. A laboratory or specimen collection centre as defined in the *Laboratory and Specimen Collection Centre Licensing Act*.

3. A private hospital as defined in the *Private Hospitals Act*.

4. A psychiatric facility as defined in the *Mental Health Act*.

5. A long-term care home as defined in the *Long-Term Care Homes Act, 2007*.

6. [Repealed O. Reg. 94/10, s. 1.]

7. [Repealed O. Reg. 94/10, s. 1.]

8. An intensive support residence or a supported group living residence as defined in the *Services and Supports to Promote the Social Inclusion of Persons with Developmental Disabilities Act, 2008*.

9. A facility where any of the following are provided: child development services or child treatment services, as defined in the *Child and Family Services Act*, or child and family intervention services, as defined in Regulation 70 of Revised Regulations of Ontario, 1990.

10. [Repealed O. Reg. 25/09, s. 1(1).]

11. Laundry facilities located in any of the facilities listed above.

12. A plant, as defined in Ontario Regulation 219/01 (*Operating Engineers*) made under the *Technical Standards and Safety Act, 2000*, that is operated primarily for one or more than one of the facilities listed above.

(2) At a laundry facility to which this Regulation applies, if the regulations under the *Occupational Health and Safety Act* relating to industrial establishments conflict with this Regulation, this Regulation prevails unless the provision in the other regulation states that it is to prevail over this Regulation.

O. Reg. 25/09 s. 1; 94/10 s. 1; 169/11 s. 1

3. In applying this Regulation, a measure or a procedure or the composition, design, size or arrangement of any physical object, device or thing may vary from that prescribed if,

(a) the variation affords protection for the health or safety of a worker equal to or greater than that prescribed by this Regulation; and

(b) notice of the variation is given to the joint health and safety committee, if any, and to the trade union, if any.

4. The employer shall keep on file all records or reports that are required to be kept under this Regulation for a period of at least one year or such longer period as is necessary to ensure that the two most recent reports are on file.

Notice of Accidents

5. (1) If a worker is killed or critically injured at a facility, the written report required by subsection 51(1) of the Act shall include,

(a) the name and address of the employer;

(b) the nature and circumstances of the occurrence and of the bodily injury sustained;

(c) a description of the machinery or thing involved, if any;

(d) the time and place of the occurrence;

(e) the name and address of the person who was critically injured or killed;

(f) the names and addresses of all witnesses to the occurrence;

(g) the name and address of the physician or surgeon, if any, who is attending to or attended to the injured or deceased person; and

(h) the steps taken to prevent a recurrence.

(2) If an accident, explosion or fire causes injury to a worker at a facility that disables the worker from performing his or her usual work, the written notice required by subsection 52(1) of the Act shall include,

(a) the name and address of the employer;

(b) the nature and circumstances of the occurrence and of the bodily injury sustained by the worker;

(c) a description of the machinery or thing involved, if any;

(d) the time and place of the occurrence;

(e) the name and address of the worker who was injured;

(f) the names and addresses of all witnesses to the occurrence;

(g) the name and address of the physician or surgeon, if any, who is attending to or attended to the worker for the injury; and

(h) the steps taken to prevent a recurrence.

(3) If an accident, explosion or fire at a facility causes injury requiring medical attention but does not disable a worker from performing his or her usual work, the employer shall keep a record of that occurrence and the record shall include,

(a) the nature and circumstances of the occurrence and of the injury sustained;

(b) the time and place of the occurrence;

(c) the name and address of the injured worker; and

(d) the steps taken to prevent a recurrence.

(4) The record kept by the employer under subsection (3) for inspection by an inspector shall be notice to a Director.

(5) The written notice required under subsection 52(2) of the Act if an employer is advised that a worker has an occupational illness or that a claim in respect of an occupational illness has been filed with the Workplace Safety and Insurance Board shall include,

    (a) the name and address of the employer;

    (b) the nature of the occupational illness and the circumstances which gave rise to such illness;

    (c) a description of the cause or the suspected cause of the occupational illness;

    (d) the period when the worker was affected;

    (e) the name and address of the worker who is suffering from the occupational illness;

    (f) the name and address of the physician, if any, who is attending to or attended to the worker for the illness; and

    (g) the steps taken to prevent further illness.

O. Reg. 25/09 s. 2

6. If an occurrence involves the collapse or failure of a temporary or permanent structure that was designed by a professional engineer or architect, the employer shall, within fourteen days after the occurrence supplement the notice or report required by section 51 or 52 of the Act with the written opinion of a professional engineer as to the cause of the collapse or failure.

7. A notice under subsection 57(9) of the Act shall be in Form 1.

General Duty to Establish Measures and Procedures

8. Every employer in consultation with the joint health and safety committee or health and safety representative, if any, and upon consideration of the recommendation thereof, shall develop, establish and put into effect measures and procedures for the health and safety of workers.

9. (1) The employer shall reduce the measures and procedures for the health and safety of workers established under section 8 to writing and such measures and procedures may deal with, but are not limited to, the following:

    1. Safe work practices.

    2. Safe working conditions.

3. Proper hygiene practices and the use of hygiene facilities.

4. The control of infections.

5. Immunization and inoculation against infectious diseases.

6. The use of appropriate antiseptics, disinfectants and decontaminants.

7. The hazards of biological, chemical and physical agents present in the workplace, including the hazards of dispensing or administering such agents.

8. Measures to protect workers from exposure to a biological, chemical or physical agent that is or may be a hazard to the reproductive capacity of a worker, the pregnancy of a worker or the nursing of a child of a worker.

9. The proper use, maintenance and operation of equipment.

10. The reporting of unsafe or defective devices, equipment or work surfaces.

11. The purchasing of equipment that is properly designed and constructed.

12. The use, wearing and care of personal protective equipment and its limitations.

13. The handling, cleaning and disposal of soiled linen, sharp objects and waste.

(2) At least once a year the measures and procedures for the health and safety of workers shall be reviewed and revised in the light of current knowledge and practice.

(3) The review and revision of the measures and procedures shall be done more frequently than annually if,

(a) the employer, on the advice of the joint health and safety committee or health and safety representative, if any, determines that such review and revision is necessary; or

(b) there is a change in circumstances that may affect the health and safety of a worker.

(4) The employer, in consultation with and in consideration of the recommendation of the joint health and safety committee or health and safety representative, if any, shall develop, establish and provide training and educational programs in health and safety measures and procedures for workers that are relevant to the workers' work.

Personal Protective Equipment

10. (1) A worker who is required by his or her employer or by this Regulation to wear or use any protective clothing, equipment or device shall be instructed and trained in its care, use and limitations before wearing or using it for the first time and at regular intervals thereafter and the worker shall participate in such instruction and training.

(2) Personal protective equipment that is to be provided, worn or used shall,

(a) be properly used and maintained;

(b) be a proper fit;

(c) be inspected for damage or deterioration; and

(d) be stored in a convenient, clean and sanitary location when not in use.

11. If a worker is exposed,

(a) to the hazard of head injury, the worker shall wear head protection appropriate in the circumstances;

(b) to the hazard of eye injury, the worker shall wear eye protection appropriate in the circumstances;

(c) to the hazard of foot injury, the worker shall wear foot protection appropriate in the circumstances; and

(d) to the hazard of slipping on a work surface, the worker shall wear footwear with slip-resistant soles.

12. If a worker has or wears long hair, loose clothing or jewellery that may present a hazard it shall be suitably confined.

13. (1) Except where work is performed from a ladder, if a worker is exposed to the hazard of falling to a surface more than three metres below the position where the worker is situated, the worker shall be provided with and shall wear a fall arrest system.

(2) The fall arrest system shall consist of a serviceable safety belt or harness and lifeline that is adequately secured to a fixed support and so arranged that the worker cannot fall freely for a vertical distance of more than 1.5 metres.

(3) The fall arrest system shall,

(a) have sufficient capacity to absorb twice the energy and twice the load that under the circumstances of its use may be transmitted to it; and

(b) be equipped with a shock absorber or other device to limit the maximum arresting force to 8.0 kilonewtons to the worker.

14. (1) If a worker is exposed to the hazard of drowning and the liquid into which the worker could fall is of sufficient depth that a flotation device would be effective,

(a) the worker shall be provided with and wear a flotation device appropriate in the circumstances;

(b) an alarm system to warn workers that a rescue operation is to be carried out shall be provided;

(c) appropriate rescue equipment including flotation devices, poles and ropes shall be available in proximity to the hazard for immediate use; and

(d) a worker trained in cardio-pulmonary resuscitation shall be immediately available.

(2) Subsection (1) does not apply to a swimming pool or a pool used for therapeutic purposes.

15. (1) A worker who supports, positions or restrains a patient or resident during X-ray radiation of the patient or resident shall be provided with and wear a protective apron and protective gloves and, where appropriate, a protective collar.

(2) The equipment provided under subsection (1) shall have a lead equivalence of at least 0.5 millimetres.

Premises

16. A warning sign shall be posted on any door, corridor or stairway,

(a) that is not a means of egress but that is located or arranged so that it could be mistaken for one; or

(b) that leads to a hazardous, restricted or unsafe area.

17. Except where the door is in a fire separation, a self-closing door in a corridor used as a passageway for vehicles or wheeled equipment shall be equipped with a hold-open device and a see-through panel.

18. (1) This section applies with respect to a hazardous room,

(a) with an area greater than fifteen square metres; or

(b) requiring a distance of travel greater than 4.5 metres from any point in the room to an egress doorway.

(2) A hazardous room shall have at least two egress doorways that are at least three-quarters of the length of the diagonal distance of the room from each other.

(3) One egress doorway in a hazardous room shall be located within a maximum distance of twenty-five metres from any point in the room.

(4) A hazardous room shall be located in a floor area that has at least two exits.

(5) In this section, "hazardous room" means a room containing a substance which because of its nature or the form in which the substance exists, is handled or stored, may explode or become easily ignited causing a fire or creating an atmosphere or condition of imminent hazard to a worker.

Ventilation

19. (1) General indoor ventilation adequate to protect the health and safety of a worker shall be provided by natural or mechanical means.

(2) A mechanical ventilation system shall be inspected every six months to ensure it is in good condition.

(3) The inspection referred to in subsection (2) shall be carried out by a person who is qualified by training and experience to make such an inspection.

(4) The person carrying out the inspection shall file a report on the inspection with the employer and with the joint health and safety committee or health and safety representative, if any.

(5) A mechanical ventilation system,

    (a) shall be serviced and have maintenance work performed on it as frequently as recommended by the manufacturer; and

    (b) shall be serviced, have maintenance work performed on it or be repaired when a report referred to in subsection (4) indicates it is necessary to ensure the system is maintained in good condition.

20. (1) The ventilation system shall be such that replacement air is provided to replace air that is exhausted.

(2) The replacement air shall,

    (a) be heated, when necessary, to maintain at least the minimum temperature in the workplace specified in subsection 21(1);

(b) be free from contamination from any hazardous dust, vapour, smoke, fume, mist or gas; and

(c) enter in such a manner so as not to cause undue drafts and prevent,

    (i) blowing of settled dust into the workplace; and

    (ii) interference with any exhaust system.

(3) Air discharged from any exhaust system shall be discharged in such a manner so as to prevent the return of contaminants to any work area.

Heating

21. (1) Subject to subsections (2) and (3), an enclosed workplace shall be maintained at a temperature,

    (a) that is suitable for the type of work performed;

    (b) that is no less than 18 degrees Celsius; and

    (c) that is not likely to cause physical stress because of heat.

(2) Clause (1)(b) does not apply to a workplace,

    (a) that is normally unheated;

    (b) where materials requiring lower temperatures are used or stored, or a process or activity is carried out or performed requiring lower temperatures;

    (c) where radiant heating is such that a worker working in the area has the degree of comfort that would result were the area heated to 18 degrees Celsius;

    (d) where the work or activity is such that a temperature of 18 degrees Celsius could cause discomfort; or

    (e) during the first hour of the main operating shift where heat from processing or equipment provides a substantial portion of the heating.

(3) If it is not practical in the circumstances to maintain the temperature of an enclosed workplace as required by clause (1)(c), the employer shall, in consultation with the joint health and safety committee or health and safety representative, if any, develop, maintain and put into effect measures and procedures to ensure that a worker is not exposed to heat stress conditions that are likely to endanger or injure the worker.

Lighting

22. (1) A workplace shall be provided with illumination in accordance with the minimum lighting requirements as set out in Part 3 of the Ontario Building Code.

(2) The brightness levels and ratios, glare, contrast and shadows shall be maintained at a level that is not likely to be a hazard to a worker.

(3) Glare and reflection that are likely to be a hazard to a worker shall be limited as far as is practicable.

23. If a glare from a direct lighting source is likely to be a hazard to a worker, the source shall be shielded by louvres, lenses, lens covers or diffusers which control the glare.

24. If a worker is required to use a video display terminal for a continuous period of one hour or more, the worker shall have at least five minutes of time free from such work in every hour.

25. If fluorescent tubes are disposed of by crushing or compacting, it shall be done in an area adequately ventilated to protect the health and safety of the worker and the worker shall be provided with and use appropriate protective equipment

26. Burned-out light bulbs and fluorescent tubes shall be promptly replaced with appropriate replacements to ensure the workplace is provided with adequate illumination to perform the work safely.

27. Lighting equipment shall be serviced and maintained at regular intervals to ensure the workplace is provided with illumination in accordance with section 22.

Hygiene Facilities

28. Toilets and washbasins for the use of workers shall,

    (a) be provided in accordance with the requirements for sanitary facilities as set out in Part 3 of the Ontario Building Code;

    (b) have hot and cold running water for the washbasins; and

    (c) have reasonable personal hygiene supplies and equipment, including soap and disposable towels.

29. (1) Potable drinking water shall be provided from a fountain with an upward jet or from a tap from a piped water supply or a covered vessel together with a supply of single-use cups in a sanitary container located near the tap.

(2) Potable drinking water shall be available,
   (a) on every floor where work is regularly performed; and
   (b) within 100 metres of any area where work is regularly performed.

30. (1) If ten or more workers are employed at a facility, a room or other space affording reasonable privacy shall be provided.

(2) The room shall be equipped with one or more cots and chairs, unless the facility has a first-aid station or infirmary room that is so equipped.

31. Refrigerators used to store cultures, specimens or biological ampules shall not be used to store food or drink.

32. No food, drink, tobacco or cosmetics shall be consumed, applied or kept in areas where infectious materials, hazardous chemicals or hazardous drugs are used, handled or stored.

Work Surfaces

33. (1) A work surface shall be kept free of,
   (a) obstructions and hazards;
   (b) cracks, holes and bumps that may endanger a worker; and
   (c) accumulations of refuse, snow and ice.

(2) A work surface shall not have any finish or protective material used on it that is likely to make the surface slippery.

(3) A worker who knows that the conditions of a work surface fails to comply with subsection (1) or (2) shall report the failure to a supervisor.

(4) If a report of a failure to comply is made to a supervisor, he or she shall ensure that steps necessary to remedy the situation are taken forthwith, and until remedied, the hazard shall be identified by a conspicuous warning sign.

34. (1) If there is a spill of a liquid or material on a work surface that is likely to cause a worker to slip or fall, it shall be cleaned up forthwith and, until cleaned up, it shall be identified by a conspicuous warning sign.

(2) If a work surface is slippery when it is being cleaned or polished, a conspicuous sign warning that the surface is slippery shall be posted during cleaning or polishing.

35. If wet processes are used, or wet conditions are present, on a work surface and they cause it to be slippery, steps necessary to remedy the situation shall be taken including,

(a) the use of non-slip work surfaces;

(b) the provision of dry-standing places or non-slip mats;

(c) the provision of drainage adequate in the circumstances; or

(d) the use of water resistant, non-slip footwear by workers who may use the work surface.

36. (1) Subject to subsection (2), there shall be a guardrail,

(a) around the perimeter of an uncovered opening in a floor, roof or other surface to which a worker has access;

(b) at an open side of,

(i) a raised floor, mezzanine, balcony, gallery, landing, platform, walkway, stile, ramp or other surface, and

(ii) a vat, bin or tank, the top of which is less than 107 centimetres above the surrounding floor, ground, platform or other surface; and

(c) around a machine, electrical installation, place or thing that is likely to endanger the safety of any worker.

(2) Subsection (1) does not apply to,

(a) a loading dock;

(b) a pit used for maintenance of vehicles or similar equipment;

(c) a roof to which access is required for maintenance purposes only;

(d) a swimming pool or a pool used for therapeutic purposes; or

(e) a stage in an auditorium or lecture theatre.

37. A guardrail shall be designed and constructed to meet the requirements for guardrails as set out in Parts 3 and 4 of the Ontario Building Code or it shall,

(a) have a horizontal top rail located not less than ninety-one and not more than 107 centimetres above the surface to be guarded;

(b) have an intermediate rail located midway between the top rail and the surface to be guarded;

(c) if tools or other objects may fall on a worker, have a toe-board that extends from the surface to be guarded to a height of not less than 125 millimetres;

(d) be constructed to meet the structural requirements for guardrails as set out in Part 4 of the Ontario Building Code; and

(e) be free of splinters and other hazardous protrusions.

38. An opening in a work surface shall be covered or shall have a guardrail around its perimeter.

39. A cover on an opening in a work surface shall be secured in place and shall be constructed to meet the structural requirements for loads due to the use of floors and roofs as set out in Part 4 of the Ontario Building Code.

40. If frequent access is required to equipment that is elevated above or is located below a work surface, permanent platforms shall be provided with access by a fixed stair or a fixed access ladder.

41. (1) A fixed access ladder shall,

    (a) be vertical;

    (b) have rest platforms at not more than nine metre intervals;

    (c) be offset at each rest platform;

    (d) where the ladder extends more than five metres above grade, floor or landing, have a safety cage beginning not more than 2.2 metres above grade, floor or landing and continuing at least ninety centimetres above the top landing with openings to permit access by a worker to rest platforms or to the top landing;

    (e) have side rails that extend ninety centimetres above the landing, and

    (f) have rungs which are at least fifteen centimetres from the wall and spaced at regular intervals.

(2) Subsection (1) does not apply to an access ladder on a tower, water tank, chimney or similar structure that has a safety device which will provide protection should a worker using the ladder fall.

O. Reg. 25/09 s. 3

Restricted Spaces

42. (1) In this section, "restricted space" means a tank, vat, vessel, duct, vault, boiler or other space from which the egress of a worker is restricted, limited or impeded because of the construction, design, location or other physical characteristics of the space.

(2) A worker shall enter a restricted space only if,

    (a) he or she is informed of and familiar with the characteristics of the restricted space which restrict, limit or impede egress and is instructed in the procedures for entering, working in and exiting from the restricted space;

(b) there are procedures and measures in place for the removal of the worker from the restricted space in the event of an emergency;

(c) at least one other worker is stationed outside the restricted space and in proximity to it and is readily available and capable of implementing emergency procedures and measures for the removal of the worker from the restricted space; and

(d) mechanical equipment in the restricted space is disconnected from its power source and is locked out.

(3) The requirements of subsection (2) apply with all necessary modifications while a worker is in a restricted space.

Confined Spaces

43. to 43.19 [Repealed O. Reg. 97/11, s. 1.]

Equipment

44. Machinery or equipment shall be,

    (a) suitable for its actual use;

    (b) constructed of materials of sufficient size and strength to withstand imposed stresses;

    (c) provided with locking devices in order to prevent accidental operation which may be a hazard to a worker;

    (d) placed on a surface that is capable of supporting it;

    (e) inspected immediately before its use and at regular intervals as recommended by the manufacturer;

    (f) serviced and maintained in accordance with the recommendations and instructions of the manufacturer;

    (g) operated by a worker trained in its use and function; and

    (h) stored in a manner that prevents its movement.

45. If a machine or prime mover or transmission equipment has an exposed moving part that may endanger the safety of any worker, it shall be equipped with and guarded by a guard or other device that prevents access to the moving part.

46. An in-running nip hazard or any part of a machine, device or thing that may endanger the safety of a worker shall be equipped with and guarded by a guard or other device that prevents access to the pinch point.

47. A machine shall be shielded or guarded so that the safety of a worker is not endangered by its product, the material being processed or its waste stock.

48. An emergency stop control on a power-driven machine shall be conspicuously identified and be located within easy reach of the operator.

49. (1) An operating control that acts as a guard for a machine that is not otherwise guarded shall,

(a) be in a location where the safety of the operator is not endangered by moving machinery; and

(b) be arranged so that it cannot be operated accidentally.

(2) An operating control that acts as a guard for a machine that is not otherwise guarded shall not be made ineffective by a tie-down device or other means.

50. (1) Subject to subsection (2), a worker shall repair, maintain or adjust a machine, transmission machinery, device or thing or a part thereof only if,

(a) the control switches or other control mechanisms are locked out;

(b) the moving parts are stopped; and

(c) the hydraulic, pneumatic or gravity-stored energy is dissipated or contained.

(2) If it is not practical to de-energize a machine or transmission equipment by locking out its controls during repair, maintenance or adjustment, a worker may do such work if barriers, shields or other effective precautions are used or taken to ensure the safety of the worker while he or she is doing the work.

51. Clearance between a moving part of any machine or any material carried by the moving part of the machine and any other machine, structure or thing shall be adequate to ensure that the safety of any worker in the area is not endangered.

52. (1) Subject to subsection (3), if a worker is repairing or altering a gas line, steam line, pipeline, drum, tank or other container, the worker shall,

(a) adjust its internal pressures to atmospheric pressure before any fastening is removed;

(b) drain and clear it or otherwise render it free from any explosive, flammable or harmful substance.

(2) If a worker is repairing or altering a gas line, steam line, pipeline, drum, tank or other container, the worker shall not refill it while there is any risk of vaporizing or igniting the substance that is being placed in it.

(3) Subsection (1) does not apply if a competent person is hot-tapping and boxing-in a pipeline under controlled conditions so as to provide for the protection of all workers.

53. If machinery or equipment is being dismantled, serviced or repaired and the collapse of any part of it may injure a worker, blocking shall be installed to prevent its collapse.

54. If a worker may pass or work under machinery, equipment or material that is temporarily elevated, it shall be securely and solidly blocked to prevent it from falling or moving.

55. Before lifting or self-propelled mobile equipment is operated after its repair or modification, a person qualified by training and experience to do so shall inspect it to ensure that it is in good condition and a record shall be kept of the inspection.

56. (1) Glassware used in a laboratory shall be inspected for chips and cracks before use.

(2) Chipped or cracked glassware shall not be used unless it is repaired to a condition that does not present a hazard to a worker and if not repaired it shall be placed in a puncture-resistant container for disposal as waste.

57. A grinding wheel shall be,

      (a) marked with the maximum speed at which it may be operated;

      (b) checked for any defect before it is mounted;

      (c) mounted in accordance with the manufacturer's specifications;

      (d) provided with protective hoods that enclose the wheel as closely as the work will permit;

      (e) operated only by a worker using eye protection;

      (f) operated at a speed which does not exceed the manufacturer's recommendations; and

      (g) stored where it will not be subjected to heat, cold or impact which may damage it.

58. A work rest used with a grinding wheel shall,

      (a) be in a position above the centre line of the grinding wheel;

      (b) have a maximum clearance of three millimetres from the grinding wheel; and

(c) be adjusted only when the grinding wheel is stationary.

59. (1) A centrifuge shall be maintained and operated in accordance with the recommendations and instructions of its manufacturer.

(2) A centrifuge shall be designed or equipped with a device to prevent it from being operated at a speed in excess of that for which it was designed and intended.

(3) The load in a centrifuge shall be balanced to minimize vibration during its operation.

(4) If a flammable or infectious material is being centrifuged, a legible sign warning of the hazard shall be posted in the area where the centrifuge is being operated.

(5) If a bench-model centrifuge is being used to centrifuge a flammable or infectious material, it shall be operated in a biological safety cabinet or be otherwise appropriately contained, unless sealed safety heads or sealed centrifugal caps are used.

(6) Cushions shall be used in centrifuging material that is in glass containers.

60. (1) An autoclave or sterilization machine shall,

    (a) if the sterilant used in it is ethylene oxide or another hazardous chemical, be vented to the outdoors;

    (b) be operated by a worker qualified by training and experience to do so;

    (c) have its operating and emergency instructions posted adjacent to it;

    (d) be maintained on a regular basis and be inspected at least once every three months;

    (e) be tested when first put into service and annually thereafter by a person qualified by training and experience to do so and a record of the test shall be kept; and

    (f) have a pressure relief valve set at a pressure not exceeding that for which it was designed and intended.

(2) After its operation or use, an autoclave or sterilization machine shall not be opened until its pressure has returned to atmospheric pressure.

61. (1) Subject to subsection (2), a worker who is loading or unloading an autoclave or sterilization machine shall be provided with and wear aprons and elbow-length insulated gloves of an impervious material.

(2) If the autoclave or sterilization machine does not use heat, the gloves are not required to be insulated.

Electrical Equipment

62. Electrical equipment, power lines, conductors and insulating materials shall,

(a) be suitable for their use;

(b) be certified by the Canadian Standards Association or by the Electrical Safety Authority, as defined in the *Electricity Act, 1998*; and

(c) be installed, maintained, modified and operated in such a manner as not to present a hazard to a worker.

O. Reg. 142/99 s. 1

63. Except where electrical work is being carried out as permitted by section 68, tools, ladders, scaffolding and other equipment or materials capable of conducting electricity shall not be stored, used or left close enough to any energized electrical installation such that they may make electrical contact with an energized conductor.

64. No person, other than a person authorized to do so by the supervisor in charge of the room or enclosure, shall enter or be permitted to enter a room or other enclosure that contains exposed energized electrical parts.

65. The entrance to a room or other enclosure containing exposed energized electrical parts shall be marked by conspicuous signs warning of the danger and stating that entry by unauthorized persons is prohibited.

66. (1) The power supply to electrical installations, equipment or power lines shall be disconnected, locked out of service and tagged before any work is done, and when any work is being done, on or near the installations, equipment or power lines.

(2) Locking out and tagging are not required,

(a) if the power lines are adequately grounded with a visible grounding mechanism; or

(b) if the voltage is less than 300 volts and there is no locking device for the circuit breakers or fuses and procedures are in place adequate to ensure that the circuit is not inadvertently energized.

(3) Before beginning the work each worker shall determine if the power supply is disconnected.

(4) If locking out and tagging are not required, the employer shall ensure that the procedures set out in clause (2)(b) are carried out.

(5) This section does not apply if it is not practicable to disconnect electrical installations, equipment or power lines from the power supply before working on, or near, the installations, equipment or power lines.

67. A tag required by subsection 66(1) shall,

    (a) be made of non-conducting material;

    (b) be secured to prevent its inadvertent removal;

    (c) be placed in a conspicuous location;

    (d) state the reason the switch is opened;

    (e) show the name of the person responsible for opening the switch; and

    (f) show the date and time on which the switch was opened.

68. (1) This section applies if it is not practicable to disconnect electrical installations, equipment or power lines from the power supply before working on, or near, the installations, equipment or power lines.

(2) Only a competent person shall perform the work.

(3) The worker shall use rubber gloves, mats, shields, electrical shock resistant footwear or other protective equipment and procedures adequate to ensure protection from electrical shocks and burns while performing the work.

(4) If the installation, equipment or power line is operating at 300 volts or over but less than 750 volts, a suitably equipped, competent person who is able to perform rescue operations, including cardiopulmonary resuscitation, shall be readily available and be able to see the worker who is performing the work.

(5) If the installation, equipment or power line is operating at 750 volts or over,

    (a) the work shall be carried out by a competent person under the authority of an electrical utility; and

    (b) a suitable equipped, competent person who is able to perform rescue operations, including cardio-pulmonary resuscitation, shall be readily available and be able to see the worker who is performing the work.

(6) Subsections (4) and (5) do not apply to troubleshooting, installing or replacing meters or to the testing of appliances or instruments by,

(a) a worker who holds a certificate of qualification issued under the *Ontario College of Trades and Apprenticeship Act, 2009*, that is not suspended, in the trade of,

(i) electrician—construction and maintenance, or

(ii) electrician—domestic and rural, if the worker is performing work that is limited to the scope of practice for that trade; or

(b) a person with equivalent qualifications by training or experience.

O. Reg. 25/09 s. 7; 89/13 s. 1

69. Cord-connected electrical equipment and tools shall be adequately grounded.

70. (1) When used outdoors or in wet locations, portable electrical tools shall be protected by a ground fault circuit interrupter installed at the receptacle or on the circuit at the electrical panel.

(2) If there is an indication of a ground fault, it shall be investigated and removed without delay.

71. Electrical equipment or power lines that are no longer used for the purpose for which they were intended or designed shall be isolated, de-energized and,

(a) removed; or

(b) left in place and locked out and permanently disconnected by removing the cables from their connections at both ends and cutting back or taping the cables.

72. (1) No object shall be brought closer to an energized electric conductor of the voltage set out in Column 1 of the following Table than the distance specified opposite to it in Column 2:

TABLE

Column 1	Column 2
Conductor Voltage	**Minimum Distance**
750 to 150,000 volts	3 metres
over 150,000 to 250,000 volts	4.5 metres
over 250,000 volts	6 metres

(2) Subsection (1) does not apply,

   (a) if mats, shields or other protective devices adequate to ensure protection from electrical shocks and burns are installed under the authority of the owner of the conductor; and

   (b) if the person who is responsible for bringing the object within the minimum distance is using procedures adequate to ensure protection from electrical shock and burns and is,

    (i) a worker who holds a certificate of qualification issued under the *Ontario College of Trades and Apprenticeship Act, 2009*, that is not suspended, in the trade of,

        (A) electrician—construction and maintenance, or

        (B) electrician—domestic and rural, if the worker is performing work that is limited to the scope of practice for that trade, or

    (ii) a person with equivalent qualifications by training or experience.

O. Reg. 25/09 s. 8; 89/13 s. 2

73. If a vehicle, crane or similar equipment is operated near a live power line and it is possible for any part of it or its load to make contact with the live power line,

   (a) a worker shall be stationed within view of the operator to warn him or her when any part of the equipment is approaching the minimum distance from the live power line; and

   (b) clearance shall be allowed for any changes in boom angle and for any swing of the hoisting cable and load.

Compressed Gas Cylinders

74. (1) A storage cylinder for compressed gas shall,

   (a) have a valve connection which prevents an inadvertent connection that would result in a hazardous mixture of gases;

   (b) be secured in position during transportation, storage or use;

   (c) not be rolled, slid or dropped;

   (d) if designed for the use of a valve protection cap, have the valve protection cap in position when the cylinder is being transported or stored;

   (e) if it contains acetylene, be in an upright position;

   (f) be protected from physical damage;

521

(g) if it is empty, be labelled accordingly and have the valve securely turned off; and

(h) be stored in a well-ventilated area, away from any source of ignition.

(2) Subsection (1) does not apply to fire extinguishers or calibration equipment.

(3) A cylinder containing compressed flammable gas shall be stored,

(a) at least six metres from any cylinder containing oxygen; or

(b) with a barrier of noncombustible material at least 1.5 metres high having a fire resistance rating of at least one-half hour separating it from any cylinder containing oxygen.

(4) The area where compressed gas cylinders are stored shall be posted as a no smoking area and no person shall smoke in the area.

Material Handling Equipment

75. In sections 76 through 79, "material handling equipment" and "lifting equipment" do not include,

(a) equipment to which Ontario Regulation 209/01 (*Elevating Devices*), made under the *Technical Standards and Safety Act, 2000*, applies; or

(b) equipment used to lift, lower or transfer a person who is not a worker.

O. Reg. 25/09 s. 9

76. (1) Material handling equipment shall not be used to support, raise or lower a worker unless the requirements of this section are met.

(2) If material handling equipment is used to support, raise or lower a worker, the worker shall be on a platform that is,

(a) equipped with adequate safety devices that automatically prevent the platform and load from falling if the platform's normal support fails;

(b) suspended from a boom that does not move; or

(c) attached to a mast or boom which,

(i) is hydraulically or pneumatically operated, and

(ii) is equipped with a safety device that will prevent free fall of the platform in the event of a pressure line failure.

(3) A worker on a platform that is suspended from a boom that does not move shall be attached to a separate lifeline suspended from the boom or a fixed support capable of supporting at least four times the weight of the worker.

(4) If the material handling equipment is not designed for the specific purpose of hoisting personnel, the load applied to it shall be less than one-half the maximum rated load.

(5) The platform shall have a sign indicating the load that may be applied to it under subsection (4).

(6) If controls are provided at more than one location,
> (a) each control station shall be provided with means that allow the operator to cut off power to the equipment; and
> (b) interlocks shall be provided so that only one station can be operative at any one time.

(7) Except when the controls are operated from the platform, a worker other than the worker on the platform shall attend to and operate them.

77. If a worker who is operating material handling equipment is exposed to overhead hazards and adequate protection from the hazards is not provided by the use of personal protective equipment, overhead protection by means of a cab, screen, canopy, guard or other adequate protection shall be provided on the equipment.

78. Except for purposes of testing, no material handling equipment shall be loaded in excess of its maximum rated load.

79. (1) Lifting equipment shall be thoroughly examined by a competent person to determine its capability of handling the maximum load as rated,
> (a) before being used for the first time; and
> (b) thereafter as often as necessary but not less frequently than recommended by the manufacturer and, in any case, at least once a year.

(2) A permanent record shall be kept of each examination conducted under subsection (1) for as long as the equipment remains on the premises and for one year after the equipment is removed and the record shall be signed by the person who conducted it.

(3) Lifting equipment shall be clearly marked with sufficient information to enable its operator to determine the maximum rated load that the equipment is capable of lifting under any operating condition.

(4) If lifting equipment is equipped with limit switches, the switches shall,

(a) automatically cut off the power;

(b) automatically apply the brake when a load reaches its permissible limit; and

(c) be used as an operating control only when designed for such use.

(5) If a limit switch is used as an operating control on lifting equipment, a second limit switch shall be located behind the first switch.

(6) The lifting equipment's controls shall be attended when its load is in the raised position.

(7) Lifting equipment shall be attended when the forks, bucket, blades or similar part is in the raised position unless,

(a) the equipment is a hydraulic or pneumatic hoist that supports the load from below and is fixed in one location; or

(b) the forks, bucket, blades or similar part is solidly supported.

Ladders

80. (1) Except for a step stool, a worker shall not stand upon a chair, box or other loose object while working.

(2) A chair, box or other loose object shall not be used to support a ladder, scaffold or working platform.

81. The maximum length of a ladder measured along the side rail shall not be more than,

(a) six metres for a step-ladder;

(b) nine metres for a single ladder; and

(c) thirteen metres for an extension or sectional ladder.

82. (1) A ladder shall,

(a) have adequate strength, stiffness and stability to support any load likely to be applied to it;

(b) be free from broken or loose members or other faults;

(c) have rungs evenly spaced; and

(d) be equipped with slip-resistant feet.

(2) A wooden ladder shall not be painted or coated with an opaque material.

83. When a ladder is being used it shall,

(a) be placed on a firm footing and secured against slipping;

(b) if the ladder is between six and nine metres in length, be securely fastened or be held in place by one or more workers while being used;

(c) if the ladder exceeds nine metres in length, be securely fastened or stabilized to prevent it from tipping or falling;

(d) when not securely fastened, be inclined so that the horizontal distance from the top support to the foot of the ladder is not less than one-quarter and not more than one-third of the length of the ladder; and

(e) if the ladder is likely to be endangered by traffic, have a worker stationed at its foot to direct such traffic or have barriers or warning signs placed at its foot.

84. (1) When a step-ladder is being used as a self-supporting unit, its legs shall be fully spread and the spreader shall be locked.

(2) No worker shall stand on the top of a step-ladder or shall use the pail shelf as a step.

Scaffolds

85. If work cannot be done from a ladder without hazard to a worker, a scaffold shall be provided for the worker.

86. Only a competent person shall supervise the erection, alteration and dismantling of a scaffold.

87. (1) Every scaffold shall be capable of supporting,

(a) two times the maximum load to which it is likely to be subjected, without exceeding the allowable unit stresses for the particular materials used; and

(b) four times the maximum load to which it is likely to be subjected, without overturning.

(2) No scaffold shall be loaded in excess of the maximum load it could reasonably be expected to support and not in excess of the maximum load set out in clauses (1)(a) and (b).

(3) The requirements in this section and in section 88 do not apply to a suspended scaffold.

88. (1) Every scaffold shall,

(a) be constructed of suitable structural material;

(b) have horizontal members that are adequately secured to prevent lateral movement and that do not have splices between the points of support;

(c) have footings, sills or supports that are sound, rigid and capable of supporting at least two times the maximum load to which the scaffold is likely to be subjected without settlement or deformation that may affect the stability of the scaffold;

(d) where it consists of a structural system of tubular metal frames, have connecting devices between components that provide positive engagement in compression and tension;

(e) have all fittings, gear, base plates and wheels installed according to the manufacturer's instructions;

(f) have safety catches on all hooks;

(g) be adequately secured at vertical intervals not exceeding three times the least lateral dimension of the scaffold, measured at the base, to prevent lateral movement;

(h) where lumber is used in its construction, be constructed only of Construction Grade spruce or Number 1 Grade spruce; and

(i) have all uprights braced diagonally in the horizontal and vertical planes to prevent lateral movement.

(2) If a scaffold is more than fifteen metres in height, it shall be designed by a professional engineer and constructed in accordance with the design.

89. A scaffold mounted on castors or wheels, other than a movable working platform to which subsection 94(1) applies, shall,

(a) have a height which does not exceed three times the least lateral dimension of the scaffold,

(i) measured at the base, or

(ii) measured between the outriggers;

(b) be equipped with a suitable braking device on each castor or wheel; and

(c) have the brakes applied when,

(i) any worker is on the scaffold or the working platform of the scaffold, or

(ii) the scaffold is unattended.

90. The working platform of a scaffold shall,

(a) be designed, constructed and maintained to support all loads to which it may be subjected without exceeding the allowable unit stresses for the materials used, and in any event shall support not less than 2.4 kilo-newtons per square metre;

(b) be at least forty-six centimetres in width;

(c) be provided, at each open side and at the ends of the platform, with guardrails that comply with section 37;

(d) if the platform consists of sawn lumber planks, have planks of Number 1 Grade spruce that,

> (i) bear a legible grade identification stamp or bear a permanent grade identification mark,
>
> (ii) are at least forty-eight millimetres in thickness by 250 millimetres in width with a span not exceeding 2.1 metres,
>
> (iii) overhang their supports by not less than 150 millimetres and not more than 300 millimetres, and
>
> (iv) are cleated or otherwise secured against slipping; and

(e) if the platform required consists of planks manufactured of laminated wood, metal or a combination of materials, consist of planks tested in accordance with good engineering practice to demonstrate structural equivalence to the sawn lumber planks specified in clause (d).

Suspended Scaffolds

91. (1) This section applies to,

(a) a suspended scaffold that is permanently installed on a building or structure;

(b) a suspended scaffold that is transported in component form and is assembled to use at a work site;

(c) a boatswain's chair or single-point suspension equipment intended for the support of one worker; and

(d) the supports and equipment for a suspended scaffold or boatswain's chair, including lines, outrigger beams, davits, receptacles for outrigger beams or davits, cornice hooks, parapet wall hooks and anchors for attachment of primary suspension line or lifelines.

(2) A worker who is on or is getting on or off a suspended scaffold, boatswain's chair or similar single-point suspension equipment shall be protected by a fall arrest system that meets the requirements of section 13.

(3) All mechanically or electrically operated equipment described in subsection (1) shall,

(a) be suitable for a purpose for which it is used;

(b) have legible operating and maintenance instructions of the manufacturer affixed to the equipment in a conspicuous location;

(c) be operated, inspected and maintained in accordance with the manufacturer's instructions;

(d) be used only in a manner which does not endanger a worker; and

(e) not be used when a component, which may affect its safe operation, is damaged or defective.

(4) Primary suspension lines and lifelines used in connection with equipment described in subsection (1) shall,

(a) be rigged in accordance with generally accepted rigging practice;

(b) be rigged so that each line hangs vertically from the roof or access level to the ground or egress level of a worker using the line;

(c) have a breaking strength of at least ten times the static load that the line is intended to bear;

(d) have each connecting end wrapped around a protective thimble and securely fastened,

(i) by means of swagged fitting or eye splice if applied by the manufacturer of the line, or

(ii) if the line is wire rope, by a minimum of three clamps; and

(e) be inspected before each day's use by a competent person who shall report any defects or damage to a supervisor.

(5) Primary suspension lines and lifelines used in connection with equipment described in subsection (1) shall not be used when they are defective or damaged.

(6) A worker on a suspended scaffold, boatswain's chair or similar single-point suspension equipment shall have an effective means of summoning assistance in case of emergency.

92. (1) A boatswain's chair or similar single-point suspension equipment shall,

(a) have a seat at least 600 millimetres long and 250 millimetres wide of one piece construction capable of supporting 225 kilograms;

(b) be supported by a sling constructed of a wire rope of at least nine millimetres that crosses underneath the seat;

(c) not be used where the descent exceeds ninety metres;

(d) only be used for areas within arm's reach of a worker freely suspended on the primary support line; and

(e) not be used in conjunction with corrosive substances or solutions.

(2) A natural or synthetic line used as primary support line for a boatswain's chair or other similar single-point equipment shall be,

(a) doubled from the anchor point or point of suspension of the line to ground or egress level;

(b) permanently identified with,

(i) the name of the manufacturer of the line,

(ii) the date of the manufacture of the line, and

(iii) the length of the line;

(c) protected from abrasion;

(d) used only with a descent control or similar device,

(i) approved by the manufacturer of the descent control or similar device for use in window cleaning operations, and

(ii) in accordance with the installation, operating and maintenance instructions of the manufacturer of the descent control or similar device, which instructions shall be kept available for the inspection of an inspector;

(e) discarded when no longer safe for use or in accordance with the manufacturer's recommendations, whichever occurs first; and

(f) tested by a recognized testing laboratory at least once every twelve months for compliance with clause 91(4)(c), and, if found not in compliance, discarded.

93. (1) Static or horizontal lines rigged between anchor points for direct attachment of lifelines or primary support lines shall meet the requirements of this section.

(2) A professional engineer shall,

(a) instruct on the use of the static or horizontal lines and primary support lines; and

(b) certify the maximum load to be applied to them.

(3) The support capability of an anchor point shall exceed the total breaking strength of all support lines attached to it.

(4) Outrigger beams, cornice hooks and parapet wall hooks for support of primary support lines shall,

(a) be capable of supporting at least four times the maximum load to which they may be subjected without overturning and without exceeding the allowable unit stress for the materials of which they are constructed;

(b) be constructed of steel or aluminum or equivalent material; and

(c) be tied back to a fixed support so as to prevent their movement.

(5) Outrigger beams for support of primary support lines shall,

(a) have counterweights,

(i) that are manufactured for the purpose,

(ii) that are marked as to weight, and

(iii) that are securely attached to the outrigger beam;

(b) be accompanied by the supplier's or manufacturer's instructions indicating the number of counterweights that are necessary for the arrangements of the beam and the load that the beam can bear for each arrangement; and

(c) if positioned on a rolling undercarriage, have the undercarriage fixed to prevent the counterweights from moving while a worker is suspended by the primary support lines.

94. (1) A movable working platform operated by mechanical or electric power, including an elevating rolling scaffold and a self-propelled elevating scaffold or work platform, shall,

(a) be designed by a professional engineer in accordance with good engineering practice to support,

(i) two times the maximum load to which it may be subjected without exceeding the allowable unit stresses for the materials used, and

(ii) four times the maximum load to which it may be subjected without overturning;

(b) be constructed and maintained in accordance with the design of the professional engineer;

(c) be capable of supporting two times the maximum load to which it may be subjected without exceeding the allowable unit stresses for the materials used;

(d) be provided with guardrails that comply with the requirements of section 37;

(e) be fitted with signs indicating the safe working load;

(f) if equipped with outriggers, have a notice indicating the circumstances when the outriggers shall be used;

(g) be equipped with a fail safe mechanism for the elevating power system in the case of a power source or system failure;

(h) be equipped with a dead man control that will cut the power off from the operating mechanism unless the control regulating the power is continuously operated by a worker; and

(i) have each component which may affect its safe operation inspected by a competent person,

(i) before initial use, and

(ii) after initial use, as often as necessary but not less frequently than recommended by the manufacturer and, in any case, at least once a year.

(2) A movable working platform of the type described in subsection (1) shall not be used when a component that may affect its safe operation is defective.

(3) This section does not apply to a suspended scaffold.

Explosive Hazards

95. A process that is likely to produce dust, fume, gas or vapour to such an extent as to be capable of forming an explosive mixture when mixed with air shall be carried out,

(a) in an area that has provision for the disposal of the mixture by burning under controlled conditions; or

(b) in another area if,

(i) the area is identified by a sign warning of the hazard,

(ii) the area is isolated from other operations,

(iii) the area has a system of ventilation adequate to ensure that the dust, fume, gas or vapour does not reach a hazardous concentration,

(iv) the area has no potential sources of ignition,

(v) any heating or air vents leading to other areas have baffles, chokes or dampers to reduce the effects of any explosion, and

(vi) the area has provision for explosion venting.

Anaesthetic Gases

96. Where anaesthetic gases are likely to be present, the following measures and procedures shall be put into effect:

1. The installation of effective scavenging systems to collect, remove and dispose of waste gases.

2. The installation and use of anaesthesia respirators and machines to reduce contamination of the air in the room during administration of anaesthetic gases.

3. The implementation and use of a maintenance program for scavenging systems and anaesthesia respirators and machines and for inspecting for leakage on a monthly basis.

4. The adoption and use of proper work practices to reduce contamination of the room air during the administration of anaesthetic gases.

5. The regular maintenance of the ventilation system including filters.

Antineoplastic Drugs

97. (1) The employer shall, in consultation with the joint health and safety committee or health and safety representative, if any, develop, establish and put into effect written measures and procedures to protect workers who may be exposed to antineoplastic agents or to material or equipment contaminated with antineoplastic agents.

(2) The measures and procedures required by subsection (1) shall include,

(a) procedures for the storing, preparing, handling, using, transporting and disposing of antineoplastic agents and material contaminated with antineoplastic agents;

(b) emergency procedures to be followed in the event of a worker's exposure to antineoplastic agents by a needle puncture, inhalation or skin contact;

(c) procedures for the maintenance and disposal of equipment contaminated with antineoplastic agents;

(d) measures for the use of engineering controls, work practices, hygiene practices and facilities or personal protective equipment appropriate in the circumstances; and

(e) measures for the use of an appropriate biological safety cabinet for the preparation of antineoplastic agents.

(3) The employer shall provide training and instruction in the measures and procedures described in subsection (2) to workers who may be exposed to antineoplastic agents or to material or equipment contaminated with antineoplastic agents.

Flammable Liquids

98. In sections 99, 100 and 101, "flammable liquid" means any liquid having a flash point below 37.8 degrees Celsius and a vapour pressure below 275 kilopascals absolute at 37.8 degrees Celsius.

99. (1) Flammable liquids shall be handled in such a manner so as to prevent the hazard of explosion or fire.

(2) Flammable liquids shall be,

(a) dispensed, removed from any potential source of ignition;

(b) if dispensed indoors, dispensed in an area equipped with ventilation adequate to remove any hazardous concentration of fume or vapour;

(c) transported in containers that prevent any leakage or spillage of the liquids or in containers equipped with spring-loaded caps; and

(d) handled in a manner that prevents any leakage or spillage of the liquids, if such leakage or spillage would result in exposing the liquids to a proximate source of potential ignition that cannot be eliminated.

(3) If flammable liquid is being dispensed from a holding container, the dispensing equipment, the containers from which the flammable liquid is dispensed and the containers into which the flammable liquid is to be placed shall be bonded and grounded so as to prevent any explosion hazard.

100. (1) Flammable liquids shall be brought into a workplace only if the liquids are contained in,

(a) sealed containers;

(b) containers that prevent any leakage or spillage of the liquids; or

(c) containers equipped with a flame arrester.

(2) If flammable liquids are brought into a workplace in sealed containers, the containers shall remain sealed until the contents or a portion of the contents is required for immediate use.

(3) After the flammable liquids that were brought into a workplace in sealed containers have been used, the remaining contents of the containers and any unused quantities of the flammable liquids shall be stored,

(a) in containers that prevent any leakage or spillage of the liquids; or

(b) in containers equipped with a spring-loaded cap.

101. (1) If more than 235 litres of flammable liquids are being stored, the liquids shall be stored,

    (a) outdoors, remote from any means of egress;

    (b) in a building used solely for the storage of flammable liquids; or

    (c) within a workplace, in a storage room that is used solely for the storage of flammable liquids and that complies with subsection (2).

(2) The storage room shall,

    (a) be separated from the rest of the building with partitions that have at least a one-hour fire resistance rating;

    (b) be equipped with,

        (i) liquid-tight seals between interior walls and the floor and a liquid-tight ramped sill at any door opening in an interior wall, or

        (ii) other means to prevent leakage or spillage of the flammable liquid from the storage room to another part of the workplace in the building;

    (c) be equipped with doors that are side hinged to swing outward and that are self-closing;

    (d) be equipped with a drain connected to a holding tank of sufficient capacity to contain any possible leakage or spillage;

    (e) be provided with a ventilation system that is adequate to render the atmosphere free of any accumulation of hazardous gas or vapour; and

    (f) if the flammable liquids are in opened containers or have flash points below 22.8 degrees Celsius and boiling points below 37.8 degrees Celsius,

        (i) be equipped with a spark-resistant floor,

        (ii) be equipped with adequate explosion venting to the outdoors, and

        (iii) have no potential source of ignition.

(3) If the quantity of flammable liquids to be stored indoors is 235 litres or less, the liquids shall be stored,

    (a) in sealed containers of no more than twenty-three litres capacity each; or

    (b) subject to section 106, in a metal cabinet of double-walled construction with a 3-point door latch and a liquid-tight door sill raised at least fifty-five millimetres above the floor.

102. (1) An internal combustion engine shall be fuelled,

(a) outside a building;

(b) only when the engine is shut off; and

(c) only if any source of ignition is more than three metres from the dispensing point.

(2) Subsection (1) does not apply to generators for emergency electrical power.

(3) A worker who is fuelling an internal combustion engine shall make an allowance for the possible expansion of the fuel due to the exposure of the equipment to higher surrounding temperature.

Material Handling

103. (1) Materials, articles or things shall be handled, stored and disposed of in a manner that will not cause a hazard.

(2) Materials, articles or things shall be transported, placed or stored so that they will not tip, collapse or fall and so that they can be removed or withdrawn without endangering the safety of any worker.

104. A container used to store, transport or dispense a hazardous material shall be,

(a) adequate to protect the worker from the substance contained in it; and

(b) protected from physical damage.

105. Incubators, refrigerators and deep freeze units used to store cultures, specimens or biological ampules shall be identified as biohazardous.

106. Flammable materials that require refrigeration shall be stored in an explosion-proof refrigerator.

107. Bottles and test tubes shall be transported in racks or containers that prevent them from breaking, leaking or spilling their contents and that protect workers from exposure to the contents.

108. Workbenches, shelves, fume hoods and safety cabinets shall have adequate space for a worker to perform the work safely.

109. (1) In a laboratory, appropriate disinfectants and decontaminants shall be provided and used to clean workbench, fume hood and safety cabinet surfaces and floors.

(2) In a laboratory where spills of a hazardous material are likely to occur, workbench, fume hood and safety cabinet surfaces and floors shall consist of a smooth nonporous or impervious material.

110. A piping system that contains a substance which is hazardous because of its toxicity, temperature, pressure, flammability, or other property, shall have its contents and direction of flow clearly identified,

    (a) at valves and fittings;

    (b) in locations where a pipe passes through a wall or floor; and

    (c) where circumstances may make its contents or direction of flow doubtful.

Housekeeping and Waste

111. (1) A room used for storing laundry or janitorial materials and equipment shall be maintained in accordance with good hygiene practices.

(2) Janitorial work that may cause dusty conditions shall be done in a manner that will minimize the contamination of air by dust.

112. Waste materials shall be removed from work areas in a building as often as is necessary to protect the health and safety of workers.

113. (1) Objects referred to in subsection (2) that are being discarded as waste materials shall be placed in puncture-resistant containers.

(2) Subsection (1) applies to needles, knives, scissors, scalpels, broken glass or other sharp objects that are capable of cutting or penetrating the skin or any part of a worker's body.

114. (1) Used needles that are being discarded as waste material shall be discarded, immediately after use and without being bent or recapped, into a puncture-resistant container.

(2) If it is impracticable to discard used needles in accordance with subsection (1),

    (a) the employer shall provide a device or equipment that protects workers from being accidentally punctured while they are recapping used needles; and

    (b) the needles shall be recapped using the device or equipment described in clause (a) by workers who have received instruction and training in the use of that device or equipment.

(3) The kind of device or equipment provided under clause (2)(a) shall be chosen by the employer after consulting with the joint health and safety committee or health and safety representative, if any, and after considering their recommendations.

115. Containers that are used for storing liquid hazardous waste in a workplace shall,

    (a) be equipped with a tight-fitting cover;

    (b) be leak-proof;

    (c) if there may be internal pressure in the container, be designed so that the pressure is relieved by controlled ventilation; and

    (d) shall be emptied daily or as the circumstances may reasonably require.

116. (1) This section applies to all waste materials at a facility other than those waste materials generated in office administration or general building maintenance at the facility.

(2) The employer in consultation with the joint health and safety committee or health and safety representative, if any, shall develop, establish and put into effect measures and procedures to ensure that waste materials contaminated or potentially contaminated with hazardous infectious agents that are likely to endanger the health or safety of a worker are collected, contained, identified, transported, handled, stored and treated in a manner that will not endanger the health and safety of a worker.

(3) The employer shall ensure that a worker who generates, collects, transports, handles or treats contaminated or potentially contaminated waste materials is trained in the measures and procedures referred to in subsection (2).

Commencement

117. This Regulation comes into force on the 1st day of June, 1993.

TABLE 1 [Repealed O. Reg. 495/09, s. 2.]

[Repealed O. Reg. 495/09, s. 2.]

Form 1
Occupational Health and Safety Act
Notice

TAKE NOTICE that this .... (specify the "place" or "thing", as the case may be) is a danger or hazard to the health or safety of workers employed in or having access to this place or thing, and the use thereof shall be discontinued immediately until the inspector's order of .... (date) to .... has been complied with. (name and address of employer or owner) No person, except an inspector, shall remove this notice unless authorized by an inspector.

Dated the .... day of ...., 19...........

(Signature of Inspector) ....

ONT. REG. 851 — INDUSTRIAL ESTABLISHMENTS

made under the *Occupational Health and Safety Act*

R.R.O. 1990, Reg. 851, as am. O. Reg. 516/92; 630/94; 230/95; 450/97; 144/99; 284/99; 528/00; 488/01; 280/05; 629/05; 565/06; 179/07; 494/09; 420/10, ss. 1-28, 29 (Fr.); 98/11; 382/15; 289/17

Definitions

1. In this Regulation,

"adequate", when used in relation to a procedure, plan, material, device, object or thing, means that it is,

    (a) sufficient for both its intended and its actual use, and

    (b) sufficient to protect a worker from occupational illness or occupational injury;

"adequately" has a meaning that corresponds to the meaning of **"adequate"**;

"architect" means a member or licensee of the Ontario Association of Architects under the *Architects Act*;

"boom" means the projecting part of a back-hoe, shovel, crane or similar lifting device from which a load is likely to be supported;

"Building Code" means Regulation 61 of Revised Regulations of Ontario, 1990 made under the *Building Code Act*;

"confined space" [Repealed O. Reg. 629/05, s. 1(2).]

"fire-resistance rating" means the rating in hours or fraction thereof that a material or assembly of materials will withstand the passage of flame and the transmission of heat when exposed to fire, as established for the material or assembly of materials under the *Building Code Act*;

"flammable liquid" means a liquid having a flash point below 37.8° Celsius, and a vapour pressure below 275 kilopascals absolute at 37.8° Celsius;

"foundry" means the part of a building or premises or the workshop, structure, room or place in which base metals or their alloys are cast in moulds, other than permanent moulds, or where core-making, shakeout or cleaning or any casting or other dust-causing operation ancillary to the casting process is carried on;

"gangway" means a defined passageway between a metal melting unit and a metal pouring area;

"lifting device" means a device that is used to raise or lower any material or object and includes its rails and other supports but does not include a device to which Ontario Regulation 209/01 (*Elevating Devices*), made under the *Technical Standards and Safety Act, 2000*, applies;

"log" includes tree-length pulpwood and a pit prop, pole, post, tie or any similar product;

"pouring aisle" means a passageway leading from a gangway where metal is poured into a mould or box;

"prime mover" means an initial source of motive power;

"professional engineer" means a member or licensee of the Association of Professional Engineers of Ontario under *the Professional Engineers Act*;

"service room" means, in relation to a building, a room that accommodates building services and includes a boiler room, furnace room, incinerator room, garbage room, elevator machine room and a room that accommodates air conditioning or heating appliances, pumps, compressors or electrical services;

"transmission equipment" means any object or objects by which the motion of a prime mover is transmitted to a machine that is capable of utilizing such motion and includes a shaft, pulley, belt, chain, gear, clutch or other device;

"working space" means any space where persons are engaged in the performance of work within a foundry but does not include offices, lunch rooms, locker rooms, change rooms, rest rooms, washrooms, shower rooms, toilet rooms, pattern shops, maintenance shops, laboratories, shipping areas, the storage space occupied by equipment or materials not regularly in use or the enclosed space where core sands and moulding sands are stored.

629/05 s. 1; 420/10 s. 1

Equivalency

2. In applying this Regulation, the composition, design, size and arrangement of any material, object, device or thing may vary from the composition, design, size or arrangement prescribed in this Regulation where the factors of strength, health and safety are equal to or greater than the factors of strength, health and safety in the composition, design, size or arrangement prescribed.

Application

3. This Regulation applies to all industrial establishments.

Part I — Safety Regulations

4. (1) Subject to subsection (2), the minimum age of,

    (a) a worker; or

    (b) a person who is permitted to be in or about an industrial establishment, shall be,

    (c) sixteen years of age in a logging operation;

    (d) fifteen years of age in a factory other than a logging operation; and

    (e) fourteen years of age in a workplace other than a factory.

(2) Clause (1)(b) does not apply to a person who,

    (a) while in the industrial establishment, is accompanied by a person who has attained the age of majority;

    (b) is being guided on a tour of the industrial establishment;

    (c) is in an area of the industrial establishment used for sales purposes; or

    (d) is in an area of the industrial establishment to which the public generally has access.

(3) Clauses (1)(d) and (e) do not apply with respect to a worker who works as a performer in the entertainment and advertising industry.

(4) In subsection (3),

"entertainment and advertising industry" means the industry of producing,

    (a) live or broadcast performances, or

    (b) visual, audio or audio-visual recordings of performances, in any medium or format;

"performance" means a performance of any kind, including theatre, dance, ice skating, comedy, musical productions, variety, circus, concerts, opera, modelling and voice-overs, and **"performer"** has a corresponding meaning.

O. Reg. 179/07 s. 1

Notice of Accidents

5. (1) The written report required by section 51 of the Act shall include,

    (a) the name and address of the constructor and the employer;

    (b) the nature and the circumstances of the occurrence and of the bodily injury sustained;

    (c) a description of the machinery or equipment involved;

    (d) the time and place of the occurrence;

    (e) the name and address of the person who was killed or critically injured;

    (f) the names and addresses of all witnesses to the occurrence; and

    (g) the name and address of the physician or surgeon, if any, by whom the person was or is being attended for the injury.

(2) For the purposes of section 52 of the Act, notice of,

    (a) an accident, explosion or fire which disables a worker from performing his or her usual work; or

    (b) an occupational illness, shall include,

    (c) the name, address and type of business of the employer;

    (d) the nature and the circumstances of the occurrence and of the bodily injury or illness sustained;

    (e) a description of the machinery or equipment involved;

    (f) the time and place of the occurrence;

    (g) the name and address of the person suffering the injury or illness;

    (h) the names and addresses of all witnesses to the occurrence;

    (i) the name and address of the physician or surgeon, if any, by whom the person was or is being attended for the injury or illness; and

(j) the steps taken to prevent a recurrence or further illness.

(3) A record of an accident, explosion or fire causing injury requiring medical attention but not disabling a worker from performing his or her usual work shall be kept in the permanent records of the employer and include particulars of,

    (a) the nature and circumstances of the occurrence and of the injury sustained;

    (b) the time and place of the occurrence; and

    (c) the name and address of the injured person.

(4) A record kept as prescribed by subsection (3) for the inspection of an inspector shall be notice to the Director.

O. Reg. 420/10 s. 2

Retention of Reports and Records

[Heading amended O. Reg. 528/00, s. 1.]

6. Where, under section 5 or 51, a report or permanent record is prescribed to be kept, it shall be kept for,

    (a) a period of at least one year; or

    (b) such longer period as is necessary to ensure that at least the two most recent reports or records are kept.

O. Reg. 629/05 s. 2

Pre-Start Health and Safety Reviews

7. (1) In this section,

"apparatus" means equipment or a machine or device;

"protective element" means a shield, a guard, an operating control acting as a guard, a locking device or any other device preventing access;

"spray booth" means a spray booth as defined in Ontario Regulation 213/07 (*Fire Code*) made under the *Fire Protection and Prevention Act, 1997*;

"Table" means the Table to this section.

(2) Subject to subsections (5), (7), (8) and (9), a pre-start health and safety review is required if, in a factory other than a logging operation, a provision of this Regulation listed in the Table applies and the circumstances described in the Table will exist,

(a) because a new apparatus, structure or protective element is to be constructed, added or installed or a new process is to be used; or

(b) because an existing apparatus, structure, protective element or process is to be modified and one of the following steps must be taken to obtain compliance with the applicable provision:

1. New or modified engineering controls are used.

2. Other new or modified measures are used.

3. A combination of new, existing or modified engineering controls and other new or modified measures is used.

(3) When a pre-start health and safety review is required, the owner, lessee or employer shall ensure that the apparatus, structure or protective element is not operated or used or that the process is not used, as the case may be, unless the review has been conducted, and,

(a) all measures identified in the review as being required for compliance with the relevant provisions of this Regulation that are listed in the Table have been taken; or

(b) if some or all of the measures specified in clause (a) are not taken, the owner, lessee or employer has provided written notice to the joint health and safety committee or the health and safety representative, if any, of what measures have been taken to comply with the relevant provisions of this Regulation that are listed in the Table.

(4) A pre-start health and safety review includes the preparation of a written report that is made to the owner, lessee or employer and contains,

(a) details of the measures to be taken for compliance with the relevant provisions of this Regulation that are listed in the Table;

(b) if testing is required before the apparatus or structure can be operated or used or before the process can be used, details of measures to protect the health and safety of workers that are to be taken before the testing is carried out; and

(c) if item 3 or 7 of the Table applies, details of the structural adequacy of the apparatus or structure.

(5) When item 2 of the Table applies, a pre-start health and safety review is not required if,

(a) the protective element was installed at the time the apparatus was manufactured and the conditions set out in paragraphs 1, 2 and 3 of subsection (6) are met; or

(b) the protective element was not installed at the time the apparatus was manufactured and the conditions set out in paragraphs 1, 2, 3 and 4 of subsection (6) are met.

(6) The following are the conditions mentioned in clauses (5)(a) and (b):
1. The apparatus was manufactured in accordance with and meets current applicable standards, or it has been modified to meet current applicable standards.
2. The apparatus is installed in accordance with the manufacturer's instructions and current applicable standards.
3. The protective element was manufactured in accordance with and meets current applicable standards, or it has been modified to meet current applicable standards.
4. The protective element is installed in accordance with the manufacturer's instructions, and current applicable standards, if any.

(7) When item 3 of the Table applies, a pre-start health and safety review is not required if the rack or stacking structure is designed and tested for use in accordance with current applicable standards.

(8) When item 4 of the Table applies, a pre-start health and safety review is not required if the process is conducted inside a spray booth that is manufactured and installed in accordance with current applicable standards.

(9) When item 7 of the Table applies, a pre-start health and safety review is not required,
(a) in the case of a lifting device or travelling crane, if it is in or on a supporting structure originally designed for it and its capacity does not exceed the capacity provided for in that original design;
(b) in the case of an automobile hoist, if it is certified that it meets current applicable standards.

(10) If no pre-start health and safety review is required because subsection (5), (7), (8) or (9) applies, the owner, lessee or employer shall keep documents establishing the exemption readily accessible in the workplace for as long as the protective element, rack or stacking structure or lifting device, travelling crane or automobile hoist remains in the workplace or the process is used in the workplace, as the case may be.

(11) A pre-start health and safety review required under item 1, 2, 3, 4, 5, 6 or 7 of the Table shall be conducted by a professional engineer.

(12) A pre-start health and safety review required under item 8 of the Table shall be conducted by a professional engineer or by a person who in the opinion of the owner, lessee or employer possesses special, expert or professional knowledge or qualifications appropriate to assess any potential or actual hazards.

(13) The person conducting a pre-start health and safety review shall,

    (a) date and sign the written report mentioned in subsection (4);

    (b) if the person is a professional engineer, affix his or her seal to the report; and

    (c) if the person is not a professional engineer, include in the report details of his or her special, expert or professional knowledge or qualifications.

(14) Reports of pre-start health and safety reviews conducted under this section shall,

    (a) be kept readily accessible in the workplace together with any supporting documents; and

    (b) be provided to the joint health and safety committee or the health and safety representative, if any, before the apparatus, structure or protective element is operated or used or the process is used.

(15) Documents kept under subsection (10) may be reviewed, on request, by,

    (a) the joint health and safety committee or the health and safety representative, if any; or

    (b) an inspector.

TABLE

It-em	Applicable provisions of this Regula-tion	Circumstances
1.	Subsections 22(1), (2) and (4)	Flammable liquids are located or dispensed in a building, room or area.
2.	Sections 24,	Any of the following are used as protective

	25, 26, 28, 31 and 32	elements in connection with an apparatus: 1. Safeguarding devices that signal the apparatus to stop, including but not limited to safety light curtains and screens, area scanning safeguarding systems, radio frequency systems and capacitance safeguarding systems, safety mat systems, two-hand control systems, two-hand tripping systems and single or multiple beam systems. 2. Barrier guards that use interlocking mechanical or electrical safeguarding devices.
3.	Clause 45(b)	Material, articles or things are placed or stored on a structure that is a rack or stacking structure.
4.	Section 63	A process involves a risk of ignition or explosion that creates a condition of imminent hazard to a person's health or safety.
5.	Section 65	The use of a dust collector involves a risk of ignition or explosion that creates a condition of imminent hazard to a person's health or safety.
6.	Sections 87.3, 87.4, 87.5 and 88, subsections 90(1), (2) and (3), and sections 91, 92, 94, 95, 96, 99, 101	A factory produces aluminum or steel or is a foundry that melts material or handles molten material.

851

	and 102	
7.	Sections 51 and 53	The construction, addition, installation or modification relates to a lifting device, travelling crane or automobile hoist.
8.	Sections 127 and 128	A process uses or produces a substance that may result in the exposure of a worker in excess of any exposure limit set out in Regulation 833 of the Revised Regulations of Ontario, 1990 (*Control of Exposure to Biological or Chemical Agents*), Ontario Regulation 278/05 (*Designated Substance—Asbestos on Construction Projects and in Buildings and Repair Operations*) or Ontario Regulation 490/09 (*Designated Substances*) all made under the Act.

O. Reg. 450/97 s. 2; 144/99 s. 1; 528/00 s. 2; 280/05 s. 1; 494/09 s. 1; 420/10 s. 3

8. [Revoked O. Reg. 450/97, s. 3.]

Fees and Forms
[Heading added O. Reg. 450/97, s. 4.]

9. The fee for each copy of a report or each copy of an order furnished under section 64 of the Act is $500.

10. A notice under subsection 57(9) of the Act shall be in Form 2.

Premises

11. A floor or other surface used by any worker shall,
    (a) be kept free of,
        (i) obstructions,
        (ii) hazards, and
        (iii) accumulations of refuse, snow or ice; and
    (b) not have any finish or protective material used on it that is likely to make the surface slippery.

12. Clearances between a moving part of any machine or any material carried by the moving part of the machine and any other machine, structure or thing shall be adequate to ensure that the safety of any worker in the area is not endangered.

13. (1) Subject to subsection (2), there shall be a guardrail,

(a) around the perimeter of an uncovered opening in a floor, roof or other surface to which a worker has access;

(b) at an open side of,

(i) a raised floor, mezzanine, balcony, gallery, landing, platform, walkway, stile, ramp or other surface, or

(ii) a vat, bin or tank, the top of which is less than 107 centimetres above the surrounding floor, ground, platform or other surface; and

(c) around a machine, electrical installation, place or thing that is likely to endanger the safety of any worker.

(2) Subsection (1) does not apply to,

(a) a loading dock;

(b) a roof to which access is required only for maintenance purposes; and

(c) a pit used for,

(i) work on an assembly line, or

(ii) maintenance of vehicles or similar equipment.

14. (1) A guardrail shall,

(a) have a top rail located not less than 91 and not more than 107 centimetres above the surface to be guarded;

(b) have a mid rail;

(c) if tools or other objects may fall on a worker, have a toeboard that extends from the surface to be guarded to a height of at least 125 millimetres; and

(d) be free of splinters and protruding nails.

(2) A guardrail shall be constructed to meet the structural requirements for guards as set out in the Building Code.

15. A cover on an opening in a floor, roof or other surface shall be,

(a) secured in place; and

(b) constructed to meet the structural requirements for loads due to the use of floors and roofs as set out in the Building Code.

16. A door,

(a) located or arranged so that it could be mistaken for an exit door; or

(b) leading to a hazardous, restricted or unsafe area, shall be identified by a warning sign posted on it.

17. A fixed walkway, service stair or stile shall be at least fifty-five centimetres in width.

18. (1) Subject to subsection (2), an access ladder fixed in position shall,

(a) be vertical;

(b) have rest platforms at not more than nine metre intervals;

(c) be offset at each rest platform;

(d) where the ladder extends over five metres, above grade, floor or landing, have a safety cage commencing not more than 2.2 metres above grade, floor or landing and continuing at least ninety centimetres above the top landing with openings to permit access by a worker to rest platforms or to the top landing;

(e) have side rails that extend ninety centimetres above the landing; and

(f) have rungs which are at least fifteen centimetres from the wall and spaced at regular intervals.

(2) Subsection (1) does not apply to an access ladder on a tower, water tank, chimney or similar structure which has a safety device which will provide protection should a worker using the ladder fall.

O. Reg. 420/10 s. 4

19. Where frequent access is required to equipment elevated above or located below floor level, permanent platforms shall be provided with access by a fixed,

(a) stair; or

(b) access ladder.

20. Barriers, warning signs or other safeguards for the protection of all workers in an area shall be used where vehicle or pedestrian traffic may endanger the safety of any worker.

Lighting

21. Where natural lighting is inadequate to ensure the safety of any worker, artificial lighting shall be provided and shadows and glare shall be reduced to a minimum.

851

Fire Prevention—Protection

22. (1) Subject to subsections (2), (3) and (4), where not required for immediate use, flammable liquids shall be,

(a) in sealed containers; and

(b) located,

(i) outdoors and remote from any means of egress,

(ii) in a building not used for any other purpose, or

(iii) in a room,

(A) separated from the rest of the building with partitions having,

1. at least a one-hour fire-resistance rating, and

2. self-closing doors, hinged to swing outwardly on their vertical axes,

(B) equipped with,

1. a drain connected to a dry sump or holding tank, and

2. liquid-tight seals between interior walls and floor and a liquid-tight ramped sill at any door opening, which is not in an exterior wall, and

(C) having natural ventilation to the outdoors by upper and lower exterior wall gravity louvres.

(2) Where not required for immediate use, flammable liquids,

(a) in opened containers; or

(b) having a flash point below 22.8° Celsius and a boiling point below 37.8° Celsius, shall,

(c) comply with the requirements of clause (1)(b);

(d) be stored in facilities having no potential source of ignition; and

(e) when located in a room, be located in a room equipped with,

(i) explosion venting to the outdoors, and

(ii) a spark resistant floor.

(3) A maximum of 235 litres of flammable liquids may be stored,

(a) in sealed containers of not more than twenty-three litre capacity each; or

(b) in a metal cabinet of double walled construction with a 3-point door latch and a liquid-tight door sill raised at least fifty millimetres above the floor.

(4) An area where flammable liquids are dispensed shall have,

(a) mechanical ventilation from floor level to the outdoors at the rate of eighteen cubic metres per hour per square metre of floor area; and

(b) containers and dispensing equipment bonded and grounded when flammable liquid is dispensed.

O. Reg. 420/10 s. 5

23. A portable container used for dispensing flammable liquid in a work area shall be made of material suitable to provide for the safety of all workers and have,

(a) a spring-loaded cap; and

(b) a flame arrestor.

Machine Guarding

24. Where a machine or prime mover or transmission equipment has an exposed moving part that may endanger the safety of any worker, the machine or prime mover or transmission equipment shall be equipped with and guarded by a guard or other device that prevents access to the moving part.

25. An in running nip hazard or any part of a machine, device or thing that may endanger the safety of any worker shall be equipped with and guarded by a guard or other device that prevents access to the pinch point.

26. A machine shall be shielded or guarded so that the product, material being processed or waste stock will not endanger the safety of any worker.

27. An emergency stop control on a power-driven machine shall,

(a) be conspicuously identified; and

(b) be located within easy reach of the operator.

28. An operating control that acts as a guard for a machine not otherwise guarded shall,

(a) be in a location where the safety of the operator is not endangered by moving machinery;

(b) be arranged so that it cannot be operated accidentally; and

(c) not be made ineffective by a tie-down device or other means.

29. A grinding wheel shall be,

(a) marked with the maximum speed at which it may be used;

(b) checked for defects before mounting;

(c) mounted in accordance with the manufacturer's specifications;

(d) operated at a speed which does not exceed the manufacturer's recommendations;

(e) provided with protective hoods that enclose the wheel as closely as the work will permit;

(f) operated only by workers protected by eye protection; and

(g) stored where it will not be subjected to,

    (i) extreme heat or cold, or

    (ii) damage from impact.

30. A work rest for a grinding wheel shall,

(a) have a maximum clearance of three millimetres from the grinding wheel;

(b) be in a position above the centre line of the grinding wheel; and

(c) not be adjusted while the grinding wheel is in motion.

31. A centrifugal extractor, separator or dryer shall have an interlocking device that will prevent,

(a) any lid or covering guard from being opened or removed while the rotating drum or basket is in motion; and

(b) the starting of the drum or basket while the lid or covering guard is open or removed.

32. A tumbling mill or tumbling dryer shall have a locking device which prevents any movement of the mill or dryer that may endanger any worker during loading or unloading.

33. Portions of conveyors or other moving machinery that are not visible from the control station, and where starting up may endanger any worker, shall be equipped with automatic start-up warning devices.

34. Guards shall be provided beneath conveyors,

(a) that pass over any worker; or

(b) from which falling material, including broken conveyor parts, may be a hazard to any worker.

35. Overhead protection shall be provided where falling material may endanger any worker.

36. (1) Subject to subsection (2), an explosive actuated fastening tool shall,

(a) have a firing mechanism that will prevent the tool from being fired,

    (i) while being loaded,

    (ii) during preparation for firing, or

851

(iii) if dropped;

(b) be capable of being operated only when the muzzle end is held against a working surface with a force of at least twenty-two newtons greater than the weight of the tool;

(c) if required to be dismantled into separate parts for loading, be capable of being operated only when the separate parts are firmly locked together;

(d) be capable of being fired only after two separate and distinct actions have been carried out by the operator, with the firing movement separate from the operation of bringing the tool into the firing position;

(e) be used only when equipped with a protective guard or shield,

(i) suitable for the particular fastening operation being performed,

(ii) mounted at right angles to the barrel,

(iii) at least seventy-five millimetres in diameter, and

(iv) placed in a central position on the muzzle end of the tool except where the fastener is intended to be driven into a surface at a point within thirty-eight millimetres of another surface that is at any angle to the surface into which the fastener is intended to be driven;

(f) be capable of being operated when the guard prescribed by clause (e) is placed in the central position only when the bearing surface of the guard is tilted not more than eight degrees from the working surface;

(g) when not in use, be stored in a locked container;

(h) not be left unattended where it may be available to a person other than a worker having the qualifications set out in subclause (k)(i);

(i) whether loaded or unloaded, not to be pointed directly at any person;

(j) not to be loaded unless it is being prepared for immediate use;

(k) be used only,

(i) by a worker who has been instructed in the proper and safe manner of its use by the manufacturer or the manufacturer's authorized and qualified agent,

(ii) by a worker wearing both head protection and eye protection,

(iii) after it has been inspected by the worker referred to in subclause (i) to ensure that,

    (A) the tool is clean,

    (B) all moving parts operate freely,

    (C) the barrel is free from any obstruction,

    (D) the tool is adequately equipped for the intended use, and

    (E) it is not defective,

(iv) in accordance with the instructions of the manufacturer,

(v) with an explosive load of a strength adequate to perform the intended work without excessive force, and

(vi) to drive a stud or other fastener suitable for insertion in the tool; and

(l) not to be used in an atmosphere containing flammable vapours, gases or dust.

(2) Clauses (1)(e) and (f) do not apply to an explosive actuated fastening tool if the velocity of the stud or other fastener does not exceed ninety metres per second measured at a distance of two metres from the muzzle end of the tool when propelled by the maximum commercially available explosive load that the tool is chambered to accept.

(3) A misfired cartridge that has been removed from an explosive actuated fastening tool shall be placed in a water filled container until the cartridge may be properly disposed of after its safe removal from the industrial establishment.

37. An explosive load for an explosive actuated fastening tool shall,

(a) be so marked or labelled that the operator can readily identify its strength;

(b) not be stored in a container where an explosive load of a different strength is stored;

(c) not be left unattended where it may be available to a person other than a worker having the qualifications set out in subclause 36 (k)(i); and

(d) when not in use, be stored in a locked container.

38. A hand-held nailing gun or similar tool shall be,

(a) capable of being operated only when in contact with the work surface; and

(b) operated only,

        (i) by a competent person, and
        (ii) when the operator is wearing eye protection.

39. A chain saw shall,
    (a) have,
        (i) a chain that minimizes the possibility of a kickback, and
        (ii) a device which will effectively stop the chain in the event of a kickback;
    (b) be in safe operating condition;
    (c) when being started, be held firmly;
    (d) when being used, be held firmly by both hands; and
    (e) have the chain stopped when not actually cutting.

40. Electrical equipment, insulating materials and conductors shall be,
    (a) suitable for their use; and
    (b) certified by,
        (i) the Canadian Standards Association, or
        (ii) the Electrical Safety Authority, as defined in the *Electricity Act, 1998.*

                          O. Reg. 144/99 s. 2; 420/10 s. 6

41. The entrance to a room or similar enclosure containing exposed live electrical parts shall have a conspicuous sign, warning of the danger, and forbidding entry by unauthorized persons.

42. (1) The power supply to electrical installations, equipment or conductors shall be disconnected, locked out of service and tagged before any work is done, and while it is being done, on or near live exposed parts of the installations, equipment or conductors.

(2) Before beginning the work, each worker shall determine if the requirements of subsection (1) have been complied with.

(3) Locking out is not required,
    (a) if the conductors are adequately grounded with a visible grounding mechanism; or
    (b) if the voltage is less than 300 volts and there is no locking device for the circuit breakers or fuses and procedures are in place adequate to ensure that the circuit is not inadvertently energized.

(4) If locking out is not required for the reason set out in clause (3)(b), the employer shall ensure that the procedures required by that clause are carried out.

(5) If more than one worker is involved in the work referred to in subsection (1), the worker who disconnected and locked out the power supply shall communicate the purpose and status of the disconnecting and locking out.

(6) If a tag is used as a means of communication, the tag,

    (a) shall be made of non-conducting material;

    (b) shall be secured to prevent its inadvertent removal;

    (c) shall be placed in a conspicuous location;

    (d) shall state the reason the switch is disconnected and locked out;

    (e) shall show the name of the worker who disconnected and locked out the switch; and

    (f) shall show the date on which the switch was disconnected and locked out.

(7) The employer shall establish and implement written procedures for compliance with this section.

O. Reg. 630/94 s. 1

42.1(1) This section applies and section 42 does not apply if it is not practical to disconnect electrical installations, equipment or conductors from the power supply before working on, or near, live exposed parts of the installations, equipment or conductors.

(2) The worker shall use rubber gloves, mats, shields and other protective equipment and procedures adequate to ensure protection from electrical shock and burns while performing the work.

(3) If the installation, equipment or conductor is operating at a nominal voltage of 300 volts or more, a suitably equipped competent person who is able to recognize the hazards and perform rescue operations, including artificial respiration, shall be available and able to see the worker who is performing the work.

(4) Subsection (3) does not apply to equipment testing and trouble-shooting operations.

O. Reg. 630/94 s. 1

42.2 Work performed on electrical transmission systems or outdoor distribution systems rated at more than 750 volts shall be performed in accordance with,

    (a) the *Rule Book, Electric Utility Operations* published in 1990 by the Electrical Utilities Association of Ontario, Incorporated; or

(b) the *Ontario Hydro Corporate Safety Rules and Policies*, dated 1994.

O. Reg. 630/94 s. 1; 144/99 s. 3

43. Tools and other equipment that are capable of conducting electricity and endangering the safety of any worker shall not be used in such proximity to any live electrical installation or equipment that they might make electrical contact with the live conductor.

44. (1) Cord-connected electrical equipment and tools shall have a casing that is adequately grounded.

(2) Subsection (1) does not apply to cord-connected electrical equipment or tools that are adequately double-insulated and whose insulated casing shows no evidence of cracks or defects.

(3) Subsection (1) does not apply to a portable electrical generator in which the electrical equipment or tools are not exposed to an external electric power source if the casing of portable electrical equipment or tools connected to the generator is bonded to a non-current-carrying part of the generator.

O. Reg. 630/94 s. 2; 420/10 s. 7

44.1 When used outdoors or in wet locations, portable electrical tools shall be protected by a ground fault circuit interrupter installed at the receptacle or on the circuit at the panel.

O. Reg. 630/94 s. 2

44.2 A ground fault that may pose a hazard shall be investigated and removed without delay.

O. Reg. 630/94 s. 2

Material Handling

45. Material, articles or things,

(a) required to be lifted, carried or moved, shall be lifted, carried or moved in such a way and with such precautions and safeguards, including protective clothing, guards or other precautions as will ensure that the lifting, carrying or moving of the material, articles or things does not endanger the safety of any worker;

(b) shall be transported, placed or stored so that the material, articles or things,

(i) will not tip, collapse or fall, and

558

(ii) can be removed or withdrawn without endangering the
safety of any worker; and

(c) to be removed from a storage area, pile or rack, shall be removed
in a manner that will not endanger the safety of any worker.

46. Machinery, equipment or material that may tip or fall and endanger
any worker shall be secured against tipping or falling.

47. Cylindrical objects stored on their side shall be piled symmetrically
with each unit in the bottom row chocked or wedged to prevent motion.

48. Barrels, drums or kegs that are piled on their ends shall have two
parallel planks placed on top of each row before another row is added.

49. A storage cylinder for compressed gas shall,

(a) have a valve connection that prevents an inadvertent connection
which would result in a hazardous mixture of gases;

(b) be secured in position during transportation, storage or use;

(c) have the valve protection cap in position when the cylinder is not
in use;

(d) when containing acetylene, be in an upright position; and

(e) be protected from physical damage.

50. A silo, bin, hopper, structure, container or thing that is not a confined
space as defined in Ontario Regulation 632/05 (*Confined Spaces*) made
under the Act, and that is used for storing or containing bulk material
may be entered only where,

(a) the supply of material thereto is stopped and precautions are
taken that will prevent any further supply;

(b) the worker entering is wearing a safety harness or other similar
equipment attached to a rope or lifeline such that the worker shall
not be endangered by any collapse or shifting of material in the silo,
bin, hopper, structure, container or thing; and

(c) at least one other worker equipped with a suitable alarm and
capable of rendering any necessary assistance is keeping watch
nearby.

O. Reg. 629/05 s. 3; 98/11 s. 1

51. (1) A lifting device shall,

(a) be so constructed, of such strength and be equipped with suitable ropes, chains, slings and other fittings so as to adequately
ensure the safety of all workers;

851

(b) be thoroughly examined by a competent person to determine its capability of handling the maximum load as rated,

  (i) prior to being used for the first time, and

  (ii) thereafter as often as necessary but not less frequently than recommended by the manufacturer and in any case, at least once a year, and a permanent record shall be kept, signed by the competent person doing the examination;

(c) be plainly marked with sufficient information so as to enable the operator of the device to determine the maximum rated load that the device is capable of lifting under any operating condition;

(d) have a cab, screen, canopy guard or other adequate protection for the operator where the operator may be exposed to the hazard of falling material; and

(e) when it is a pneumatic or hydraulic hoist, have controls that automatically return to their neutral position when released.

(2) A lifting device shall be operated,

  (a) only by,

    (i) a competent person, or

    (ii) a worker being instructed who is accompanied by a competent person; and

  (b) in such a way that,

    (i) no part of the load passes over any worker,

    (ii) where a worker may be endangered by the rotation or uncontrolled motion of a load, one or more guide ropes is used to prevent rotation or other uncontrolled motion, and

    (iii) subject to subsection (3), when its load is in a raised position the controls are attended by an operator.

(3) Subclause (2)(b)(iii) does not apply to,

  (a) a hydraulic hoist that supports the load from below and is fixed in one location; and

  (b) an assembly line hoist temporarily unattended during a stoppage of the assembly line.

(4) Hoisting controls operated from other than a cab or cage shall,

  (a) be located so that they can be operated at a safe distance from a load being lifted; and

  (b) automatically return to their neutral position when released.

(5) Where a lifting device is equipped with one or more limit switches,

(a) each limit switch shall automatically cut off the power and apply the brake when the limit is reached; and

(b) no limit switch shall be used as an operating control unless,

(i) the limit switch is designed for such use, and

(ii) the lifting device has a second limit switch in addition to the control limit switch.

O. Reg. 420/10 s. 8

52. A crane, lift truck or similar equipment shall be used to support, raise or lower a worker only when,

(a) the worker is on a platform,

(i) equipped with adequate safety devices that will automatically prevent the platform and load from falling if the platform's normal support fails,

(ii) suspended from a boom that does not move, and the person is attached to a separate lifeline suspended from the boom or a fixed support capable of supporting at least four times the weight of the worker, or

(iii) attached to a mast or boom which,

(A) is hydraulically or pneumatically operated, and

(B) is equipped with a safety device that will prevent free fall of the platform in the event of a pressure line failure;

(b) where the equipment is not designed for the specific purpose of hoisting personnel, the load applied to the crane, lift truck or similar equipment is less than one half the maximum rated load;

(c) the platform has a sign indicating the load that may be applied to the crane, lift truck or similar equipment under clause (b);

(d) where controls are provided at more than one location,

(i) each control station is provided with means whereby the operator can shut off power to the equipment, and

(ii) interlocks have been provided so that only one station can be operative at any time; and

(e) except when the controls are operated from the platform, the controls are attended and operated by another worker.

O. Reg. 420/10 s. 9

53. Where a travelling crane is operated on a crane runway, there shall be,

(a) rail stops or bumpers extending at least as high as the centre of the wheels at both ends of the crane runway; and

(b) where applicable, similar rail stops at the ends of the crane bridge.

54. (1) Mobile equipment shall,

(a) when lighting conditions are such that its operation may be hazardous, have head lights and tail lights that provide adequate illumination;

(b) when exposed to the hazard of falling material, have a screen or canopy guard adequate to protect the operator;

(c) be used to transport a person, other than the operator, only when that worker is seated in a permanently installed seat; and

(d) subject to subsection (2), be operated only by a competent person.

(2) Clause (1)(d) does not apply to mobile equipment operated by a worker while the worker is being instructed and accompanied by a competent person.

55. A vehicle used to transport structural steel, logs or similar loads shall have a bulkhead between the operator's cab and the load that is reasonably capable of resisting any impact caused by the shifting of the load under emergency stop conditions.

56. Where the operator of a vehicle, mobile equipment, crane or similar material handling equipment does not have a full view of the intended path of travel of the vehicle, mobile equipment, crane or similar material handling equipment or its load, the vehicle, mobile equipment, crane or similar material handling equipment shall only be operated as directed by a signaller who is a competent person and who is stationed,

(a) in full view of the operator;

(b) with a full view of the intended path of travel of the vehicle, mobile equipment, crane or similar material handling equipment and its load; and

(c) clear of the intended path of travel of the vehicle, mobile equipment, crane or similar material handling equipment and its load.

57. A vehicle left unattended shall be immobilized and secured against accidental movement.

58. Powered equipment shall not be left unattended unless forks, buckets, blades and similar parts are in the lowered position or solidly supported.

59. Except for the purpose of a test of the material handling equipment, no material handling equipment shall be loaded in excess of its maximum rated load.

60. (1) Except as prescribed by section 42.2, where a vehicle, crane or similar equipment is operated near a live power line carrying electricity at more than 750 volts, every part of the equipment shall be kept at least the minimum distance from the live power line set out in Column 2 of the Table for the particular voltage set out opposite thereto in Column 1 of the Table:

851

TABLE

Minimum distance from live power lines for electricity	
Column 1	Column 2
Voltage of live power line	Minimum Distance
750 to 150,000 volts	3 metres
150,001 to 250,000 volts	4.5 metres
250,001 volts and over	6 metres

(2) Subject to section 42.2, where a vehicle, crane or similar equipment is operated near a live power line, and it is possible for any part of the vehicle, crane or similar equipment or its load to make contact with the live power line,

    (a) a worker shall be stationed within the view of the operator to warn the operator when any part of the equipment is approaching the minimum distance from the live power line; and

    (b) clearance shall be allowed for any change in boom angle and for any swing of the hoisting cable and load.

O. Reg. 630/94 s. 3

61. Gasoline engines on mobile or portable equipment shall be refuelled,

    (a) outdoors;

    (b) with the engine on the equipment stopped;

    (c) with no source of ignition, within three metres of the dispensing point; and

    (d) with an allowance made for expansion of the fuel should the equipment be exposed to a higher ambient temperature.

62. (1) Subject to subsection (2), a piping system containing a substance which, because of its toxicity, temperature, pressure, flammability or other property, is hazardous, shall have its contents and direction of flow positively identified,

    (a) at valves and fittings;

    (b) where a pipe passes through a wall or floor; and

    (c) where circumstances may make such contents or direction of flow doubtful.

(2) Subsection (1) does not apply to a piping system in a petro-chemical plant where processing and maintenance are carried out by a competent person under controlled conditions so as to provide for the protection of all workers.

O. Reg. 420/10 s. 10

63. A process that is likely to produce a gas, vapour, dust or fume, to such an extent as to be capable of forming an explosive mixture with air shall be carried out in an area which has provision for safe disposal by burning under controlled conditions or in an area which,

    (a) is isolated from other operations;

    (b) has a system of ventilation adequate to ensure that the gas, vapour, dust or fume does not reach a hazardous concentration;

    (c) has no potential sources of ignition;

    (d) has provision for explosion venting; and

    (e) has, where applicable, baffles, chokes or dampers to reduce the effects of any explosion.

64. Where the hazard of a dust explosion may be created by the entry of foreign particles into equipment, the equipment shall have separators which prevent such entry.

65. (1) Subject to subsection (2), a collector that collects aluminum, magnesium or other fine dust of an easily ignitable nature shall be located,

    (a) outdoors; or

    (b) in a room used solely for the housing of dust-collecting equipment which is,

        (i) separated from the rest of the building by a dust-tight partition having a minimum fire-resistance rating of one hour, and

        (ii) constructed to provide explosion venting to the outdoors.

(2) Subsection (1) does not apply to a collector,

(a) that uses an inert liquid as a medium to collect dust;

(b) that is used for a wood-working operation other than wood flour manufacturing and having less than 0.47 cubic metres per second capacity;

(c) that will safely contain explosions; or

(d) that will resist explosions and is equipped with effective explosion venting to the outdoors.

66. A compressed air or other compressed gas blowing device shall not be used for blowing dust or other substances,

(a) from clothing worn by a worker except where the device limits increase in pressure when the nozzle is blocked; or

(b) in such a manner as to endanger the safety of any worker.

Confined Space

67. [Repealed O. Reg. 629/05, s. 4.]

68. [Repealed O. Reg. 629/05, s. 4.]

69. [Repealed O. Reg. 629/05, s. 4.]

70. [Repealed O. Reg. 629/05, s. 4.]

71. [Repealed O. Reg. 629/05, s. 4.]

Maintenance and Repairs

72. (1) Where a structure is damaged to the extent that a collapse of the structure or any part of the structure is likely to occur and cause injury to a worker,

(a) the structure shall be braced and shored to prevent the collapse of the structure; or

(b) effective safeguards shall be provided to prevent access to the area.

(2) The bracing and shoring or other safeguards prescribed by subsection (1) shall be installed progressively to ensure that a worker installing the bracing and shoring or other safeguards is not in danger.

73. A portable ladder shall,

(a) be free from broken or loose members or other faults;

(b) have non-slip feet;

(c) be placed on a firm footing;

(d) where it,
    (i) exceeds six metres in length and is not securely fastened, or
    (ii) is likely to be endangered by traffic, be held in place by
    one or more workers while being used; and
(e) when not securely fastened, be inclined so that the horizontal
distance from the top support to the foot of the ladder is not less
than 1/4 and not more than 1/3 of the length of the ladder.

74. Machinery, equipment or material that is temporarily elevated and
under which a worker may pass or work shall be securely and solidly
blocked to prevent the machinery, equipment or material from falling or
moving.

75. A part of a machine, transmission machinery, device or thing shall be
cleaned, oiled, adjusted, repaired or have maintenance work performed on
it only when,
(a) motion that may endanger a worker has stopped; and
(b) any part that has been stopped and that may subsequently move
and endanger a worker has been blocked to prevent its movement.

76. Where the starting of a machine, transmission machinery, device or
thing may endanger the safety of a worker,
(a) control switches or other control mechanisms shall be locked
out; and
(b) other effective precautions necessary to prevent any starting
shall be taken.

O. Reg. 230/95 s. 1

77. Safety chains, cages or other protection against blown-off side or lock
rings shall be used when inflating a tire mounted on a rim.

78. (1) Subject to subsection (2), where repairs or alterations are to be
made on a drum, tank, pipeline or other container, the drum, tank, pipeline or other container shall,
(a) have internal pressures adjusted to atmospheric pressure before
any fastening is removed;
(b) be drained and cleaned or otherwise rendered free from any
explosive, flammable or harmful substance; and
(c) not be refilled while there is any risk of vaporising or igniting the
substance that is being placed in the drum, tank, pipeline or other
container.

(2) Clauses (1)(a) and (b) do not apply to a pipeline where hot-tapping and boxing-in are carried out by a competent person under controlled conditions so as to provide for the protection of all workers.

O. Reg. 420/10 s. 11

Protective Equipment

79. A worker required to wear or use any protective clothing, equipment or device shall be instructed and trained in its care and use before wearing or using the protective clothing, equipment or device.

O. Reg. 420/10 s. 12

80. A worker exposed to the hazard of head injury shall wear head protection appropriate in the circumstances.

81. A worker exposed to the hazard of eye injury shall wear eye protection appropriate in the circumstances.

O. Reg. 420/10 s. 13

82. A worker exposed to the hazard of foot injury shall wear foot protection appropriate in the circumstances.

83. (1) Long hair shall be suitably confined to prevent entanglement with any rotating shaft, spindle, gear, belt or other source of entanglement.

(2) Jewellery or clothing that is loose or dangling or rings shall not be worn near any rotating shaft, spindle, gear, belt or other source of entanglement.

84. A worker exposed to the hazard of injury from contact of the worker's skin with,

    (a) a noxious gas, liquid, fume or dust;

    (b) a sharp or jagged object which may puncture, cut or abrade the worker's skin;

    (c) a hot object, hot liquid or molten metal; or

    (d) radiant heat,

shall be protected by,

    (e) wearing apparel sufficient to protect the worker from injury; or

    (f) a shield, screen or similar barrier, appropriate in the circumstances.

85. Where a worker is exposed to the hazard of falling and the surface to which he or she might fall is more than three metres below the position where he or she is situated,

    (a) the worker shall wear a serviceable safety belt or harness and lifeline that is adequately secured to a fixed support and so arranged that the worker cannot fall freely for a vertical distance of more than 1.5 metres; and

    (b) the fall arrest system described in clause (a), shall,

        (i) have sufficient capacity to absorb twice the energy and twice the load that under the circumstances of its use may be transmitted to it, and

        (ii) be equipped with a shock absorber or other devices to limit the maximum arresting force to 8.0 kilonewtons to the worker.

O. Reg. 420/10 s. 14

86. Where a worker is exposed to the hazard of falling into liquid that is of sufficient depth for a life jacket to be effective as protection from the risk of drowning, there shall be an alarm system and rescue equipment, appropriate in the circumstances, to ensure the worker's rescue from the liquid and,

    (a) the worker shall wear a life jacket; or

    (b) the employer shall develop written measures and procedures to prevent the worker from drowning and shall implement them.

O. Reg. 284/99 s. 1

Molten Material
[Heading added O. Reg. 230/95, s. 2.]

87. Section 87.1 to 87.6 apply to foundries.

O. Reg. 230/95 s. 2

87.1 An employer who is required to develop and implement measures and procedures under sections 87.2 to 87.6 shall consult with the committee or health and safety representative, if any, in the development of the measures and procedures.

O. Reg. 230/95 s. 2

87.2(1) Every employer shall develop and implement measures and procedures to prevent molten material from coming into contact with damp, rusty or cold surfaces, moisture or water, or other substances, if the contact might endanger the health or safety of workers.

(2) A worker shall work in compliance with the measures and procedures developed under subsection (1).

(3) The employer shall ensure that a device used to contain molten material is,

    (a) examined immediately before each use; and

    (b) not used if found to be defective or contaminated by a substance that, on contact with molten material, might endanger the health or safety of workers.

O. Reg. 230/95 s. 2

87.3(1) In this section, "spillage" refers to the spillage of molten material that could endanger the health or safety of workers.

(2) The employer shall use engineering controls, to the fullest extent that is reasonably possible in the circumstances, to prevent spillage.

(3) If spillage cannot be prevented by the use of engineering controls alone, the employer shall also develop and implement other measures and procedures to be used in combination with the engineering controls to prevent spillage.

(4) If the use of engineering controls is not reasonably possible in the circumstances, the employer shall develop and implement other measures and procedures to prevent spillage.

(5) The measures and procedures referred to in subsections (3) and (4) may include the use of personal protective equipment and the exclusion of workers from locations where they might be exposed to spillage.

O. Reg. 230/95 s. 2

87.4 The employer shall provide adequate means of egress from all locations where workers may be exposed to molten material.

O. Reg. 230/95 s. 2

87.5(1) Subsections (2) to (4) apply to a location if the following conditions are met:

    1. The location is a runout, pouring or moulding pit or other working space that is,

        i. more than 60 centimetres below the adjacent floor level, or

851

569

      ii. surrounded by a wall that is more than 60 centimetres high
      and that a person must pass over to leave the working space.

2. The location was constructed or altered after May 1, 1995.

3. Workers may be exposed to molten material at the location.

(2) Egress shall be provided by means of doorways, ramps or stairs of non-combustible material.

(3) Egress ramps and stairs shall be made of slip-resistant material.

(4) If the location is more than 15 square metres in area, or if any point within the location is more than 5 metres from an egress doorway, ramp or stair,

    (a) at least two doorways, ramps or stairs shall be provided, situated at a distance from each other that is at least three-quarters of the greatest diagonal dimension of the location, measured on the horizontal plane; and

    (b) a doorway, ramp or stair shall be provided within 25 metres of any point within the location.

O. Reg. 230/95 s. 2

87.6 The employer shall develop and implement measures and procedures for communicating to workers the existence of emergency situations relating to molten material.

O. Reg. 230/95 s. 2

88. (1) A clear space adequate for safe operating and maintenance purposes shall be provided between the outer shell of any cupola or other melting unit and any wall, structure, equipment or operation.

(2) Subject to subsection (5), the width of any passageway or aisle adjacent to a melting unit shall not be less than 1.2 metres.

(3) The firing portion and fuel supply controls of each melting unit shall be accessible from an aisle or be in a location remote from a melting unit.

(4) Subject to subsection (5), the dimensions of the working space at any melting unit shall not be less than 1.8 metres measured horizontally from the furnace shell or pouring spout or such additional clearance as is required for safe working.

(5) Subsections (2) and (4) do not apply to a melting unit installed before the 31st day of July, 1964.

89. Permanent gangways shall be clearly marked.

90. (1) Subject to subsections (2) and (3), where molten metal is conveyed, the minimum width of a gangway for one-way traffic shall be as specified in the following Table:

TABLE

Type of Metal Container	Number of Workers Conveying Metal	Minimum Width
Hand shank ladles and crucibles	2 or less	90 centimetres
Hand shank ladles and crucibles	More than 2	120 centimetres
Ladle or crucible on truck, buggy or over-head track		60 centimetres wider than greatest width of ladle, crucible, truck, buggy or container support

(2) Where a gangway is used for traffic in both directions but molten metal is conveyed in one direction only, the width required by subsection (1) shall be increased by at least ninety centimetres.

(3) Where a gangway is used for carrying molten metal in both directions, the width required by subsection (1) shall be doubled.

(4) Where a ladle is carried by an overhead crane,

    (a) adequate warning shall be given before the ladle is moved; and

    (b) the danger area over which it is transported shall be clear of any worker.

91. Where a hand shank ladle or crucible is used to pour metal, the minimum width of a pouring aisle shall be as specified in the following Table:

TABLE

Height of Mould Above Aisle Level	Number of Workers Allocated to the Pouring Operation	Minimum Width of a Pouring Aisle
Less than 50 centimetres	Not more than 2	40 centimetres
50 centimetres or greater	Not more than 2	60 centimetres
Any height	More than 2	90 centimetres

O. Reg. 420/10 s. 15

92. Where molten metal is poured from a crane, trolley or truck ladle, the minimum width of a pouring aisle shall not be less than thirty centimetres greater than the greatest width of the ladle equipment, except where a bottom-pour ladle is used, in which case the aisle width shall be ninety centimetres or more.

93. Where a worker is engaged in the handling of molten metal, gaiter-type boots shall be worn together with leggings or other protective clothing such that the tops of the boots are overlapped to protect the worker from injury due to molten metal.

94. A tilting ladle for molten metal shall be secured against accidental overturning.

95. A cupola shall have,
    (a) legs and supports protected from damage by molten metal;
    (b) doors on the top hinged to act as explosion vents to the outdoors when equipped with a closed top;
    (c) a positive means of preventing the accumulation of combustible gases in the air supply system when the air supply fails; and
    (d) a continuous open flame or other means of ignition maintained above the charging level of the cupola while the cupola is in operation and until all combustible material in the cupola is consumed.

96. (1) Subject to subsection (2), the bottom of a cupola shall be supported by one or more adequate metal props with metal bases and wedges supported on concrete or other solid footing.

(2) The bottom of a cupola shall be dropped only,

    (a) after a visual and audible warning signal has been given for at least three minutes; and

    (b) by having the prop or props removed by a winch or similar device operated from outside a wall or shield at the cupola or from another safe location.

(3) As soon as is practicable after a cupola is emptied, coke slag and unmelted metal from the dropping of the cupola bottom shall be removed by a mechanical rake or other mechanical means.

97. (1) Subject to subsection (2), material to be changed into molten metal shall be free from ice or moisture.

(2) Subsection (1) does not apply where precautions have been taken to ensure that any resultant reaction will not endanger any worker.

98. A completely enclosed vessel shall be broken open prior to its being charged into a furnace.

99. Where metal castings or scrap are broken by means of a dropping device, or similar device, a permanent shield of wood planking at least thirty-eight millimetres thick shall be provided to protect workers from flying metal fragments.

100. A container used for holding or transporting molten metal shall be dry before use.

101. The floor and any water system immediately surrounding a melting unit shall be so constructed as to prevent the accumulation of moisture under or near the melting unit.

102. Where molten metal is handled on a gallery, mezzanine or other area having any working space below it, the gallery, mezzanine or area shall have a solid floor that will prevent molten metal from leaking or burning through it and the gallery, mezzanine or other area shall have a solid barrier, of not less than 1.05 metres in height, on all exposed sides to prevent metal spillage from the gallery, mezzanine or other area.

Logging

103. In this section and in sections 104 to 119,

"bucking" means the act of sawing a log or a tree that has been felled into smaller pieces;

"chicot" means,

    (a) a dead tree, or

    (b) a dead limb of a tree that may endanger a worker;

"felling area" means an area where trees are being felled and into which they might fall;

"hang up" means a tree that has not fallen to the ground after being,

    (a) partly or wholly separated from its stump, or

    (b) displaced from its natural position;

"haul road" means a road, other than a highway as defined in the *Highway Traffic Act*, on which vehicles used to haul logs are operated;

"landing area" means a cleared area where trees or logs are stored, measured, processed, unloaded or loaded and includes a log dump;

"limbing" means the act of removing limbs from a tree before or after felling;

"logger" means a worker who engages in logging and includes the employer and any person under the control of the employer;

"skidding" means the operation of moving logs or trees by pulling across terrain;

"snag" means any material or object that may interfere with the safe movement of a tree or log or that may endanger a person or any equipment;

"spring pole" means a section of tree, or bush which is, by virtue of its arrangement in relation to other materials, under tension;

"stake" means a wooden or metal post used to support and prevent the lateral movement of logs;

"tree" means a tree that is standing or is down and from which the limbs have not been removed.

630/94 s. 4

104. (1) Sections 105 to 106.2 apply to employers who undertake logging operations.

(2) In sections 105 to 106.2,

"registered" means registered with the Ministry of Training, Colleges and Universities in order to complete a training program referred to in subsection 105(1).

488/01 s. 1

105. (1) Every employer shall establish and maintain the following training programs, approved by the Ministry of Training, Colleges and Universities:

    1. For cutters and skidder operators,

        i. Cutter-Skidder Operator (Program # P750000),

        ii. Cutter (Program # P750010), and

        iii. Skidder-Operator (Program # P750020).

    2. For mechanical harvesting equipment operators, Mechanical Harvesting Equipment Operator—Common Core (Program # P750025) and,

        i. Feller Buncher Operator (Program # P750035),

        ii. Cut-to-Length Processor Operator (Program # P750045),

        iii. Grapple Skidder Operator (Program # P750055),

        iv. Forwarder/Transporter Operator (Program # P750065),

        v. Delimber Operator (Program # P750075),

        vi. Slasher Operator (Program # P750085),

        vii. Chipper Operator (Program # P750095).

(2) A document issued by the Ministry of Training, Colleges and Universities, showing that a worker is registered for a training program referred to in subsection (1) or has successfully completed it, is conclusive proof, for the purposes of sections 106, 106.1 and 106.2, of the worker being registered for the program or of his or her successful completion of the program, as the case may be.

(3) In accordance with the *Agreement on Internal Trade, 1995* and the *Protocols of Amendment*, a worker shall be deemed to hold a document showing successful completion referred to in subsection (2) if he or she has successfully completed equivalent training in another province or territory of Canada, as determined by the Director.

488/01 s. 1

106. (1) The employer shall ensure that,

(a) every cutter has successfully completed Cutter-Skidder Operator (Program # P750000) or Cutter (Program # P750010); and

(b) every skidder operator has successfully completed Cutter-Skidder Operator (Program # P750000) or Skidder Operator (Program # P750020).

(2) The employer shall ensure that every cutter or skidder operator who has not successfully completed the training required under subsection (1) is registered for the appropriate program before performing work to which the program relates.

(3) Despite subsection (2), the employer shall ensure that every worker employed to work as a cutter or as a skidder operator on May 31, 2002 who has not successfully completed the training required under subsection (1) is registered for the appropriate program by June 3, 2002.

(4) The employer shall ensure that every worker who is registered under subsection (2) or (3) successfully completes the appropriate program within one year after being registered.

488/01 s. 1

106.1(1) The employer shall ensure that every worker who operates mechanical harvesting equipment has successfully completed the appropriate program referred to in subparagraphs 2 i to vii of subsection 105(1).

(2) The employer shall ensure that every worker who operates mechanical harvesting equipment and has not successfully completed the training required under subsection (1) is registered for the appropriate program before performing work to which the program relates.

(3) Despite subsection (2), the employer shall ensure that every worker employed to operate mechanical harvesting equipment on May 31, 2002 who has not successfully completed the training required under subsection (1) is registered for the appropriate program by June 3, 2002.

(4) The employer shall ensure that every worker who is registered under subsection (2) or (3) successfully completes the appropriate program within one year after being registered.

O. Reg. 488/01 s. 1

106.2(1) The employer shall ensure that every worker who supervises the operation of mechanical harvesting equipment has successfully completed Mechanical Harvesting Equipment Operator—Common Core (Program

P750025) before performing supervisory work relating to mechanical harvesting equipment.

(2) Despite subsection (1), the employer shall ensure that every worker employed to supervise the operation of mechanical harvesting equipment on May 31, 2002 who has not successfully completed the training required under subsection (1) successfully completes the program no later than December 31, 2002.

O. Reg. 488/01 s. 1

107. (1) Subject to subsection (2), a felling area shall be kept clear of workers.

(2) Subsection (1) does not apply to,

(a) a worker authorized by the employer or supervisor to be in the felling area; or

(b) an inspector or worker accompanying an inspector in the course of their duties.

108. A landing area shall have sufficient space cleared of any hazard to enable operations to be performed without endangering any worker.

109. A tree shall,

(a) be felled only,

(i) after all workers other than the logger felling the tree are cleared from the danger area,

(ii) after all snags have been cut and cleared away,

(iii) after the chicots and spring poles in the vicinity of the tree being felled have been lowered safely to the ground, and

(iv) in such a manner that the logger felling the tree is able to stand clear of the tree during its fall;

(b) be felled alongside or across a road only after the road has been blocked off or controlled by signaller; and

(c) be limbed, bucked or topped only when the logger is in a position so that the limb, log or top when severed cannot roll or drop on the logger.

110. When a hang up occurs,

(a) the logger shall keep the felling area clear of all workers; and

(b) the hang up shall,

(i) be felled forthwith by winching or pulling using a chain or cable from a safe distance or by other safe means,

(ii) not be climbed by any worker,

(iii) not be lowered by felling another tree into or onto it, and

(iv) not be removed by cutting the supporting tree.

111. A spring pole shall be severed or cut in a manner that will not endanger,

(a) the logger cutting or severing the spring pole; or

(b) any other worker.

112. Skidding shall be done,

(a) only when all loggers, other than the operator of the vehicle doing the skidding, are clear of the danger area; and

(b) so as not to raise the log being skidded to a height that might,

(i) cause the vehicle moving the log to upend or overturn, or

(ii) otherwise endanger the operator of the vehicle moving the log.

113. A log shall be loaded or unloaded only when,

(a) the requirements of section 56 are met; and

(b) the immediate area is clear of all workers except those engaged or assisting in the loading or unloading.

114. Except for a truck, a vehicle used in logging shall be equipped with a canopy that is,

(a) of sufficient strength and construction to protect any worker in the cab from any load likely to fall on the canopy; and

(b) installed by welding or bolting to the frame of the vehicle.

420/10 s. 16

115. A truck used in logging shall have all rear windows guarded against penetration by any part of its load by a guard the strength of which is equivalent to the strength of the cab in which the window is located.

116. (1) A vehicle used for hauling logs shall,

(a) comply with section 55;

(b) be so loaded that no log extends,

(i) outside the stakes, or

(ii) farther than one-half its diameter above the stakes;

(c) have its load secured with chains or cables so as to prevent the dislodging or other movement of the load or any part thereof;

(d) while any worker is in the cab, not be loaded or unloaded by a method in which a boom or part of the load is likely to pass over the cab;

(e) have the cab occupied by more than two workers only in an emergency;

(f) subject to clause (e), be operated only when all workers are clear of the vehicle and of its load; and

(g) when unable to be unloaded completely by mechanical means,

    (i) be equipped with a tripping device for releasing the load that is so located that the worker operating the device is not endangered, and

    (ii) have its load released only in compliance with subclause (i).

(2) Where a truck or trailer used for hauling logs is equipped with stakes and the stakes are trip stakes, such stakes shall only be located on the right-hand side or rear of the truck or trailer.

O. Reg. 420/10 s. 17

117. A haul road shall,

(a) be adequate to provide for the safe operation of vehicles;

(b) have by-passes or turnout spaces at sufficiently frequent intervals to permit the safe passing of vehicles using the road; and

(c) have signs warning of the approach to every,

    (i) bridge,

    (ii) crossroads,

    (iii) blind curve,

    (iv) steep grade, and

    (v) railway crossing.

118. A bridge on a haul road shall,

(a) be structurally adequate to support any load likely to be applied to it;

(b) have curbs of a height of not less than fifteen centimetres on each side of the travelled portion of the bridge;

(c) be of sufficient width between curbs to permit the passage of vehicles using the bridge; and

(d) have markers which clearly indicate the width and ends of the bridge.

119. A vehicle used to transport loggers shall have the part of the vehicle in which the loggers are transported,

(a) structurally adequate to support any load likely to be applied to it;

(b) provided with an adequate number of seats securely attached to the vehicle so that all loggers being transported may be seated;

(c) illuminated by an electrical lighting system;

(d) equipped with a means of communication between the loggers and operator of the vehicle to enable the loggers to signal the operator to stop;

(e) adequately ventilated to protect loggers from noxious fumes and gases;

(f) free of tools, equipment or flammable liquid, which may be in racks outside the logger compartment;

(g) when used in inclement weather,

  (i) enclosed to provide protection from the weather, and

  (ii) adequately heated to protect the passengers from undue discomfort due to cold; and

(h) provided with emergency exits in accordance with the provisions of the *Highway Traffic Act.*

Part I.1

[Heading repealed O. Reg. 98/11, s. 2.]

119.1 - 119.20 [Repealed O. Reg. 98/11, s. 2.]

Part II — Buildings

120. Except as prescribed in this Part, the Building Code applies to all industrial establishments with respect to,

  (a) access to an exit;

  (b) exit from a floor area;

  (c) structural adequacy;

  (d) washrooms;

  (e) service rooms;

  (f) the fire-resistance rating of a separation for an access to an exit, service room and a process room that contains a flammable substance;

  (g) the fire protection rating of a closure.

420/10 s. 23

121. In this Part, "hazardous room" means, with respect to an industrial establishment, a room containing a substance which, because of its chemical nature, the form in which the substance exists or its handling or processing, may explode or become easily ignited creating a condition of imminent hazard to a person's health or safety.

122. (1) This section applies with respect to a hazardous room,

    (a) with an area greater than fifteen square metres; or

    (b) requiring a distance of travel greater than 4.5 metres from any point in the room to an egress doorway.

(2) A hazardous room shall be located in a floor area that has at least two exits.

(3) A hazardous room shall have at least two egress doorways that are at least three-quarters of the length of the diagonal distance of the room from each other.

(4) One egress doorway must be located within a maximum distance of twenty-three metres from any point in a hazardous room.

123. (1) The requirements of the Fire Code respecting fire extinguishers apply at industrial establishments.

(2) The requirements of the Fire Code respecting keeping egress doorways, public corridors and exits free from obstruction apply at industrial establishments.

(3) In this section,

"Fire Code" means Ontario Regulation 213/07 (*Fire Code*) made under the *Fire Protection and Prevention Act, 1997*.

420/10 s. 24

Part III — Industrial Hygiene

124. Where a worker is exposed to a potential hazard of injury to the eye due to contact with a biological or chemical substance, an eyewash fountain shall be provided.

125. Where a worker is exposed to a potential hazard of injury to the skin due to contact with a substance, a quick-acting deluge shower shall be provided.

126. Removal of material shall be done in such a way as not to cause a hazard.

127. An industrial establishment shall be adequately ventilated by either natural or mechanical means such that the atmosphere does not endanger the health and safety of workers.

128. (1) Replacement air shall be provided to replace air exhausted.

(2) The replacement air shall,

   (a) be heated, when necessary, to maintain at least the minimum temperature in the work place specified in section 129;

   (b) be free from contamination with any hazardous dust, vapour, smoke, fume, mist or gas; and

   (c) enter in such a manner so as,

      (i) to prevent blowing of settled dust into the work place,

      (ii) to prevent interference with any exhaust system, and

      (iii) not to cause undue drafts.

(3) The discharge of air from any exhaust system shall be in such a manner so as to prevent the return of contaminants to any work place.

129. (1) Subject to subsection (2), an enclosed work place shall be at a temperature,

   (a) suitable for the type of work performed; and

   (b) not less than 18° Celsius

(2) Clause (1)(b) does not apply to a work place,

   (a) that is normally unheated;

   (b) where the necessity of opening doors makes the heating of the area to the temperature specified in clause (1)(b) impracticable;

   (c) where perishable goods requiring lower temperatures are processed or stored;

   (d) where radiant heating is such that a worker working in the area has the degree of comfort that would result were the area heated to the temperature specified in clause (1)(b);

   (e) where the process or activity is such that the temperature specified in clause (1)(b) could cause discomfort; or

   (f) during the first hour of the main operating shift where process heat provides a substantial portion of building heat.

130. A worker who may be exposed to a biological, chemical or physical agent that may endanger the worker's safety or health shall be trained,

   (a) to use the precautions and procedures to be followed in the handling, use and storage of the agent;

(b) in the proper use and care of required personal protective equipment; and

(c) in the proper use of emergency measures and procedures.

131. No food, drink or tobacco shall be taken into, left or consumed in any room, area or place where any substance that is poisonous by ingestion is exposed.

132. (1) Subject to subsection (2), the regulations made under the Act respecting designated substances and an order by a Director under section 33 of the Act, potable drinking water shall be provided,

(a) from,

(i) a fountain with an upward jet, or

(ii) a tap from a piped water supply or a covered vessel, together with a supply of single-use cups in a sanitary container located near the tap;

(b) on every floor where work is regularly performed; and

(c) within 100 metres of any area where work is regularly performed.

(2) Subsection (1) does not apply to logging, except in logging camps.

O. Reg. 565/06 s. 1; 420/10 s. 25

133. (1) Except for emergency facilities, hot and cold water shall be provided at each shower.

(2) Hot water required under subsection (1) shall not,

(a) be less than 30° Celsius;

(b) exceed 60° Celsius; or

(c) be directly mixed with steam.

O. Reg. 420/10 s. 26

134. Where workers are exposed to a substance that,

(a) is poisonous by ingestion; and

(b) can contaminate the skin, shower rooms and individual lockers for street and work clothes shall be provided.

135. Where ten or more workers are employed, a room or other space shall be provided,

(a) affording reasonable privacy; and

(b) equipped with one or more cots and chairs, unless such facilities are provided at a first-aid station.

136. A place suitable for eating purposes shall be provided where,

(a) thirty-five or more workers are employed; or

(b) there is any room, area or place in which there is exposure to a substance that is poisonous by ingestion.

137. Protective clothing or other safety device that has been worn next to the skin shall be cleaned and disinfected prior to being worn by another worker.

138. (1) Where a worker is likely to be exposed to an atmosphere at atmospheric pressure with an oxygen content of less than 19.5 per cent, the worker shall be protected by mechanical ventilation so that the worker's safety and health is not endangered.

(2) Where the measures prescribed by subsection (1) are not practicable, the worker shall be protected by air supplied breathing equipment so that the worker's safety and health is not endangered.

O. Reg. 289/17, s. 1

139. [Repealed O. Reg. 382/15, s. 1.]

TABLE 1 [Repealed O. Reg. 494/09, s. 3.]

[Repealed O. Reg. 494/09, s. 3.]

Form 1 [Repealed O. Reg. 420/10, s. 28.]

[Repealed O. Reg. 420/10, s. 28.]

Form 2
Notice

TAKE NOTICE that this .... (specify the "place", "matter" or "thing", as the case may be) is a danger or hazard to the safety of workers employed in or having access to these premises and the use thereof shall be discontinued immediately until the inspector's order of .... (date) to .... (name of employer or owner) (address of employer or owner) has been complied with.

No person, except an inspector, shall remove this notice unless authorized by an inspector.

Dated the .... day of ...., 19..........

.... (signature of inspector)

ONTARIO COURT OF JUSTICE Fines — Reg. 851

Schedule 67.3

	Occupational Health and Safety Act **(as it relates to Regulation 851 of the Revised Regulations of Ontario, 1990)**		
ITEM	**COLUMN 1**	**COLUMN 2 SECTION**	**SET FINE (INCL. COSTS OF $5.00)**
1.	Employer failing to ensure a safe work surface for worker under s. 11 of Reg. 851	clause 25(1)(c)	$300.00
2.	Supervisor failing to ensure worker is working on a safe work surface under s.11 of Reg. 851	clause 27(1)(a)	$200.00
3.	Worker failing to work on a safe work surface under s.11 of Reg. 851	clause 28(1)(a)	$200.00
4.	Supervisor failing to ensure worker works with guarded opening under s. 13(1) of Reg. 851	clause 27(1)(a)	$300.00

	Occupational Health and Safety Act (as it relates to Regulation 851 of the Revised Regulations of Ontario, 1990)		
ITEM	**COLUMN 1**	**COLUMN 2 SECTION**	**SET FINE (INCL. COSTS OF $5.00)**
5.	Worker failing to work with guarded opening under s.13(1) of Reg. 851	clause 28(1)(a)	$200.00
6.	Supervisor failing to ensure worker works with covered opening under s. 15 of Reg. 851	clause 27(1)(a)	$300.00
7.	Worker failing to work with covered opening under s. 15 of Reg. 851	clause 28 (1) (a)	$200.00
8.	Supervisor failing to ensure worker uses a machine with adequate guarding under s. 24 of Reg. 851	clause 27 (1) (a)	$300.00
9.	Worker failing to use a machine with adequate guarding under s. 24 of Reg. 851	clause 28 (1) (a)	$300.00
10.	Supervisor failing to ensure worker uses a machine with adequate guarding under s. 25 of Reg. 851	clause 27 (1) (a)	$300.00

Occupational Health and Safety Act (as it relates to Regulation 851 of the Revised Regulations of Ontario, 1990)			
ITEM	COLUMN 1	COLUMN 2 SECTION	SET FINE (INCL. COSTS OF $5.00)
11.	Worker failing to use a machine with adequate guarding under s. 25 of Reg. 851	clause 28 (1) (a)	$300.00
12.	Supervisor failing to ensure worker uses a machine with adequate guarding under s. 26 of Reg. 851	clause 27 (1) (a)	$300.00
13.	Worker failing to use a machine with adequate guarding under s. 26 of Reg. 851	clause 28 (1) (a)	$200.00
14.	Supervisor failing to ensure worker works with effective operating control that acts as a guard under s. 28 (c) of Reg. 851	clause 27 (1) (a)	$300.00
15.	Worker failing to work with effective operating control that acts as a guard under s. 28 (c) of Reg. 851	clause 28 (1) (a)	$300.00
16.	Employer failing to provide safe chain saw under s. 39 of Reg. 851	clause 25 (1) (a)	$300.00

851

Occupational Health and Safety Act (as it relates to Regulation 851 of the Revised Regulations of Ontario, 1990)			
ITEM	COLUMN 1	COLUMN 2 SECTION	SET FINE (INCL. COSTS OF $5.00)
17.	Employer failing to ensure that chain saw provided under s. 39 of Reg. 851 is used safely	clause 25 (1) (d)	$300.00
18.	Supervisor failing to ensure worker uses a chain saw safely under s. 39 of Reg. 851	clause 27 (1) (a)	$200.00
19.	Worker failing to use chain saw safely under s. 39 of Reg. 851	clause 28 (1) (a)	$200.00
20.	Supervisor failing to ensure no work is done on or near live exposed parts of electrical installations, equipment or conductors without the power supply being disconnected, locked out and tagged under s. 42 (1) of Reg. 851	clause 27 (1) (a)	$300.00

	Occupational Health and Safety Act (as it relates to Regulation 851 of the Revised Regulations of Ontario, 1990)		
ITEM	COLUMN 1	COLUMN 2 SECTION	SET FINE (INCL. COSTS OF $5.00)
21.	Worker working on or near live exposed parts of electrical installations, equipment or conductors without the power supply being disconnected, locked out and tagged under s. 42 (1) of Reg. 851	clause 28 (1) (a)	$300.00
22.	Supervisor failing to ensure worker uses protective equipment and procedures while doing electrical work under s. 42.1 (2) of Reg. 851	clause 27 (1) (a)	$300.00
23.	Employer failing to provide portable electrical tool protected by a ground fault circuit interrupter under s. 44.1 of Reg. 851	clause 25 (1) (a)	$300.00
24.	Employer failing to ensure portable electrical tool protected by a ground fault circuit interrupter provided under s. 44.1 of Reg. 851 is used	clause 25 (1) (d)	$300.00

851

	Occupational Health and Safety Act (as it relates to Regulation 851 of the Revised Regulations of Ontario, 1990)		
ITEM	**COLUMN 1**	**COLUMN 2 SECTION**	**SET FINE (INCL. COSTS OF $5.00)**
25.	Supervisor failing to ensure worker using a portable electrical tool protected by a ground fault circuit interrupter under s. 44.1 of Reg. 851	clause 27 (1) (a)	$200.00
26.	Worker failing to use a portable electrical tool protected by a ground fault circuit interrupter under s. 44.1 of Reg. 851	clause 28 (1) (a)	$200.00
27.	Employer failing to ensure that lifting device is operated safely under s. 51 (2) (b) of Reg. 851	clause 25 (1) (c)	$300.00
28.	Supervisor failing to ensure operator of a lifting device works safely under s. 51 (2) (b) of Reg. 851	clause 27 (1) (a)	$300.00
29.	Operator of lifting device failing to work safely under s. 51 (2) (b) of Reg. 851	clause 28 (1) (a)	$200.00

	Occupational Health and Safety Act (as it relates to Regulation 851 of the Revised Regulations of Ontario, 1990)		
ITEM	**COLUMN 1**	**COLUMN 2 SECTION**	**SET FINE (INCL. COSTS OF $5.00)**
30.	Supervisor failing to ensure worker works on or near an immobilized and secure unattended vehicle under s. 57 of Reg. 851	clause 27 (1) (a)	$300.00
31.	Worker failing to immobilize and secure unattended vehicle under s. 57 of Reg. 851	clause 28 (1) (a)	$200.00
32.	Supervisor failing to ensure worker works around attended lifting equipment when forks, bucket, blades and similar parts are unsupported under s. 58 of Reg. 851	clause 27 (1) (a)	$300.00
33.	Worker working around unattended lifting equipment when forks, bucket, blades and similar parts are unsupported under s. 58 of Reg. 851	clause 28 (1) (a)	$200.00

851

	Occupational Health and Safety Act **(as it relates to Regulation 851 of the Revised Regulations of Ontario, 1990)**		
ITEM	**COLUMN 1**	**COLUMN 2 SECTION**	**SET FINE (INCL. COSTS OF $5.00)**
34.	Supervisor failing to ensure that worker does not bring object closer than specified distance to overhead electric supply line under s. 60 of Reg. 851	clause 27 (1) (a)	$300.00
35.	Worker bringing object closer than specified distance to overhead electric supply line under s. 60 of Reg. 851	clause 28 (1) (a)	$300.00
36.	Employer failing to provide safe portable ladder under s. 73 of Reg. 851	clause 25 (1) (a)	$300.00
37.	Employer failing to ensure that a portable ladder pro-vided under s. 73 of Reg. 851 is used safely	clause 25 (1) (d)	$300.00
38.	Supervisor failing to ensure worker uses a portable ladder safely under s. 73 of Reg. 851	clause 27 (1) (a)	$200.00

ITEM	COLUMN 1	COLUMN 2 SECTION	SET FINE (INCL. COSTS OF $5.00)
	Occupational Health and Safety Act (as it relates to Regulation 851 of the Revised Regulations of Ontario, 1990)		
39.	Worker failing to use portable ladder safely under s. 73 of Reg. 851	clause 28 (1) (a)	$200.00
40.	Supervisor failing to ensure worker works around safely secured temporarily elevated machinery, equipment or material under s. 74 of Reg. 851	clause 27 (1) (a)	$300.00
41.	Worker failing to work around safely secured temporarily elevated machinery, equipment or material under s. 74 of Reg. 851	clause 28 (1) (a)	$200.00
42.	Supervisor failing to ensure worker works on a safely secured machine under s. 75 of Reg. 851	clause 27 (1) (a)	$300.00
43.	Worker failing to work on a safely secured machine under s. 75 of Reg. 851	clause 28 (1) (a)	$300.00

851

	Occupational Health and Safety Act (as it relates to Regulation 851 of the Revised Regulations of Ontario, 1990)		
ITEM	COLUMN 1	COLUMN 2 SECTION	SET FINE (INCL. COSTS OF $5.00)
44.	Supervisor failing to ensure worker works on a machine with proper precautions where starting may endanger the safety of a worker under s. 76 of Reg. 851	clause 27 (1) (a)	$300.00
45.	Worker failing to work on a machine with proper precautions where starting may endanger the safety of a worker under s. 76 of Reg. 851	clause 28 (1) (a)	$300.00
46.	Employer failing to ensure appropriate head protection provided under s. 80 of Reg. 851 is used	clause 25 (1) (d)	$300.00
47.	Supervisor failing to ensure worker wears appropriate head protection under s. 80 of Reg. 851	clause 27 (1) (a)	$200.00

	Occupational Health and Safety Act (as it relates to Regulation 851 of the Revised Regulations of Ontario, 1990)		
ITEM	**COLUMN 1**	**COLUMN 2 SECTION**	**SET FINE (INCL. COSTS OF $5.00)**
48.	Employer failing to ensure appropriate eye protection provided under s. 81 of Reg. 851 is used	clause 25 (1) (d)	$300.00
49.	Supervisor failing to ensure worker wears appropriate eye protection under s. 81 of Reg. 851	clause 27 (1) (a)	$200.00
50.	Employer failing to ensure appropriate foot protection provided under s. 82 of Reg. 851 is used	clause 25 (1) (d)	$300.00
51.	Supervisor failing to ensure worker wears appropriate foot protection under s. 82 of Reg. 851	clause 27 (1) (a)	$200.00
52.	Employer failing to ensure proper skin protection provided under s. 84 of Reg. 851 is used	clause 25 (1) (d)	$300.00

851

	Occupational Health and Safety Act (as it relates to Regulation 851 of the Revised Regulations of Ontario, 1990)		
ITEM	COLUMN 1	COLUMN 2 SECTION	SET FINE (INCL. COSTS OF $5.00)
53.	Supervisor failing to ensure worker works with proper skin protection under s. 84 of Reg. 851	clause 27(1)(a)	$200.00
54.	Worker failing to work with proper skin protection under s. 84 of Reg. 851	clause 28 (1) (a)	$200.00
55.	Supervisor failing to ensure worker wears fall protection equipment under s. 85 of Reg. 851	clause 27 (1) (a)	$300.00
56.	Employer failing to ensure protective clothing provided is worn to protect from hazards caused by molten metal under s. 93 of Reg. 851	clause 25 (1) (d)	$300.00
57.	Supervisor failing to ensure worker wears protective clothing provided to protect from hazards caused by molten metal under s. 93 of Reg. 851	clause 27 (1) (a)	$200.00

851

ITEM	COLUMN 1	COLUMN 2 SECTION	SET FINE (INCL. COSTS OF $5.00)
	Occupational Health and Safety Act (as it relates to Regulation 851 of the Revised Regulations of Ontario, 1990)		
58.	Worker failing to wear protective clothing provided to protect from hazards caused by molten metal under s. 93 of Reg. 851	clause 28 (1) (a)	$200.00
59.	Employer failing to ensure a tree is felled, limbed, bucked or topped safely under s. 109 of Reg. 851	clause 25 (1) (c)	$300.00
60.	Supervisor failing to ensure logger fells, limbs, bucks or tops a tree safely under s. 109 of Reg. 851	clause 27 (1) (a)	$300.00
61.	Logger failing to fell, limb, buck or top a tree in safely under s. 109 of Reg. 851	clause 28 (1) (a)	$300.00
62.	Employer failing to ensure a hang up is dealt with safely under s. 110 of Reg. 851	clause 25 (1) (c)	$300.00
63.	Supervisor failing to ensure worker deals with a hang up safely under s. 110 of Reg. 851	clause 27 (1) (a)	$300.00

	Occupational Health and Safety Act (as it relates to Regulation 851 of the Revised Regulations of Ontario, 1990)		
ITEM	**COLUMN 1**	**COLUMN 2 SECTION**	**SET FINE (INCL. COSTS OF $5.00)**
64.	Worker failing to deal with a hang up safely under s. 110 of Reg. 851	clause 28 (1) (a) (v)	$200.00
65.	Employer failing to ensure a spring pole is cut safely under s. 111 of Reg. 851	clause 25 (1) (c)	$300.00
66.	Supervisor failing to ensure worker cuts a spring pole safely under s. 111 of Reg. 851	clause 27 (1) (a)	$300.00
67.	Worker failing to cut spring pole safely under s. 111 of Reg. 851	clause 28 (1) (a)	$200.00
68.	Employer failing to ensure that skidding is done under s. 112 of Reg. 851	clause 25 (1) (c)	$300.00
69.	Supervisor failing to ensure logger skids under s. 112 of Reg. 851	clause 27 (1) (a)	$300.00
70.	Logger failing to skid under s. 112 of Reg. 851	clause 28 (1) (a)	$200.00

	Occupational Health and Safety Act (as it relates to Regulation 851 of the Revised Regulations of Ontario, 1990)		
ITEM	COLUMN 1	COLUMN 2 SECTION	SET FINE (INCL. COSTS OF $5.00)
71.	Employer failing to provide a vehicle used for hauling logs that complies with s. 116 (1) of Reg. 851	clause 25 (1) (a)	$300.00
72.	Employer failing to ensure vehicle provided for hauling logs is used in compliance with s. 116 (1) of Reg. 851	clause 25 (1) (d)	$300.00
73.	Supervisor failing to ensure worker uses a vehicle used for hauling logs in compliance with s. 116 (1) of Reg. 851	clause 27 (1) (a)	$300.00
74.	Worker failing to use a vehicle used for hauling logs in compliance with s. 116 (1) of Reg. 851	clause 28 (1) (a)	$200.00
75.	Employer failing to provide vehicle used to transport loggers in compliance with s. 119 of Reg. 851	clause 25 (1) (a)	$300.00

851

599

Occupational Health and Safety Act (as it relates to Regulation 851 of the Revised Regulations of Ontario, 1990)			
ITEM	COLUMN 1	COLUMN 2 SECTION	SET FINE (INCL. COSTS OF $5.00)
76.	Supervisor failing to ensure worker uses a vehicle used to transport loggers in compliance with s. 119 of Reg. 851	clause 27 (1) (a)	$200.00
01/05			

Schedule 67.4

Regulation 851 of the Revised Regulations of Ontario, 1990 under the Occupational Health and Safety Act			
ITEM	COLUMN 1	COLUMN 2 SECTION	SET FINE (INCL. COSTS OF $5.00)
1.	Worker failing to use protective equipment and procedures while doing electrical work	subsection 42.1 (2)	$300.00
2.	Worker failing to wear appropriate head protection	section 80	$200.00

Regulation 851 of the Revised Regulations of Ontario, 1990 under the Occupational Health and Safety Act			
ITEM	**COLUMN 1**	**COLUMN 2 SECTION**	**SET FINE (INCL. COSTS OF $5.00)**
3.	Worker failing to wear appropriate eye protection	section 81	$200.00
4.	Worker failing to wear appropriate foot protection	section 82	$200.00
5.	Worker failing to wear fall protection equipment	section 85	$300.00
01/05			

851

ONT. REG. 852 — INVENTORY OF AGENTS OR COMBINATIONS OF AGENTS FOR THE PURPOSE OF SECTION 34 OF THE ACT

made under the *Occupational Health and Safety Act*

R.R.O. 1990, Reg. 852, as am. O. Reg. 208/91 (Fr.); 517/92.

1. The Ministry of Labour hereby adopts, as an inventory of agents or combinations of agents that are not new biological or chemical agents or combinations of such agents for the purpose of section 34 of the Act, the Chemical Substances initial Inventory including the User Guides and Indices and Trademarks and Product Names reported in conjunction therewith of May, 1979, together with the Cumulative Supplement to the Initial Inventory of June, 1980, published by the Administrator of the Environmental Protection Agency of the United States of America under the *The Toxic Substances Control Act* (P.L. 94-469).

R.R.O. 1980, Reg. 693 s. 1

2. Inquiries concerning Inventory and Cumulative Supplement may be addressed to:

> Inventory of Agents,
> Occupational Health and Safety Branch
> Ministry of Labour,
> 400 University Avenue,
> Toronto, Ontario.
> M7A 1T7 ·

R.R.O. 1980, Reg. 693 s. 2; O. Reg. 517/92 s. 1

ONT. REG. 385/96 — JOINT HEALTH AND SAFETY COMMITTEES — EXEMPTION FROM REQUIREMENTS

made under the *Occupational Health and Safety Act*

O. Reg. 385/96, as am. O. Reg. 131/98; 19/09 (Fr.).

1. In this Regulation,

"ordinary worker" does not include a participant in community participation under the *Ontario Works Act, 1997*;

"volunteer worker" means a worker who performs work or supplies a service but who receives no monetary compensation for doing so other than an allowance for expenses or an honorarium.

O. Reg. 131/98 s. 1

385/96

2. A workplace at which fewer than 20 ordinary workers are regularly employed is exempted from clause 9(2)(a) of the Act.

3. A project at which fewer than 20 ordinary workers are regularly employed is exempted from clause 9(2)(c) of the Act.

4. The following workplaces are exempt from subsection 9(12) of the Act:
    1. A workplace at which fewer than 20 ordinary workers (who are not volunteer workers) are regularly employed.
    2. A project at which fewer than 50 ordinary workers (who are not volunteer workers) are regularly employed.

5. Ontario Regulations 334/95 and 39/96 are revoked.

6. This regulation comes in force on September 1, 1996.

ONT. REG. 854 — MINES AND MINING PLANTS

made under the *Occupational Health and Safety Act*

R.R.O. 1990, Reg. 854, as am. O. Reg. 583/91; 584/91;
171/92; 384/92; 571/92; 693/92; 60/94; 779/94; 68/96; 272/97;
236/99; 486/99; 174/01; 251/01; 291/02; 31/04; 630/05; 84/07;
496/09; 99/11; 296/11; 92/13; 34/14, ss. 1-19, 20 (Fr.); 265/15;
383/15; 167/16.

Definitions

1. In this Regulation,

"adequate", when used in relation to a procedure, plan, material, device, object or thing, means that it is,

(a) sufficient for both its intended and its actual use, and

(b) sufficient to protect a worker from occupational illness or occupational injury;

"adequately" has a meaning that corresponds to the meaning of **"adequate"**;

"authorized" means authorized to do a specific task by a supervisor who is in charge of the workplace;

"automatic hoist" means a mine hoist that can be operated by controls situated at shaft stations or on the shaft conveyance;

"breaking strength" means the breaking strength of a shaft rope as determined by a cable testing laboratory approved by the Minister;

"bulkhead" means a structure for the impoundment of water, compressed air, hydraulic backfill or any material in an underground opening where the potential pressure against the structure will be in excess of 100 kilopascals;

"charge" means,

(a) an explosive and a detonator, or

(b) an explosive, a detonator and primer that is exploded as a single unit;

"CSA Standard" means a standard published by the Canadian Standards Association;

"dam" means a structure for the impoundment of more than twenty-five tonnes of water in an underground opening and constructed so as to permit an unobstructed overflow of the water;

"destructive test" means a test on a sample of shaft rope wherein the shaft rope is broken during the test by a tensile testing machine;

"detonator" means a device used in firing a charge of explosive and includes blasting cap and electric blasting cap;

"Director" [Repealed O. Reg. 571/92, s. 1.]

"drum hoist" means a hoist where the rope is wound on a drum or drums;

"electrical mobile equipment" [Repealed O. Reg. 272/97, s. 1.]

"electromagnetic device" means a testing device using an electromagnetic system for examining a shaft rope;

"explosive" means a substance that is made, manufactured or used to produce an explosion or detonation and includes gunpowder, propellant powder, dynamite, detonating cord, shock tube, blasting agent, slurry, water gel and detonator;

"factor of safety" means the number of times the breaking strength of a shaft rope exceeds the weight it supports at a specified location on the rope;

"fire-extinguishing equipment" means a fire hose, an extinguisher or other similar equipment used to fight a fire;

"fire hazard area" means,

(a) an area where a fire hazard may be created by smoking, matches or other means of producing heat or fire and which has been designated as such by the supervisor in charge of the mine, or

(b) a storage area where oil, grease or flammable liquids are stored in excess of 500 litres;

"fire-resistance rating" means the rating in hours or fraction thereof that a material or assembly of materials will withstand the passage of flame and the transmission of heat when exposed to fire, as established for the material or assembly of materials under the *Building Code*;

"fire suppression system" means an installation for the specific purpose of controlling a fire in a particular place;

"friction hoist" means a hoist where the driving force between the drum and rope or ropes supporting the shaft conveyance is obtained through friction;

"hoist" means a drum or friction hoist used for transporting persons or materials in an underground mine;

"licensed magazine" [Repealed O. Reg. 272/97, s. 1.]

"lifting device" means a permanently installed system for the purpose of raising, lowering or swinging materials, which includes its rails and supports but does not include a crane, elevator, mine hoist, utility hoist or tugger hoist;

"locomotive" means a unit propelled by any form of energy or a combination of such units operated from a single control running only on rails of a standard gauge railroad and used for moving standard gauge railroad cars but does not include a self-propelled track crane, motorized equipment used for the maintenance of a standard gauge railroad, a motor vehicle equipped with rail wheels in addition to rubber-tired wheels or other similar equipment;

"magazine" means a building, place or structure in which an explosive is kept or stored and includes a detonator storage building, or place, but does not include a storage container being used in an underground mine containing less than 160 kilograms of explosive;

"mine hoisting plant" means a hoist for an underground mine and includes the prime mover, transmission equipment, head-frame, sheaves, ropes, shaft, shaft conveyances, shaft sinking equipment, shaft furnishings, hoist controls, counterweight, signalling and communications equipment and any other equipment used in connection with a hoist;

"motor vehicle" means a vehicle propelled by other than muscular power, including an automobile, a caterpillar-tracked vehicle, a truck, a tractor and a motor vehicle running on rails but does not include a locomotive;

"noncombustible" has the same meaning as in Ontario Regulation 332/12 (Building Code) made under the *Building Code Act, 1992*;

854

"nondestructive test" means the examination of a part without subjecting it to physical distortion, damage or destruction;

"prime mover" means an engine or other device that provides an initial source of motive power;

"primer" means a small charge placed within the main charge to initiate an explosion;

"production crane" means an electrically operated device that travels on fixed overhead track or tracks, and,

    (a) is used to handle hot or molten materials, or

    (b) has a duty rating equal to or greater than Class C or D as determined under Part 3.4 of CSA Standard B167-1964, "General Purpose Electric Overhead Travelling Cranes";

"professional engineer" means a person who is registered as a professional engineer or licensed as a professional engineer under the *Professional Engineers Act*;

"railroad" means a standard gauge railroad at a mine or mining plant;

"rockburst" means an instantaneous failure of rock causing an expulsion of material at the surface of an opening or a seismic disturbance to a surface or underground mine;

"SABS" means South African Bureau of Standards;

"service crane" means an electrically operated device that travels on fixed overhead track or tracks and has a duty rating equal to or less than Class A or B as determined under Part 3.4 of CSA Standard B167-1964, **"General Purpose Electric Overhead Travelling Cranes"**;

"shaft conveyance" means a conveyance raised or lowered by a mine hoist in a shaft and includes a bucket, a single or multi-deck cage, a skip or a combination of skip and cage;

"shaft rope" means a hoisting, tail, balance, guide or rubbing rope;

"shot" means the sound of a charge or charges being exploded;

"standard gauge" means that the space between the rails of a railroad is approximately 1,435 millimetres;

"surface mine" means a pit or quarry where metallic or non-metallic rock, mineral bearing substance, earth, clay, sand or gravel is being or has been removed by means of an excavation open to the surface to supply material for construction, industrial or manufacturing purposes and includes any work, undertaking or facility used in connection therewith but does not include a cutting for a right of way for a highway or a railroad;

"train",

(a) except in Parts V and VI, means one or more locomotives without railroad cars or coupled with railroad cars, and

(b) in Parts V and VI, means one or more motor vehicles running on rails without cars or coupled with cars;

"transmission equipment" means any object or objects by which the motion of a prime mover is transmitted to a machine that is capable of utilizing such motion and includes a shaft, pulley, belt, chain, gear, clutch or other device;

"uncontrolled fall of ground" means a fall of ground, such as rock or fill falling from the walls or back of an underground or surface mine but does not include falls occurring as part of blasting or scaling operations;

"underground mine" means a mine that is not a surface mine and includes any work, undertaking or facility used in connection therewith;

"vehicle" includes a locomotive, railroad cars, motor vehicle, trailer or any vehicle propelled, drawn or driven by any kind of power.
O. Reg. 584/91 s. 1; 571/92 s. 1; 272/97 s. 1; 174/01 s. 1; 31/04 s. 1; 630/05 s. 1; 34/14 s. 1; 167/16, s. 2

Part I — General

2. (1) Subject to subsection (2), this Regulation applies to all mines and mining plants and to mining development.

(2) Ontario Regulation 213/91 applies,

(a) during the construction of a mining plant on the surface; and

(b) to construction at the surface of a mine for the purpose of developing the mine.

O. Reg. 571/92 s. 2

3. An owner, constructor or employer may vary a procedure required by this Regulation or the composition, design, size or arrangement of a material, object, device or thing as required by this Regulation,

(a) if the procedure, composition, design, size or arrangement as varied affords protection for the health and safety of workers that is at least equal to the protection that would otherwise be given; and
(b) if the owner, constructor or employer gives written notice of the varied procedure, composition, design, size or arrangement to the joint health and safety committee or the health and safety representative, if any, for the workplace and to any trade union representing workers at the workplace.

O. Reg. 583/91 s. 1

4. Notices shall be posted in conspicuous places at each mine or mining plant, setting out the name, business address and business telephone number of,

(a) the inspector for the district in which the mine or mining plant is located;
(b) the person in charge of the mine or mining plant;
(c) the employer of workers at the mine or mining plant; and
(d) the owner of the mine or mining plant.

5. (1) Before proceeding with,

(a) the development or construction of a mine or a mining plant;
(b) the introduction of new process technology;
(c) the major alteration of mining technique or mining technology;
(d) the use of new methods of construction or of equipment installation;
(e) the making of a major addition or alteration;
(f) the design of a system and procedure for the transfer of fuel by gravity from the surface to an underground fuelling station;
(g) the construction of a bulkhead or dam;
(h) the construction of a tailings dam or any surface structure for the impoundment of tailings; or
(i) the design of a trolley line system, if the lines of the system are to have an operating voltage greater than 300 volts, the owner of a mine or mining plant shall ensure that the drawings, plans and specifications are prepared or checked by a professional engineer under his or her seal and signature and are in compliance with the Act and this Regulation.

(2) The owner of a mine or mining plant shall ensure that the drawings, plans and specifications required under subsection (1) are kept readily available at the mine site.

(2.1) A written statement of the proposed development, construction, introduction, alteration or use shall be given to the joint health and safety committee or health and safety representative, if any.

(3) The employer shall notify an inspector,

(a) when portable crushing, screening or associated washing equipment is installed in or about a surface mine; and

(b) before a test drill is operated at the surface to prove mineral bearing substances, rock, earth, clay, sand or gravel.

(c) [Repealed O. Reg. 84/07, s. 1.]

(d) [Repealed O. Reg. 84/07, s. 1.]

(4) [Revoked O. Reg. 272/97, s. 2(4).]

O. Reg. 60/94 s. 1; 272/97 s. 2; 236/99 s. 1; 84/07 s. 1

5.1 (1) An employer shall conduct a risk assessment of the workplace for the purpose of identifying, assessing and managing hazards, and potential hazards, that may expose a worker to injury or illness.

(2) A risk assessment must take into consideration the nature of the workplace, the type of work, the conditions of work at that workplace and the conditions of work common at similar workplaces.

(3) The results of an assessment must be provided, in writing, to the joint health and safety committee or the health and safety representative, if any.

(4) If no joint health and safety committee or health and safety representative is required at the workplace, the results of an assessment must be communicated to workers at the workplace and provided, in writing, to any worker at the workplace who requests them.

(5) The requirement in subsection (1) to conduct a risk assessment is in addition to any specific assessments required by the Act or any Regulation made under it.

O. Reg. 167/16, s. 3

5.2 (1) An employer shall, in consultation with the joint health and safety committee or the health and safety representative, if any, develop and maintain measures to eliminate, where practicable, or to control, where the elimination is impracticable, the hazards, and potential hazards, identified in a risk assessment conducted under subsection 5.1(1).

(2) The measures referred to in subsection (1) shall be put in writing and shall include each of the following, as applicable and reasonable in the circumstances:

854

1. Substitution or reduction of a material, thing or process.
2. Engineering controls.
3. Work practices.
4. Industrial hygiene practices.
5. Administrative controls.
6. Personal protective equipment.

(3) Personal protective equipment shall only be used as a measure if the measures referred to in paragraphs 1 to 5 of subsection (2) are not obtainable, are impracticable or do not eliminate or fully control hazards and potential hazards.

O. Reg. 167/16, s. 3

5.3 (1) The risk assessment required by section 5.1 must be reviewed as often as necessary and at least annually.

(2) When conducting the review, the employer shall ensure that,

    (a) new hazards or new potential hazards are assessed;

    (b) existing hazards or potential hazards that have changed are re-assessed; and

    (c) the measures required by section 5.2 continue to effectively protect the health and safety of workers.

(3) Subsections 5.1(3) and (4) and section 5.2 apply with necessary modifications in respect of any new hazards and potential hazards and any existing hazards or potential hazards that have changed.

O. Reg. 167/16, s. 3

6. (1) The owner of a surface mine producing metallic ore or of an underground mine shall prepare and maintain a mine design assessing the ground stability of the active and proposed workings of the mine.

(2) The mine design shall consist of drawings, plans, specifications or procedures to be used and shall be prepared under the direction of a competent person.

(2.1) The mine design shall be based upon sound geotechnical engineering practices and shall,

    (a) describe the geology of the mine;

    (b) outline the geometry of existing and proposed excavations;

    (c) describe previous occurrences of ground instability;

    (d) describe the mining method including stope sequencing and blasting methods;

(e) specify the ground support system; and

(f) describe measures planned and used to assess potential ground instability such as instrumentation and computer modelling.

(3) The mine design shall be assessed and updated at least annually and also before any alteration is made to the mine that may significantly affect the ground stability of the mine.

(4) The mine design shall be kept readily available at the mine site for review by an inspector and by the joint health and safety committee or health and safety representative, if any.

(5) [Revoked O. Reg. 272/97, s. 3.]

O. Reg. 571/92 s. 3; 60/94 s. 2; 272/97 s. 3

6.1(1) In an underground mine, the geometry of an existing excavation that does not have ground support shall not be altered unless,

(a) the owner of the mine arranges for a professional engineer to prepare, in accordance with sound geotechnical engineering practices, a written report on the proposed alteration; and

(b) the report states that the safety of workers will not be endangered by the proposed alteration.

(2) In an underground mine, a new excavation that is planned to have no ground support shall not be made unless,

(a) the owner of the mine arranges for a professional engineer to prepare, in accordance with sound geotechnical engineering practices, a written report on the proposed excavation; and

(b) the report states that the safety of workers will not be endangered by the proposed excavation.

(3) The owner of the mine shall ensure that copies of reports prepared under subsections (1) and (2) are,

(a) kept readily available at the mine site; and

(b) given to the joint health and safety committee or health and safety representative, if any, and to any trade union representing workers at the workplace.

O. Reg. 31/04 s. 2

7. A tailings dam or any other surface structure for the impoundment of tailings shall be,

(a) designed in accordance with good engineering practice by a professional engineer;

(b) constructed in accordance with the design; and

(c) maintained so that the structure provides stability against any static and dynamic loading to which it may be subjected.

8. (1) Subject to subsection (2), the minimum age of,

(a) a worker; or

(b) a person who is permitted to be in or about a mine or mining plant, shall be,

(c) sixteen years of age at a mining plant or a surface mine, excluding the working face; and

(d) eighteen years of age at an underground mine or at the working face of a surface mine.

(2) Subsection (1) does not apply to prohibit tours of, or visits to, a mine or mining plant by persons under the prescribed ages who are accompanied by and under the direction of a guide.

9. (1) No worker shall remain or be requested to remain in an underground mine for more than eight hours in any consecutive twenty-four hours, measured from the time the worker enters an underground mine until the time the worker leaves the underground mine.

(2) Despite subsection (1), a worker may remain underground in a mine,

(a) when an emergency causes an extension of the time;

(b) for more than eight hours in any consecutive twenty-four hours on one day of a week but only for the purpose of changing shift or for the purpose of avoiding work on Sunday or on a holiday; or

(c) if the worker is a supervisor, pump operator, cagetender, or is a person engaged solely in surveying or measuring or in emergency repair work necessary to permit production.

(3) A worker shall not be permitted to operate a mine hoist for more than eight hours in any consecutive twenty-four hours, except in a case provided for in clause (2)(a) or (b) or in subsection (4), but,

(a) where no competent substitute is available, the worker may work extra time not exceeding four hours in any consecutive twenty-four hours for a period not exceeding fourteen calendar days in any four week period; or

(b) where the work is not carried out continuously on three shifts per day, the worker may work such extra time as is necessary for lowering or hoisting the workers employed on the shift, at the beginning and end of their shift.

(4) An employer at an underground mine may schedule hours of work in excess of eight hours in any 24-hour period with the consent of the trade unions representing the workers at the underground mine or, if there is no trade union, consent of the workers themselves.

O. Reg. 272/97 s. 4

10. A supervisor, deck attendant, shaft conveyance attendant or mine hoist operator shall be capable of communicating effectively in the English language.

11. (1) Employers in the following types of mines and mining plants shall establish and maintain the following training programs:

    1. Hard rock underground mine,

        i. Common Core for Basic Underground Hard Rock Miner (Program #P770010),

        ii. Specialty Modules for Underground Hard Rock Miner (Program #P770010),

        iii. Common Core for First Line Underground Mine Supervisor—Underground Hard Rock Mining (Program #P770121).

    2. Soft rock underground mine,

        i. Common Core for Basic Underground Soft Rock Miner (Program #P770130),

        ii. Specialty Modules for Underground Soft Rock Miner (Program P#770130),

        iii. Common Core for First Line Underground Mine Supervisor—Underground Soft Rock Mining (Program #P770131).

    3. Mill process operation,

        i. Common Core for Basic Mill Process Operator—Mineral Ore (Program #P810050),

        ii. Specialty Modules for Mill Process Operator—Mineral Ore (Program #P810050).

    4. Mines and mining plants other than hard rock underground mines, soft rock underground mines, and mill, smelter and refinery process operations,

        i. Common Core module for Generic First Line Supervisor—Surface Mining, Surface and Underground Diamond Drilling Operations, and Underground and Surface Mining Trades (Program #P770141).

854

(2) An employer shall train each worker in the modules of the programs described in subsection (1) appropriate for that worker.

(3) The employer shall ensure that a worker completes all of the modules of the appropriate basic common core program before work covered by that program is assigned to the worker.

(4) The employer shall ensure that a worker completes all of the modules of the appropriate supervisor's common core program within 12 months after the worker begins performing supervisory duties.

(5) The employer shall ensure that a worker completes a specialty module within 12 months after the worker begins performing work covered by that module.

(6) Subsections (2) to (5) do not apply to a worker with respect to a module if the worker,

    (a) successfully completed the module before being employed by the employer and gives the employer proof of successful completion; or

    (b) was accredited under a predecessor of this section and gives the employer proof of accreditation.

(7) A worker who would otherwise be required to be trained in the program described in subparagraph 1 iii of subsection (1) is not required to be trained in that program if he or she completed Program #P770120 (Common Core for First Line Production Supervisors, Underground Hard Rock Mining) on or before April 1, 2007.

(8) A document issued by the Ministry of Training, Colleges and Universities showing that a worker has successfully completed a module of a program referred to in subsection (1) or (7) is conclusive proof for the purposes of this section of the worker's successful completion of the module.

                O. Reg. 571/92 s. 4; 174/01 s. 2; 84/07 s. 2; 296/11 s. 1

11.1 (1) Employers engaged in underground diamond drilling operations shall establish and maintain the following components of the Underground Diamond Driller training program:

    1. Common Core for Underground Diamond Driller — Helper Level (Program #P770150).

    2. Common Core for Underground Diamond Driller — Runner Level (Program #P770150).

(2) An employer shall train each worker who commences employment after March 31, 1996 in the modules of the program described in subsection (1) appropriate for that worker, and the training shall be completed before the worker has completed a total of 12 months of employment as a helper or runner in underground diamond drilling operations.

(3) Subsection (2) does not apply to a worker with respect to a module if the worker successfully completed the module before being employed by the employer and gives the employer proof of successful completion.

(4) A document issued by the Ministry of Training, Colleges and Universities showing that a worker has successfully completed a module of a program referred to in subsection (1) is conclusive proof for the purposes of this section of the worker's successful completion of the module.

O. Reg. 68/96, s. 1; 174/01, s. 3; 296/11, s. 2; 167/16, s. 4

11.1.1 (1) Employers engaged in surface diamond drilling operations shall establish and maintain the following components of the Surface Diamond Driller training program:

    1. Common Core for Surface Diamond Driller — Part 1 (Basic Level) (Program #P770200).

    2. Common Core for Surface Diamond Driller — Part 2 (Helper Level) (Program #P770200).

    3. Common Core for Surface Diamond Driller — Part 3 (Runner Level) (Program #P770200).

    4. Speciality Modules for Surface Diamond Driller (#P770200).

(2) employer shall train each worker who performs work as a surface diamond driller in the modules of the program described in subsection (1) appropriate for that worker and shall ensure that the training is completed in accordance with the following requirements:

    1. Part 1 (Basic Level) shall be completed before the worker begins performing work covered by the modules of that component of the program.

    2. Part 2 (Helper Level) shall be completed within 12 months after the day the worker begins performing work covered by the modules of that component of the program.

    3. Part 3 (Runner Level) shall be completed within 12 months after the day the worker begins performing work covered by the modules of that component of the program.

4. Each specialty module shall be completed within 12 months after the day the worker begins performing work covered by the applicable module.

(3) Subsection (2) does not apply to a worker with respect to a module if the worker successfully completed the module before being employed by the employer and gives the employer proof of successful completion.

(4) A document issued by the Ministry of Training, Colleges and Universities showing that a worker has successfully completed a module of the program referred to in subsection (1) is conclusive proof for the purposes of this section of the worker's successful completion of the module.

O. Reg. 167/16,   s. 5

11.2(1) Employers engaged in surface mine operations shall establish and maintain the following training programs:

1. Common Core for Surface Miner (Program #770210).
2. Specialty Modules for Surface Miner (Program #770210).

(2) An employer shall train each worker in the modules of the programs described in subsection (1) appropriate for that worker.

(2.1) The employer shall ensure that a worker completes all of the common core modules within 12 months after the worker begins performing work covered by those modules.

(3) Subsection (2) does not apply to a worker with respect to a module if the worker successfully completed the module before being employed by the employer.

(4) A worker shall be trained in the appropriate common core modules before beginning training in a specialty module.

(4.1) The employer shall ensure that a worker completes a specialty module described in subsection (1) within 12 months after the worker begins performing work covered by that module.

(5) A document issued by the Ministry of Training, Colleges and Universities showing that a worker has successfully completed a module of a program referred to in subsection (1) is conclusive proof for the purposes of this section of the worker's successful completion of the module.

O. Reg. 251/01 s. 1; 296/11 s. 3

11.2.1(1) Employers engaged in hard rock underground mine operations shall establish and maintain the training program described as Basic

Underground Hard Rock Mine Service Types—Common Core (Program #P770225).

(2) An employer shall train each worker in the program described in subsection (1), as appropriate for that worker.

(2.1) The employer shall ensure that a worker completes all of the modules of the program described in subsection (1) within 12 months after the worker begins performing work covered by those modules.

(3) Subsection (2) does not apply if the worker successfully completed the program described in subsection (1) before being employed by the employer.

(4) A document issued by the Ministry of Training, Colleges and Universities showing that a worker has successfully completed a module of the program referred to in subsection (1) is conclusive proof for the purposes of this section of the worker's successful completion of the module.

O. Reg. 291/02 s. 1; 296/11 s. 4

11.2.2(1) Employers engaged in contiguous underground mine operations and smelter operations shall establish and maintain the following training programs:

    1. Common Core for Basic Smelter Operations—Mineral Ore (Program #P810080).

    2. Common Core for Non-Production Workers in a Smelter Operation—Mineral Ore (Program #P810090).

(2) An employer shall train each worker in the modules of the programs described in subsection (1) appropriate for that worker.

(2.1) The employer shall ensure that a worker completes all of the modules of the appropriate program within 12 months after the worker begins performing work covered by those modules.

(3) Subsection (2) does not apply if the worker successfully completed the program described in subsection (1) before being employed by the employer.

(4) A document issued by the Ministry of Training, Colleges and Universities showing that a worker has successfully completed a module of the program referred to in subsection (1) is conclusive proof for the purposes of this section of the worker's successful completion of the module.

O. Reg. 31/04 s. 3; 296/11 s. 5

854

11.2.3 The training programs described in sections 11 to 11.2.2 must be developed jointly by labour and management in the mining industry and the Ministry of Training, Colleges and Universities and must be approved by that Ministry.

O. Reg. 296/11 s. 6; 265/15 s. 1

11.3 In accordance with the *Agreement on Internal Trade, 1995* and the *Protocols of Amendment*, a worker shall be deemed to hold a certificate referred to in subsection 11(8), 11.1(4), 11.2(5) or 11.2.1(4) if he or she has successfully completed equivalent training in another province or territory of Canada, as determined by the Director.

O. Reg. 251/01 s. 1; 291/02 s. 2; 84/07 s. 3

12. (1) Every worker who is exposed to the hazard of head injury shall wear a protective hat that consists of a shell and suspension system that will adequately protect a worker's head against impact and from flying or falling small objects.

(2) Every worker who is exposed to the hazard of foot injury shall wear protective footwear consisting of a boot or shoe which incorporates a protective box toe that will protect a worker's toes against injury due to impact and which is capable of resisting at least 125 joules of impact energy.

(3) An employer shall require a worker to wear or use such personal protective equipment, clothing and devices as are necessary to protect the worker from the particular hazard to which the worker may be exposed.

(4) Every worker shall be properly fitted with personal protective clothing or equipment by a competent person or persons.

(5) Loose clothing, adornments and hair shall be suitably confined to prevent entanglement with any machinery, device or thing in a workplace.

13. (1) Where, in an emergency, the health or safety of a worker is likely to be endangered by lack of oxygen or the presence of a noxious gas, fume or dust,

> (a) emergency breathing equipment and resuscitating equipment shall be provided for use in such emergency; and
> (b) a worker trained in the use of the breathing equipment and the resuscitating equipment required by clause (a) shall be conve-niently available on each shift.

(2) The emergency breathing equipment and the resuscitating equipment required by clause (1)(a) shall each be stored in a dust-proof container.

14. (1) Subject to subsection (5), where a worker is exposed to the hazard of falling more than three metres, a fall arrest system shall be used to protect the worker.

(2) The fall arrest system required by subsection (1) shall consist of a suitable combination of a belt, a full body harness, a lanyard, an anchor and a rope-grabbing device or lifeline.

(3) The belt, full body harness, lanyard and lifeline shall,

    (a) be made of material with elastic properties capable of absorbing and minimizing the arrest force in case of a fall;

    (b) be designed to distribute a fall arrest force in such a manner that the possibility of injury to the worker is minimized;

    (c) be of sufficient strength to absorb twice the energy that may be transmitted to the fall arrest system; and

    (d) not be knotted or allowed to become knotted, when used or worn.

(4) When being used and worn against the hazard of falling, the lifeline of the fall arrest system shall be,

    (a) anchored so that a worker will fall free of arrest not more than one metre; and

    (b) connected to an object that is,

        (i) capable of resisting the arrest force in case of a fall, and

        (ii) free of sharp edges.

(5) Subsection (1) does not apply to a worker employed in shaft sinking where measures and procedures are adopted and put into effect that will provide equal or greater protection to the worker.

15. (1) No person under the influence of, or carrying, intoxicating liquor, shall enter or knowingly be permitted to enter a mine or mining plant.

(2) Subject to subsection (3), no person under the influence of, or carrying, a drug or narcotic substance shall enter or knowingly be permitted to enter a mine or mining plant.

(3) A person required to use a prescription drug and able to perform his or her work may enter a mine or mining plant upon establishing medical proof thereof.

854

16. (1) This section applies with respect to a worker who is working alone in an underground mine. However, it does not apply with respect to a supervisor working alone in an underground mine.

(2) For the purposes of this section, a worker is not working alone if he or she,

(a) is assigned to work with at least one other worker and is in regular visual contact with the other worker;

(b) is in visual contact with another worker at least once every hour; or

(c) has ready access to a system of two-way communication such as radio, telephone or other electronic means.

(3) Only a competent worker shall work alone in an underground mine.

(4) Except as otherwise provided by this section, a supervisor or a competent worker designated by the supervisor shall visit a worker at least three times during the worker's shift, if the worker is working alone in an underground mine.

(5) In the following circumstances, a supervisor or competent worker designated by the supervisor is required to visit a worker only once during the worker's shift, if the worker is working alone in an underground mine:

1. The work conditions are standard.

2. A supervisor or competent worker designated by the supervisor visits or communicates with the worker at least once every two hours.

3. A record of the communications with the worker is kept.

(6) The communication required by paragraph 2 of subsection (5) must be either face-to-face communication or by a system of two-way communication such as radio, telephone or another electronic means.

O. Reg. 272/97 s. 5

17. (1) Mine rescue stations may be established, equipped, operated and maintained, as the Minister may direct, by an entity specified by the Minister that, in the opinion of the Minister, is qualified to perform those functions.

(2) An entity specified under subsection (1) shall,

(a) appoint mine rescue officers; and

(b) establish mine rescue crews.

(3) Mine rescue officers shall,

(a) administer mine rescue stations;

(b) train mine rescue crew members; and

(c) ensure that each mine rescue crew member is competent to perform and physically capable of performing the functions of a mine rescue crew member.

(4) The owner of a mine shall make available, at the owner's expense,

(a) an adequate number of workers to be taught and trained in mine rescue work; and

(b) training facilities and adequate storage for training materials and equipment.

(5) [Repealed O. Reg. 296/11, s. 7.]

(6) [Repealed O. Reg. 296/11, s. 7.]

(7) A mine rescue operation at a mine shall be under the direction of the supervisor in charge of the mine and the costs of the rescue operation shall be at the expense of the owner of the mine.

(8) Notice shall be given immediately to a mine rescue officer and to an inspector when the services of a mine rescue crew are required.

O. Reg. 272/97 s. 6; 263/99 s. 2; 296/11 s. 7

18. (1) Surface mines and openings on the surface to underground mines shall be protected to prevent inadvertent access where,

(a) the surface mine or opening is a hazard by reason of its depth;

(b) approaches and openings are not readily visible; or

(c) the hazard caused by the surface mine or opening is greater than the hazard caused by the natural topographical features of the area.

(2) Prior to operations at a mine being terminated, a shaft or raise opening shall be,

(a) capped with a stopping of reinforced concrete; or

(b) filled and kept filled with material so that any subsidence of the material will not endanger any person.

(3) The stopping prescribed in clause (2)(a) shall be,

(a) secured to solid rock or to a concrete collar secured to solid rock; and

(b) capable of supporting a uniformly distributed load of 18 kilopascals or a concentrated load of 81 kilonewtons, whichever is greater.

(4) Where an underground mine is being developed after the 1st day of October, 1979, shafts or raise openings shall be provided with a collar of concrete secured to bedrock.

O. Reg. 265/15 s. 2

19. (1) Subject to subsection (2), a pillar sixty metres thick shall be established on either side of a party boundary between adjoining underground mining properties.

(2) Except for exploration headings and diamond drilling, before the pillar is mined, drawings, plans, specifications, mining methods and procedures for the mining of the pillar shall be prepared or checked by a professional engineer in accordance with good engineering practice, filed with the owners of adjoining mining properties and kept readily available at each mine site.

(3) The drawings, plans, specifications, mining methods and procedures to be filed shall be maintained and kept up to date in accordance with subsection 29(2) of the Act.

(4) The pillar dimensions and mining methods and procedures shall,

    (a) provide ground support to control rockbursting, ground falls or pillar failures; and

    (b) withstand inrush of water or waterbearing materials across the party boundary.

(5) Subject to subsections (2), (3) and (4), the party boundary pillar may be mined if the owners of the adjoining mines agree.

O. Reg. 272/97 s. 7

20. (1) The Minister may approve a laboratory for the purpose of testing or examining shaft ropes or other hoisting appliances.

(2) For a mine in Ontario, the fee for testing a rope at an approved laboratory shall be determined in accordance with subsections (3) and (4).

(3) The fee for testing a rope described in Column 1 of a Table to subsection (4) is the corresponding base amount set out in Column 2 plus the corresponding additional fees set out in Columns 3 and 4 that apply with respect to the rope, if any.

(4) The fees set out in the Tables to this subsection are effective as follows:

    1. Table 1 is effective from January 1, 2016 to December 31, 2016.

    2. Table 2 is effective from January 1, 2017 to December 31, 2017.

    3. Table 3 is effective from and after January 1, 2018.

TABLE 1

Column 1 Rope Construction (diameter in millimetres)	Column 2 Base Fee (in dollars)	Column 3 Additional Fee (in dollars) for PVC Filled Ropes	Column 4 Additional Fee (in dollars) for Compacted/Die Form Ropes
6 strand (up to 19.05)	403.28	277.09	55.42
6 strand (greater than 19.05 up to 44.45)	432.48	277.09	55.42
6 strand (greater than 44.45 up to 63.50)	483.96	277.09	55.42
6 strand (greater than 63.50)	593.84	277.09	55.42
7 to 24 strand (up to 19.05)	541.82	207.82	83.13
7 to 24 strand (greater than 19.05 up to 44.45)	571.02	207.82	83.13
7 to 24 strand (greater than 44.45 up to 63.50)	622.50	207.82	83.13
7 to 24 strand (greater than 63.50)	732.38	207.82	83.13
25 to 35 strand (up to 19.05)	715.00	554.18	110.84
25 to 35 strand (greater than 19.05 up to 44.45)	709.57	554.18	110.84
25 to 35 strand (greater than 44.45 up to 63.50)	761.05	554.18	110.84
25 to 35 strand (greater than 63.50)	870.93	554.18	110.84
36 strand or more (up to 19.05)	784.28	623.46	124.69
36 strand or more (greater than 19.05 up to 44.45)	778.84	623.46	124.69

36 strand or more (greater than 44.45 up to 63.50)	830.32	623.46	124.69
36 strand or more (greater than 63.50)	940.20	623.46	124.69
Full lock Coil Rope (up to 19.05)	403.28		
Full lock Coil Rope (greater than 19.05 up to 44.45)	432.48		
Full lock Coil Rope (greater than 44.45 up to 63.50)	483.96		
Full lock Coil Rope (greater than 63.50)	593.84		
Half lock Coil Rope (up to 19.05)	264.73		
Half lock Coil Rope (greater than 19.05 up to 44.45)	293.93		
Half lock Coil Rope (greater than 44.45 up to 63.50)	345.41		
Half lock Coil Rope (greater than 63.50)	455.29		

TABLE 2

Column 1 Rope Construction (diameter in millimetres)	Column 2 Base Fee (in dollars)	Column 3 Additional Fee (in dollars) for PVC Filled Ropes	Column 4 Additional Fee (in dollars) for Compacted/Die Form Ropes
6 strand (up to 19.05)	537.70	369.46	73.89
6 strand (greater than 19.05 up to 44.45)	576.64	369.46	73.89
6 strand (greater than 44.45 up to 63.50)	645.27	369.46	73.89
6 strand (greater than 63.50)	791.78	369.46	73.89
7 to 24 strand (up to 19.05)	722.43	277.09	110.84
7 to 24 strand (greater than 19.05 up to 44.45)	761.37	277.09	110.84
7 to 24 strand (greater than 44.45 up to 63.50)	830.00	277.09	110.84
7 to 24 strand (greater than 63.50)	976.51	277.09	110.84
25 to 35 strand (up to 19.05)	953.34	738.91	147.78
25 to 35 strand (greater than 19.05 up to 44.45)	946.09	738.91	147.78
25 to 35 strand (greater than 44.45 up to 63.50)	1014.73	738.91	147.78
25 to 35 strand (greater than 63.50)	1161.24	738.91	147.78
36 strand or more (up to 19.05)	1045.70	831.28	166.26
36 strand or more (greater than 19.05 up to 44.45)	1038.46	831.28	166.26

854

36 strand or more (greater than 44.45 up to 63.50)	1107.09	831.28	166.26
36 strand or more (greater than 63.50)	1253.60	831.28	166.26
Full lock Coil Rope (up to 19.05)	537.70		
Full lock Coil Rope (greater than 19.05 up to 44.45)	576.64		
Full lock Coil Rope (greater than 44.45 up to 63.50)	645.27		
Full lock Coil Rope (greater than 63.50)	791.78		
Half lock Coil Rope (up to 19.05)	352.97		
Half lock Coil Rope (greater than 19.05 up to 44.45)	391.91		
Half lock Coil Rope (greater than 44.45 up to 63.50)	460.55		
Half lock Coil Rope (greater than 63.50)	607.06		

TABLE 3

Column 1 Rope Construction (diameter in millimetres)	Column 2 Base Fee (in dollars)	Column 3 Additional Fee (in dollars) for PVC Filled Ropes	Column 4 Additional Fee (in dollars) for Compacted/Die Form Ropes
6 strand (up to 19.05)	672.13	461.82	92.36
6 strand (greater than 19.05 up to 44.45)	720.80	461.82	92.36
6 strand (greater than 44.45 up to 63.50)	806.59	461.82	92.36
6 strand (greater than 63.50)	989.73	461.82	92.36
7 to 24 strand (up to 19.05)	903.04	346.36	138.55
7 to 24 strand (greater than 19.05 up to 44.45)	951.71	346.36	138.55
7 to 24 strand (greater than 44.45 up to 63.50)	1037.50	346.36	138.55
7 to 24 strand (greater than 63.50)	1220.64	346.36	138.55
25 to 35 strand (up to 19.05)	1191.67	923.64	184.73
25 to 35 strand (greater than 19.05 up to 44.45)	1182.62	923.64	184.73
25 to 35 strand (greater than 44.45 up to 63.50)	1268.41	923.64	184.73
25 to 35 strand (greater than 63.50)	1451.55	923.64	184.73
36 strand or more (up to 19.05)	1307.13	1039.09	207.82
36 strand or more (greater than 19.05 up to 44.45)	1298.07	1039.09	207.82

854

36 strand or more (greater than 44.45 up to 63.50)	1383.87	1039.09	207.82
36 strand or more (greater than 63.50)	1567.00	1039.09	207.82
Full lock Coil Rope (up to 19.05)	672.13		
Full lock Coil Rope (greater than 19.05 up to 44.45)	720.80		
Full lock Coil Rope (greater than 44.45 up to 63.50)	806.59		
Full lock Coil Rope (greater than 63.50)	989.73		
Half lock Coil Rope (up to 19.05)	441.22		
Half lock Coil Rope (greater than 19.05 up to 44.45)	489.89		
Half lock Coil Rope (greater than 44.45 up to 63.50)	575.68		
Half lock Coil Rope (greater than 63.50)	758.82		

(5) A laboratory shall issue a Certificate of Test for each sample of shaft rope submitted to it for testing, setting out the breaking strength of the rope, and the breaking strength, as set out in the Certificate of Test, shall be the breaking strength of the rope from which the sample was taken.

O. Reg. 384/92 s. 1; 265/15 s. 3

21. **(1)** The written report required by section 51 of the Act shall include,

(a) the name and address of the employer;

(b) the nature and the circumstances of the occurrence and the bodily injury sustained;

(c) a description of the machinery or equipment involved;

(d) the time and place of the occurrence;

(e) the name and address of the person who was killed or critically injured;

(f) the names and addresses of all witnesses to the occurrence and of all supervisors and workers who were involved; and

(g) the name and address of the physician or surgeon, if any, by whom the person was or is being attended for the injury.

(2) For the purposes of section 52 of the Act, notice of,

(a) an accident, explosion or fire which disables a worker from performing his or her usual work; or

(b) an occupational illness, shall include,

(c) the name, address and type of business of the employer;

(d) the nature and the circumstances of the occurrence and the bodily injury or illness sustained;

(e) a description of the machinery or equipment involved;

(f) the time and place of the occurrence;

(g) the name and address of the person suffering the injury or illness;

(h) the names and addresses of all witnesses to the occurrence;

(i) the name and address of the physician or surgeon, if any, by whom the person was or is being attended for the injury or illness; and

(j) the steps taken to prevent a recurrence.

(3) A record of an accident, explosion or fire causing injury requiring medical attention but not disabling a worker from performing his or her usual work shall be kept in the permanent records of the employer and include particulars of,

854

(a) the nature and the circumstances of the occurrence and the injury sustained;

(b) the time and place of the occurrence; and

(c) the name and address of the injured person.

(4) A record kept as prescribed by subsection (3) for the inspection of an inspector shall be notice to the Director.

(5) In addition to the occurrences referred to in section 53 of the Act, a notice in writing shall be given where,

(a) a failure occurs in or to a hoist, sheave, hoisting rope, shaft conveyance, shaft timbering or shaft lining;

(b) flammable gas is present in a workplace in an underground mine;

(c) spontaneous heating with evolution of gas occurs in a workplace;

(d) a major failure or major damage occurs or is caused to electrical equipment, standard gauge railroad equipment, a crane or a motor vehicle underground;

(e) a rockburst occurs causing damage to equipment or the displacement of more than five tonnes of material;

(f) an uncontrolled fall of ground occurs causing damage to equipment or the displacement of more than fifty tonnes of material;

(g) a fuse, a detonator or an explosive is found to be defective;

(h) a structural failure occurs in any matter or thing for which a design by a professional engineer is prescribed by this Regulation; or

(i) an unexpected and uncontrolled run of material, water or slimes in excess of one cubic metre occurs that could have endangered a worker.

O. Reg. 60/94 s. 3; 34/14 s. 2

22. (1) For the purpose of subsection 29(2) of the Act, drawings, plans and specifications to be kept and maintained shall be,

(a) a surface plan showing,

(i) the boundaries of a mining property,

(ii) the co-ordinates of the section of a mining property under which mining has been done,

(iii) all lakes, streams, roads, railways, electric power transmission lines, main pipe lines, buildings, adits, surface workings, diamond drill holes, out-croppings of rock, dumps, tailing-disposal sites and openings to an underground mine, and

(iv) stopping of openings on the surface to an underground mine;

(b) plans on a horizontal plane with separate drawings for each level showing all underground workings, including shafts, tunnels, diamond drill holes, dams and bulkheads;

(c) plans on a vertical plane of all mine sections at suitable intervals and azimuths, showing all shafts, tunnels, drifts, stopes and other mine workings in relation to the surface, including the location of the top of the bedrock, the surface of the overburden and the bottom and surface of any known watercourse or body of water; and

(d) a plan or diagram showing,

(i) the position of all fixed electrical apparatus and communication systems in the mine,

(ii) the routes of all fixed power feeders and fixed branch feeders properly noted and referenced, and

(iii) the rating of all electrical feeder control apparatus and equipment.

(2) The surface plan prescribed by clause (1)(a) shall show,

(a) the boundaries of the mining property,

(i) related to the lot fabric where the property is in a subdivided township,

(ii) connected to the nearest mile post on a surveyed township boundary where the property is in an unsubdivided township, or

(iii) connected to the nearest,

(A) mile post on a surveyed township boundary,

(B) base line, or

(C) meridian line, where the property is in unsurveyed territory, and

(iv) connected to a co-ordinate control survey monument if one exists within ten kilometres of the property; and

(b) the position and form of a permanent bench mark to which all elevations are related, and the permanent bench mark shall be related,

      (i) where a Canadian Geodetic Datum bench mark exists within ten kilometres, to that bench mark, and

      (ii) to the permanent bench mark of each adjoining property.

(3) The measurements under clause (2)(a) shall be consistent with accuracy standards for third order horizontal control surveys based on Ontario Specifications for Horizontal Control Surveys, 1979.

(4) Where operation at a mine is terminated or suspended, copies of the plans mentioned in subsection (1) shall be filed with the Ministry.

(5) Copies of all plans shall be on a legible scale and suitable for micro-filming.

23. (1) If an underground mine has been permanently shut down or abandoned or if operations at the mine have been discontinued or suspended for more than three months, the owner shall, before dewatering, exploring or resuming work at the mine,

      (a) notify an inspector of the owner's intention to enter the mine; and

      (b) furnish an inspector with such drawings, plans, specifications and descriptions of procedures as are necessary to determine whether it is safe to enter the mine.

(2) Subject to subsection (4), where a decision is made to discontinue or suspend operations at a mine or mining plant, notice shall be given forthwith to an inspector.

(3) Where operations at a mine or mining plant are discontinued or suspended, the notice mentioned in subsection (2) shall advise whether,

      (a) stopping and protection has been done as prescribed in section 18;

      (b) explosives have been disposed of as prescribed in subsection 122(5);

      (c) removal and disposition of hoisting ropes has been done as prescribed in subsection 228(17);

      (d) disconnection from the electrical power source has been done and has been confirmed in writing by the appropriate electrical utilities inspection department; and

      (e) plans required by section 22 have been filed with the Ministry.

(4) Subsections (2) and (3) do not apply to gravel pit operations that are discontinued during the winter months.

O. Reg. 779/94 s. 1; 272/97 s. 8

24. [Repealed O. Reg. 167/16, s. 6.]

Part II — Fire Protection

25. (1) Procedures in case of a fire in an underground mine, or in a structure or building on the surface at an underground mine, that may be a hazard to workers in the mine shall be prepared by the supervisor in charge of the mine.

(2) An alarm system, that is effective to warn workers in an underground mine of a fire that is likely to endanger their safety, shall be provided.

(3) The procedures required by subsection (1), or extracts therefrom, and a notice explaining the alarm system shall be set out in writing and shall be posted and kept posted in the shaft house and in a conspicuous place or places where they are most likely to come to the attention of a worker.

(4) Every worker shall be advised by a supervisor of the procedures and the alarm system.

(5) Once in at least every twelve months during each production shift a fire alarm test of the procedures shall be conducted.

(6) The alarm system in an underground mine shall,

    (a) consist of the introduction into all workplaces of sufficient quantities of ethyl mercaptan gas or similar gas to be readily detectable by all workers; and

    (b) be kept ready for immediate use.

(7) Despite clause (6)(a), an alternative means of alarm may be used if the alarm system is agreed upon by the employer and the joint health and safety committee or the health and safety representative, if any, for the workplace.

(8) A report of each fire alarm test of the procedures mentioned in subsection (5) shall be kept available at the mine for three years.

O. Reg. 779/94 s. 2; 272/97 s. 9

26. Where the procedure in case of a fire in an underground mine provides for the use of a refuge station for workers, the refuge station shall,

    (a) be constructed with materials having at least a one hour fire-resistance rating;

(b) be of sufficient size to accommodate the workers to be assembled therein;

(c) be capable of being sealed to prevent the entry of gases;

(d) have a means of voice communication with the surface; and

(e) be equipped with a means for the supply of,

    (i) compressed air, and

    (ii) potable water.

27. **(1)** A fresh air base shall be provided underground where necessary to serve as a base for rescue and recovery work.

(2) A fresh air base shall be,

(a) at least thirty square metres in area; and

(b) equipped with a means for the supply of potable water and compressed air.

28. **(1)** Fire extinguishing equipment of suitable type and size for use on a fire shall be provided,

(a) at a fire hazard area;

(b) where an electrical installation or equipment may be a fire hazard;

(c) in or about a headframe;

(d) in a building or structure on surface where a fire might endanger the mine entrance; and

(e) at a shaft station in an underground mine.

(2) A fire suppression system consisting of sprinklers, foam or other suitable means of suppressing fire shall be provided,

(a) in an underground mine,

    (i) on equipment containing more than 100 litres of flammable hydraulic fluids,

    (ii) in every storage area where more than 500 litres of oil, grease or flammable liquids are stored,

    (iii) in every service garage; and

    (iv) in every permanent fuelling station; and

(b) on the surface, in a building or structure, except a fan house, located above or adjacent to an opening to an underground mine.

(3) At least once each month in an underground mine,

(a) fire extinguishing equipment;

(b) fire suppression systems;

(c) fire hydrants; and

(d) fire doors,

shall be inspected by a competent person who shall report in writing thereon to the supervisor in charge of the underground mine.

O. Reg. 486/99 s. 1

29. (1) In an underground mine or in or about a headframe or shaft house, flammable refuse shall be,

(a) deposited in covered, fire-resistive containers; and

(b) removed at least once a week from the mine or headframe or shaft house.

(2) Scrap timber shall safely be disposed of or removed from an underground mine.

(3) A written report certifying that there is no accumulation of flammable refuse in the area under his or her supervision shall be made weekly by a supervisor to the supervisor in charge of the mine.

30. (1) Oil, grease and other flammable material shall not be kept or stored in a shafthouse or in a portal house.

(2) Oil, grease and flammable liquids with a flashpoint below 52° Celsius shall,

(a) when being used underground, be transported and stored only in metal containers or receptacles or in portable plastic containers for Petroleum Fuels as specified in CSA Standard B376-M1980, "Portable Containers for Gasoline and Other Petroleum Fuels"; and

(b) when stored underground, be restricted in quantity to the requirement for,

(i) the current day's work in the case of volatile flammable liquids, and

(ii) seven days in the case of oil and grease.

(3) No device for the generation of acetylene gas shall be used in an underground mine.

(4) No internal combustion engine that uses gasoline, propane or other volatile substance as a fuel shall be used in an underground mine.

(5) Except when used for burning or cutting, propane or other similar fuel that is heavier than air when in a gaseous state shall not be permitted to be or be kept underground.

854

(6) When propane or other similar fuel that is heavier than air is being used underground for burning or cutting, the cylinders for the fuel shall be of a type approved by Transport Canada and shall not be larger than five kilograms in capacity.

O. Reg. 584/91 s. 2; 34/14 s. 3

31. No worker shall build or set a fire in an underground mine unless the worker is specifically authorized to do so and has immediately available suitable fire extinguishing equipment.

32. Every workshop and lunchroom in an underground mine shall,

(a) be constructed of material with at least a one hour fire-resistance rating; and

(b) be located and maintained so as to reduce the fire hazard to a minimum.

33. A structure housing a fan used in connection with a ventilation system for an underground mine shall be constructed of noncombustible material.

O. Reg. 167/16, s. 1

34. (1) A fire hazard area shall be identified by suitable warning signs.

(2) Except where special precautions are taken and written instructions issued, no use of matches, smoking or other means of producing heat or fire shall be permitted in a fire hazard area.

35. (1) If a flow of flammable gas is encountered in a mine or in an enclosed building housing a diamond drill on the surface and the concentration of the flammable gas is unknown,

(a) all sources of ignition in the affected area shall be eliminated;

(b) all electrical equipment in the affected area shall be de-energized;

(c) the affected area shall be evacuated;

(d) precautions shall be taken to prevent persons from entering the affected area inadvertently;

(e) a supervisor shall be notified;

(f) the affected area shall be tested by a competent person; and

(g) the affected area shall be designated as a fire hazard area.

(2) Subject to subsections (3), (4) and (5), work may resume if the concentration of flammable gas is below 1.0 per cent.

(3) If the concentration is less than 0.25 per cent and the affected area is tested periodically to ensure that the level of concentration is known, no precautions are required.

(4) If the concentration is 0.25 per cent or greater but not more than 0.5 per cent, all of the following precautions shall be taken:

1. The supervisor shall provide written instructions of any special precautions.
2. The instructions, if any, shall be communicated to the workers.
3. The affected area shall be designated as a fire hazard area.
4. The affected area shall be tested at least once per shift before work begins and, again, on release of any further flow of gas.
5. A flammable gas detector shall remain in the affected area for the purpose of continued testing.

(5) If the concentration is 0.5 per cent or greater but not more than 1.0 per cent, all of the precautions set out in subsection (4) shall be taken and the electrical equipment, diesel engines, tools and other material used in the workplace shall be designed to function safely in a flammable gas atmosphere.

(6) If concentrations of flammable gas exceed 1.0 per cent in an area, all of the following precautions shall be taken:

1. All sources of ignition in the affected area shall be eliminated.
2. All electrical equipment in the affected area shall be de-energized.
3. All persons, other than competent persons necessary to measure the concentration of flammable gas and to make ventilation changes, shall be removed from the affected area.

(7) In mines where flammable gas is known to occur, workers who are underground or diamond drillers who are on the surface shall be advised of,

(a) the probability of encountering a flow of the gas; and

(b) the measures and procedures prescribed in this section.

(8) For the purposes of this section, the concentration of flammable gas means the percentage, by volume, of flammable gas in the general atmosphere.

O. Reg. 236/99 s. 3

36. (1) Where a blow torch or welding, cutting or other hot work equipment is used underground, or in a headframe, shaft house or other surface building in which a fire may endanger the mine entrance or the underground workings, a procedure for the safe use of hot work equipment shall be prepared in writing and signed by the supervisor in charge of the mine.

(2) Only a worker who is a competent person or is under the direction of a competent person shall use hot work equipment.

(3) In addition to the hot work procedure required by subsection (1), written instructions shall be issued to the worker by a supervisor before the hot work equipment is used respecting,

    (a) the type of work;

    (b) the location of the work;

    (c) when the work is to be done; and

    (d) any special measures and procedures to be taken before, during and after the work.

(4) Where hot work equipment is used in a shaft, timbered area or fire hazard area,

    (a) the area adjacent to the particular workplace shall be wet down,

        (i) before the work is begun, and

        (ii) when the work is stopped and the worker using the hot work equipment intends to leave;

    (b) the area adjacent to the particular workplace shall be examined for potential fire hazards,

        (i) before the work is begun, and

        (ii) when the work is stopped and the worker intends to leave the area, and

        (iii) on at least one other occasion approximately two hours after the work is stopped;

    (c) fire-fighting equipment suitable for extinguishing any potential fire shall be available; and

    (d) workers shall be protected from fumes, vapours or gases by,

        (i) ventilation, or

        (ii) the wearing of respirators.

(5) Subsection (1) does not apply to hot work being performed in a repair station or garage protected by a fire suppression system.

(6) Clause (4)(a) does not apply where the wetting down will create a hazard because of freezing or the presence of electrical equipment.

37. (1) Except during the initial stages of exploration and development of an underground mine, in addition to the opening through which workers are let into or out of the mine and the ore extracted, a separate escapement exit shall be provided.

(2) The escapement exit required by subsection (1) shall be,

(a) located more than thirty metres from the main hoisting shaft or ramp;

(b) of sufficient size to afford an easy passageway;

(c) where necessary, provided with ladders from the deepest workings to the surface;

(d) marked on all levels by signs and arrows pointing the way of exit in a manner to expedite escape;

(e) made known to all underground workers who shall be instructed as to the route to the escapement exit; and

(f) inspected at least once a month by a competent person who shall give a written report of such inspection to the supervisor in charge of the mine.

(3) A structure covering the escapement exit shall be constructed of material with at least a one hour fire-resistance rating.

O. Reg. 265/15 s. 4

38. (1) Subject to subsection (2), unless there is a second means of exit from an underground mine, no building shall be erected within fifteen metres of any closed-in part of a headframe or portal house.

(2) A building erected within fifteen metres of any closed-in part of a headframe or portal house shall be constructed of material with at least a one hour fire-resistance rating.

(3) No steam boiler or diesel engine shall be installed in such a manner that any part thereof is within thirty metres of the centre of the collar of a shaft or other entrance to a mine.

(4) No internal combustion engine shall be installed, serviced, garaged or stored in or within fifteen metres of the building housing the hoist nor within thirty metres of the centre of the collar of a shaft or other entrance to a mine.

(5) Except for the fuel tanks of motor vehicles, no gasoline or liquid fuel shall be stored within thirty metres of the centre of the collar of a shaft or other entrance of a mine.

854

(5.1) Subsections (3), (4) and (5) do not apply with respect to a diesel engine and an attached diesel fuel tank (other than an engine installed on a motor vehicle) if,

    (a) the engine and tank are enclosed by a structure constructed of material that has a fire-resistance rating of at least one hour;

    (b) the structure separates the enclosed area from the hoist or a shaft or other entrance to a mine; and

    (c) the enclosed area has a fire suppression system and an automatic fire alarm.

(6) The natural drainage shall drain away from the shaft collar or other mine entrance.

(7) Where a hoist is located above the mine shaft, the supporting and enclosing structures shall be constructed of material with at least a one hour fire-resistance rating.

                                            O. Reg. 272/97 s. 10

39. Fire doors in an underground mine shall,

    (a) where practical, be installed to close off the shaft or main entrance to the mine and the mine openings directly associated with it from the other workings;

    (b) be installed to close off,

        (i) service garages, and

        (ii) oil storage areas where a total of more than 500 litres of oil, grease or flammable liquid are stored;

    (c) have at least a one hour fire-resistance rating; and

    (d) be maintained in proper order and kept clear of all obstructions so as to be readily usable at all times.

40. (1) Where, in an underground or tower mounted hoistroom, the normal air supply may become contaminated in an emergency, uncontaminated air shall be available to the hoist operator and cagetender by means of,

    (a) an enclosed booth with a positive supply of uncontaminated air; or

    (b) one or more units of self-contained demand air or oxygen breathing apparatus, together with a fully charged cylinder of compressed air of at least 8.5 cubic metres capacity.

(2) Every hoist operator and cagetender who may be required to use demand breathing apparatus shall be competent in its use.

41. (1) Procedures in case of a fire at,
    (a) the surface of an underground mine;
    (b) a surface mine; or
    (c) a mining plant,
shall be prepared by the supervisor in charge of the mine or mining plant.

(2) The procedures required by subsection (1) or extracts therefrom shall be set out in writing and shall be posted and kept posted in a conspicuous place or places where they are most likely to come to the attention of a worker.

(3) A suitable number of workers at each mine and mining plant shall be trained in the fire-fighting procedures and,
    (a) the names of such workers shall be posted in a conspicuous place;
    (b) such workers shall be tested for proficiency at least once a year; and
    (c) a written report of the results of the tests shall be made and kept on file.

(4) Fire-extinguishing equipment of a suitable type and size shall be provided at,
    (a) the surface of every underground mine;
    (b) every surface mine; and
    (c) mining plant.

(5) At least once each month, the,
    (a) fire-extinguishing equipment;
    (b) fire suppression systems;
    (c) fire hydrants; and
    (d) fire doors,
at the surface of an underground mine, a surface mine and a mining plant shall be inspected by a competent person who shall report thereon to the supervisor in charge of the mine or mining plant, as the case may be.

42. (1) The fuel tank of an internal combustion engine installed in a building shall be arranged so that the transfer of fuel to the tank takes place at a point outside the building and the fuel is conducted to the tank in a tightly jointed pipe or conduit.

(2) The air displaced from the fuel tank shall be conducted to a safe point outside the building before being discharged into the atmosphere.

854

43. Any dangerous, flammable or explosive material or substance in a solid, liquid or gaseous state, or any combination thereof, other than explosive, that is kept, stored or handled, in a mining plant shall,

   (a) be kept in a container that is suitable having regard to the nature and state of the material or substance;

   (b) have labels on the container identifying the material or substance and warning of the hazards involved therewith;

   (c) be kept apart or insulated from any source of ignition or from temperatures likely to cause combustion; and

   (d) where the material or substance is not intended for immediate use, be kept, stored or handled,

      (i) outside any building,

      (ii) in a building not used for any other purpose, or

      (iii) in a well ventilated compartment with at least a one hour fire-resistance rating which is located in conformity with clause (c).

44. (1) In addition to the main exit, a building at a mining plant, except a magazine, shall be provided with a second means of exit, convenient to and having easy communication with all rooms regularly occupied by a worker, including,

   (a) tower stairs equipped with doors and hardware with at least a one hour fire-resistance rating at each storey including the basement; or

   (b) metal or other noncombustible fire escapes consisting of exterior stairways with railings and with landings at each storey connecting directly with the interior of the building through metal or other doors with at least a one hour fire-resistance rating.

(2) No means of exit from a plant building shall be obstructed and no door to a fire escape, tower stair or other smokeproof enclosure shall be prevented from closing or remaining closed.

O. Reg. 167/16, s. 1

45. A process that is likely to produce a gas, vapour, dust or fume to such an extent as to be capable of forming a flammable mixture with air shall be carried out in an area which,

   (a) is isolated from other operations;

   (b) has a system of ventilation which removes the gas, vapour, dust or fume;

   (c) has no potential sources of ignition; and

(d) has vents, baffles, chokes, dampers or other means to reduce the effects of any explosion, as may be required.

Part III — Access to Workplaces

46. (1) A safe means of access to a workplace shall be provided by a walkway, stairway or ladderway.

(2) Where workers are required to work, operate, maintain or service equipment, a safe means of access shall be provided as prescribed in subsection (1).

(3) Every walkway and every working platform more than 1.5 metres above the ground shall be provided with,

    (a) a handrail not less than 0.91 metre or more than 1.07 metres above the floor of the walkway or platform;

    (b) a second rail placed at the mid-point between the top rail and the floor of the walkway or platform or have the space between the top rail and the floor closed by a screen; and

    (c) toeboards which shall extend from the floor a height of not less than 100 millimetres.

(4) The handrail required by clause (3)(a) shall be capable of withstanding a load applied in any direction to the top rail of at least 0.9 kilonewton.

(5) Despite clauses (3)(b) and (c), toeboards and second rails are not required on a temporary walkway or working platform or on an underground drilling platform that is normally not more than three metres above the ground.

(6) When a platform consists of wooden planks, the planks shall,

    (a) be sound, unpainted and free of large knots;

    (b) provide a minimum safety factor of three times the maximum load to which it is likely to be subjected; and

    (c) be nailed or otherwise secured against movement.

(7) Where a means of access to a workplace is inclined at more than twenty degrees and less than fifty degrees to the horizontal, a stairway or ladderway shall be provided.

(8) Where a means of access to a workplace is inclined at more than fifty degrees to the horizontal, a ladder shall be provided.

(9) A stairway shall,

854

(a) be at an angle not greater than fifty degrees to the horizontal;

(b) not have the rise or vertical distance between landings of a flight exceed 3.6 metres;

(c) have the treads and risers uniform in width and height respectively in any one flight; and

(d) be provided with handrails of adequate strength not less than 0.91 metre and not more than 1.07 metres in height above the treads of the stairs.

47. (1) A ladder shall,

(a) be of strong construction;

(b) be free from broken or loose members or other faults;

(c) be installed and maintained so as to reduce to a minimum the hazard of a person falling therefrom;

(d) if made of wood,

(i) be of sound straight-grain lumber,

(ii) not be painted or otherwise treated in a manner to obscure the grain;

(e) have a distance between centres of the rungs not greater than 300 millimetres or less than 250 millimetres;

(f) have the spacing between rungs not vary more than fifteen millimetres in a ladderway;

(g) have not less than 100 millimetres clearance behind any rung from a wall or any timber or obstruction underneath the ladder; and

(h) project at least one metre above the landing or opening unless strong handholds are provided above the top of the ladder.

(2) A fixed ladder shall be securely fastened in place.

48. (1) Except in an underground mine, a ladderway at an angle steeper than seventy degrees to the horizontal shall be fixed in place and be provided with,

(a) platforms at intervals not greater than seven metres;

(b) a safety cage; or

(c) a protective device which when used will prevent a worker from falling.

(2) Except in an underground mine, where platforms are used in conjunction with a ladderway,

(a) the ladders shall be offset;

(b) a platform shall be provided at each place where ladders are offset; and

(c) the platform shall be not less than 600 millimetres in width by 1.2 metres in length.

49. A portable ladder shall,

(a) be equipped with non-slip feet or otherwise secured;

(b) where any activity in the vicinity may create a hazard to a person thereon, be protected at its base; and

(c) where the ladder has metal or metal-reinforced side rails, not be used near exposed and energized electrical circuits or equipment.

50. (1) Subject to subsection (2), a suitable ladderway shall be provided in every shaft.

(2) An independently powered conveyance may be used in place of a ladderway.

(3) Except for an auxiliary ladder used in shaft-sinking operations, a shaft ladder shall be inclined.

(4) During shaft-sinking operations, if a permanent ladder is not provided to the bottom, an auxiliary ladder that will reach from the permanent ladders to the bottom shall be provided in such convenient position that it may be promptly lowered to any point at which a worker is working.

O. Reg. 272/97 s. 11

51. (1) Where a ladderway is installed in an underground mine or in a headframe used in conjunction with a shaft and the ladderway is inclined at more than seventy degrees from the horizontal,

(a) the ladderway shall be provided with substantial platforms at intervals not greater than seven metres;

(b) the ladders shall be offset at the platform;

(c) except for openings large enough to permit the passage of a worker, the platforms shall be fully closed; and

(d) if installed in a shaft manway, the ladders shall be placed over the openings of the platforms below.

(2) Where the ladderway is inclined at less than seventy degrees to the horizontal, the ladders may be continuous and the provisions of clauses (1)(a) and (c) shall apply.

(3) Where a ladderway is inclined at less than fifty degrees to the horizontal, no platform is required except at points of offset.

(4) Where a ladderway is the only means of access for mine rescue purposes, the opening shall be large enough for such purpose.

52. Wire ropes used for climbing purposes shall not be frayed or have projecting broken wires.

53. No person shall be, or be permitted to be, in a combined ladderway and hoistway compartment while a bucket or material is being,

    (a) loaded or unloaded at the top; or

    (b) hoisted or lowered.

54. (1) A walkway, stairway or ladderway shall be,

    (a) maintained in a safe condition;

    (b) free from obstructions;

    (c) of sufficient size to ensure that crowding does not occur; and

    (d) cleared of hazardous accumulation of material without undue delay.

(2) Any opening in a floor or other surface which may be a hazard to a worker shall be,

    (a) protected by a guardrail; or

    (b) covered with securely fastened planks or other material capable of supporting any load to which it is likely to be subjected.

Part IV — Protection of Workers

55. No worker shall work in a location where another worker is working overhead unless measures are taken to protect the worker.

56. Where a gas, liquid or vapour is contained at a pressure other than atmospheric pressure, before any fastening of the container or system connected therewith,

    (a) is loosened, any flow into or out of the container or system shall be effectively stopped; or

    (b) is removed, the container or system shall be drained or bled so that the pressure in the container or system equals atmospheric pressure.

57. No liquids or solids shall be transferred from one location or container to another location or container by the application of air under pressure except where equipment specifically designed for the purpose is used.

58. Plastic pipe and fittings shall,

(a) meet CSA Standards B137.0-M 1981 and B137.3-M 1981 or, if installed after the 1st day of September, 1992, meet CSA Standards B137.0-M1986, "Definitions, General Requirements and Methods of Testing For Thermoplastic Pressure Piping" and B137.3-M1986, "Rigid Polyvinyl Chloride PVC Pipe For Pressure Applications";

(b) be properly supported;

(c) not be used for the main supply or discharge of compressed air or water in mine shafts; and

(d) not be forced around bends that may unreasonably stress the pipe or its connections.

O. Reg. 571/92 s. 5

59. (1) All openings, sumps, vessels, bins, hoppers, elevated platforms or pits, other than grease pits, which constitute a hazard, shall be fenced or otherwise guarded.

(2) Every power-operated door through which vehicles or pedestrians travel,

(a) shall be clearly distinguished from its surroundings; and

(b) shall be operated in accordance with the procedures adopted by the employer for its use.

60. (1) Before a worker enters any silo, bin, hopper or other container or structure containing bulk material, all further supply of material thereto shall be stopped and any removal of material therefrom shall be prevented.

(2) When working on top of bulk material in any silo, bin, hopper or other container or structure,

(a) a worker shall use a fall arrest system; and

(b) at least one other worker, who is a competent person, equipped with a suitable alarm shall be in constant attendance outside the silo, bin, hopper or other container or structure.

61. (1) Stockpiles of unconsolidated material shall be,

(a) inspected for hazardous conditions regularly by a competent person; and

(b) made safe before a worker is allowed to work close to or on top of the stockpile.

(2) Bulk or packaged material shall be piled or stacked in a manner to prevent accidental movement or collapse.

(3) When a tunnel is used under a stockpile for the purpose of reclaiming material from the stockpile at least two exits shall be provided from the tunnel.

62. A procedure shall be established and maintained at an underground mine to record every worker and other person who is underground in the mine.

62.1(1) This section applies with respect to tasks at a workplace that are determined to be non-routine hazardous tasks jointly by the employer and the joint health and safety committee or the health and safety representative, if any, for the workplace.

(2) The employer and the joint health and safety committee or the health and safety representative shall jointly establish safe procedures for performing a non-routine hazardous task.

(3) The employer shall ensure that the safe procedures are set out in writing.

(4) The employer shall ensure that workers are informed that a task is a non-routine hazardous task and are informed about the procedures for performing it before beginning the task.

(5) A worker performing a non-routine hazardous task shall follow the established procedures.

O. Reg. 60/94 s. 4

63. (1) Every place where drilling and blasting is being carried on in an underground mine shall be examined by a supervisor during each work shift.

(2) Every place other than where drilling and blasting is being carried on in an underground mine and where workers carry on work shall be examined by a supervisor at least once each work week.

64. (1) Where in an underground mine a potential or actual danger to the health or safety of a worker has not been remedied or removed at the end of a work shift, a record in writing shall be made by the supervisor of the work shift and signed by the supervisor describing,

    (a) the dangerous condition; and

    (b) the state of corrective measures taken.

(2) The record required by subsection (1) shall be read and countersigned by the supervisor of the next work shift before a worker on such shift does any work in the area of the dangerous condition and the workers on such shift who may be affected by the dangerous condition shall be advised of,

    (a) the dangerous condition;

    (b) the state of corrective measures undertaken; and

    (c) the work required to be done to remove or remedy the dangerous condition.

65. (1) An employer in an underground mine, in consultation with the joint health and safety committee, if any, for the mine, shall develop a written program to provide for the timely communication of information between workers and supervisors in the mine respecting ground stability, ground movement, falls of ground, ground monitoring equipment and emergencies.

(2) The communications program shall set out,

    (a) means and procedures for communicating information;

    (b) the kind of information to be communicated; and

    (c) the actions to be taken by supervisors and workers with respect to information that is communicated to them.

66. (1) Before work is begun in a workplace in an underground mine, the ground conditions of the workplace shall be examined for dangers and hazards and, if required, made safe.

(2) [Revoked O. Reg. 571/92, s. 6.]

O. Reg. 571/92 s. 6

67. (1) An employer shall prepare written procedures to be used at an underground mine concerning,

    (a) activities relating to the installation of ground support at the mine; and

    (b) activities that require a worker to be exposed to unsupported ground before the ground support is installed.

(2) The procedures shall state the methods for undertaking the activities and for preventing workers' exposure to unsafe ground conditions.

(3) The employer shall consult with the joint health and safety committee or, if no committee exists, with the health and safety representative in preparing the procedures.

O. Reg. 571/92 s. 7

67.1 During scaling procedures in a workplace in an underground mine, no other work shall be carried on that hinders the scaling procedures.

O. Reg. 571/92 s. 7

68. Where a workplace, travelway, manway or other area of an underground mine is under repair or where there is danger or hazard to a worker,

> (a) the workplace, travelway, manway or other area shall be closed by barricades, fencing or other suitable means; and
>
> (b) warning signs shall be posted indicating that it is under repair or indicating the nature of the danger or hazard.

O. Reg. 486/99 s. 2

69. (1) Illumination shall be provided in an underground mine adequate for a worker to visually assess ground conditions at the worker's workplace.

(2) Where a cap lamp is used to provide the illumination as required by subsection (1), it shall be capable of providing a peak illuminance of at least 1500 lux at 1.2 metres from the light source.

(3) An employer in an underground mine who supplies cap lamps to workers shall develop a procedure for assessing and maintaining cap lamps and a copy of the procedure shall be available at the mine site for review by the joint health and safety committee or health and safety representative, if any, for the mine.

(4) A record of cap lamp maintenance test results shall be kept.

(5) Despite subsection (2), if the ground to be assessed is at a distance that is greater than the effective range of a cap lamp, the employer shall supply, and the worker shall use, auxiliary lighting that will provide the illumination required by subsection (1).

O. Reg. 272/97 s. 12

70. [Revoked O. Reg. 272/97, s. 13.]

71. (1) An overhead protective device to protect the operator from falling objects shall be installed on every motor vehicle that is used,

> (a) in an underground mine that is developed after June 1, 1988; or
>
> (b) in an area in an underground mine with respect to which the Director has given the owner a written opinion that local ground stability presents a hazard to the operators.

(2) Clause (1)(a) does not apply to a motor vehicle while it is being used in an area in an underground mine that is made safe,

(a) by scaling, timbering or rockbolting; or

(b) by measures that provide safety equal to or better than scaling, timbering or rockbolting.

(3) An overhead protective device required by subsection (1) shall comply with the falling-object protective structures requirements of International Standard ISO 3449-05 (R2014) "Earth-Moving Machinery – Falling Object Protective Structures – Laboratory Tests and Performance Requirements".

(4) An overhead protective device shall be maintained in good condition.
O. Reg. 272/97 s. 14; 84/07 s. 4; 167/16, s. 7

72. (1) In the event of an occurrence listed in subsection (2) at an underground mine, a record of that occurrence shall be kept in writing and shall provide the following:

1. The time, location and extent of the occurrence.

2. A description of any injuries caused to workers.

3. Any other relevant information, including the records of any monitoring instruments or devices before the occurrence.

(2) For the purposes of subsection (1), the following are considered occurrences:

1. A rockburst.

2. An uncontrolled fall of ground.

3. A seismic event that is of a magnitude that is likely to cause significant rock mass damage or may compromise the effectiveness of the ground support system.

4. A seismic event that occurs in or near an active area of a mine that is of a magnitude that may cause ground instability.
O. Reg. 167/16, s. 8

73. (1) An employer shall develop a quality control program for work in an underground mine to ensure that the ground support systems that are specified in the mine design are properly installed and remain effective while in use.

(2) The employer shall maintain a record of the tests that are required under the quality control program.

(3) If requested, the employer shall provide a copy of the quality control program and of the record of tests under the program to the joint health and safety committee or, if no committee exists, to the health and safety representative.

O. Reg. 571/92 s. 8

74. A shaft, raise or other opening in an underground mine shall be securely fenced, covered or otherwise guarded.

75. (1) A shaft shall be securely cased, lined or timbered.

(2) During shaft-sinking operations, the casing, lining or timbering shall be maintained within a distance of the bottom not exceeding twenty metres.

76. (1) Except during shaft-sinking operations, a shaft compartment used for the handling of material shall be enclosed at the collar and at all levels, except the side on which material is loaded on or off the shaft conveyance.

(2) The enclosure referred to in subsection (1) shall,

    (a) be made of substantial materials;

    (b) extend above the collar and each level a distance of not less than the height of the shaft conveyance plus two metres but need not exceed seven metres;

    (c) extend below the collar and each level a distance of not less than two metres; and

    (d) conform to the size of the shaft conveyance, allowing for necessary operating clearance.

77. (1) Subject to subsection (2), the manway in a shaft shall be separated from the hoisting or counterweight compartments by a partition which complies with subsection 76(2).

(2) Between levels, the partition may consist of metal of suitable weight and mesh to prevent,

    (a) a falling object from entering the manway; or

    (b) the intrusion of an object from the manway into the hoisting compartment.

(3) A safe passageway and standing room for a person outside the shaft shall be provided at all workings opening into a shaft and the manway shall be directly connected with such openings.

78. (1) Except when the hoisting compartment at a shaft station is securely closed off, a substantial gate shall be installed.

(2) The gate required by subsection (1) shall,

(a) be kept closed except when the shaft conveyance is being loaded or unloaded at the station;

(b) have a minimum of clearance beneath it; and

(c) be reinforced against impact of,

(i) a locomotive, train or car when rail tracks lead to the compartment, or

(ii) a motor vehicle when motor vehicles are used in the vicinity of the shaft.

79. Where a counterweight is used in a shaft, the counterweight compartment shall be enclosed except when the counterweight travels on guides.

80. During shaft-sinking operations, no work shall be done in any place in a shaft while a worker is working in another part of the shaft below such place unless the worker in the lower position is protected from the danger of falling material by a securely constructed covering extending over a sufficient portion of the shaft to afford complete protection.

81. Hooks used in connection with the suspension of any equipment or material in a shaft or raise or over a worker shall be choked or equipped with a safety latch.

82. When work or an examination is taking place in the compartment of a shaft or in that part of the headframe used in conjunction therewith,

(a) hoisting operations in that compartment, except for those necessary to perform the work or examination, shall be suspended;

(b) protection from accidental contact with any moving shaft conveyance or counterweight, or falling objects shall be provided for a worker performing the work or examination; and

(c) the power supply to all conveyor belts, gates and other devices that are located above a worker and that could cause material to flow into the shaft shall be locked and tagged in the safe position and the gates shall be mechanically secured in the closed position.

O. Reg. 571/92 s. 9

82.1 Before the commencement of work or of an examination below a loading pocket in a shaft, a competent person who is authorized by the employer to proceed, and who proceeds, below the loading pocket shall inspect it to ensure that the work or examination can proceed safely.

O. Reg. 583/91 s. 2

83. (1) This section applies when a raise is being developed and there are workers in the raise.

(2) A raise that is inclined at an angle greater than 50 degrees and is longer than 10 metres from the collar to the face shall be divided into at least two compartments, one of which shall be a ladderway.

(3) Subsection (2) does not apply where a raise climber is used.

(4) The ladderway shall be maintained within five metres of the face of the raise.

O. Reg. 272/97 s. 15

84. (1) If a worker may be endangered by the withdrawal, collapse, shifting or movement of bulk material such as rock, ore or other material in a stope, pass or chute or in a storage area, the employer shall ensure that written procedures for the precautions to be taken before, during and after removal of the material are established and followed.

(2) The written procedures required by subsection (1) shall address the following matters:

    1. The conditions under which workers are required to wear a fall arrest system.

    2. The communication of hazards to all persons who may be at risk.

    3. The identification of those locations that are not safe for workers to enter.

    4. The need to post warning signs that indicate the nature of the danger or hazard and the need to erect barriers to prevent inadvertent access to the area.

    5. Any additional protection to be provided to workers required to enter or work in the area.

(3) No worker shall be positioned so that when the worker is pulling a chute his or her access to an exit from the area may be blocked by an uncontrolled run of material, water or slime.

(4) A mechanical locking device shall be installed on overcut power operated chute gates, so that the gate may be locked in the open or closed position.

(5) A power-operated safety guard or gate shall be designed and installed to minimize hazards when the power fails.

O. Reg. 571/92 s. 10; 291/02 s. 3

85. Where the entrance or exit to a workplace in an underground mine cannot be used at all times, a second means of entrance or exit shall be provided.

86. A diamond drill hole in an underground mine shall at the time that drilling is discontinued or an intersection with the drill hole is made,

(a) be clearly marked at the collar and any points of intersection or breakthrough, with a single capital letter "H" that is,

(i) located within one metre of the collar or intersection, and

(ii) at least 300 millimetres by 300 millimetres in size;

(b) have the approach to the collar or to any intersection or breakthrough securely closed off or guarded,

(i) when mining is in progress towards the hole, and

(ii) when blasting is to be done within five metres of an intersection of the hole; and

(c) be shown on the plans of the mine.

O. Reg. 68/96 s. 2

87. (1) A workplace in an underground mine shall,

(a) be kept free from accumulations or flows of water which might endanger a worker in the area; and

(b) have a water removal and drainage system to remove excess or unwanted water from the mine to the surface through a pumping system or by other means.

(2) The water removal and drainage systems referred to in clause (1)(b) shall be maintained in good condition.

(3) A positive displacement water pump shall be equipped with a relief valve or system.

(4) Any drain hole in an underground mine shall be,

(a) clearly marked by signs that are visible, readable by workers and clearly distinguished from their surroundings; and

(b) identified on any drawings, plans and specifications relating to that area of the mine.

(5) An employer and supervisor shall take all reasonable precautions in the circumstances to do the following:

1. Prevent an accumulation or flow of water, either of which might endanger a worker.

2. Guard against an accumulation of water in a chute, raise or waste or ore pass where material in the chute, raise or waste or ore pass may block drainage.

3. Control an accumulation or flow of water in areas of a mine where an accumulation or flow of water is likely to be present.

(6) Where an accumulation of water is likely to be present, a borehole shall be drilled at least six metres ahead of the working face to protect against a sudden breakthrough of water.

(7) A drill or blast hole that is located in an area of the mine where an accumulation or flow of water is likely to be present shall be identified on any drawings, plans and specifications relating to that area of the mine.

(8) A drill or blast hole that could allow water to enter a chute, raise or waste or ore pass shall be filled or plugged to prevent water from entering the chute, raise or waste or ore pass.

(9) If, despite the requirements in subsections (1), (5), (6), and (8), an accumulation or flow of water that may endanger a worker occurs in an area of an underground mine,

(a) the employer shall ensure that the supervisor for that area is informed of the accumulation or flow of water;

(b) the employer shall ensure that all workers in that area are notified of the accumulation or flow of water;

(c) the employer shall ensure that the area is adequately barricaded to prevent access; and

(d) the employer and the supervisor shall not permit any worker to enter that area unless the purpose of the work directly relates to the management and removal of the water and all reasonable precautions in the circumstances have been taken for the protection of such workers.

O. Reg. 167/16, s. 9

87.1 (1) An owner of an underground mine shall, in consultation with the joint health and safety committee or health and safety representative, if any, develop and maintain a written water management program.

(2) The program shall include measures and procedures to,

(a) identify areas of the mine where water is likely to accumulate;

(b) control the volume of water that may enter the mine, either naturally or as a result of the mining process;

(c) prevent unwanted or uncontrolled flows of water in all areas of the mine;

(d) effectively and safely manage and remove water that poses a risk of injury to a worker; and

(e) maintain water removal and drainage systems and all of the components of such systems.

(3) A copy of the program shall be provided to the joint health and safety committee or health and safety representative, if any, and shall be kept readily available at the mine site.

(4) Subject to subsection (5), the program shall be reviewed at least annually.

(5) The program shall be reviewed as soon as possible following any significant alteration to the water removal or drainage system and if such a review is required, the next annual review required by subsection (4) shall be within one year of the date of the review under this subsection.

O. Reg. 167/16, s. 9

88. (1) Where earth, clay, sand or gravel is being removed from a surface mine by means of powered equipment,

(a) the working face shall be sloped at the angle of repose; or

(b) the vertical height of the working face shall not be more than 1.5 metres above the maximum reach of the equipment.

(2) Where earth, clay, sand or gravel is being removed from a surface mine by means other than powered equipment,

(a) the working face shall be sloped at its angle of repose; or

(b) the vertical height of the working face shall not be more than three metres.

(3) No undercutting of the working face shall be permitted or done.

(4) Except when mining operations are being actively pursued, benches and walls shall be sloped to less than the angle of repose.

89. Where metallic or non-metallic rock is being removed from a surface mine,

(a) the vertical height of the working face shall not be more than twenty-five metres; and

(b) except where a tunnelling method is used to remove the rock, no undercutting of the working face shall be permitted or done.

90. Every surface mine,

(a) that is dangerous because of its condition or depth shall be securely fenced or otherwise guarded against inadvertent access; and

(b) shall have a safe travelway leading from the working level to the surface.

91. (1) Trees and other vegetation and unconsolidated materials such as earth, clay, sand or gravel and rocks within two metres of the rim of a surface mine and likely to endanger any person shall be removed.

(2) Overburden beyond two metres of the rim of a surface mine shall be sloped to an angle less than its natural angle of repose.

92. (1) Subject to subsection (2),

(a) where earth, clay, sand or gravel is being removed from a surface mine no mining operations shall be carried on within a distance from the property boundary of half the total depth of the surface mine and earth, clay, sand or gravel that sloughs from within this distance shall not be removed; and

(b) where metallic or non-metallic rock is being removed from a surface mine, no mining operations shall be carried on within a distance of six metres from the property boundary.

(2) Adjoining owners may, by agreement in writing, waive the provisions of subsection (1).

93. (1) In a surface mine where metallic or non-metallic rock is being removed, no work shall be carried on,

(a) near a working face following a blast; or

(b) near a face on which mining operations have been discontinued for a period of more than seven days,

until a supervisor examines the face for any potential or actual hazard to the health or safety of a worker.

(2) When a surface mine is worked in benches, loose rock on berms or benches shall not be permitted to accumulate so that a worker on a lower bench is endangered.

94. A worker barring loose rock, or scaling or cleaning on a face of a surface mine shall use and wear a fall-arrest system.

95. (1) An employer shall provide personal protective equipment, shield, appliance or other device where a worker is exposed to the hazard of being burned by molten materials.

(2) An employer shall require a worker to use or wear personal protective equipment, shield, appliance or other device provided by the employer where the worker is exposed to the hazard of being burned by molten material.

96. (1) Precautions shall be taken to prevent contact between molten material and damp surfaces, rusty surfaces, cold surfaces, moisture, water, or other substance where such contact may cause an explosion, and where such explosion may endanger a worker.

(2) Precautions shall be taken to prevent spillage of molten material from a ladle, slag pot or similar vessel where such spillage may endanger a worker.

(3) A ladle, slag pot or similar vessel shall be examined immediately before use and, if found to be defective or contaminated by a substance which may cause an explosion, shall not be used for molten material.

97. (1) Where a worker is required to go above the casting floor level of an operating blast furnace, the worker shall notify a supervisor.

(2) When a worker is above the casting floor level of an operating blast furnace, a second competent worker shall,

    (a) be in attendance to render assistance to the worker; and

    (b) remain in a safe place until such assistance is required.

98. A suitable working platform shall be provided on the bustle pipe of a blast furnace.

99. A system of communication shall be provided and maintained between all dangerous workplaces of a blast furnace, including the blast furnace top structure and,

    (a) the cast house;

    (b) the skip operator's room; and

    (c) every other place where workers are continuously on duty.

100. A ladderway or stairway shall be provided from the foundation to the top of a blast furnace.

101. When a blast furnace is hanging, no worker or other person shall be, or be permitted to be, above the level of the casting floor.

102. Where a major repair is to be carried out at the top structure of a blast furnace that requires the blast furnace to be shut down,

(a) the blast furnace area shall be cleared of workers other than those carrying out the repair; and

(b) the major repair area shall be tested for gases likely to endanger the health and safety of a worker before the repair is commenced and during the carrying out of the repair.

Part V — Haulage

103. (1) When in use, a motor vehicle running on rails, other than a standard gauge railroad, shall,

(a) be in safe working condition;

(b) have brakes that will stop and hold the vehicle or cars under full load condition;

(c) have headlights;

(d) have an audible warning system that shall be sounded,

(i) where a worker may be endangered by the movement of the vehicle and cars, if any, or

(ii) whenever the vehicle and cars, if any, are about to move underground or in an enclosed building;

(e) be provided, where possible, with a fixed seat for the operator;

(f) have a guard that will provide protection for the operator from collision or other impact;

(g) when manually operated, be operated only when the operator is in the proper position at the controls;

(h) when operated by remote control or by an automated system, be so arranged that in the event of failure of part of the control or system, the vehicle and cars, if any, will be brought to a stop immediately;

(i) when left unattended, have,

(i) the control placed in the parking position, and

(ii) the brake fully applied; and

(j) when electrically powered by storage battery or from a trolley wire, have control levers so arranged that they cannot be moved accidentally or removed when the power is on.

(2) Except for clauses (1)(a) and (g), this section does not apply to a motor vehicle propelled by compressed air.

O. Reg. 34/14 s. 4

104. Except when used in areas where natural or artificial lighting provides good visibility, a train shall have a tail light on the last car.

105. (1) When in use, a motor vehicle, other than a motor vehicle running on rails, shall,

(a) be in safe working condition;

(b) have brakes which will stop and hold the vehicle under full load conditions on all operating grades, slopes and ramps;

(c) subject to subsection (2), have headlights and tail lights;

(d) where,

(i) equipped with power-assisted steering, and

(ii) operated on surface,

have a system such that in the event of a failure of the power-assistance element of the system, the vehicle can be held on course by the steering until the vehicle is stopped;

(e) except for purposes of training or testing, be operated only by a competent operator;

(f) be provided, where practical, with a fixed seat for the operator;

(g) when manually operated, be operated only when the operator is in a proper position at the controls;

(h) where operated by remote control or by an automated system, be so arranged that in the event of the failure of part of the control or system, the vehicle will be brought to a stop;

(i) when left unattended, have,

(i) the control placed in the parking position, and

(ii) the brake fully applied;

(j) except when used in an underground mine, have lights or reflectors that show the width of the vehicle to a person in the path of its direction of travel;

(k) where the motor vehicle is to be operated in reverse and the operator or another person may be endangered thereby, be operated only when another worker is stationed to direct and warn the operator of any hazard to himself or another person; and

(l) be equipped with a type BC fire extinguisher.

(2) In areas where natural or artificial lighting is adequate to enable the operator to have a clear view of the areas and persons, a motor vehicle may be operated without headlights or tail lights.

(3) Where the view of the operator of a motor vehicle in the direction of its travel is limited,

> (a) the vehicle shall be equipped with an audible or visible alarm that will warn a worker who may be endangered by the movement of the vehicle; and

> (b) the alarm shall be activated before the vehicle is put in motion.

(4) Except when the motor vehicle is used in an underground mine, a rear view mirror shall be installed in the motor vehicle where the view to the rear of the operator is limited.

(5) The windshield and windows of the cab of a motor vehicle shall consist of safety glass and be maintained so as to provide unobstructed vision.

(6) Where motor vehicles that restrict the view of the operator because of size or design are used, procedures to control and govern the movement of such vehicles, other vehicles and pedestrians shall be established.

(7) A procedure for the testing, maintenance and inspection of each motor vehicle shall be adopted and the procedure shall,

> (a) schedule the testing of brakes, steering, lighting and other safety components prior to initial use of the motor vehicle for the shift;

> (b) schedule the motor vehicle for routine inspections and maintenance, taking into consideration the recommendations of the manufacturer and the conditions of use;

> (c) itemize the tests to be carried out following maintenance work and before first use of the motor vehicle;

> (d) provide a record of the testing, maintenance, inspection and testing that has been carried out; and

> (e) provide for the testing, maintenance and inspections to be performed by competent persons.

(8) Except for clauses (1)(a), (e) and (g), this section does not apply to a motor vehicle propelled by compressed air.

O. Reg. 31/04 s. 4; 84/07 s. 5

105.1 (1) An employer at a mine shall, in consultation with the joint health and safety committee or health and safety representative, if any, develop and maintain a written traffic management program.

(2) The program shall include measures and procedures to,

666

(a) prevent collisions, of motor vehicles, that may endanger the health and safety of workers by addressing hazards relating to reduced or impeded visibility of motor vehicle operators; and

(b) protect the health and safety of workers and pedestrians who may be endangered by the movement of a motor vehicle.

(3) A copy of the program shall be provided to the joint health and safety committee or health and safety representative, if any, and shall be kept readily available at the mine site.

(4) The program shall be reviewed at least annually.

O. Reg. 167/16, s. 10

106. (1) Where a motor vehicle is operated on a grade or ramp, traffic control procedures shall be established including provision for the control of emergency situations.

(2) Where a motor vehicle is disabled or parked in the travelled portion of a roadway, a warning to approaching traffic shall be provided by,

(a) flashing lights;

(b) flares;

(c) reflectors;

(d) lamps; or

(e) a worker suitably equipped to be readily seen, who directs traffic approaching the area.

(3) In the operation of a motor vehicle in an underground mine,

(a) the maximum load to be carried;

(b) the maximum speed; and

(c) the gear selection to be used,

on a grade or ramp shall be established and made known to the operator by the supervisor in charge of the mine.

(4) Before ascending or descending a main access ramp in an underground mine, the operator of a motor vehicle shall,

(a) fully engage the forward-reverse lever;

(b) select the proper gear; and

(c) test the service and emergency brakes.

107. (1) A motor vehicle in a mine shall be equipped with wheel chocks that comply with Society of Automotive Engineers Standard SAE J348 JUN90 "Wheel Chocks".

854

(2) The wheel chocks shall be used to block movement whenever the vehicle,

    (a) is left unattended on a slope; or

    (b) is being maintained or repaired.

(3) Despite subsections (1) and (2), an alternative means of blocking the movement of a motor vehicle in the circumstances described in subsection (2) may be used if the alternative means is developed by the employer in consultation with the joint health and safety committee or the health and safety representative, if any, for the workplace.

(4) [Repealed O. Reg. 296/11, s. 8.]

(5) [Repealed O. Reg. 296/11, s. 8.]

O. Reg. 31/04 s. 5; 296/11 s. 8

107.1(1) An employer shall establish written procedures for work performed on tire and wheel assemblies.

(2) The procedures shall address the hazards associated with the work in a manner that protects the health and safety of workers.

(3) Where possible, the procedures shall require the use of devices to protect the health and safety of workers.

(4) An employer shall train workers in work performed on tire and wheel assemblies and in the procedures established under subsection (1) before the workers perform that kind of work.

O. Reg. 296/11 s. 9

108. (1) When the controls are left unattended,

    (a) the bucket of a front-end loader, backhoe or other excavating machine;

    (b) the blade of a bulldozer; or

    (c) the load of a fork-lift truck, mobile crane or other hoisting machine, shall be in the lowered position or adequately supported.

(2) Any part of a motor vehicle or other equipment, including the blade or bucket or dump box of a truck, the lowering of which may endanger a worker, shall be blocked so as to prevent its lowering accidentally.

(3) A crane or other hoisting machine shall be operated in such a way that no part of its load will pass over a person, other than a worker receiving the load and a worker receiving a load shall, so far as is practicable, position himself or herself so that the load does not pass over him or her.

(4) A shovel, backhoe or similar excavating machine shall be operated in such a way that no part of its load will pass over a person.

(5) An operator who may be endangered during the loading of a vehicle shall vacate the vehicle.

109. (1) A rail track switch in which a person's foot may become trapped shall have guards at the frog and switch point to effectively protect against the hazard.

(2) Rail tracks in use shall be in good working condition.

110. (1) Vehicles being used for transporting workers shall,

    (a) be provided with suitable seats or other facilities;

    (b) be limited to a maximum number of passengers, which number shall be posted in or on the vehicle; and

    (c) when enclosed, be equipped with an emergency exit.

(2) Whenever the face of an inclined tunnel in a mine exceeds a vertical depth of 100 metres without intermediate access to the tunnel from a shaft with hoisting facilities for people, a vehicle shall be provided to transport workers down and up the tunnel.

(3) Except for training purposes, only those workers authorized and required to handle the load shall ride on a vehicle that is transporting,

    (a) explosives;

    (b) steel or timber; or

    (c) heavy equipment.

(4) The load on a vehicle shall be adequately secured.

(5) A worker may carry personal hand tools or equipment on a vehicle when,

    (a) the vehicle is not crowded;

    (b) the tools and equipment are properly protected by guards; or

    (c) the tools or equipment are isolated in separate containers.

(6) The maximum speed and the maximum load of a vehicle transporting workers or a service vehicle shall be posted on the vehicle in a conspicuous location.

111. (1) Subject to subsections (2) and (3), a haulageway for a motor vehicle running on rails in an underground mine shall have,

854

(a) a walkway on one side so that there is at least 0.6 metres clearance between the sides of the haulageway and the motor vehicle running on rails or the train; or

(b) safety stations as prescribed in section 114 at intervals not exceeding thirty metres.

(2) Despite subsection (1), a haulageway that is used by a motor vehicle running on rails that travels more than 12 kilometres per hour shall have a walkway on one side of at least 1.2 metres between the side of the haulageway and the motor vehicle and pedestrian traffic shall be restricted to designated periods during which no motor vehicle running on rails shall be used in the haulageway.

(3) Where pedestrian traffic is permitted in a haulageway to which subsection (2) applies and the walkway is less than two metres in width, safety stations, as prescribed in section 114, shall be provided at intervals not exceeding thirty metres.

(4) Subsection (1) does not apply to any haulageway that was driven prior to the 1st day of October, 1979 if the haulageway complies with section 245 of *The Mining Act*, being chapter 274 of the Revised Statutes of Ontario, 1970, as it read on the 30th day of September, 1979.

112. A haulageway used by motor vehicles, other than motor vehicles running on rails, shall,

(a) except where pedestrian traffic is effectively prevented, be at least 1.5 metres wider than the maximum width of a motor vehicle using the haulageway; and

(b) where it is regularly used by pedestrians and it is less than two metres wider than the maximum width of a motor vehicle using the haulageway, have safety stations as prescribed in section 114 at intervals not exceeding thirty metres.

113. Except in an underground mine with a low clearance roof in which equipment designed to be operated herein is used, a haulageway used by a motor vehicle shall have sufficient clearance below the roof, support or overhead installations to enable the operator of a motor vehicle to sit erect at all times.

114. (1) A safety station shall consist of a recess in the wall of a haulageway that shall be,

(a) at least,

        (i) 0.6 metre in depth, in addition to any existing clearance between the vehicle and the wall,
        (ii) two metres in height, and
        (iii) 1.5 metres in length;
    (b) plainly marked; and
    (c) clean and free of obstruction.

(2) Clause (1)(a) does not apply to a safety station in a haulageway that was driven before the 1st day of October, 1979, if the safety station complies with section 245 of *The Mining Act*, being chapter 274 of the Revised Statutes of Ontario, 1970, as it read on the 30th day of September, 1979.

115. (1) Subject to subsection (2), where the view of rail traffic at railway tracks on surface is obstructed in one or both directions, guardrails shall be placed at the approach to the tracks.

(2) Subsection (1) does not apply where,
    (a) restricted clearance makes guardrails impracticable; and
    (b) a warning signal which automatically functions at the approach of a locomotive or train gives a warning signal that is both audible and visible; or
    (c) a worker is guarding the approach.

116. (1) Haulage roads on surface shall be designed, constructed and maintained to,
    (a) minimize hazards from the slipping or skidding of vehicles;
    (b) enable vehicles to pass each other safely; and
    (c) avoid steep grades wherever practical.

(2) The open side of a ramp haulage road in a surface mine shall be provided with a suitable protective barrier.

(3) Every haulage road on surface shall be kept in good repair.

                          O. Reg. 693/92 s. 1

117. (1) Where, on surface at a mine or mining plant, the clearance between the sides of a train or motor vehicle and the wall of a building or other structure is less than 500 millimetres, the location shall be plainly marked showing the danger.

(2) Where the operator may be exposed to overhead hazards on surface at a mine or mining plant, a cab, screen or other adequate overhead protection shall be provided on,

854

    (a) a power-driven crane, shovel or similar machine;

    (b) a fork-lift truck; and

    (c) a front-end loader or other excavating machine.

118. (1) When material is dumped from a vehicle that is occupied by a person, the dump point shall include features designed to prevent the vehicle from going over a bank, over a bench or into a raise or other open hole.

(2) In an underground mine, the features referred to in subsection (1) shall not include the use of a ridge of material.

O. Reg. 272/97 s. 16; 291/02 s. 4

119. (1) In this section and in sections 119.1 and 119.2,

"emergency brake system" means a secondary brake system that is used for stopping a motor vehicle in the event of any single failure in the service brake system.

(2) The brake system on a motor vehicle that is operated on a grade, slope or ramp shall be able to perform the individual system function requirements of,

    (a) a service brake system;

    (b) an emergency brake system; and

    (c) a parking brake system.

(3) The capacity of retarders shall not be considered in determining the capacity of the brake systems described in clauses (2)(a), (b) and (c).

(4) Any combination of the system function requirements described in clauses (2)(a), (b) and (c) may be performed by a single brake system.

(5) Each brake system shall be capable of being,

    (a) tested independently; and

    (b) readily applied by a worker seated in the driver's seat.

(6) A service brake system may consist of a hydraulic pump motor drive system.

(7) The service brake system and the emergency brake system shall be capable of safely stopping the motor vehicle while it is being operated,

    (a) on the maximum grade, slope or ramp in its area of operation;

    (b) at its maximum authorized speed; and

    (c) with its maximum authorized load.

(8) The parking brake system shall be capable of holding the motor vehicle stationary, with its maximum authorized load, on the maximum grade, slope or ramp in its area of operation.

(9) The emergency brake system shall be set up so that, whether the brake is applied automatically or manually, a deliberate act is required to release it.

(10) Before a motor vehicle is first put into service, the following systems shall be tested by a competent person for proper operation:
1. Service brake.
2. Emergency brake.
3. Parking brake.
4. Steering.
5. Warning devices.
6. Lighting.

(11) A record of the tests described in subsection (10),
    (a) shall be signed by the competent person who performed the tests;
    (b) shall be kept as long as the motor vehicle is in service; and
    (c) shall be made available to the joint health and safety committee or the health and safety representative, if any.
        O. Reg. 571/92 s. 11; 693/92 s. 2; 272/97 s. 17; 84/07 s. 6

119.1(1) The brake system of a rubber-tired motor vehicle that was first used in an underground mine after September 1, 1992 shall meet the requirements of CSA Standard M424.3-M-90, "Braking Performance—Rubber-Tired, Self-Propelled Underground Mining Machines".

(2) The brake system of a rubber-tired motor vehicle that was first used in a surface mine on or after October 1, 2007 shall meet the requirements of CSA Standard M3450-03, "Braking systems of rubber-tired machines—Performance requirements and test procedures".

(3) The brake system of a tracked motor vehicle that was first used in an underground mine or in a surface mine on or after October 1, 2007 shall meet the requirements of ISO 10265: 1998 "Earth-moving machinery—Crawler Machines—Performance requirements and test procedures for braking systems".

(4) [Repealed O. Reg. 84/07, s. 6.]

(5) [Repealed O. Reg. 84/07, s. 6.]

(6) [Repealed O. Reg. 84/07, s. 6.]

O. Reg. 272/97 s. 18; 84/07 s. 6; 34/14 s. 5

119.2(1) This section applies with respect to motor vehicles, other than vehicles operating on rails, that are,

  (a) first put into service by the employer on or after August 16, 1997; and

  (b) equipped with a stored energy brake system that uses a pneumatic system or a full hydraulic system to apply the service brakes.

(2) For the purposes of this section, the critical level of pressure is the level of pressure in a motor vehicle's stored energy brake system, torque converter or transmission below which the manufacturer has determined that the vehicle is unsafe to operate.

(3) A motor vehicle that is operated on the surface must be equipped with a device that warns the operator that the vehicle's stored energy brake system is approaching the critical level of pressure, so that the vehicle can be safely stopped.

(4) A motor vehicle that is operated underground must be equipped with,

  (a) a device that automatically applies the emergency brake system and stops the vehicle before the vehicle's stored energy brake system, torque converter or transmission pressure reaches the critical level of pressure; and

  (b) a device that warns the operator that the emergency brake system is about to be applied.

O. Reg. 84/07 s. 6

120. (1) A service garage, service bay or fuelling station in an underground mine shall,

  (a) be designed and protected to prevent inadvertent entry of an uncontrolled motor vehicle;

  (b) be located so that in the event of a fire or explosion in the garage, bay or station there will be a minimum effect on working areas of the mine or on underground installations including shafts, magazines, refuge stations, transformer installations and other installations;

  (c) have a concrete floor without service pits in the floor; and

  (d) be equipped with a system to contain spills of oil and grease.

(2) A service garage or service bay shall be of sufficient size to,

(a) accommodate the longest and widest vehicle that will use the garage or bay; and

(b) provide clearance around the vehicles being serviced to permit the safe performance of all work in the garage or bay.

(2.1) A vehicle shall be serviced where practicable at a service garage or a service bay.

(2.2) Only one vehicle may be serviced at a service bay at any one time.

(3) A fuelling station shall be established before a heading has advanced 250 metres from the ramp or shaft unless vehicles can be fuelled at another fuelling station.

(4) A fuelling station shall be separate from a service garage.

(5) A vehicle shall be fuelled where practicable at a fuelling station.

(6) Where a mobile fuelling supply tank is used the tank shall be clearly labelled with "No Smoking" signs.

(7) Any spillage of oil or fuel shall be taken up at once, deposited in a fireproof receptacle and removed from the mine without undue delay.

(8) All fuel handling, transfer, storage and dispensing systems in an underground mine shall be designed according to good engineering standards and subjected to a fire safety hazard review before first use.

(9) The employer, in consultaion with the joint health and safety committee or the health and safety representative, if any, shall develop appropriate safeguards and procedures for the safe handling, transfer, storage and dispensing of fuel in an underground mine.

O. Reg. 291/02 s. 5; 31/04 s. 6

Part VI — Explosives

121. Where an explosive is used in an underground mine,

(a) it shall be of Fume Class 1 rating as established by the Explosives Regulatory Division of Natural Resources Canada; or

(b) if other than of Fume Class 1 rating, a procedure shall be prepared and adopted by the supervisor in charge of the mine, to ensure that no worker is exposed to fumes that endanger his health or safety.

O. Reg. 34/14 s. 6

122. (1) Explosives stored or kept at a mine or mining plant shall be used only for authorized purposes and if not so used, returned to the supplier of the explosives.

(2) Smoking shall not be permitted and no fire or naked flame shall be taken,

    (a) within a magazine; or

    (b) within eight metres of any explosive.

(3) Any careless act of placing or handling explosive shall be,

    (a) reported forthwith to a supervisor in charge of the workplace;

    (b) investigated by the supervisor; and

    (c) reported forthwith by the supervisor to an inspector.

(4) No explosive shall be used to blast or break up ore, salamander or other material where, by reason of its heated condition, there is any danger or risk of premature explosion of the charge.

(5) When operations at a mine are discontinued or suspended for more than three months, all explosives shall be disposed of in a safe manner.

O. Reg. 272/97 s. 19; 236/99 s. 4

123. (1) Explosives kept or stored on the surface shall be kept or stored in compliance with the *Explosives Act* (Canada) and the regulations under that Act.

(2) If a magazine is required, it shall be,

    (a) constructed in conformity with "Storage Standards for Industrial Explosives, May 2001" published by the Explosives Regulatory Division of Natural Resources Canada;

    (b) located in conformity with the User Manual, Quantity Distance Tables published by the Explosives Regulatory Division of Natural Resources Canada; and

    (c) protected by a fire break.

(3) A copy of the notification given to an inspector under subsection (4) shall be posted in the magazine.

(4) An operator of a surface magazine or a mine using explosives shall give written notice to an inspector and the joint health and safety committee or health and safety representative, if any,

    (a) before a magazine is or explosives are first used; and

    (b) annually after the magazine is or explosives are first used.

(5) The notice shall contain the following information:

1. The address of the operator.

2. Specific location of any surface magazine or a statement that the explosives are delivered directly to the underground workings.

3. The identification number provided by the Ministry.

4. The nature and quantity of explosives to be stored or delivered.

5. A statement that any surface magazine conforms to this Regulation and to the *Explosives Act* (Canada) and the regulations under that Act.

O. Reg. 272/97 s. 20; 84/07 s. 7; 34/14 s. 7; 265/15 s. 5

124. [Revoked O. Reg. 272/97, s. 20.]

125. (1) Explosives in an underground mine shall be kept or stored in a magazine but where less than 160 kilograms of explosives are kept or stored in the underground mine they may be kept or stored in suitable storage containers at locations removed from drilling and blasting operations.

(2) If the necessary supply of explosives exceeds five working days, the explosives shall be kept or stored in a magazine.

(3) The employer shall ensure that suitable plans and specifications showing the following are prepared, kept up to date and kept readily available at the mine site:

1. The design and location of magazines.

2. The design and location of explosive storage areas other than magazines.

3. The maximum explosive storage capacity at each magazine and at each explosive storage area that is not a magazine.

(4) The employer shall, in consultation with the joint health and safety committee or the health and safety representative, if any, establish a procedure for,

(a) identifying the location of explosives that are being kept in explosive storage areas other than magazines; and

(b) ensuring that they are recorded under subsection (3).

(5) Despite subsection (1), where long hole blasts or similar blasting operations are being carried on in an underground mine, such quantities of explosives as can be loaded in a twenty-four hour period together with an amount that may be necessary to maintain that supply may be kept in a suitable storage area that is not a magazine.

O. Reg. 272/97 s. 21; 84/07 s. 8

126. (1) A magazine, storage container or explosive storage area referred to in section 125 that is in an underground mine shall be,

    (a) located at least 60 metres from,

        (i) the main access into or from a mine,

        (ii) key mechanical and electrical installations that remain in service during a mine emergency,

        (iii) areas of refuge or other areas where workers may congregate, and

        (iv) storage areas for fuels or other potential sources of fire;

    (b) located and designed to protect explosives from vehicle impact or vehicle fires; and

    (c) conspicuously marked by a "DANGER EXPLOSIVES" sign.

(2) Subclause (1)(a)(i) does not apply during the initial stages of exploration and development of a mine.

O. Reg. 272/97 s. 22; 84/07 s. 9

127. (1) A magazine in an underground mine shall be under the control and direction of a competent person.

(2) A weekly inspection of a magazine in an underground mine shall be carried out by a competent person who shall report in writing to a supervisor,

    (a) as to the condition of the magazine and the explosives; and

    (b) as to the quantities of explosives stored therein.

(3) Reports required by subsection (2) shall be kept for a period of at least six months.

O. Reg. 272/97 s. 23

128. (1) Every magazine and every storage container shall be kept clean, dry and free from grit at all times.

(2) The floors and shelves of a magazine where nitroglycerine explosives are kept shall be treated with a neutralizing agent to remove any traces of nitroglycerine.

(3) When explosive is issued or removed from a magazine, the explosive longest in the magazine, if not defective, shall be used first.

(4) Explosive that is damaged shall be disposed of in accordance with the following rules:

1. The employer shall establish, in consultation with the joint health and safety committee or the health and safety representative, if any, a procedure for safely disposing of damaged explosive.

2. The procedure shall state,

  i. what maximum accumulation of damaged explosive is permitted in a magazine or storage place before the damaged explosive must be disposed of,

  ii. what means of disposal shall be used, and

  iii. how frequently damaged explosive shall be disposed of, in addition to disposal under subparagraph i.

(5) Explosive that is unattended shall not be left in or about any working place but shall be returned to storage.

(6) Detonators and capped fuse shall be stored in a separate, suitable, closed storage container located at least eight metres from any other explosive.

(7) Explosive shall not be heated above the ambient temperature of its storage place.

O. Reg. 31/04 s. 7

129. (1) All electrical equipment and wiring installed or used in a magazine or in an explosives storage area that is not a magazine,

  (a) shall comply with,

    (i) the requirements of the Ontario Electrical Safety Code with respect to Class II, Division 2 hazardous locations, and

    (ii) "Storage Standards for Industrial Explosives, May 2001", published by the Explosives Regulatory Division of the Department of Natural Resources (Canada); and

  (b) shall be protected against lightning strikes and electrical surges.

(2) The reference to the Ontario Electrical Safety Code in subclause (1)(a)(i) is to the 23rd edition (2002), published by the Electrical Safety Authority.

O. Reg. 84/07 s. 10

854

130. [Revoked O. Reg. 272/97, s. 24.]

131. A motor vehicle when transporting explosives on the surface at a mine or plant shall,

  (a) be kept in sound mechanical condition;

(b) be conspicuously marked by red signals or flags easily visible from front, rear and both sides;

(c) have all metal parts that could come in contact with containers of explosives covered with wood, tarpaulin or similar non-sparking material;

(d) not be used to transport other goods or materials at the same time as explosives are being transported;

(e) be equipped with a type BC fire extinguisher;

(f) not be loaded in excess of its rated carrying capacity;

(g) have explosives secured or fastened so as to prevent any part of the load from becoming dislodged;

(h) transport detonators with other explosives only if the detonators are,

(i) in a suitable container in a separated compartment, and

(ii) 5,000 or less in number;

(i) be attended at all times; and

(j) carry only those persons necessary for handling explosives.

132. (1) Except as provided for in subsection (2), explosives transported at a mine shall,

(a) be in suitable closed containers;

(b) have detonators, blasting caps and capped fuses kept separate from other explosives.

(2) Capped fuses may be transported with other explosives without placing them in a container if they are kept separate from other explosives.

(3) Primers shall be made up,

(a) as near to their point of use as is practicable; and

(b) only in sufficient numbers for the immediate work in hand.

(4) Made-up primers shall be transported,

(a) in separate, suitable, closed containers conspicuously marked with the words "DANGER—EXPLOSIVES"; and

(b) in a separate vehicle or conveyance from other explosives.

133. (1) When transporting explosives in a shaft conveyance the worker in charge of the operation shall give or cause to be given notice of the operation to the deck attendant and hoist operator.

(2) No worker shall,

(a) place in;

(b) have while in; or

(c) take out of, a shaft conveyance any explosive except under the immediate supervision of a worker authorized for the purpose by a supervisor.

(3) No other material shall be transported with explosives in a shaft conveyance.

134. (1) Explosives shall be removed without delay from,
    (a) near the shaft collar;
    (b) other entrances to the underground workings; and
    (c) a shaft station.

(2) Explosives underground shall be transported from a magazine to other magazines or place of use,
    (a) without delay; and
    (b) by the most direct and safe route.

135. (1) Where explosives are transported underground by means of a motor vehicle or a train,
    (a) the speed of the vehicle or train shall not exceed ten kilometres per hour;
    (b) specific arrangements for the right of way of the vehicle or train shall be made before the vehicle or train is put in motion;
    (c) the explosives shall be in suitable containers;
    (d) the requirements prescribed by section 131, except clauses (b) and (c), apply with necessary modifications; and
    (e) the motor vehicle or train shall display and operate a flashing red light whenever explosives are being transported.

(2) Where explosives are transported underground by means of a train,
    (a) the motor vehicle running on rails shall be maintained on the forward end of the train unless a worker walks in front of the train to effectively guard it;
    (b) a car carrying explosives shall be separated from the motor vehicle by an empty car or spacer of equivalent length;
    (c) no explosives shall be carried on the motor vehicle; and
    (d) every car carrying explosives shall be protected from contact with a trolley wire.

O. Reg. 84/07 s. 11

135.0.1(1) In this section,

854

"bulk explosives vehicle" means a motor vehicle that is used to transport bulk explosives underground.

(2) A bulk explosives vehicle shall be provided with a fire suppression system that uses sprinklers, foam or some other suitable means of suppressing fire.

(3) Whenever a bulk explosives vehicle is not in use, it shall be parked in a place designated as a safe parking place by the employer.

(4) A place may be designated as a safe parking place for the purpose of subsection (3) only if it is located at least 60 metres away from,

(a) the main access into or from a mine;

(b) key mechanical and electrical installations that remain in service during a mine emergency;

(c) areas of refuge or other areas where workers may congregate; and

(d) storage areas for fuel or other potential sources of fire.

(5) Plans and specifications showing the design and location of the designated safe parking places shall be kept readily available at the mine site.

(6) Subsections (3), (4) and (5) do not apply during the initial stages of development and exploration in a mine.

(7) A bulk explosives vehicle shall not be parked in a magazine.

(8) The employer shall, in consultation with the joint health and safety committee or health and safety representative, if any, develop a procedure for the regular power washing of bulk explosives vehicles.

(9) Without limiting the generality of subsection (8), the procedure shall specify how often washing is to take place.

(10) Before a bulk explosives vehicle enters a garage for maintenance,

(a) all explosives, detonators and explosive residue shall be removed from the vehicle; and

(b) the vehicle shall undergo power washing in accordance with the procedure mentioned in subsection (8).

O. Reg. 84/07 s. 12

135.1(1) This section applies when detonators are being transported otherwise than by means of a motor vehicle or train.

(2) Detonators shall be carried in containers that are,

(a) suitable for the purpose; and

(b) clearly marked as containing detonators.

(3) The employer shall make containers that comply with subsection (2) readily available to workers.

O. Reg. 31/04 s. 8

136. (1) Subject to subsection (2), before drilling or sampling is commenced in a working place in an underground mine, the exposed faces shall be,

(a) washed with water; and

(b) carefully examined for misfires, cut-off holes and remnants of blasted holes.

(1.1) Despite subsection (1), if it is not practical to examine for misfires, cut-off holes or remnants of blasted holes, drilling or sampling may be done using methods and procedures described in subsection (7).

(2) In gypsum mines and in mines containing soluble minerals and salts where water cannot be used,

(a) an alternate method shall be used for checking each face for misfires and cut-off holes; and

(b) a written procedure detailing the method shall be prepared and followed.

(3) Where practical, after the face has been checked all remnants of blasted holes shall be conspicuously marked by,

(a) a ring of contrasting paint or crayon; and

(b) inserting sticks or plugs into the holes for lifter remnants in a heading.

(4) In a mine, no drilling or sampling shall be done within 160 millimetres of the bottom remnant, or an intact portion, of a hole that has been charged and blasted unless the methods and procedures described in subsection (7) are followed.

(5) In a mine, no drilling or sampling shall be done within one metre of any hole containing explosives unless the methods and procedures described in subsection (7) are followed.

(6) No development heading shall be abandoned or work therein discontinued until,

(a) the material broken at the firing of the last round has been cleared from the face; and

854

(b) the whole face of the heading examined for explosives in misfires or remnants of holes.

(7) For the purposes of subsections (1.1), (4), (5) and 139(3), drilling or sampling may be done using methods and procedures developed by the employer and the workers involved in the task and agreed upon by the joint health and safety committee or the health and safety representative for the workplace,

(a) if the employer gives notice, at least ten days before implementing the methods and procedures, to each union representing workers at the workplace;

(b) if the employer ensures that workers are trained in the methods and procedures; and

(c) if the employer publicizes the methods and procedures and displays them in the workplace before implementing them.

(8) Subject to subsection (9), if a frozen cut is encountered, drilling may be done only if it is done in accordance with methods and procedures developed by the employer and the workers involved in the task and agreed on by the joint health and safety committee or the health and safety representative for the workplace.

(9) No collaring may be done within 300 millimetres of a frozen cut or if there is a possibility of intersecting any portion of a frozen cut, unless the methods and procedures of subsection (7) are used.

(10) In subsections (8) and (9),

"frozen cut" means the first holes blasted in a development round that do not break the rock as intended, but rather shatter and cover over with no explosives visible.

O. Reg. 584/91 s. 3; 171/92 s. 1; 272/97 s. 25; 291/02 s. 6

137. (1) Subject to subsection (2), any explosive charge that has misfired or cut off,

(a) shall not be withdrawn; and

(b) shall be blasted without undue delay at a safe and suitable time.

(2) Except for nitroglycerine sensitized explosives, water soluble explosives may be washed out of the hole by means of an approved device.

(3) A worker who fires any charges shall, where possible, count the number of shots and if a misfire is suspected shall report it to his or her supervisor.

(4) Where at the end of a shift a misfire is suspected, or if a misfire has been reblasted and it has not been checked, such fact, together with the location of the hole, shall be recorded in the shift log.

(5) An employer shall establish and maintain a system for reporting to the employer and recording misfired explosives.

(6) An employer shall use reasonable efforts to determine the cause of a misfiring of an explosive and shall take such preventive action as is reasonable in the circumstances.

O. Reg. 583/91 s. 3

138. (1) Drill holes shall be of sufficient size to admit the free insertion to the bottom of the hole of a cartridge of explosive or a loading hose.

(2) Before charging a hole with explosives, the hole shall be cleared of all obstructions.

139. (1) Drilling or undercutting and charging operations at a mine shall not be carried on simultaneously,

(a) on the same face above or below each other; or

(b) within eight metres horizontal distance of each other.

(2) In charging holes for blasting, no iron or steel tool or rod shall be used.

(3) No iron or steel tool shall be used in a hole that contains an explosive unless the methods and procedures described in subsection 136(7) are followed.

(4) Drill holes charged with explosives shall,

(a) have a properly prepared detonating agent placed in the charge;

(b) be fired in their proper sequence;

(c) when loaded in one loading operation, be blasted in one blasting operation, except where a procedure for doing otherwise has been prepared and adopted by the supervisor in charge of the mine; and

(d) when primed, not be left unfired, but shall be fired at the time for blasting required by the supervisor in charge of the mine.

(5) Except when blasting electrically or when only one charge is to be fired, there shall be at least two workers present at a blasting operation.

(6) Except when the blasting operation is conducted on surface in daylight or under artificial light, every worker engaged in a blasting operation shall carry a light.

(7) Where detonating cord is used,

(a) loading shall be completed in all holes; and

(b) all equipment not required for the loading operation shall be removed from the blast site before,

    (i) cords are interconnected between holes or attached to trunk line circuits, and

    (ii) delay devices or initiating detonators are attached to trunk line circuits.

O. Reg. 171/92 s. 2

140. Where holes are loaded pneumatically with explosives,

(a) only semi-conductive hoses manufactured for such purpose shall be used;

(b) pneumatic loading equipment shall not be grounded directly to pipes, rails or other similar continuous conductors; and

(c) where electrical blasting caps are used,

    (i) no plastic or other non-conducting liners shall be used, and

    (ii) the cap shall not be placed in the hole until the pneumatic loading of the hole has been completed, except where a procedure for doing otherwise has been prepared and adopted by the supervisor in charge of the mine.

141. (1) Before blasting,

(a) a worker shall be stationed at each entrance or approach and instructed to prevent inadvertent access to every place where,

    (i) the blasting is to take place,

    (ii) the safety of persons may be endangered by the blasting, or

    (iii) a diamond drill hole intersection may connect with the blast;

(b) the worker doing the blasting shall,

    (i) give or cause to be given due warning in every direction by shouting "FIRE", or give warning of a primary blast by siren where the extent of the operation makes shouting ineffective,

    (ii) satisfy himself or herself that all persons have left the workplace or the vicinity except those required to assist him or her in blasting and guarding, and

    (iii) take necessary precautions to ensure that all areas of the mine to be affected by the blasting operation are vacated.

(2) In surface mines,

(a) the warning of a primary blast by siren shall be given,

(i) at least five minutes prior to the blast, and

(ii) again at one minute prior to the blast;

(b) where it is necessary to stop traffic on a public road,

(i) signs shall be posted to warn traffic of the impending blast, and

(ii) guards equipped with suitable red flags shall be posted to stop traffic prior to the blast;

(c) an all-clear signal shall be sounded after all danger from the blast has passed; and

(d) where a worker is required near the blast area, blasting shelters shall be provided.

(3) If there is a disagreement as to the time of setting off blasts in contiguous or adjacent claims or mines, the owners or employers shall jointly determine times at which blasting operations may be performed.

O. Reg. 272/97 s. 26

141.1(1) In a blasting operation, the worker who makes the final connections necessary to allow the blast to be fired is the only person who is permitted to fire the blast.

(2) Despite subsection (1), if it is not possible for the same worker to perform both functions in a particular blasting operation,

(a) the employer, in consultation with the joint health and safety committee, or the health and safety representative, if any, shall establish safe procedures for performing the blasting operation;

(b) the employer shall ensure that the safe procedures are set out in writing and that the workers involved in the blasting operation are informed about the safe procedures before performing any tasks in connection with the blasting operation; and

(c) every worker involved in the blasting operation shall follow the safe procedures.

O. Reg. 31/04 s. 9

142. (1) A competent person shall be appointed to design each primary blast at a surface mine.

(2) The design of a primary blast shall include,

(a) the number of holes to be blasted;

(b) the burden, spacing and depth of each hole;

(c) the type and weight of explosives;

(d) the length of stemming and firing delay detonator used for each hole;

(e) the firing sequencing of the holes;

(f) the weight of explosives used per estimated tonne broken; and

(g) the guarding procedures necessary to protect the safety of workers.

(3) A competent person shall ensure that each blast is carried out according to the design.

(4) The person in charge of a blast shall keep a record of the design data for the blast and shall sign it.

O. Reg. 571/92 s. 13; 60/94 s. 5

143. (1) The person in charge of a primary blast at a surface mine shall keep a record setting out,

(a) the date, time and location of the blast;

(b) the wind direction and velocity at the time of the blast; and

(c) the atmospheric conditions at the time of the blast.

(2) The person shall sign the record.

O. Reg. 571/92 s. 13

144. A vehicle shall not be driven, parked or located over or under loaded holes except where a procedure for doing so has been prepared and adopted by the supervisor in charge of the mine.

145. Before a connection is made between two underground working places,

(a) an examination shall be made of the workings towards which the active working is advancing, where practicable, to determine that the work can proceed in a safe manner; and

(b) when the distance between the working places is less than,

(i) twice the length of the longest drill steel used, or

(ii) a minimum of five metres from the bottom of the longest hole,

all approaches to both working places shall be guarded before blasting.

146. Where safety fuse is used in any blasting operation,

(a) no fuse shorter than one metre shall be used;

(b) no fuse shall be lighted at a point closer than one metre from the capped end;

(c) capped fuses shall be supplied in standard lengths;

(d) the uncapped ends of fuses of the same length shall be identified;

(e) where more than one charge is to be fired, each fuse connected to a charge shall be lighted by a suitable and reliable timing device;

(f) where igniter cord is used, no connections shall be made to fuses until all holes are loaded; and

(g) where igniter cord is used, a worker shall, immediately after the ignition of the igniter cord, leave the workplace which will be affected by the blasting operation.

147. **(1)** A worker performing blasting operations shall not permit any person to return to a workplace affected by the operation until the applicable minimum period of time described in this section has elapsed.

(2) If safety fuses are used, the minimum period is,

(a) 10 minutes after the worker performing the blasting operations hears the last shot, if a single fuse is used; or

(b) 30 minutes after the worker performing the blasting operations hears the last shot, if more than one fuse is used.

(3) In the case of a misfire when at least one safety fuse is used, the minimum period is 30 minutes after a reblast.

(4) If detonators that are not safety fuses are used, the minimum period is,

(a) the time for the blasting contaminants to clear, if one detonator is used; or

(b) 10 minutes after the worker performing the blasting operations hears the last shot, if more than one detonator is used.

(5) If the worker performing the blasting operations does not hear a shot when using detonators that are not safety fuses, the minimum period is 10 minutes after,

(a) the worker has disconnected the lead wires from the power source and short-circuited them and locked the blasting switch, if any, in the open position; or

(b) the worker has disconnected the initiation device from the blasting system.

O. Reg. 779/94 s. 3

147.1(1) No worker shall use safety fuses in an underground mine to blast hang-ups in chutes, passes, millholes or drawpoints.

(2) No worker shall insert a safety fuse into a drilled hole in an underground mine.

O. Reg. 60/94 s. 6; 779/94 s. 4; 68/96 s. 3

148. (1) Blasting in a shaft, shaft station or other workings being driven from a shaft shall be done by means of electricity,

(a) after the first three metres of advance has been made in the shaft; and

(b) until such time as the permanent timbers and ladders have reached the level upon which blasting is being done.

(2) Blasting in a raise, where free escape is not readily available, shall be done by means of electricity from a safe location outside the raise.

149. When blasting by means of electricity,

(a) where balanced circuits are required, each circuit shall be tested before firing with a suitable galvanometer or other similar suitable instrument;

(b) where electric blasting caps are used,

(i) the protective shunt shall not be removed from the leg wire until connections are made,

(ii) the leg wire shall not be shortened to less than one metre,

(iii) the firing cables leading to the face or faces shall be short-circuited while the leads from the blasting caps are being connected to each other and to the firing cables,

(iv) the short-circuit prescribed in subclause (iii) shall not be removed until all workers have left the workplaces to be affected by the blasting operation, and

(v) the short-circuit prescribed in subclause (iii) shall be located so that a premature explosion will be harmless to the worker opening the short-circuit; and

(c) before any person returns to the workplace affected by the blasting operation,

(i) the firing cables shall be removed from the battery, blasting machine or other source of electricity and shall be short-circuited, and

(ii) the blasting switch shall be locked in the open position.

150. (1) Where the source of current is a portable direct current battery or blasting machine the firing cables or wires shall,

(a) not be connected to the source of current until,

(i) the workplace to be affected by the blasting operation has been cleared of persons, and

(ii) immediately prior to blasting; and

(b) be disconnected and short-circuited immediately after the blast has been fired.

(2) A blasting machine shall,

(a) be of a type and design specifically manufactured for the purpose;

(b) be kept in good mechanical and electrical condition;

(c) be tested regularly using methods specified by the manufacturer;

(d) be tested before any blasts that may require the maximum output of the machine;

(e) be clearly marked with the capacity of the machine; and

(f) not be used in excess of its rated capacity.

(3) A portable direct current battery shall be of a type and design specifically manufactured for the purpose.

O. Reg. 265/15 s. 6

151. Blasting cables and blasting wires shall,

(a) be distinguished from other cables and wires;

(b) be used for blasting purposes only; and

(c) not come into contact with,

(i) detonating cords,

(ii) power, lighting or communication cables, or

(iii) pipes, rails or other continuous metal grounded circuits.

152. (1) When a common electrical source is used to fire blasts in more than one workplace provision shall be made for,

(a) the continued shorting of the blasting cables;

(b) a three-way switch for each individual blasting circuit which can be locked in either the shorted or closed position to provide for,

(i) shorting of the circuit,

(ii) energizing the circuit, and

(iii) testing of the circuit;

(c) identification of blasting cables and switches; and

(d) a written blasting procedure setting forth,

(i) the method of connecting the blasting wires to the electrical supply,

(ii) the evacuation of all workers from the area of the blast, and

(iii) the method of testing the system to ensure that the proper connections have been made.

(2) The written blasting procedure shall be followed.

153. (1) Circuits from a source other than from a portable hand-operated device used for blasting shall be,

(a) from an isolated, ungrounded power source; and

(b) used for blasting only.

(2) A blasting device shall,

(a) be designed for the purpose;

(b) be kept in good mechanical and electrical condition;

(c) be constructed so that it automatically opens the circuit by gravity to short-circuit the blasting conductor;

(d) have the live side enclosed within a fixed box with a door,

(i) that can be locked and unlocked only by the worker doing the blasting, and

(ii) so arranged that the door cannot be closed unless the contacts of the firing circuit are in the opened and shorted position; and

(e) where the power source exceeds 300 volts be electromagnetically operated.

154. (1) No electrical blasting circuit connections shall be made on or near to surface or in or near to a shaft during an electrical storm in the vicinity.

(2) If electrical blasting operations are undertaken, an employer shall ensure that the operations are conducted so as to ensure that there is no interference from any system, device or controller capable of producing radio frequencies or radiating electromagnetic energy.

(3) An employer shall ensure that a system, device or controller that is capable of producing radio frequencies or radiating electromagnetic energy does not set off detonators.

(4) Subsections (1), (2) and (3) do not apply with respect to blasting operations that use,

(a) a combination blast initiation device and high-frequency radio signal that have been designed for that purpose; or

(b) a high-frequency impulse-initiated detonator.

O. Reg. 272/97 s. 27

Part VII — Electrical

155. (1) If electrical equipment is installed or modified, the work shall be done in accordance with good electrical practices.

(2) The electrical equipment shall be operated in accordance with good electrical practices.

(3) The quantity and trade name of any liquid insulant or coolant when in excess of one litre shall be shown on the name plate of the electrical equipment in which it is contained.

(4) A person who is competent in the electrical trade shall be appointed to be in charge of electrical equipment.

O. Reg. 486/99 s. 3

156. If the employer intends to make a major electrical installation or a major alteration to existing electrical installation, the employer shall give the joint health and safety committee or the health and safety representative, if any, written notice of that fact.

O. Reg. 272/97 s. 28; 486/99 s. 4

157. [Revoked O. Reg. 486/99, s. 5.]

158. (1) This section applies with respect to all work done on electrical equipment or conductors, other than work that is performed on energized equipment as permitted under subsection 159(1).

(2) An employer shall establish a written locking and tagging program to protect the health and safety of workers.

(3) Before doing any work to which this section applies, a worker shall verify, by testing, that the following requirements have been complied with:

    1. All hazardous sources of electrical supply to the electrical equipment or conductors are isolated.

    2. Subject to subsection (4), all energy isolating devices are properly engaged, locked and tagged in accordance with subsection (5).

    3. All hazardous stored electrical energy is discharged.

(4) A locking device required under paragraph 2 of subsection (3) may be omitted where,

    (a) the locking device in itself creates a hazard due to the design of the energy isolating device; or

854

(b) circuit breakers or fuses for voltages of less than 150 volts to ground are not equipped with a means of locking.

(5) A tag required under paragraph 2 of subsection (3) shall,

(a) be secured to prevent its inadvertent removal;

(b) state the reason the energy isolating devices are locked and tagged;

(c) show the name of the person responsible for locking and tagging the energy isolating devices;

(d) show the date on which the energy isolating devices were locked and tagged;

(e) be made of nonconducting materials; and

(f) be installed so as not to become energized.

O. Reg. 265/15 s. 7

159. (1) Electrical work shall not be performed on energized equipment except where,

(a) de-energizing the equipment,

(i) would increase or introduce additional hazards, or

(ii) is not feasible due to equipment design or operational limitations;

(b) equipment and personal protective devices and clothing that are appropriate to the work are provided and used;

(c) the employer has established written measures and procedures for energized work to protect the health and safety of workers;

(d) no hazard from explosive or flammable materials exists; and

(e) all necessary precautions to work safely are taken.

(2) Except as provided for in subsection (1), no object shall be brought closer than the distance specified in Column 2 of the following Table to an exposed, energized overhead electric supply line of the voltage specified in Column 1:

TABLE

Column 1	Column 2	
Voltage of Powerline	**Minimum Distance**	
300 to 150,000 volts	3	metres
150,000 to 250,000 volts	4.5	metres

Over 250,000 volts	6	metres

(3) Precautions to guard workers against injury by moving or energized parts shall be taken before maintenance, repair or adjustment work is performed on a machine that is energized.

(4) When located less than 1.5 metres measured in a horizontal plane or 2.5 metres measured in a vertical plane from a walkway or landing, any bare part of electrical equipment energized in excess of 150 volts DC or 50 volts AC shall be guarded.

(5) Machines that have movable or extendable booms must not be operated in close proximity to energized electrical supply lines unless,

(a) they are operated in accordance with subsection (1); or

(b) the operator of the machine has been authorized to perform such work; and

(i) there is a clearance between any part of the machine and the energized line that is more than the greater of,

(A) one-half the maximum horizontal reach of the boom, or

(B) the distance determined under subsection (2),

(ii) the lines are disconnected and grounded;

(iii) the machine is a railroad crane operating on railroad tracks and the supply line is energized to less than 750 volts direct current, or

(iv) the supply lines are guarded against contact by any part of the machine or its load.

(6) Subsections (2) to (5) apply only with respect to electrical lines installed on the surface and electrical equipment used on the surface.

O. Reg. 60/94 s. 7; 486/99 s. 6; 265/15 s. 8

160. [Repealed O. Reg. 265/15, s. 9.]

161. A portable ladder which has metal or metal reinforced side rails shall not be,

(a) stored in or about electrical equipment having energized and exposed parts; or

(b) used about electrical equipment having energized exposed parts.

162. [Revoked O. Reg. 486/99, s. 7.]

854

163. (1) The supports for electrical equipment and the compartments in which it is installed shall be of such material and arranged in such a manner as to reduce the potential for a fire to a minimum.

(2) No flammable material shall be stored or placed in the same compartment as electrical equipment.

(3) Lamps or heating units shall be installed and protected so as to prevent the heat generated from causing a fire.

(4) A fire extinguishing device shall be provided in each area where electrical equipment creates a fire hazard.

(5) The fire extinguishing device prescribed in subsection (4) shall be,

    (a) of a type approved for use on electrical fires;

    (b) of a size recommended for the size and type of equipment;

    (c) located convenient to an exit from the area; and

    (d) maintained in condition for immediate use.

164. (1) Electrical mobile equipment operating at more than 300 volts to ground shall be supplied by a system wherein,

    (a) the neutral is grounded through a current limiting device in such a manner as to limit the possible rise of ground fault potential to a maximum of 100 volts to ground; and

    (b) ground fault protection is provided.

(2) Electrical mobile equipment operating at more than 300 volts to ground must have a fail safe circuit that prevents the supply of electricity to the equipment when the conductivity of the ground return circuit is not continuous.

(3) In this section,

"electrical mobile equipment" means equipment which, during its operating cycle, is required to move along the ground while energized and which receives its current through a trailing cable and includes drills which connect to an electrical power supply.

O. Reg. 272/97 s. 29

165. [Revoked O. Reg. 486/99, s. 7.]

166. [Revoked O. Reg. 486/99, s. 7.]

167. [Repealed O. Reg. 167/16, s. 11.]

168. [Revoked O. Reg. 486/99, s. 7.]

169. [Revoked O. Reg. 486/99, s. 7.]

170. (1) The power supply to a motor shall not be run through the enclosure of the controller for another motor.

(2) [Repealed O. Reg. 296/11, s. 10.]

O. Reg. 296/11 s. 10

171. [Revoked O. Reg. 486/99, s. 7.]

172. (1) [Revoked O. Reg. 486/99, s. 8.]

(2) [Revoked O. Reg. 486/99, s. 8.]

(3) Switchboards shall be made of materials that are noncombustible.

O. Reg. 486/99 s. 8; 167/16, s. 1

173. [Revoked O. Reg. 486/99, s. 9.]

174. (1) This section applies with respect to equipment that can be operated or moved by remote control using a system, device or controller that produces radio frequencies or radiates electromagnetic energy.

(2) An employer shall ensure that the system, device or controller is not capable of operating or moving equipment unless it is intended to do so.

(3) An employer shall ensure that only one system, device or controller can be used at a time to operate or move the equipment.

(4) The system, device or controller must be equipped with a device that enables the operator to stop the equipment in an emergency.

(5) The employer shall establish procedures to ensure that the operator and other workers are in a safe location when the equipment is being operated or moved.

O. Reg. 272/97 s. 31

175. (1) Cables supplying electrical power from surface to underground shall be fed through a circuit breaker located on surface.

(2) [Revoked O. Reg. 486/99, s. 10.]

(3) [Revoked O. Reg. 486/99, s. 10.]

(4) [Revoked O. Reg. 486/99, s. 10.]

(5) [Revoked O. Reg. 486/99, s. 10.]

(6) [Revoked O. Reg. 486/99, s. 10.]

O. Reg. 486/99 s. 10

176. [Revoked O. Reg. 486/99, s. 11.]

177. [Revoked O. Reg. 486/99, s. 11.]

178. [Revoked O. Reg. 486/99, s. 11.]

179. The voltage of any underground lighting circuit shall not exceed 150 volts to ground except in circuits using direct current where the voltage shall not exceed 300 volts to ground.

180. (1) In an underground mine with trolley lines installed underground, the owner shall ensure that the requirements of this section are met.

(2) The lines must be designed to have a nominal voltage less than 1,200 volts and operated with a nominal voltage less than 1,200 volts.

(3) The lines must have ground fault protection if they use alternating current.

(4) If the operating voltage of the lines is greater than 300 volts, there must be,

    (a) lighting or reflectors sufficient to indicate the location of the lines; and

    (b) warning signs installed at points of access to the lines.

(5) Trolley lines of the bare conductor type must be protected by guards made of insulating materials.

(6) The guards must extend at least 75 millimetres below the lowest point of the trolley line and must be placed not more than 150 millimetres from the nearest line.

(7) Despite subsection (5), guards are not required on trolley lines of the bare conductor type that use alternating current if the trolley lines have ground fault protection that prevents a worker from being exposed to an electrical current sufficient to cause ventricular fibrillation.

(8) Trolley lines of the bare conductor type that are installed underground after December 31, 1994 must be located,

    (a) at least 2.4 metres above grade, if the operating voltage is 300 volts or less;

    (b) at least 2.7 metres above grade, if the operating voltage is more than 300 volts but less than 750 volts;

    (c) at least 4.0 metres above grade, if the operating voltage is 750 volts or more.

(9) Trolley lines of the busway conductor type that are installed underground after December 31, 1994 must be located at least 2.4 metres above grade.

(10) Subsections (8) and (9) do not apply with respect to trolley lines that are an extension of a trolley line system,

    (a) if the system is installed before January 1, 1995;

    (b) if the system has an operating voltage of 300 volts or less; and

    (c) if the extension is located at least 1.8 metres above grade.

(11) The employer shall establish written procedures to require all necessary precautions to work safely around trolley lines.

O. Reg. 779/94 s. 5; 486/99 s. 12

Part VIII — Mechanical

181. (1) An explosive actuated fastening tool shall,

    (a) when in storage be,

        (i) accessible only to an authorized worker, and

        (ii) kept in a locked container; and

    (b) be of a type and design that conforms to CAN3-Z166-M85 Series "Powder Actuated Fastening Tools".

(1.1) An explosive actuated tool or explosive actuated system shall be,

    (a) maintained in proper condition; and

    (b) serviced in accordance with the manufacturer's recommendations.

(2) The shells for use with an explosive actuated tool or explosive actuated system shall,

    (a) be identified as to size and strength;

    (b) be kept in containers which contain only one size and strength;

    (c) not be left unattended except when in storage; and

    (d) when in storage be,

        (i) accessible only to an authorized worker, and

        (ii) kept in a locked container.

(3) The operator of an explosive actuated tool or explosive actuated system shall,

    (a) be a competent person;

    (b) operate the tool or system in accordance with the manufacturer's instructions; and

854

(c) ensure before use that the barrel is clean and free from any obstruction.

O. Reg. 584/91 s. 4; 174/01 s. 4; 34/14 s. 8

181.1 Sections 182, 183, 183.1 and 183.2 apply only with respect to work done in underground mines.

O. Reg. 296/11 s. 11

182. (1) Diesel-powered equipment shall not be used in an underground mine unless a form obtained from the Ministry has been completed with information relating to the equipment and the completed form is readily available at the mine site.

(1.1) [Repealed O. Reg. 296/11, s. 12(1).]

(2) Non-rail-bound diesel-powered equipment that is first used in an underground mine after June 1, 1995 must meet the requirements set out in CSA Standard M424.2-M90 "Non-Rail-Bound Diesel-Powered Machines for use in Non-Gassy Underground Mines" excluding the requirements in sections 4.5, 5.3 and 5.4 of that document.

(3) Gasoline or another volatile fuel shall not be used in the starting mechanism of diesel-powered equipment.

(4) The fuel used in a diesel engine shall conform to the Canadian General Standards Board National Standard of Canada CAN/CGSB 3.517-2013 "Diesel Fuel".

(5) An employer shall ensure that the undiluted exhaust emissions from diesel-powered equipment contain less than 600 parts per million by volume of carbon monoxide.

(6) [Repealed O. Reg. 296/11, s. 12(2).]

O. Reg. 779/94 s. 6; 272/97 s. 32; 174/01 s. 5; 296/11 s. 12; 34/14 s. 9; 265/15 s. 10

183. (1) An employer shall maintain a chart of procedures for the use and operation of diesel-powered equipment that sets out,
(a) the actual volume of air flowing in the underground haulageways and workings where the equipment is operating; and
(b) the total ventilation requirements for the equipment when it is operating normally in a single continuous course of air.

(2) The employer shall post the chart in a location where it is clearly visible and readily accessible to the operator of the diesel-powered equipment.

O. Reg. 583/91 s. 4; 779/94 s. 7

183.1(1) The employer shall ensure that a flow of air that meets the requirements of this section is provided to the workplace where diesel-powered equipment is operating.

(2) The flow of air must be provided by a mechanical ventilation system.

(3) The flow of air must be at least 0.06 cubic metres per second for each kilowatt of power of the diesel-powered equipment operating in the workplace.

(4) The flow of air must reduce the concentration of toxic substances in diesel exhaust emissions to prevent exposure of a worker to a level in excess of the limits prescribed under section 4 of Regulation 833 of the Revised Regulations of Ontario, 1990 (*Control of Exposure to Biological or Chemical Agents*) made under the Act.

(5) The flow of air must,

    (a) reduce the time-weighted average exposure of a worker to total carbon to not more than 0.4 milligrams per cubic metre of air; or

    (b) reduce the time-weighted average exposure of a worker to elemental carbon, multiplied by 1.3, to not more than 0.4 milligrams per cubic metre of air.

O. Reg. 779/94 s. 7; 496/09 s. 1; 296/11 s. 13; 265/15 s. 11

183.2(1) The employer shall ensure that tests are conducted to determine the following matters at the times indicated:

    1. The volume of air flowing in underground haulageways and workings where diesel-powered equipment is operating. This must be tested at least weekly.

    2. The carbon monoxide content of the undiluted exhaust discharging from diesel-powered equipment to the atmosphere. This must be tested,

        i. immediately after repairs are made to the engine or the exhaust system or both, and

        ii. at routine intervals for maintenance as the manufacturer recommends or, if there is no such recommendation, at least once a month.

    3. The volume of air flow and the carbon monoxide, nitrogen dioxide, formaldehyde or total carbon contents of the atmosphere. These must be tested at the request of a worker.

854

(1.1) The employer shall ensure that the following rules are complied with in relation to tests conducted under paragraph 2 of subsection (1):

    1. The employer shall develop and implement testing measures and procedures in consultation with the joint health and safety committee or health and safety representative, if any, and shall take into consideration any recommendations made by the committee or representative.

    2. Each individual piece of equipment must be tested under consistent conditions so that results from different tests can be compared.

    3. Testing must be carried out, as far as is practical, on equipment under full load.

(2) The employer shall provide the results of every test conducted under subsection (1) to the joint health and safety committee or the health and safety representative, if any, for the workplace.

(3) The employer shall record the results of every test conducted under paragraphs 2 and 3 of subsection (1) and shall maintain the record.

(4) If a test indicates that a worker has been exposed to diesel exhaust emissions containing a toxic substance in excess of the level set out in subsection 183.1(4) or clause 183.1(5)(a) and if this test result could not have been predicted in the circumstances, the employer shall,

    (a) investigate the cause and take remedial action, if possible, to prevent a recurrence of the situation;

    (b) notify the worker and the joint health and safety committee or the health and safety representative, if any, for the workplace; and

    (c) conduct tests of the emissions until the results show that the concentration of the toxic substance does not exceed the level set out in subsection 183.1(4) or clause 183.1(5)(a).

O. Reg. 779/94 s. 7; 296/11 s. 14

184. The exhaust of an internal combustion engine which is temporarily or permanently installed within a building on surface shall be,

    (a) conducted to a point outside the building; and

    (b) prevented from,

        (i) re-entering the building,

        (ii) entering the intake of any compressor,

        (iii) contaminating the atmosphere of another building, and

        (iv) contaminating mine workings.

184.1 A temporary attachment used to connect a lifting device to its load or to anchor it,

    (a) shall be appropriate for the use;

    (b) shall be designed and installed in accordance with safety factors recognized by good engineering practice; and

    (c) shall be used in a manner that minimizes shock loading.

O. Reg. 571/92 s. 14

185. (1) In this section,

"machine" includes a prime mover, transmission equipment and thing.

(2) A machine that has an exposed moving part that may endanger the safety of any person shall be fenced or guarded unless its position, construction or attachment provides equivalent protection.

(3) A machine shall be provided with a device that automatically prevents a worker operating it from coming in contact with any moving part.

(4) The travelway of a counterweight shall be guarded or located to prevent,

    (a) inadvertent entry thereto by a worker; and

    (b) injury to a worker should the counterweight become detached from its fastenings.

(5) Clearance sufficient for the safety of a worker shall be provided from the path of travel of,

    (a) a load carried by a machine;

    (b) a moving part of a machine; and

    (c) another machine.

(6) A revolving set screw, bolt, key or other similar device shall be recessed, encased or guarded to prevent inadvertent contact by a worker.

(7) If any work is being done on a machine,

    (a) the moving parts shall be stopped;

    (b) any hydraulic, pneumatic or gravity stored energy shall be dissipated or contained;

    (c) energy isolating devices shall be installed if the machine is not already equipped with them; and

    (d) all energy isolating devices shall be properly engaged, locked and tagged.

(8) Before doing any work to which subsection (7) applies, a worker shall verify, by testing, that the requirements of that subsection have been complied with.

(9) A tag required by clause (7)(d) shall,

(a) be secured to prevent its accidental removal;

(b) state the reason the energy isolating devices are locked and tagged;

(c) show the name of the person responsible for locking and tagging the energy isolating devices; and

(d) show the date on which the energy isolating devices were locked and tagged.

(10) If it is not practical to comply with subsection (7) work to which that subsection applies may be done if, while it is being done, barriers, shields or other effective precautions are used or taken for the safety of a worker.

O. Reg. 31/04 s. 10; 265/15, s. 12

186. (1) Subject to subsection (10), no elevator shall be put into service without a professional engineer giving written statement to the owner setting out,

(a) the location of the elevator;

(b) the maximum loading of number of persons and material that may be carried by the elevator when it is installed, maintained and operated in compliance with this Regulation;

(c) that the elevator is designed and manufactured in accordance with appropriate engineering standards and installed where it is to be put into service in compliance with good engineering practice.

(2) Subsection (1) does not apply to an elevator that is operated for testing purposes.

(3) The owner shall ensure that a copy of the statement is posted at the mine site in a location readily visible to workers and that a copy is given to the joint health and safety committee or the health and safety representative, if any.

(4) The maximum loading set out in the statement required under subsection (1) or a permit referred to in subsection (10) shall not be exceeded.

(5) An elevator installation shall meet the following standard:

1. If it was installed before October 15, 1991, CSA Standard B44-1975, "Safety Code for Elevators, Dumbwaiters, Escalators and Moving Walks".

2. If it was installed on or after October 15, 1991 and before April 23, 1999, CSA Standard B44-M90, "Safety Code for Elevators".

3. If it was installed on or after April 23, 1999 and before October 1, 2007, CSA Standard B44-94, "Safety Code for Elevators".

4. If it was installed on or after October 1, 2007, CSA Standard B44-00, "Safety Code for Elevators".

(6) Each component that may affect the safe operation of an elevator shall be examined and tested by a competent person before an elevator is initially used and thereafter at intervals not exceeding one month.

(7) A log book shall be kept in which the date, findings and name of the competent persons performing the examinations and tests prescribed in subsection (6) shall be recorded.

(8) In addition to the standards required to be met under subsection (5), an elevator shall,

(a) have a safe means of access to the machinery room which access shall be located outside the hoistway;

(b) not have hoisting or balance ropes that are spliced;

(c) have the entry to the machinery room restricted to authorized persons;

(d) have a means by which a person stranded in an elevator can alarm persons outside the elevator when the elevator is operated on automatic control; and

(e) have its controls and machine parts protected against physical damage, moisture, dust or extreme temperatures.

(9) The machinery room of the elevator shall be kept clean and contain only those materials required for the elevator.

(10) Subsections (1) and (3) do not apply to an elevator being operated under a permit issued by the Ministry of Labour before August 16, 1997. O. Reg. 779/94 s. 8; 272/97 s. 33; 236/99 s. 5; 84/07 s. 13; 34/14 s. 10

187. A dumbwaiter, escalator or moving walk shall meet the following standard:

1. If it was installed before April 1, 1994, CSA Standard B44-1975, "Safety Code for Elevators, Dumbwaiters, Escalators and Moving Walks".

2. If it was installed on or after April 1, 1994 and before April 23, 1999, CSA Standard B44-M90, "Safety Code for Elevators".

3. If it was installed on or after April 23, 1999 and before October 1, 2007, CSA Standard B44-94, "Safety Code for Elevators".

4. If it was installed on or after October 1, 2007, CSA Standard B44-00, "Safety Code for Elevators".

O. Reg. 60/94 s. 8; 236/99 s. 6; 84/07 s. 14; 34/14 s. 11

188. [Repealed O. Reg. 167/16, s. 11.]

189. (1) No worker shall be raised or lowered or be permitted to be raised or lowered by any hoist, derrick, crane or similar device unless,

(a) such device is examined and tested by a competent person before being used to raise or lower the worker;

(b) a safe procedure for raising or lowering the worker is established in accordance with subsection (2) and is used; and

(c) there is a device by which the hoist operator and the worker being raised or lowered can exchange movement signals except where the worker being transported is visible at all times to the hoist operator.

(2) The procedure must be jointly developed by the employer and the joint health and safety committee or health and safety representative, if any, for the workplace.

O. Reg. 571/92, s. 15; 60/94 s. 9

190. A worker using a bosun's chair, suspended scaffold or mobile staging shall be protected by a fall arrest system as prescribed by section 14 if the worker may fall more than three metres from the chair, scaffold or staging.

191. No elevator, dumbwaiter, escalator, moving walk or manlift shall be used when a component, which may affect its safe operation, is defective.

192. (1) A lifting device shall be,

(a) designed to safety factors recognized by good engineering practice;

(b) installed in accordance with such design criteria;

(c) provided with overwind protection if power operated; and

(d) provided with an identification plate.

(2) The maximum load that a lifting device may carry, based on its design criteria, shall be established by its designer.

(3) A notice showing the maximum load established under subsection (2) shall be posted in a location visible to the operator of the device.

(4) Except during testing, the maximum load established under subsection (2) shall not be exceeded.

(5) Each component that may affect the safe operation of a lifting device shall be examined and tested by a competent person before initial use and thereafter at intervals not exceeding one year.

(6) The dates, findings and names of the competent persons performing the examinations and tests prescribed in subsection (5) shall be recorded and the records shall be kept available for inspection.

(7) Where a combination of lifting devices is used simultaneously, the work shall be supervised by a competent person.

O. Reg. 34/14 s. 12

193. (1) A grinder shall be assembled and adjusted in accordance with the manufacturer's specifications.

(2) The maximum speed at which a grinding wheel may be operated shall be indicated on the grinding wheel or in a manner by which the speed may be readily ascertained.

(3) A grinding wheel shall be,
    (a) enclosed by a protective hood except for the area at the workrest;
    (b) stored where it will not be damaged by impact, extreme heat and cold;
    (c) stopped when the grinder or workrest is being adjusted; and
    (d) not operated in excess of the manufacturer's recommended maximum speed.

(4) The operator of a grinder shall wear eye protection.

(5) The workrest of a grinder shall be mounted above the centre line of the grinding wheel not more than three millimetres from the wheel.

(6) An air operated grinder shall have a governor to prevent its operation in excess of the rated speed of the grinding wheel.

(7) The governor required by subsection (6) shall be inspected regularly and maintained in proper operation.

194. (1) A person directing workers who perform welding, burning or cutting operations shall be a competent person.

854

(2) Every worker who as part of his or her work performs welding, burning or cutting operations shall be a competent person.

(3) Protection for workers to protect them against injury from fumes, radiation and electric arcs produced during welding, burning or cutting operations shall be provided and used.

(4) A device to extinguish a fire that may be caused by heat or cuttings produced during welding, burning or cutting shall be provided with each oxygen-acetylene unit.

(5) The device required by subsection (4) shall,

    (a) have a capacity for extinguishing a fire that is equal to or greater than a minimum Underwriters' Laboratories of Canada classification of 1A 10B; and

    (b) be suitable for class A and B fires.

(6) Equipment for welding, burning or cutting shall be protected against physical damage and from damage by heat, fire and sparks.

(7) No gas welding, burning or cutting equipment shall be used unless it is free from defects, leaks, oil and grease.

(8) Acetylene cylinders shall be placed in an upright position for at least thirty minutes before use.

(9) The valve protection cover or cap of an oxygen or acetylene cylinder shall be secured in place when the cylinder is not in use and, in the case of a threaded cover or cap, the cover or cap shall be secured at least hand-tight.

(10) The valves of oxygen and acetylene cylinders shall be closed when,

    (a) a job is completed;

    (b) the oxygen and acetylene cylinders are on portable units and unattended underground; and

    (c) the oxygen and acetylene cylinders are transported.

(11) The regulators and manifolds of oxygen and acetylene cylinders shall be disconnected when the cylinders are being transported underground.

(12) Unless procedures for safe use have been established by a supervisor in charge of the workplace, a charged gas system installed for welding, burning or cutting shall not be used for any other purpose.

(13) An insulated conductor of adequate size shall be used to carry the welding current back to an electric welder unless another safe return path has been provided.

(14) No welding, cutting, burning or soldering shall be done on a container in which an explosive or flammable substance has been stored unless the substance,

(a) has been completely removed; or

(b) has been made non-flammable or non-explosive.

(15) No explosive or flammable substance shall be put in a container on which welding, burning, cutting or brazing has been done until the container has cooled sufficiently to prevent ignition of the substance.

(16) A second worker who is a competent person shall attend oxygen and acetylene control devices when oxygen and acetylene cylinders are set up in,

(a) a position not readily available to the worker performing cutting, welding or burning operations; and

(b) a shaft conveyance while a worker is welding, burning or cutting on or from the conveyance.

195. (1) A multi-girder top-running electric overhead travelling crane for general use shall meet the standards set out in CSA Standard B167-1964, "General Purpose Electric Overhead Travelling Cranes".

(2) An electric overhead travelling crane for steel mill service shall meet the standards set out in the Association of Iron and Steel Engineers Standard No. 6, "Specifications for Electric Overhead Travelling Cranes for Steel Mill Service".

(3) Every production crane shall be provided with,

(a) a safe means of access and egress for the operator from the cab mounted on the crane when,

(i) it is parked in the normal parking position, and

(ii) it cannot be brought to the normal parking position; and

(b) an alarm by which the operator can warn persons that may be endangered by the moving crane.

(4) Every service crane shall be provided with an alarm that is visible to persons in the vicinity of the crane when the crane is operating on,

(a) pendant control, where the worker controlling the crane does not have a clear view of the area in which the crane is operating; or

854

(b) radio frequency control.

(5) Every production crane and every service crane shall be provided with,

(a) protection against inadvertent operation by radio frequencies when equipped with radio frequency controls;

(b) an operating procedure to guard against colliding with other cranes on the same track;

(c) a load rating plate, stating the maximum load that can be carried by the crane, posted on the crane;

(d) a means by which the power conductors for the crane can be safely disconnected from the source of electrical supply; and

(e) a switch or circuit breaker by which the maximum power to the crane can be safely interrupted from the cab on the crane, unless the crane collectors can be safely removed.

(6) Before a crane is first used, a person trained in and using the test requirements contained in CSA Standard B167-1964 "General Purpose Electric Overhead Travelling Cranes" shall test devices that may affect the safe operation of the crane.

(6.1) While a crane is in use a trained person shall examine and service devices that may affect the safe operation of the crane at a frequency at least equal to that recommended by its manufacturer or, if there is no manufacturer's recommendation, at a frequency at least equal to that specified by a competent person.

(7) In addition to the requirements of subsection (6), devices that may affect the safe operation of,

(a) a production crane shall be tested daily when in use; and

(b) a service crane shall be tested daily when in use and the test shall be made before the first use of the crane on that day.

(8) A trained person shall examine, using non-destructive testing techniques, the shafting of each hoist drive train of a production crane to determine if it is in sound condition before the crane is first used.

(8.1) After a production crane has been first used, a trained person shall examine, using non-destructive techniques, the shafting of each hoist drive train of the crane at a frequency at least equal to that recommended by its manufacturer or, if there is no manufacturer's recommendation, at a frequency at least equal to that specified by a competent person in order to determine if it is in sound condition.

(9) A log book shall be kept for each crane and the log book shall contain,

(a) a record of the dates on which testing, servicing and inspections were performed;

(b) a record of the findings of any tests and examinations;

(c) a record of repairs and modifications performed and the signature of the person performing such work; and

(d) the signature of the supervisor authorizing the repairs or modifications referred to in clause (c).

(10) No crane shall be operated,

(a) when in the hoisting rope,

(i) the number of broken wires in one lay length exceeds 5 per cent of the total in the rope, or

(ii) defects that seriously affect its strength are known to exist;

(b) when a person is in the vicinity of the wheel tracks unless precautions have been taken to ensure his or her safety;

(c) by an unauthorized person;

(d) by a person who is not a competent person, except for the purpose of training;

(e) when any device that may affect safe operation is found to be faulty; and

(f) when the load exceeds the load rating of the crane, except for the purpose of a test.

(11) No person shall ride or be permitted to ride,

(a) on the load being carried by a crane;

(b) on a crane except,

(i) the crane operator and any trainee,

(ii) personnel performing maintenance, inspection, or testing of the crane,

(iii) supervisors, and

(iv) for the purpose of maintenance repairs from the crane when precautions for the safety of workers doing the repair have been implemented.

(12) A production crane shall be operated by a competent person who is in possession of a subsisting crane operator's medical certificate.

(13) A person operating a production crane shall,

(a) be physically and mentally fit to discharge the duties of a crane operator;

854

(b) undergo a medical examination by a physician before commencing work as a crane operator and every twelve months thereafter;

(c) obtain a crane operator's medical certificate from the physician certifying that the person is physically fit to operate a crane and is not subject to any infirmity of body or mind that may interfere with the duties of a crane operator.

(14) The crane operator's medical certificate shall,

(a) expire one year from its date; and

(b) be kept on file and recorded on a posted list of active crane operators.

(15) The crane operator's medical certificate shall be in the following form:

Occupational Health and Safety Act

CRANE OPERATOR'S MEDICAL CERTIFICATE

I have this day examined

name: .... and certify he (she) is physically fit to operate a crane and is not subject to any infirmity of body or mind that may interfere with the duties of a crane operator.

....
(signature of physician)

....
(date)

O. Reg. 571/92 s. 16; 296/11 s. 15

196. (1) No person shall ride on a conveyor belt.

(2) A conveyor shall have,

(a) a means to safely apply belt dressing while the conveyor is in motion; and

(b) if the conveyor is started automatically, by remote control or if a portion or portions of the conveyor are not visible from the operator's position, a start-up warning device.

(3) Subsections (3.1) and (3.2) apply to the following pinch points on a conveyor:

1. The head, tail, drive, deflection and tension pulleys.

2. If the lift of the belt is restricted, the return rollers and the carry rollers.

(3.1) Subject to subsection (3.2), the pinch points referred to in subsection (3) shall be guarded by a guard that, unless it would render the pinch point inaccessible, extends at least 0.9 metres from the pinch point.

(3.2) If it is impracticable to comply with subsection (3.1),

(a) a fence shall be in place that prevents access to the pinch points;

(b) a barricade shall be in place that prevents access to the pinch points; or

(c) a gate equipped with an interlocking device, which has a manual reset switch, shall be in place that prevents access to the pinch points while the conveyor is operating.

(3.3) Subsections (3.1) and (3.2) do not apply if the position or construction of the conveyor provides equivalent protection that renders the pinch points inaccessible.

(4) Guards shall be provided beneath a conveyor,

(a) that passes over a worker; or

(b) from which falling materials or parts may endanger a worker.

(5) A conveyor in an underground mine shall have,

(a) devices that guard against excessive slip between the belt and the driving pulley; and

(b) a fire suppression system at the driven end unless fire retardant belting is used or the conveyor is continually attended by a worker.

(6) A conveyor shall be stopped and the prime mover de-energized, locked and tagged out when the conveyor is undergoing repairs, adjustments or maintenance unless,

(a) it is necessary to run the conveyor during such work; and

(b) effective precautions are taken to prevent injury to a worker from moving parts.

O. Reg. 68/96, s. 4; 167/16, s. 12

196.1 (1) Every conveyor shall have an emergency stopping system that operates a manual reset switch that stops the conveyor.

(2) If a conveyor is accessible to a worker, the emergency stopping system is required,

(a) at any pinch point on the conveyor that is not set out in subsection 196(3) and the emergency stopping system must be within easy reach of a worker at each of those pinch points; and

(b) at any other locations along the conveyor in order to ensure that the system is always within easy reach of a worker.

(3) If a conveyor is inaccessible to a worker by any means listed in sub-section (4), the emergency stopping system is required at a location or locations determined by the employer following consultation with the joint health and safety committee or health and safety representative, if any.

(4) For the purposes of subsection (3), the following are considered means by which a conveyor is inaccessible:

1. A fence.
2. A barricade.
3. A gate equipped with an interlocking device, which has a manual reset switch that renders the conveyor inoperative when the gate is moved or opened.
4. The location of the conveyor renders it inaccessible.
5. Any combination of paragraphs 1 to 4.

O. Reg. 167/16, s. 13

197. (1) A power driven raise climber shall,

(a) have at least two independent means of braking,

(i) one of which shall be as close as practical to the final drive of the motor,

(ii) each capable of stopping and holding the climber with its maximum rated load, and

(iii) each arranged to permit independent testing;

(b) have the maximum load that it may carry as certified by its manufacturer, displayed on the climber or at the raise service position;

(c) be operated within the maximum load limit;

(d) except when the track on which it operates is being extended, have a stop block to prevent the climber being taken beyond the track;

(e) have an effective means for communication between the climber and the raise service position; and

(f) have an overspeed safety device that,

(i) will stop the climber and hold it in place if it begins to travel faster than its design speed,

(ii) is approved by the manufacturer of the climber,

(iii) is overhauled at least once every three years by the manufacturer or by another competent person, and

(iv) bears a suitable mark identifying the device's serial number, the most recent date on which the device was overhauled and the name of the person who performed the overhaul.

(2) A raise climber that is electrically powered shall,

(a) not be operated in excess of 750 volts;

(b) be protected by a ground fault system;

(c) have a visible break switch at the raise service area by which its power can be isolated;

(d) have a switch at the raise service area by which its power can be safely interrupted; and

(e) have a control switch on the climber by which power to its motor can be removed.

(3) The electrical supply to a raise climber shall be disconnected while explosives and electric caps are being loaded into a position for blasting.

(4) A means by which workers can be reached and removed from a raise climber shall be available for use.

(5) Devices that may affect the safe operation of a raise climber shall be examined by a competent person,

(a) before the raise climber is first used at the raise and daily thereafter when in use; and

(b) during every major overhaul of the raise climber.

(6) A major overhaul shall be performed on a raise climber at the frequency recommended by the manufacturer of the climber or a competent person, whichever is the more frequent.

(7) A raise climber being used at a raise shall be cleaned thoroughly weekly.

(8) The brakes and controls of the raise climber shall be tested prior to first being used during a workshift.

(9) The main shafting of the drive train of a raise climber shall be subjected to a nondestructive test by a competent person to determine if it is in sound condition,

(a) before the raise climber is first put into service; and

(b) during every major overhaul of the raise climber and not less frequently than once for every 4,000 hours of use.

(10) A log book shall be kept for each raise climber and the log book shall contain,

(a) a record of the dates the examinations prescribed in subsections (5) and (9) are performed;

(b) a record of the findings during the examinations referred to in clause (a);

(c) a record of any repairs and modifications, and the signature of the person performing such examinations, repairs and modifications; and

(d) the signature of the supervisor authorizing the repairs and modifications referred to in clause (c).

(11) The owner shall give written notice to the joint health and safety committee or a health and safety representative, if any, of a proposed raise climber installation.

(12) A raise climber shall be,

(a) designed, maintained and operated in accordance with good engineering practice; and

(b) built and installed in accordance with the design.

(13) The employer of workers operating the raise climber shall ensure that a notice showing the maximum number of persons or load weight is posted on or near the raise climber and that the number or weight is not exceeded.

(14) [Revoked O. Reg. 236/99, s. 7(3).]

O. Reg. 60/94 s. 10; 272/97 s. 35; 236/99 s. 7; 174/01 s. 6; 84/07 s. 15

198. (1) Procedures for the safe operation of a steam or compressor plant shall be prepared in writing and made available to the workers operating and maintaining the plant.

(2) A steam boiler or compressor to which Ontario Regulation 220/01 (Boilers and Pressure Vessels) made under the *Technical Standards and Safety Act, 2000* does not apply shall be regularly cleaned and examined for proper and safe condition.

O. Reg. 31/04 s. 11

199. (1) An air compressor driven by a prime mover exceeding twenty-five kilowatts when installed in an underground mine shall be,

(a) designed and installed so as to minimize the hazard of fire or explosion due to the accumulation of carbonaceous materials in the air system;

(b) provided with protective devices that prevent its operation if,

(i) the temperature of the air at the discharge line is in excess of normal,

(ii) the temperature of the compressor cooling water and cooling air is in excess of normal, or

(iii) the flow and pressure of compressor lubricating oil is below normal;

(c) provided with an alarm that,

(i) is audible and visible to the worker in charge of the compressor,

(ii) operates when a device as prescribed in clause (b) is activated,

(iii) operates as long as the conditions exist that cause a device as prescribed in clause (1)(b) to operate.

(2) No protective device prescribed in clause (b) shall be,

(a) capable of automatically restarting the compressor; and

(b) used unless tested and found to function properly.

200. (1) A reciprocating type air compressor driven by a prime mover exceeding thirty kilowatts, that is lubricated by oil and discharges to a closed system over 100 kilopascals, shall have,

(a) a temperature-indicating device installed at the high-pressure discharge pipe; and

(b) the normal operating temperature marked on the device.

(2) The discharge air temperature shall be,

(a) read at least once every operating shift; and

(b) recorded in a compressor log book.

201. (1) An operator of mobile cranes, shovels and boom trucks, or similar equipment, whereby rope is wound onto a drum driven by an engine for the purpose of raising, lowering or swinging materials, shall,

(a) hold a certificate of qualification issued under the *Ontario College of Trades and Apprenticeship Act, 2009*, that is not suspended, or, if the worker is an apprentice, be working pursuant to a training agreement registered under that Act, that is not suspended, in the trade of,

(i) hoisting engineer—mobile crane operator 1, if the mobile crane, shovel and boom truck or similar equipment is capable of raising, lowering or swinging any material that weighs more than 30,000 pounds,

(ii) hoisting engineer—mobile crane operator 1 or hoisting engineer—mobile crane operator 2, if the mobile crane, shovel and boom truck or similar equipment is capable of raising, lowering or swinging only material that weighs more than 16,000 pounds but no more than 30,000 pounds, or

(iii) hoisting engineer—tower crane operator, if the equipment is a tower crane; or

(b) be qualified in accordance with a program approved by the Director, when the person is an employee of the mine or mining plant.

(2) An approved program referred to in clause (1)(b) shall consist of,

(a) instruction time;

(b) field time;

(c) familiarization with the equipment to be used; and

(d) a method of examination.

(3) Mobile cranes, shovels, boom trucks and similar equipment shall be inspected for safe and proper condition by a competent person,

(a) before being used at the start of each workshift; and

(b) at regular intervals as recommended by the manufacturer.

O. Reg. 60/94 s. 11; 92/13 s. 1

Part IX — Railroads

202. (1) Standard practices to govern the safe operation of a standard gauge railroad, a self-propelled track crane, motorized equipment used for the maintenance of a standard gauge railroad, a motor vehicle equipped with rail wheels in addition to rubber-tired wheels or other similar equipment shall be prepared in writing.

(2) A copy of the standard practices prepared in accordance with subsection (1) shall be provided to each railroad worker and each railroad worker,

(a) shall be trained and instructed in and be knowledgeable of the standard practices for his or her work; and

(b) shall have a copy of the standard practices readily available while on duty.

(3) Where a railroad of a mine or mining plant interconnects with a railroad of a railway company a standard procedure shall be established and followed for carrying on operations on the first mentioned railroad.

(4) A railroad shall be built to safely withstand speeds and loads to which it will normally be subjected by a train.

(5) A low bridge warning sign shall be installed at an approach of a railroad to an overhead structure, where the clearance between the underside of the structure and the top of any railroad car is less than two metres.

(6) Guard rails shall be placed at the approach to railroad tracks where the view is obstructed in one or both directions.

(7) A locomotive shall,

(a) have an audible warning system in proper working condition;
(b) have a suitable headlight for each travel direction when operating in areas without adequate lighting;
(c) be equipped with brakes in proper working condition; and
(d) have the control lever so mounted as to prevent its inadvertent removal.

(8) The locomotive operator shall be in position at the controls when operating the locomotive on manual control.

(9) Before leaving a locomotive unattended, the operator shall,

(a) set the controls in position for parking;
(b) set the brakes; and
(c) on a grade, use hand brakes or wheel chocks to prevent movement of the locomotive.

(10) The owner shall give notice to the joint health and safety committee or the health and safety representatives, if any, before installing remote or automatic controls for the operation of a locomotive.

(11) A standard practice shall be prepared for the use of radio communications systems on a railroad.

(12) Only authorized persons shall ride on a train.

(13) One or more workers shall be stationed to direct the operator of a locomotive when backing a train in a location where persons may be endangered.

(14) A car shall not be permitted to run free unless,

  (a) adequate control thereof is maintained; and

  (b) there is no hazard to a worker.

O. Reg. 272/97 s. 36; 34/14 s. 13

Part X — Mine Hoisting Plant

203. (1) Subject to subsection (5), no mine hoisting plant shall be operated without a professional engineer giving written statement to the owner setting out,

  (a) the location of the plant;

  (b) the maximum loading of number of persons and material that may be carried by the plant when it is installed, maintained and operated in compliance with this Regulation;

  (c) that the plant is designed and manufactured in accordance with appropriate engineering standards and installed where it is being operated in compliance with good engineering practice.

(2) Subsection (1) does not apply to a plant that is operated for testing purposes.

(3) The owner shall ensure that a copy of the statement for each plant is available at the mine site and readily reviewable by the workers and that a copy is given to the joint health and safety committee or health and safety representative, if any.

(4) The mine owner shall ensure that the mine hoisting plant is installed, maintained and operated in compliance with this Regulation.

(5) Subsections (1) and (3) do not apply to a plant being operated under a permit issued by the Ministry of Labour before August 16, 1997.

O. Reg. 571/92 s. 17; 272/97 s. 37

204. (1) Subject to subsection (5), no shaft conveyance shall be operated without a professional engineer giving written statement to the owner setting out,

  (a) the location of the conveyance;

(b) the maximum loading of number of persons and material that may be carried by the conveyance when it is installed, maintained and operated in compliance with this Regulation;

(c) that the conveyance is designed and manufactured in accordance with appropriate engineering standards and installed where it is being operated in compliance with good engineering practice.

(2) Subsection (1) does not apply to a conveyance that is operated for testing purposes.

(3) The owner shall ensure that a copy of the statement is posted at the shaft collar and that a copy is given to the joint health and safety committee or health and safety representative, if any.

(4) The owner shall ensure that the conveyance is installed, maintained and operated in compliance with this Regulation.

(5) Subsections (1) and (3) do not apply to a conveyance being operated under a permit issued by the Ministry of Labour before August 16, 1997.

O. Reg. 272/97 s. 37

205. Tests for compliance with this Regulation shall be conducted on a mine hoisting plant before being put into initial service in a particular location.

206. (1) In determining the maximum weight to be included in the written statement required under subsection 204(1), the professional engineer shall take into consideration the maximum load that a mine hoisting plant is capable of safely carrying.

(2) Subject to subsection (3), the maximum number of persons that can be carried on a shaft conveyance shall be determined as follows:

1. Where the clear floor area of a deck of a shaft conveyance is 1.86 square metres or less, there shall be at least 0.19 square metre for each person.

2. Where the clear floor area of a deck of a shaft conveyance is more than 1.86 square metres and less than 4.64 square metres, there shall be at least 0.16 square metre for each person.

3. Where the clear floor area of a deck of a shaft conveyance is 4.64 square metres or more, there shall be at least 0.14 square metre for each person.

(3) The maximum number of persons that may be carried by a shaft conveyance shall not exceed 85 per cent of the maximum weight of materials divided by ninety kilograms.

O. Reg. 272/97 s. 38

207. The following log books shall be obtained from the Ministry and used for each mine hoisting plant:

1. Electrical Hoisting Equipment Record Book.
2. Hoisting Machinery Record Book.
3. Hoist operator's Log Book.
4. Rope Record Book.
5. Shaft Inspection Record Book.

208. A headframe on surface or underground in an underground mine shall,

(a) be designed in accordance with good engineering practice;
(b) have the plans of the design certified by a professional engineer;
(c) be constructed in accordance with the design;
(d) be of sufficient strength to safely withstand all loads to which it is likely to be subjected; and
(e) be of sufficient height to provide a distance for an overwind that exceeds the greater of,

   (i) twice the stopping distance of the hoist at the maximum speed permitted by the hoist controls, or

   (ii) three metres.

209. (1) A mine shaft shall,

(a) be designed in accordance with good engineering practice;
(b) have a means to guide each shaft conveyance to prevent contact with another shaft conveyance or shaft furnishings;
(c) have underwind clearances that exceed the stopping distance of the shaft conveyance when travelling at the maximum speed permitted by the hoist-controls, except,

   (i) during shaft sinking, or

   (ii) when chairs are used to land a skip during loading; and

(d) where a friction hoist is installed, have tapered guides or other such devices above and below the limits of regular travel of the shaft conveyance and counterweight, arranged to act as a direct physical brake to decelerate and stop the counterweight and shaft conveyance in the event of an over-travel.

(2) A barrier or obstruction to prevent a shaft conveyance from being lowered into water in the shaft bottom must be installed in the shaft except,

  (a) when the shaft is being sunk; or

  (b) where a friction hoist is installed.

(3) A probe indicating the high water level shall be installed below the lowest working level in a shaft in which natural drainage is not provided and in which flooding may occur due to equipment failure.

(4) The probe shall be installed so that it can be read by the person in control of the hoist.

(5) The probe shall be installed so that,

  (a) it enables the person in control of the hoist to prevent a shaft conveyance from being lowered into water; or

  (b) it prevents a shaft conveyance from being lowered into water.

(6) If a probe is installed, a procedure must be established to prevent a conveyance with occupants from being lowered into water.

(7) The employer shall establish the procedure in consultation with the joint health and safety committee.

(8) The procedure shall be implemented when the probe indicates that there is water at the high water level.

O. Reg. 779/94 s. 9

210. (1) Subject to subsection (5), protective devices and procedures shall be used to prevent a shaft conveyance or counterweight from coming into contact with an intermediate shaft obstruction.

(2) A device which may become an intermediate shaft obstruction shall be positively locked out of the shaft compartment to prevent inadvertent entry into the compartment.

(3) The location of the intermediate shaft obstruction shall be marked on the depth indicator of a hoist.

(4) The protective procedure for operating the intermediate shaft obstruction shall be prepared in writing and posted for use by the hoist operator.

(5) Doors for covering the shaft at the collar to facilitate the maintenance of a shaft conveyance are not an intermediate shaft obstruction if,

(a) they are positively latched out of the shaft compartments when not in use; and

(b) dual lights are installed to indicate to the hoist operator whether such doors are in or out of the shaft compartment.

(6) Equipment used to directly discharge material into a skip shall operate in such a way that actuating power is required before any gate will open.

O. Reg. 583/91 s. 5

211. (1) This section applies if a shaft conveyance is being used to transport persons.

(2) The hoist shall be equipped with control devices that prevent the shaft conveyance from being taken,

(a) to the dump position, unless a procedure is established and followed that ensures persons on the shaft conveyance remain securely in place if the conveyance is taken to the dump position; or

(b) below a loading pocket, unless the controls for loading the shaft conveyance from that pocket have been made inoperative or the persons are being transported in a separate compartment of the shaft.

(3) If a shaft conveyance that is being used to transport persons is not a cage or a combination skip and cage designed to normally transport persons, the hoist shall not be permitted to travel at a speed that is more than the lesser of,

(a) one-half the normal speed of the hoist; or

(b) five metres per second.

(4) The control devices of the hoist shall be designed and installed to be fail safe.

(5) An audible or visible signal that the control devices for the hoist are set in operation shall be given to persons entering the shaft conveyance.

O. Reg. 31/04 s. 12

212. (1) Chairs used for landing a cage shall be,

(a) arranged to fall clear and remain clear of the shaft compartment when the cage is lifted off the chairs;

(b) operable only from outside the cage; and

(c) so arranged as not to distort the cage.

(2) Chairs fastened to shaft station posts shall be of a chain type.

213. A certificate for each hoist shall be obtained from the manufacturer of the hoist or a professional engineer competent in the design of mine hoisting plants certifying,

(a) the maximum rope pull;

(b) the maximum suspended load; and

(c) the maximum unbalanced load in the case of a friction hoist, and no hoist shall be loaded above the maximums as certified.

214. (1) No hoist shall be used for the transporting of persons unless it has a braking system consisting of at least two sets of mechanical brakes to stop and hold the drum for the shaft conveyance transporting the persons.

(2) Each set of mechanical brakes shall,

(a) stop and hold the drum when the shaft conveyance or counterweight is operating at its maximum load;

(b) be so arranged to be capable of being tested independently; and

(c) be arranged to apply normal braking effort before a linkage or brake piston reaches a limit of travel.

(3) At least one of the mechanical brakes shall be designed and arranged so that the brake,

(a) applies directly to the drum; and

(b) applies automatically when,

(i) the safety circuit of the hoist is interrupted, or

(ii) the pressure in the hydraulic or pneumatic system for applying brakes has dropped below normal.

(4) The braking system shall be arranged so that,

(a) the brakes are applied by control levers that are pulled unless brake and power control levers are common;

(b) any brake weights installed to provide auxiliary braking force can be readily tested for freedom of movement; and

(c) the hoist brakes are applied automatically upon the loss of electrical, hydraulic or pneumatic power.

(5) Subject to subsection (6), the brakes of a drum hoist shall be arranged to decelerate the hoist at a rate greater than 1.5 metres per second per second and less than 3.7 metres per second per second where braking is initiated by an interrupted safety circuit and the hoist is,

(a) normally used for the transporting of persons; and

(b) operating in the normal full speed zone.

854

(6) Subsection (5) does not apply to a drum hoist installed at a particular location prior to the 1st day of October, 1979.

(7) The brakes of a drum hoist installed in a particular location before the 1st day of October, 1979 and that is normally used for transporting persons shall be tested to determine its deceleration rates.

(8) [Repealed O. Reg. 34/14, s. 14.]

(9) The braking system of a hoist not normally used to transport persons shall be designed and arranged to safely stop and hold the hoist under all conditions of normal load, speed and direction of travel.

(10) Clause (4)(a) does not apply to a hoist that was installed before the 1st day of October, 1979.

O. Reg. 486/99 s. 13; 34/14 s. 14

215. (1) A clutch of a drum hoist shall be interlocked with the brake so that,

> (a) the clutch can be disengaged only when the brake of the drum is fully applied;
> (b) the clutch is fully engaged before the brake of the drum can be released; and
> (c) the brake will apply if the clutch begins to disengage inadvertently.

(2) The controls for engaging and disengaging a clutch shall be guarded to prevent their inadvertent operation.

(3) No band type friction clutch shall be used.

(4) A device must be installed that indicates to the hoist operator whether or not the clutch is fully engaged.

(5) The following apply if a hoist is installed on or after October 25, 2002 or if a brake control system or clutch control system on a hoist is modified after that date:

> 1. The hoist shall be designed and equipped with at least two independent clutch brake interlocking systems to prevent any single component from causing a failure.
> 2. The hoist shall be designed so that the clutch brake interlocking systems may be safely examined.
> 3. The clutch control shall be designed so that the selection of clutch disengagement automatically applies the clutch drum brake.

O. Reg. 60/94 s. 12; 291/02 s. 7

216. (1) Except as prescribed in subsections (2), (3) and (4), the drum diameter to rope diameter ratio for a drum hoist shall be equal to or greater than,

(a) 60 to 1, where the nominal rope diameter is 25.4 millimetres or less; or

(b) 80 to 1, where the nominal rope diameter is greater than 25.4 millimetres.

(2) The drum diameter to rope diameter ratio for a drum hoist in use for shaft sinking or for preliminary development work during shaft sinking shall be equal to or greater than,

(a) 48 to 1, where the nominal rope diameter is 25.4 millimetres or less; and

(b) 60 to 1, where the nominal rope diameter is greater than 25.4 millimetres.

(3) The drum diameter to rope diameter ratio of a friction hoist shall be equal to or greater than,

(a) 80 to 1, for stranded ropes; and

(b) 100 to 1, for locked coil ropes.

(4) Subsection (1) does not apply to a drum hoist where the drum diameter to rope diameter is,

(a) 54 to 1, where the nominal rope diameter is 25.4 millimetres or less; or

(b) 72 to 1, where the nominal rope diameter is greater than 25.4 millimetres, so long as the drum hoist was manufactured prior to 1954 and the original load rating given by its manufacturer is not exceeded.

217. (1) No drum hoist shall have,

(a) more than three layers of rope where the drum has helical or spiral grooving or does not have grooving;

(b) more than four layers of rope if the drum has parallel and half pitch grooving; and

(c) less than three dead turns of the rope on the drum.

(2) Despite clause (1)(b), a drum hoist may have a maximum of five layers of rope if,

(a) the mine hoisting plant meets the standards set out in SABS Code of Practice 0294, Ed. 1, "The performance, operation, testing and maintenance of drum winders relating to rope safety", as approved according to procedures of SABS on August 4, 2000; and

(b) the rope is used, maintained and examined according to the requirements set out in SABS Code of Practice 0293:1996, "Condition assessment of steel wire ropes on mine winders", as approved by the President of SABS on September 16, 1996.

O. Reg. 31/04 s. 13

218. (1) Subject to subsection (2), the drum of a drum hoist shall be provided with,

(a) grooves that properly fit the rope, unless the hoist is being used for shaft sinking or preliminary development work during shaft sinking in which case the drum may be smooth; and

(b) flanges of sufficient height to contain all the rope and which are strong enough to withstand any loading by the rope.

(2) A conical drum hoist shall be provided with grooves that prevent the rope from slipping off.

219. A drum hoist and a sheave shall be arranged so that the rope,

(a) coils properly across the face of the drum;

(b) winds smoothly from one layer to another; and

(c) winds without cutting into the rope layer beneath.

220. Bolts and other fittings of a mine hoisting plant shall be properly secured.

221. A hoist shall be provided with depth indicators that continuously, accurately and clearly show to the hoist operator the position,

(a) of a shaft conveyance and counterweight, if any;

(b) in an inclined shaft, of a change in gradient that requires a reduction in hoist speed;

(c) at which the overwind, underwind and track limit devices are set to operate;

(d) of any intermediate shaft obstruction;

(e) of the limits of normal travel for the shaft conveyance and counterweight, if any; and

(f) of any collar doors, dump doors and crosshead landing chairs.

222. (1) A steam or air powered hoist shall be provided with devices that,

(a) protect against an overwind;

(b) protect against an underwind, except during shaft sinking;

(c) indicate the air or steam pressure for the hoist operator; and

(d) permit the air or steam supply to the hoist engine to be readily shut off by the hoist operator.

(2) Where the hoisting plant consists of a single shaft conveyance without a counterweight, the compression of the engine of an air or steam powered hoist may be used as an automatic brake if,

(a) the engine is non-reversing;

(b) the exhaust restraining valve is fail safe;

(c) the piping system is strong enough to withstand the air or steam pressures;

(d) the compression has sufficient braking capacity to stop the hoist carrying its maximum load;

(e) the normal speed of the hoist is less than 2.5 metres per second; and

(f) specifications and arrangements of the hoist have been prepared or checked by a professional engineer and comply with this section.

O. Reg. 272/97 s. 39

223. A hoist being used as a tugger or a utility hoist shall be maintained and used so as not to endanger the safety of a worker.

224. A hoist that is relocated shall comply with the requirements of this Regulation.

225. (1) Before a sheave is used, a certificate for the sheave shall be obtained from the manufacturer of the sheave or a professional engineer competent in sheave design certifying as to,

(a) the maximum rated load;

(b) the diameter of rope for which it was designed;

(c) the breaking strength of the rope for which it was designed; and

(d) the maximum amount of groove wear that shall be permitted.

(2) No sheave shall be,

(a) loaded above the maximum rated load; or

(b) used other than in compliance with the certificate.

(3) The ratio of the diameter of the sheave to the diameter of the rope shall be as prescribed in section 216.

(4) A sheave shall,

(a) be made of materials which will safely withstand the ambient temperatures;

(b) be fitted with a groove to fit the rope being used; and

(c) bear a serial number and the date of its manufacture.

(5) The shaft of a sheave shall be examined for flaws by a non-destructive test by a person competent in such testing,

(a) before being put into service in a particular location;

(b) after installation; and

(c) at a regular frequency as recommended by a person competent in such testing.

226. (1) No hoist that is electrically powered shall be used unless it has a safety circuit that,

(a) is fail safe;

(b) when interrupted, operates to,

(i) set the brakes,

(ii) remove power from the hoist motor or motors, and

(iii) stop the mine hoist when in motion.

(2) The safety circuit of a hoist shall be interrupted when,

(a) there is a failure of a power supply to the hoist electrical system which may affect safe operation;

(b) there is an overload on the hoist motors of a magnitude and duration exceeding normal;

(c) there is a short circuit in the hoist electrical system; and

(d) a prescribed safety device has operated.

(3) A switch to interrupt the safety circuit of a hoist shall be installed and the switch shall be,

(a) manually operable;

(b) located within easy reach of the hoist operator when at the controls;

(c) readily recognizable; and

(d) readily operable.

(4) A track limit device shall be installed in each shaft compartment that will be operated directly by the shaft conveyance or counterweight to interrupt the safety circuit of a hoist in the case of an overwound shaft conveyance or counterweight.

(5) Devices shall be installed to protect a shaft conveyance or counterweight against,

(a) an overwind;

(b) an underwind, except during shaft sinking;

(c) approaching the limits of travel at an excessive speed; and

(d) operating or being operated at an overspeed in excess of that for which the hoisting plant was designed and intended.

(6) The devices required by subsection (5) shall,

(a) operate to interrupt the safety circuit when activated;

(b) be driven directly by the drum;

(c) be protected for loss of motion;

(d) prevent the paying out of excess rope during shaft sinking; and

(e) be set to stop the hoist before a shaft conveyance, counterweight and their attachments make contact with a fixed part of a mine shaft or headframe.

(7) Devices shall be installed for a friction hoist that are set to interrupt the safety circuit where,

(a) there is abnormal slip between the hoist drum and the hoist ropes;

(b) there is abnormal wear of the rope treads or the tread wear limit has been reached;

(c) a shaft conveyance and counterweight approaches the collar of a mine shaft at excessive speed; or

(d) a violent swing or large rise in the loop of a balance rope occurs.

(8) The devices required for the purposes of clause (7)(c) shall be installed in the mine shaft.

(9) On a friction hoist, a device shall be installed that synchronizes the position of the shaft conveyance with safety devices driven from the drum.

(10) A hoist that is electrically powered shall,

(a) have an ammeter within plain view of the hoist operator to indicate the hoist motor current;

(b) except when the slowdown control at the limits of travel is automatic, have a device to warn the operator, audibly, that the hoist is approaching the limit where a reduction in speed is necessary for safe manual braking; and

(c) have a speed indicator if the normal speed exceeds 2.5 metres per second;

(d) have a device from which a voltage signal that is proportioned to the speed of the hoist can be obtained;

(e) have a backout device as prescribed in subsection (11) by which a shaft conveyance or counterweight can be removed from an overwound or underwound position;

854

(f) if equipped with an underwind by-pass device, have such device,
  (i) manually operable only, and
  (ii) restrict the hoist operation to slow speed;

(g) have overwind by-pass devices that,
  (i) are manually operable only,
  (ii) when in use restrict hoist operation to slow speed, and
  (iii) allow hoist travel beyond the first device providing overwind protection;

(h) have a master controller that has a neutral or brake reset position;

(i) have any brake operating levers arranged so that upon an interruption of the safety circuit the power to the hoist cannot be restored until the levers are in the brake applied position;

(j) have accurate and sensitive safety controllers; and

(k) have each safety-related device capable of being effective under the environmental conditions in which it is installed.

(11) A backout device shall,
  (a) be manually operable only; and
  (b) prevent the brake or brakes from being released until sufficient torque has been developed to ensure movement in the correct direction.

(12) The adjustment of a protective device shall be altered only by a competent person authorized to do so.

226.1(1) Every drum hoist in a mine that is regularly used to transport persons in a cage or skip must be equipped with a slack rope protection system that,
  (a) will interrupt the safety circuit when activated; and
  (b) is effective over the entire operating length of the shaft.

(2) Subsection (1) does not apply to a drum hoist that was installed at or relocated within a mine before January 1, 2012.

O. Reg. 296/11 s. 16

227. (1) A device that permits changing from manual to automatic control shall be installed on an automatic hoist and the device shall be,
  (a) located where it is readily accessible to the manual controls; and
  (b) operated only by an authorized worker.

(2) Where a hoist is designed to be operated from control stations located at shaft levels and within a shaft conveyance, the switch for affecting the change-over of the control mode between that at the shaft levels and at the shaft conveyance shall be effective only at the shaft level at which the shaft conveyance is stopped.

(3) Devices installed on the levels for the purpose of selecting the shaft conveyance destination and initiating hoist movement shall be effective only when,

    (a) the shaft conveyance is stopped at that level; and

    (b) the installation is designed for call operation.

(4) When an executive signal for hoist motion is given from controls at a level, at least five seconds shall lapse before the hoist moves.

(5) Except for jogging, devices at shaft level control stations for initiating hoist motion shall be effective only when the shaft gate at the level where the conveyance is stopped is closed.

(6) Except for jogging, devices located within a cage for initiating hoist motion shall be effective only when the door of the cage and the gate of the shaft are closed.

(7) Where the controls for initiating hoist motion are located within a cage, a device shall be installed in the cage by which the safety circuit of the hoist can be interrupted.

228. (1) A shaft rope shall not be used unless,

    (a) a 2.5 metre representative sample has been subjected to a destructive test in accordance with CSA Standard G4-00 "Steel Wire Rope for General Purpose and for Mine Hoisting and Mine Haulage"; and

    (b) a Certificate of Test has been obtained from a cable testing laboratory approved by the Minister.

(2) The test described in subsection (2.1) shall be performed not more than six months after a hoisting rope is first used on a drum hoist, and afterwards at intervals of not more than six months.

(2.1) A piece of the rope at least 2.5 metres long located at the lower end above the attachment to the conveyance shall be cut off, have its ends fastened to prevent unravelling and be tested in accordance with CSA Standard G4-00 "Steel Wire Rope for General Purpose and for Mine Hoisting and Mine Haulage".

(2.2) The date of each test under subsections (1) and (2.1) and the results obtained shall be recorded in the Rope Record Book for the rope.

(3) A Certificate of Test issued under section 20 shall be kept available for inspection, and a copy shall be given to the joint health and safety committee or health and safety representative, if any.

(4) A hoisting rope being used as a shaft rope shall be tested throughout its working length by a competent person using an electromagnetic testing device designed, built and tested according to appropriate engineering standards,

    (a) within six months of being put into service; and

    (b) thereafter at regular intervals not exceeding four months; or

    (c) at intervals shorter than four months where, by extrapolation from past tests, the loss in breaking strength will exceed 10 per cent before the next prescribed test.

(5) A balance rope and, where practical, a guide and a rubbing rope in use, shall be tested throughout its working length by a competent person using an electromagnetic testing device designed, built and tested according to appropriate engineering standards,

    (a) within twelve months of being put into service; and

    (b) thereafter at regular intervals not exceeding eight months except where a test discloses a loss exceeding 5 per cent of the breaking strength recorded on the Certificate of Test, in which case the regular intervals shall not exceed four months.

(6) The date of each electromagnetic test and the results obtained shall be recorded in the Rope Record Book for the rope.

(7) A person competent to do so shall interpret the electromagnetic test and graphs and shall sign the record consisting of the test, the graphs and the interpretation.

(8) The record shall be kept readily available at the mine site while the rope is in service.

(9) If a test shows a loss exceeding 7.5 per cent of the breaking strength recorded on the Certificate of Test, the person who signs the record shall send a copy of the record of the test to the owner and the joint health and safety committee or health and safety representative, if any, within 14 days after the test is completed.

(10) A rope shall not be used as a shaft rope if it has been spliced.

(10.1) A shaft rope shall not be reversed unless it is used on a friction hoist.

(11) The minimum nominal diameter of a hoisting rope shall exceed,

    (a) 15.9 millimetres where only one rope supports a shaft conveyance or counterweight; and

    (b) 12.7 millimetres where more than one rope supports a shaft conveyance or counterweight.

(12) The factor of safety of a hoisting rope installed on a drum hoist shall not be less than,

    (a) 8.5 at the point the rope is attached to a shaft conveyance or counterweight, subject to clause (b);

    (b) 7.5 at the point the rope is attached to a skip or counterweight where the material load was accurately weighed; and

    (c) 5.0 at the point the rope leaves the head sheave when the shaft conveyance or counterweight is at its lowest point of normal travel, subject to subsection (12.1).

(12.1) Clause (12)(c) does not apply if,

    (a) the drum hoist is being used in a vertical shaft;

    (b) at the point that the rope leaves the head sheave when the shaft conveyance or counterweight is at its lowest point of normal travel, the rope has a breaking strength at the time of installation of not less than that obtained from the formula, 25,000 divided by the quantity (4,000 plus L) multiplied by the maximum suspended load to be carried by the rope, including the load represented by the weight of the rope itself, where L is the maximum length of the rope in metres, in the shaft compartment below the head sheave;

    (c) the mine hoisting plant meets the standards set out in SABS Code of Practice 0294, Ed. 1, "The performance, operation, testing and maintenance of drum winders relating to rope safety", as approved according to procedures of SABS on August 4, 2000; and

    (d) the rope is used, maintained and examined according to the requirements set out in SABS Code of Practice 0293:1996, "Condition assessment of steel wire ropes on mine winders", as approved by the President of SABS on September 16, 1996.

(13) The factor of safety of a hoisting rope installed on a friction hoist shall not be less than the greater of,

    (a) the factor obtained from the formula 8.0 minus 0.00164 L, where L is the maximum length of the rope in metres, in the shaft compartment below the head sheave or the drum of a friction hoist; or

    (b) 5.5.

854

(14) The factor of safety of a tail or balance rope shall not be less than 7.

(15) The factor of safety of a guide or a rubbing rope shall not be less than 5.

(16) Notice in duplicate in the form set out in the Rope Record Book of the installation of a shaft rope and containing the information set out in the said Book shall be kept readily available at the mine site.

(17) When a shaft rope is removed from service notice thereof shall be kept readily available at the mine site for one year and the notice shall,

    (a) state,

        (i) the date of removal,

        (ii) the reason for removal, and

        (iii) the disposition of the removed rope; and

    (b) be in the form of the detachable part of the white Rope Installation Sheet in the Rope Record Book.

(18) No rope shall be used as a shaft rope where the breaking strength of the rope has dropped below the breaking strength set out in the Certificate of Test as follows:

    1. In any part of a hoisting rope, 90 per cent.

    2. In any part of a multi-layer, multi-strand balance rope, 90 per cent.

    3. In any part of a single layer stranded balance rope, 85 per cent.

    4. In any part of a guide or rubbing rope, 75 per cent.

(19) Despite subsection (18), no rope shall be used as a shaft rope where,

    (a) the extension of a test piece has decreased to less than 60 per cent of its original extension when tested to destruction and marked corrosion or considerable loss in wire torsions has occurred;

    (b) the number of broken wires, excluding filler wires, in any section equal to one lay length exceeds 5 per cent of the total; or

    (c) the rate of stretch in a friction hoisting rope shows a rapid increase over its normal stretch recorded during its service.

(20) If hoisting is discontinued or suspended in a shaft compartment, each shaft rope shall be removed from the shaft immediately.

(21) Despite subsection (20), shaft ropes may be left in a shaft compartment if the ropes are continually maintained and tested in accordance with this Regulation.

            O. Reg. 779/94 s. 10; 272/97 s. 40; 31/04 s. 14

229. (1) Shaft ropes shall be attached by closed type devices that will not inadvertently disconnect.

(2) In a drum hoist installation, the hoisting rope from a shaft conveyance and counterweight shall be attached to the drum of the hoist.

(3) No wedge type attachments shall be used unless the attachments are,

    (a) in sound condition; and

    (b) certified at least once every six years of use as being in sound condition by a competent person or by the manufacturer.

(4) When the attachments for a shaft hoisting rope are first installed, or re-installed after disassembling, the following measures and procedures shall be taken before the hoist is put to use:

    1. Two test trips of the conveyance or counterweight through the working part of the shaft, while the conveyance or counterweight is carrying normal load shall be performed.

    2. An examination of the attachments upon the completion of the two test trips shall be made.

    3. Any necessary adjustments shall be made.

    4. A record of any adjustments, examinations and test trips shall be made in the Hoisting Machinery Record Book by the person or persons making the adjustments, examinations and test trips.

(5) Where shaft rope attachments are made using rope clips, the number of clips to be used and their torque shall be in accordance with good engineering standards.

(6) A socket attachment used between a shaft conveyance of counter-weight and a shaft rope shall be,

    (a) designed to be suitable for mine hoisting;

    (b) installed by a person who,

        (i) is competent in the installation of the type of socket being used, and

        (ii) complies with the manufacturer's current installation standard; and

    (c) if it is used for hoisting ropes, made with a socket long enough to ensure that the embedded length of rope in the socket is greater than seven times the rope diameter.

(7) Each component of an attachment between a shaft conveyance or counterweight and a shaft rope, except for a rope clip, shall be designed to ensure that when in service and carrying the rated load, the component is

854

capable of withstanding at least four times the maximum allowable design stresses without permanent distortion.

(8) For the purpose of subsection (7), the maximum allowable design stresses are those established by good engineering practice and shall take into account the effects of,

(a) the weight of the conveyance or counterweight;

(b) the rated load;

(c) any impact load;

(d) any dynamic load;

(e) stress concentration factors;

(f) corrosion;

(g) metal fatigue; and

(h) dissimilar materials.

(9) The rope attachments, other than rope clips, installed after October 7, 1999 shall be identified and load rated by the manufacturing or a professional engineer.

O. Reg. 486/99 s. 14; 84/07 s. 16

230. (1) A certificate shall be obtained for each shaft conveyance or counterweight showing its,

(a) rated load, as certified by a professional engineer; and

(b) serial number, date of manufacture and the name of the manufacturer.

(2) Each shaft conveyance and counterweight shall be examined and inspected at least once in every five years of use by a competent person and a record of such examination and inspection shall be kept available for inspection.

(3) All parts of a shaft conveyance or counterweight when in service and carrying the rated load shall be capable of withstanding at least four times the maximum allowable design stresses without permanent distortion.

(4) The maximum allowable design stresses shall be those established by good engineering practice and include the effects of,

(a) the weight of the conveyance or counterweight;

(b) the rated load;

(c) any impact load;

(d) any dynamic load;

(e) stress concentration factors;

(f) corrosion;

(g) metal fatigue; and

(h) dissimilar materials.

(5) Where a worker performs work from the top of a shaft conveyance or counterweight, there shall be provided for the worker,

(a) a safe footing; and

(b) overhead protection, except when changing shaft guides.

(6) Devices shall be provided in a shaft conveyance by which any equipment or supplies within the conveyance may be safely secured.

231. (1) This section applies when a suspended or movable work platform that is not a shaft conveyance is used to transport or support a worker who is performing work in a shaft or in a raise.

(1.1) The work platform shall be designed by a professional engineer in accordance with good engineering practices and shall be built in accordance with the design.

(2) Before the initial use of a work platform, the employer shall give notice to the joint health and safety committee or to the health and safety representative, if any.

O. Reg. 571/92 s. 18; 68/96 s. 5; 272/97 s. 41; 236/99 s. 8

232. (1) A cage, being used to transport persons, shall,

(a) where it is supported by only a single rope or attachment point have the safety catches and mechanisms prescribed in subsection (6);

(b) except on any side which has a door, be enclosed by sheet steel at least three millimetres thick;

(c) have ventilation, adequate for the persons being transported;

(d) have a hood of steel plate, at least five millimetres thick;

(e) have a door or doors as prescribed in subsection (2);

(f) have an internal height greater than 2.1 metres;

(g) have a clearance at the door that is greater than 1.8 metres; and

(h) have where practical, an exit for the persons in the roof which can be opened from inside or outside the cage.

(2) The door or doors on a cage shall,

(a) be at least 1.5 metres high;

(b) be mounted and arranged so they cannot be opened outward from the cage;

(c) have devices for positive latching in the closed position;

854

(d) be of solid materials, except for a viewing window;

(e) be so arranged that they may be closed at all times that persons or materials, except rolling stock, are being transported in the cage;

(f) be mounted so as to provide only enough clearance at the floor to permit free closing or opening; and

(g) be of adequate strength to withstand normal shock loads.

(3) A skip used to transport workers in a shaft shall meet the following requirements unless it is being used to transport workers for shaft inspection or shaft maintenance or unless it is being used in an emergency:

1. The skip must have the safety catches and mechanisms required by subsection (6) if the skip is supported by only a single rope or attachment point.

2. The skip must provide an enclosure at least 1.07 metres high for the persons being transported.

3. The skip must have ventilation that is adequate for the persons being transported.

4. The skip must have a suitable floor that is adequately fastened.

5. The skip must have a means for safe entry and exit.

(3.1) For the purposes of subsection (3), a skip is considered to be being used in an emergency if it is being used to hoist injured people, to evacuate people, to fight fire or to enable people to perform emergency repair work necessary to maintain the mine or the mine dewatering system, electrical system or ventilation system.

(4) The openings between a shaft and a skip box over which persons must pass to enter or leave a skip shall be closed off sufficiently to prevent a person from falling through the opening.

(5) The shaft signal pull cord shall be located in a convenient place for the skip tender.

(6) Safety catches and mechanisms on a cage or skip shall,

(a) be of a type and design that meets good engineering practice;

(b) stop and hold a cage or skip transporting persons should the supporting rope or attachment break; and

(c) be subjected to the tests prescribed in subsection (7) and successfully pass the free fall test prescribed in subsection (8),

(i) prior to the cage or skip first being used to transport persons, and

(ii) prior to the cage or skip first being used after repairs to correct distortion of the safety catches and mechanisms.

(7) Free fall tests shall be performed under the following conditions:

1. The cage or skip must carry a weight equal to its maximum permitted load of persons and any material permitted to be carried at the same time.

2. The cage or skip must travel at a speed equal to,

   i. the normal hoisting speed when transporting persons, or

   ii. the speed attained by a free fall of 1.5 metres.

3. The guides on which the test is made must be of the same specifications as those in the shaft in which the conveyance will operate.

(7.1) A free fall test shall not be performed at the speed attained by a free fall of 1.5 metres unless the design and configuration of the safety dogs and loading on the cage or skip have been tested at normal hoisting speed before the free fall test.

(7.2) If a free fall test is to be performed at the speed attained by a free fall of 1.5 metres, the person performing the test shall record the rate of deceleration and the rate of change in deceleration of the cage or skip on a chart suitable for determining the deceleration of the conveyance.

(8) A free fall test shall be successfully passed if,

(a) the skip or cage decelerates to a stop at an average rate that is not less than nine or greater than 20 metres per second per second.

(b) there is no damage to the safety dogs and mechanisms;

(c) the safety dogs engage the guides continuously during deceleration; and

(d) a calculation shows that the safety dogs will stop the cage or skip when it is carrying its maximum material load.

(9) A report of a free fall test shall be made in the Hoisting Machinery Record Book for the hoist.

O. Reg. 571/92 s. 19; 68/96 s. 6; 272/97 s. 42

233. (1) A system for communicating by voice shall be installed and maintained at an underground mine.

(2) The communication system required by subsection (1) shall permit communication between persons at,

(a) the collar of the shaft, including the collar of an internal shaft;

854

(b) the landing stations in use in a shaft;

(c) the hoist room for the shaft including the hoist room for an internal shaft;

(d) an underground refuge station; and

(e) an attended place on surface.

234. Where a call system is installed for a cage, the call system shall,

(a) not be operated in excess of 150 volts; and

(b) be arranged so that the call signals are inaudible to the hoist operator.

235. (1) A signalling system shall be installed at an underground mine by which signals may be exchanged between the tender of a shaft conveyance and the hoist operator for the purpose of controlling the hoist.

(2) The system prescribed in subsection (1) shall,

(a) not be operated in excess of 150 volts;

(b) be supplied with power from a transformer which supplies no other load;

(c) where the primary voltage of the transformer exceeds 750 volts,

(i) have one conductor of the power supply grounded, or

(ii) have the conductors ungrounded if,

(A) an isolating transformer with a 1 to 1 ratio supplies the power for the signal, and

(B) the circuit has a device to indicate a ground fault;

(d) have the non-current carrying metal parts of the signalling unit grounded unless the unit is mounted at least 2.4 metres above the floor;

(e) except as prescribed in subsection (3), be capable of providing signals that are,

(i) audible and clear,

(ii) separate for each shaft compartment, and

(iii) distinctive in sound for each compartment;

(f) be arranged so that the hoist operator can return a signal to the worker signalling; and

(g) be installed at every working level, landing deck and any other necessary shaft location.

(3) The system shall be capable of providing a signal that is both audible and visible when installed on a multi-deck sinking stage.

(4) Signalling systems using radio frequencies for transmitting signals shall comply with section 174.

236. (1) A signal for hoist movement shall be given only,

    (a) by an authorized worker; and

    (b) when the shaft conveyance or counterweight is at the same location as the worker signalling, except during,

        (i) shaft sinking and preliminary shaft development, or

        (ii) maintenance work in a shaft or on a mine hoisting plant.

(2) No hoist shall be moved on manual control unless,

    (a) the signal prescribed under this section is given;

    (b) the signal is returned by the hoist operator; and

    (c) at least four seconds have elapsed after the executive signal has been given.

(3) Signals shall be given in the following sequence:

    1. Cautionary.

    2. Destination.

    3. Executive.

(4) The following basic code of signals to a hoist operator shall be used:

1.	Stop immediately	1 signal
2.	Where the shaft conveyance is stationary, hoist	1 signal
3.	Lower	2 signals
4.	Persons entering or leaving a shaft conveyance	3 signals
5.	Caution—blasting to take place	4 signals
6.	Release of shaft conveyance	5 signals
7.	Danger	9 signals
8.	Chairing	1 signal followed by 2 signals
9.	Hoist slowly	3 signals, followed by 3 signals, followed by 1 signal

854

| 10. | Lower slowly | 3 signals, followed by 3 signals, followed by 2 signals |

(5) In addition to the basic code of signals prescribed by subsection (4), the tender of a shaft conveyance shall comply with the Code of Standard Signals issued by the Ministry.

(6) Where it is necessary for the operation of a shaft conveyance, the supervisor in charge of an underground mine may establish signals in addition to those prescribed by subsections (4) and (5).

(7) The basic code of signals and destination signals shall be posted in every hoistroom, working level and landing deck.

O. Reg. 265/15 s. 13

237. (1) This section applies during shaft sinking and preliminary development work during shaft sinking at an underground mine.

(2) A bucket used to transport persons shall,

    (a) be provided when the vertical depth of a shaft below the collar exceeds fifty metres;

    (b) be at least 1.07 metres high; and

    (c) be designed as prescribed by subsections 230(3) and (4).

(3) Where the distance between a head sheave and the shaft bottom exceeds 100 metres a crosshead shall be used with a bucket.

(4) A crosshead shall be,

    (a) landed on at least two chairs at the bottom crosshead stop to prevent distortion;

    (b) attached to the rope by a safety appliance in such manner that where the crosshead jams in the shaft compartment, the bucket is stopped; and

    (c) of a type that encloses the bucket unless,

        (i) the shaft compartment is tightly lined, and

        (ii) the bucket is barrel-shaped.

(5) Dual lights shall be installed to indicate to the hoist operator that,

    (a) the crosshead and bucket are descending together from the bucket dumping position;

    (b) the service doors are in or out of the shaft compartment; and

    (c) the dump doors are in or out of the shaft compartment.

(6) A service door or doors as prescribed by subsection (7), to cover the sinking compartment of a shaft, shall be provided.

(7) The service door or doors required by subsection (6) shall,

(a) be installed at the collar and any place in the shaft where tools and other materials are loaded or unloaded into or from the bucket;

(b) be automatically latched out by mechanical devices when out of the shaft compartment;

(c) be closed when a bucket is being loaded or unloaded with tools and other materials; and

(d) be closed when persons are entering or leaving a bucket, except where the closed crosshead provides equal protection for persons.

(8) Dump doors shall be installed and maintained that,

(a) prevent a bucket from being dumped when the dump doors are open;

(b) prevent any material from falling down the shaft while the bucket is being dumped; and

(c) are provided with devices that securely latch the dump doors out of the shaft compartment automatically.

(9) Where a multi-deck stage is being used, the stage shall be,

(a) designed by a professional engineer in accordance with good engineering practice; and

(b) built in accordance with the design.

(10) Before the initial use of a multi-deck stage, the employer shall give notice to the joint health and safety committee or to the health and safety representative, if any.

(11) A bucket shall be filled so that no piece of loose rock projects above the level of the rim.

(12) No person shall ride on the rim of a bucket.

(12.1) A person who is being transported by a bucket shall ride inside the bucket.

(13) The worker authorized to give signals for hoist movement shall,

(a) maintain proper discipline of persons riding in the bucket; and

(b) enforce the loading restrictions of the conveyance permit.

(14) No person shall obstruct the worker mentioned in subsection (13) from performing his or her prescribed duties.

(15) A bucket shall not be allowed to leave the top or bottom of the shaft until the bucket has been steadied.

(16) A bucket returning to the shaft bottom shall be,

(a) stopped at a distance at least five metres and not more than ten metres above the bottom of the shaft; and

(b) lowered slowly below the point described in clause (a) only on a separate signal.

(17) On the initial trip following a blasting operation, no bucket transporting workers shall be lowered below a point,

(a) less than fifteen metres above the blasting set or bulkhead; or

(b) where the health and safety of workers is likely to be endangered.

(18) Below the point prescribed in subsection (17), the bucket shall be lowered slowly on the signal of the workers being transported and only a sufficient number of workers shall be transported on the initial trip as are required to conduct a proper examination of the part of the shaft that may be affected by the blast.

(19) Persons may be at the bottom of the shaft during the dumping cycle of the shaft conveyance.

O. Reg. 272/97 s. 43; 263/99 s. 9; 296/11 s. 17

238. (1) No person shall operate, or be permitted to operate, a hoist, unless that person,

(a) is in possession of a subsisting hoist operator's medical certificate;

(b) is over eighteen years of age;

(c) [Revoked O. Reg. 60/94, s. 13.]

(d) is a competent person or, in the case of a worker being trained to operate the hoist, is under the direct supervision of a competent person; and

(e) is physically and mentally fit to discharge the duties of a hoist operator.

(2) A person operating a hoist shall,

(a) undergo a medical examination by a physician before commencing work as a hoist operator and every twelve months thereafter; and

(b) obtain a hoist operator's medical certificate from the physician certifying that the person is physically fit to operate a hoist and is not subject to any infirmity of body and mind that may interfere with the duties of a hoist operator.

(3) A hoist operator's medical certificate shall,

    (a) be kept available for inspection; and

    (b) expire twelve months after its date.

(4) A hoist operator's medical certificate shall be in the following form:
Occupational Health and Safety Act

HOIST OPERATOR'S MEDICAL CERTIFICATE

I have this day examined

Name ....

and certify he/she is physically fit to operate a hoist and is not subject to any infirmity of body or mind that may interfere with the duties of a hoist operator.

....
Signature of physician

....
(date)

O. Reg. 60/94 s. 13; 296/11 s. 18

239. (1) A report shall be made by the hoist operator in the Hoist Operator's Log Book for each shift performed by him or her of,

    (a) the working condition of,

        (i) the hoist brakes, clutches and clutch brake interlocks,

        (ii) the depth indicator,

        (iii) the signal system,

        (iv) the hoist controls,

        (v) the overwind and underwind devices, and

        (vi) other devices which may affect safe hoist operation;

    (b) any instructions given to him or her affecting hoist operations;

    (c) any unusual circumstances in connection with the operation of the hoist;

    (d) the results of any tests prescribed by this Regulation;

    (e) any trial trips;

    (f) any inadvertent stoppages; and

    (g) his or her actual starting and finishing time.

(2) The hoist operator shall,

854

(a) review and countersign all entries in the Hoist Operator's Log Book for the preceding two shifts; and

(b) sign in the Hoist Operator's Log Book for his or her period of duty.

(3) A person issuing instructions to the hoist operator shall record and sign such instructions in the Hoist Operator's Log Book.

(4) The supervisor in charge of a mine hoist shall review and countersign each working day the entries in the Hoist Operator's Log Book for the preceding twenty-four hour work period.

(5) The Hoist Operator's Log Book shall be kept in the hoistroom and available for inspection.

240. (1) A hoist operator shall,

(a) at least once during his or her shift, in accordance with sub-section (2),

(i) test for the satisfactory working conditions and holding capacity of the hoist brakes, and

(ii) test the holding capacity of any friction clutch;

(b) at least once in twenty-four hours of use of a hoist, test the overwind and underwind protective devices by operating the hoist into them;

(c) make a trial trip of a shaft conveyance,

(i) through the working part of a shaft if hoisting has been stopped for a period exceeding two hours and the hoist operator has reason to believe that an event may have occurred to cause damage or obstruction to the free and normal movement of the conveyances in the shaft, and

(ii) below any part of a shaft that has been under repair, after the repairs have been completed;

(d) remain at the hoist controls when the hoist is in motion under manual control;

(e) except when the hoist is on automatic control due to a temporary absence of the operator from the hoist controls, set the brakes and controls so that at least two separate and distinct actions are required to put the hoist in motion;

(f) not be in voice communication when the hoist is in motion and under his or her manual control, except during an emergency or during maintenance and examination;

(g) not operate the hoist to transport any person unless at least two brakes can be applied to stop the hoist drum;

(h) not lower persons on an unclutched drum;

(i) when heavy loads or irregularly shaped loads are on or under the shaft conveyance, operate the hoist with caution;

(j) complete the hoist movement required by an executive signal after the hoist movement is begun unless there is a signal to stop or an emergency signal; and

(k) upon receiving three signals, remain at the hoist controls unless advised orally by the person in charge of the conveyance that hoist movement will not be required.

(2) The following applies with respect to the tests required by clause (1)(a):

1. The tests shall be conducted in accordance with a procedure established for the hoist.

2. The hoist operator shall conduct the tests immediately before the hoist is used to move a shaft conveyance that is transporting persons.

3. If the tests have been conducted under paragraph 2 during a shift, it is not necessary to conduct them again during the same shift.

O. Reg. 584/91 s. 6; 31/04 s. 15; 34/14 s. 15

241. No person shall,

(a) operate or interfere with devices or controls for operating a hoist unless authorized;

(b) speak to the hoist operator while he or she is operating the hoist on manual control, except in an emergency or when the hoist is being repaired, maintained or adjusted;

(c) be on a cage while it is being placed onto or removed from chairs;

(d) be in, on or under a shaft conveyance or counterweight which is supported by an unclutched drum unless the conveyance or counterweight is secured in position or unless permitted by subsection 237(19);

(e) leave a shaft conveyance that has inadvertently stopped at a point other than a shaft station, except upon instruction from an autho-rized person outside the conveyance;

(f) put to use any chairs for landing a cage, unless,

(i) a signal for chairing has been made and returned, or

(ii) special arrangements have been made to operate a cage with a car, in balance, from that location;

(g) permit the normal operation of a mine hoist if an object which may be a hazard to the operation of a shaft conveyance or counterweight has fallen down a mine shaft until,

(i) a shaft inspection or a trial trip through the affected part has been made,

(ii) any obstructions have been removed, and

(iii) any damage affecting safe operation has been repaired.

O. Reg. 34/14 s. 16

242. (1) The hoist operator shall be instructed in the procedures to follow in operating the hoist where there is,

(a) an intermediate shaft obstruction;

(b) an emergency; and

(c) an inadvertent hoist stoppage,

and shall be instructed in the procedures for operating any safety devices for people.

(2) A notice shall be posted in the hoistroom warning that no person shall speak to the hoist operator while the hoist operator is operating the hoist on manual control, except in an emergency or when the hoist is being repaired, maintained or adjusted.

(3) A hoist operator shall be available at a mine to manually operate an automatically controlled mine hoist when persons are underground.

(4) A competent person or persons shall be designated to,

(a) give mine shaft signals;

(b) be in charge of a shaft conveyance;

(c) maintain discipline of persons riding in a shaft conveyance;

(d) enforce the load limits for the shaft conveyance; and

(e) notify the hoist operator of heavy loads or irregular shaped loads on or under the shaft conveyance.

(5) Procedures shall be adopted for removing persons from a shaft conveyance which has stopped inadvertently at a place in a shaft other than a shaft station.

(6) The person or persons designated to carry out the functions set out in subsection (4) shall be readily available to perform those functions.

243. (1) When equipment or supplies are being transported in a shaft, they shall,

(a) when in a shaft conveyance, be loaded and secured in a manner to prevent shifting;

(b) when secured to a hoisting rope of the conveyance, be secured in a manner to prevent damage to the rope and permit the safety mechanisms of the conveyance to operate; and

(c) when transported below the shaft conveyance or crosshead, be suspended in a manner to prevent contact with shaft furnishings.

(2) The suspension system or arrangement used to transport equipment or supplies below the shaft conveyance or crosshead shall be capable of withstanding at least four times the maximum allowable design stresses without permanent distortion to any component of the system or arrangement and shall meet the requirements prescribed by subsection 230(4).

244. (1) No person shall be transported in a shaft conveyance,

(a) that is a cage, unless the cage doors are closed;

(b) while the hoist that is raising or lowering the shaft conveyance is being used to transport ore or waste;

(c) that is a multi-deck cage, where supplies or service rolling stock are being transported, except that persons may be carried on the top deck when,

(i) such materials are carried on another deck,

(ii) the materials are adequately secured,

(iii) the doors of the top deck are closed,

(iv) the combined load does not exceed 85 per cent of the material load limit of the conveyance, and

(v) the scheduled trips for persons have been completed;

(d) where personal hand tools or equipment are being transported, unless such tools or equipment are,

(i) protected by guards,

(ii) secured, and

(iii) the combined load does not exceed 85 per cent of the material load limit of the conveyance;

(e) unless a worker authorized to give signals is in charge of the conveyance; and

(f) with explosives, supplies or service rolling stock.

(2) Despite clause (1)(f), those workers required to handle explosives, supplies or service rolling stock may be transported with the explosives, supplies or service rolling stock if space is provided for the safety of the workers and the combined load does not exceed 85 per cent of the material load limit of the conveyance.

245. Where a mine shaft exceeds 100 metres in vertical depth, a shaft conveyance shall be provided for the raising and lowering of workers.

246. No mine hoisting plant shall be put to, or continued in, normal service if it is or ought to be known to have a defect or be in an improper state of repair except for the purpose of correcting the defect or improper state of repair.

247. (1) One or more competent persons shall be appointed to examine the following parts of an electrically-powered or electrically-controlled hoist:

    1. Hoist motors.
    2. Hoist controls.
    3. Electrical safety devices.
    4. Signalling devices.

(2) The examination shall be done at least once each week when the hoist is being used.

(2.1) If the parts were not examined during the week before the hoist is to be used, the examination shall be done immediately before it is used.

(3) A record of the examination, servicing and repair shall be made in the Electrical Hoisting Equipment Record Book.

(4) The entries in the Electrical Hoisting Equipment Record Book shall be dated and signed by the person performing the examination, servicing or repairs.

(5) A record of a failure or accident involving an electrical component of a hoist motor and controls, electrical safety and signalling devices shall be made in the Electrical Hoisting Equipment Record Book by the supervisor in charge of electrical hoisting equipment.

(6) The supervisor in charge of the mine hoisting plant shall,

    (a) review the entries made in the Electrical Hoisting Equipment Record Book within one week after each entry is made;

    (b) ascertain that the examinations required by this section and all necessary work have been done; and

(c) upon completion of each review required by clause (a), certify in the Electrical Hoisting Equipment Record Book that he or she has complied with clauses (a) and (b).

O. Reg. 68/96 s. 7

248. (1) A competent person or persons shall be appointed to examine the mechanical parts of a mine hoisting plant in accordance with subsections (2), (2.1) and (2.2).

(2) An examination shall be made,

(a) immediately before the hoisting plant is used if it was not examined the previous day, and at least once each day thereafter that it is in use,

(i) of the exterior of each hoisting and tail rope to detect the presence of kinks or other damage and to note the appearance of the rope dressing, and

(ii) of the safety catches of the shaft conveyance for any defects;

(b) [Repealed O. Reg. 68/96, s. 8(2).]

(c) if the hoist is being used, at least once every month of,

(i) the shaft ropes to determine,

(A) the amount of wear, distortion and corrosion,

(B) the need for lubrication,

(C) the need for changing the wear patterns,

(ii) the hoisting ropes for the number and location of broken wires, and

(iii) the friction treads of a friction hoist;

(d) at least once every six months of service of,

(i) the hoisting rope of a drum hoist at the drum spout and at the attachments to the drum, and

(ii) the hoisting rope of a friction hoist within attachments at the shaft conveyance or counterweight in accordance with an established procedure; and

(e) at least once every twelve months of,

(i) bolt locking devices, foundation bolts and all bolts critical to hoist safety, and

(ii) the bails, suspension gear and structure of the shaft conveyance and counterweight.

(2.0.1) If any of the equipment described in clause (2)(c) was not examined in accordance with that clause during the month before the hoist is to be

854

used, the examination shall be done immediately before the hoist is to be used.

(2.1) The following parts shall be examined at least once a week when they are in use:

  1. Any conveyance safety mechanisms for proper adjustment and freedom of movement.

  2. Any head, deflection or idler sheaves, their shafting and bearer and sole plates.

  3. The attachments of each shaft rope.

  4. The attachments on any shaft conveyance or counterweight.

  5. Any shaft conveyance, counterweight and work platform.

  6. The hoist parts, brakes, clutch, brake-clutch interlocks and depth indicators.

  7. Any hoisting equipment being used for shaft sinking.

  8. Any auxiliary brake operating weights, to assure their freedom of movement and holding capacity.

(2.2) If the parts listed in subsection (2.1) were not examined during the week before they are to be used, the examination shall be done immediately before they are used.

(2.3) An examination of the clutch and brake-clutch interlocks under subsection (2.1) shall include an operational check to ensure their performance.

(3) At least once every three months, the safety catches and mechanisms of the cage or other shaft conveyance shall be tested and such tests shall consist of releasing the empty conveyance suddenly in some suitable manner from rest, so that the safety catches have the opportunity to grip the guides and, where the safety catches do not act satisfactorily, the cage or other shaft conveyance shall not be used for lowering or raising workers until the safety catches have been repaired and tested and shown to act satisfactorily.

(4) Hoisting ropes in use on a drum hoist shall be cleaned when necessary and shall be dressed with lubricant at least once each month so as to maintain a good coating and a record of the cleaning and dressing shall be entered in the Hoisting Machinery Record Book and the entry shall be dated and signed by the supervisor in charge of the work.

(5) [Repealed O. Reg. 779/94, s. 11.]

(6) The portion of the hoisting rope and tail rope that is within a wedge attachment of a friction hoist shall be examined at least once after every 18 months of service and shall be cut off when an examination reveals that,

    (a) there are one or more broken wires;

    (b) there is advanced corrosion;

    (c) there is excessive pitting; or

    (d) there is excessive deformation of one or more wires.

(6.1) The portion of the hoisting rope and tail rope that is within a socket attachment of a friction hoist shall be cut off,

    (a) after 24 months of service, in the case of tail rope within a resin socket attachment;

    (b) after 18 months of service, in all other cases.

(7) An examination shall be made by a competent person, using non-destructive methods acceptable to a professional engineer, to determine the condition of the,

    (a) mine hoist shafting, brake pins and linkages; and

    (b) structural parts, attachment pins and draw bars of a shaft conveyance and counterweight.

(7.1) The examination shall be made before the parts are first used and at regular intervals that are no greater than those recommended by the competent person performing the examination.

(8) Drawings of the parts to be examined under subsection (7) shall be made available, upon request, to the person performing the examination.

(9) A record of the examinations required by this section and any servicing and repairs shall be entered in the Hoisting Machinery Record Book and the entries in the Record Book shall be dated and signed by the person performing the examination, servicing or repairs.

(10) A record of a failure or accident involving a mechanical part of a mine hoisting plant shall be made in the Hoisting Machinery Record Book by the supervisor in charge of the mechanical hoisting equipment.

(11) The supervisor in charge of the mechanical parts of the mine hoisting plant shall countersign each entry made in the Hoisting Machinery Record Book with respect to examinations made under subsection (7).

(12) The supervisor in charge of the mine hoisting plant shall,

(a) review the entries made in the Hoisting Machinery Record Book within one week after each entry is made;

(b) ascertain that the examinations required by this section have been made and all necessary work done; and

(c) upon completion of the review required by clause (a), certify in the Hoisting Machinery Record Book that he or she has complied with clauses (a) and (b).

O. Reg. 779/94 s. 11; 68/96 s. 8; 272/97 s. 44; 236/99 s. 10; 486/99 s. 15; 296/11 s. 19; 34/14 s. 17; 167/16, s. 14

249. (1) An examination shall be made by a competent person of,

(a) the mine shaft, at least once a week when it is being used;

(b) if the hoist is being used, the shaft guides, timbers, walls, and compartments used for hoisting, at least once every month;

(c) the headframe, headframe foundation and backlegs, sheave deck, dump, bin and bin supports, at least once every year;

(d) the shaft sump, at such frequency as is necessary to assure that the tail, guide and rubbing rope connections are clear of water and spillage; and

(e) water in the shaft sump at least once every year to determine its pH.

(1.1) If the mine shaft is not examined during the week before it is to be used, the examination shall be done immediately before it is used.

(1.2) If the shaft guides, timbers, walls and compartments used for hoisting are not examined during the month before the hoist is used, the examination shall be done immediately before the hoist is used.

(2) A record of the examinations required by subsection (1) and any servicing and repairs shall be entered in the Shaft Inspection Record Book and such entries shall be dated and signed by the person performing the examination, servicing or repairs.

(3) The supervisor in charge of the mine shaft and headframe shall,

(a) review the entries made in the Shaft Inspection Record Book within one week after each entry is made;

(b) ascertain that the examinations required by subsection (1) have been made and all necessary work done;

(c) upon completion of the review required by clause (a), certify in the Shaft Inspection Record Book that he or she has complied with clauses (a) and (b).

O. Reg. 68/96 s. 9; 488/99 s. 16

250. The ropes, sheaves, brakes, attachments and other parts of a utility or tugger hoist shall be regularly examined by a competent person and kept in safe condition.

Part XI — Working Environment

251. (1) [Repealed O. Reg. 272/97, s. 45.]

(2) A direct gas fired non-recirculating make-up heater being used for heating a mine or a mining plant shall be installed, operated and maintained to conform to CSA Standard 3.7-77, Direct Gas-Fired Non-Recirculating Make-Up Air Heaters.

(3) All liquid or gas fuel for a heating system shall be piped and stored so that any leakage will not accumulate at or enter an underground mine.

(4) A heating system shall be operated and maintained so as to eliminate the risk of fire or explosion.

(5) A record of service, maintenance and tests on the heating system shall be kept in a log book.

O. Reg. 584/91 s. 7; 272/97 s. 45; 34/14 s. 18

252. (1) In a mining plant building, a ventilation system shall be provided, maintained and used, that will,

(a) provide an oxygen content in the atmosphere of at least 19.5 per cent by volume to all workplaces therein; and

(b) dilute and remove contaminants from all workplaces therein to prevent exposure of a worker to contaminants in excess of the limits prescribed under section 4 of Regulation 833 of the Revised Regulations of Ontario, 1990 (*Control of Exposure to Biological or Chemical Agents*) made under the Act.

(2) Accurate plans and records of a mining plant building ventilation system shall be kept and maintained, showing,

(a) the location of all ventilation openings;

(b) the location of all ventilation fans;

(c) the volumes of air in cubic metres per second handled by the fans and openings;

(d) the volumes of air in cubic metres per second withdrawn by processing equipment; and

854

(e) the location and functions of all ventilation regulating doors, louvres or other devices.

(3) Where in a mining plant the atmosphere may contain chemical or physical agents that are likely to endanger the health and safety of a worker, equipment for the detection of such agents shall be provided and such equipment shall be readily accessible.

O. Reg. 272/97 s. 46; 496/09 s. 2; 265/15 s. 14

253. (1) In an underground mine, a mechanical ventilation system shall be provided, maintained and used that will,

(a) provide an oxygen content in the atmosphere of at least 19.5 per cent by volume; and

(b) dilute and remove contaminants from all workplaces therein to prevent exposure of a worker to contaminants in excess of the limits prescribed under section 4 of Regulation 833 of the Revised Regulations of Ontario, 1990 (*Control of Exposure to Biological or Chemical Agents*) made under the Act.

(2) Accurate plans and records of a mechanical ventilation system in an underground mine shall be kept and maintained showing,

(a) the location of all ventilation fans;

(b) the volumes of air in cubic metres per second handled by the ventilation fans;

(c) the fan operating gauge pressure;

(d) the direction of flow of main ventilating airflows;

(e) the location and function of all fire doors; and

(f) the location and function of all ventilation doors, brattices, stoppings and regulators controlling airflows.

O. Reg. 272/97 s. 47; 496/09 s. 3; 265/15 s. 15

254. (1) In an underground mine,

(a) subject to clause (b), a development, exploration or production workplace shall be ventilated throughout by an auxiliary ventilation system for any advance in excess of sixty metres from a mechanical mine ventilation system; and

(b) if Regulation 833 of the Revised Regulations of Ontario, 1990 (*Control of Exposure to Biological or Chemical Agents*) made under the Act applies, a continuous supply of fresh air shall be provided and used to dilute and remove contaminants in a raise, and in a sub-drift for any advance in excess of 10 metres from a mechanical mine ventilation system, to prevent exposure of a worker to contaminants in excess of the limits prescribed under section 4 of that regulation.

(2) The fresh air supply prescribed by clause (1)(b) shall be,

(a) independent of the air supplied by any drill or machine used;

(b) controlled only at the beginning of the raise or sub-drift; and

(c) operating when a blast is detonated.

O. Reg. 272/97 s. 48; 496/09 s. 4; 265/15 s. 16

255. (1) An underground area that is not part of an underground mine ventilation system shall,

(a) be effectively barricaded to prevent inadvertent entry;

(b) be posted with signs to warn a person that entry is prohibited; and

(c) subject to subsection (3), be examined by a competent person before any other person enters or is permitted to enter the underground area.

(2) The examination prescribed in clause (1)(c) shall consist of an examination for,

(a) oxygen deficiency due to an oxygen content in the atmosphere that is less than 19.5 per cent by volume;

(b) the presence of a toxic gas, vapour, dust, mist or fume; and

(c) any other dangerous condition.

(3) Before a competent person examines the underground area he or she shall be provided with instructions in writing setting out,

(a) the hazard involved;

(b) the use of testing equipment required;

(c) the personal protective devices he or she is required to use or wear; and

(d) any other precautions and procedures to be taken for his or her protection.

O. Reg. 265/15 s. 17

256. (1) Before material containing cyanide is used for back fill in an underground mine, an assessment shall be conducted to determine the precautions to be taken to protect the health and safety of workers.

(2) The assessment shall be done in consultation with the joint health and safety committee or the health and safety representative, if any.

O. Reg. 272/97 s. 49

257. In an underground mine, clean water under pressure shall be made available for dust control purposes in a workplace where rock or ore is drilled, blasted, loaded or transported.

258. In an underground mine, broken rock or ore shall be thoroughly wetted by water,

>   (a) during blasting operations or immediately thereafter; and
>   (b) when the ore or rock is being loaded or scraped.

259. Sections 257 and 258 do not apply at a salt mine or any other operation where the ore or rock is hygroscopic.

260. No person shall enter or remain, or be permitted to enter or remain, in a workplace affected by blasting contaminants until the ventilation system has removed the contaminants or rendered them harmless.

261. In an underground mine a battery-charging station shall be ventilated to prevent the accumulation of an explosive mixture of gases.

262. (1) Effective illumination by means of stationary lighting shall be provided in an underground mine,

>   (a) at all active shaft stations and shaft conveyance landings where workers are required to travel or work; and
>   (b) where the nature of the equipment or the operation may create a hazard due to insufficient illumination.

(2) Every worker in an underground mine shall wear,

>   (a) high visibility safety apparel that makes the worker visible to others in the workplace and that meets the requirements set out in subsection (3); and
>   (b) retro-reflective material applied to the front, back and sides of head gear.

(3) High visibility safety apparel must meet the following requirements:

>   1. It shall be made of fluorescent or bright-coloured background material.
>   2. It shall have retro-reflective striping that,
>>   i. is located on the outside of the garment,
>>   ii. measures at least 50 mm in width,
>>   iii. completely encircles the waist, each arm and each leg below the knee,

iv. is arranged in two vertical lines on the front of the garment, extending over the shoulders and down to the waist, and

v. is arranged in the form of an "X" on the back of the garment, extending from the shoulders and down to the waist.

(4) All high visibility safety apparel and all retro-reflective material on head gear must be maintained in good condition so that they adequately visually identify a worker.

O. Reg. 174/01 s. 7; 265/15, s. 18

263. (1) Effective illumination appropriate for the task shall be provided at all workplaces on the surface, including,

(a) in those areas adjacent to the workplace where workers are required to travel; and

(b) in those circumstances where the nature of the equipment or the operation may create a hazard to a worker due to insufficient lighting.

(2) Subject to subsection (3), between sunset and sunrise, every worker on the surface shall wear,

(a) high visibility safety apparel that makes the worker visible to others in the workplace and that meets the requirements set out in subsection 262(3); and

(b) retro-reflective material applied to the front, back and sides of head gear.

(3) A worker is not required to comply with subsection (2) if the worker is in a booth, vehicle cab or another protective enclosure or if a work area is provided with fixed lighting that enables the worker to be seen.

(4) All high visibility safety apparel and all retro-reflective material on head gear must be maintained in good condition so that they adequately visually identify a worker.

O. Reg. 174/01 s. 8; 291/02 s. 8; 265/15, s. 19

264. In a workplace in a building which is solely dependent on artificial lighting and where a failure of the regular lighting system would create conditions that might endanger the safety of any person in the building, emergency lighting shall be provided which,

(a) turns on automatically when the regular lighting fails;

(b) is independent of the regular lighting source;

(c) provides adequate lighting for evacuation of the building; and

(d) shall be tested as frequently as necessary to ensure the system will function in an emergency but not less frequently than recommended by the manufacturer.

265. An air supplied respirator that provides compressed air for breathing purposes shall comply with CSA Standard Z180.1-00, "Compressed Breathing Air and Systems".

O. Reg. 571/92 s. 20; 84/07 s. 17

266. Where dust or other material is likely to cause a hazard by becoming airborne, the dust, or other material, shall be removed with a minimum of delay by,

(a) vacuuming;

(b) wet sweeping;

(c) wet shovelling; or

(d) other suitable means.

267. (1) An annual survey of potentially hazardous minor elements shall be conducted on all feed streams to and concentrates coming from a mining plant.

(2) An assessment shall be made of the potential hazard from the elements detected in the survey required by subsection (1) due to the processes used in the mining plant.

(3) Workplaces in the mining plant shall be monitored for the hazardous elements and compounds revealed by the assessment required by subsection (2).

(4) The results of the survey, the assessment and description and results of the monitoring program shall be reported annually to the joint health and safety committee or health and safety representative, if any.

(5) This section does not apply to a mining plant at a gravel pit or quarry.

O. Reg. 272/97 s. 50

268. An annual survey of use by mass of potentially hazardous chemical reagents shall be made in a mining plant.

269. Where a potentially hazardous chemical reagent has caused a medical or compensable injury,

(a) an annual record shall be maintained for the reagent,

(i) specifying its trade name and chemical composition, and

(ii) identifying all possible toxic chemical elements and compounds of the reagent;

(b) a record of the injury caused by the reagent shall be kept.

270. A copy of the records and the surveys required under sections 267, 268 and 269 shall be sent to the joint health and safety committee or health and safety representative, if any, annually.

O. Reg. 272/97 s. 51

271. [Repealed O. Reg. 630/05, s. 2.]

272. [Repealed O. Reg. 630/05, s. 2.]

273. [Repealed O. Reg. 630/05, s. 2.]

274. [Repealed O. Reg. 630/05, s. 2.]

275. [Repealed O. Reg. 630/05, s. 2.]

276. (1) Subject to subsections (3), (4) and (5), toilets and wash-basins in a mining plant shall be provided in accordance with the following Table:

TABLE

Number of Workers			Number of facilities	
			Toilets	Washba-sins
1	to	9	1	1
10	to	24	2	2
25	to	49	3	3
50	to	74	4	4
75	to	100	5	5
Add one toilet and one washbasin for each additional thirty workers or fraction thereof.				

(2) In a washroom,

(a) a toilet shall be enclosed by walls or partitions and a door that is capable of being locked from the inside to provide privacy to a person using the toilet;

(b) hot and cold water shall be supplied to each washbasin;

(c) ventilation to the outdoors capable of providing ten changes of air per hour shall be provided;

(d) a reasonable supply of personal hygiene supplies and equipment shall be provided, and where separate washrooms are provided for each sex, a legible sign indicating the sex by which the washroom is to be used shall be posted at the door.

(3) In calculating the number of toilets and washbasins required by the Table in subsection (1), the number of workers in the Table in subsection (1) shall be that number of workers who are normally present on the premises for more than 25 per cent of their working shift.

(4) Urinals may be substituted for one-half of the required number of toilets for males and for this purpose each 600 millimetres of straight trough urinal may be counted as one urinal.

(5) For the purpose of this section, each 500 millimetres of circumference of a circular wash fountain or length of straight trough washbasin may be counted as one washbasin.

(6) Water that is to be used for personal washing purposes shall not,

(a) exceed 60° Celsius at any outlet; or

(b) be directly mixed with steam.

277. (1) Suitable sanitary conveniences must be provided at a mine in accordance with this section.

(2) If workers are employed in an underground mine, one toilet must be provided for each group of twenty-five workers or less employed on a shift.

(3) If workers are employed at a surface mine, one toilet and one urinal must be provided for each group of twenty-five workers or less employed on a shift.

(4) A toilet at a mine must meet the following requirements:

1. It must be the water-flushing type or of a sanitary design.
2. It must be located in an individual compartment that has a suitable floor and a door that can be locked.
3. It must be provided with clothes hooks.
4. It must be provided with a means for cleansing hands.
5. It must be supplied with toilet paper and, if any of the workers using it are women, with a means for disposing of feminine hygiene products.

6. If electricity is available, the toilet must be provided with lighting.

7. If electricity is available, the toilet must be provided with heating if the toilet is in a location that is colder than 10° Celsius or is in an area that is cold, damp and drafty.

(5) A toilet in an underground mine must be located in a well-ventilated part of the mine and must be conveniently placed having regard to the number of workers employed on the different levels of the mine.

(6) A toilet at a mine must be provided with disinfectant and cleansers and must be cleaned and maintained as often as is required to keep it sanitary and at least once a week.

(7) The waste from a toilet at a surface mine must be disposed of on a regular basis.

(8) The waste from a toilet in an underground mine must on a regular basis be removed, placed in a sturdy leak-proof container and brought to the surface for disposal.

(9) Despite subsection (8), the employer may use a different hygienic underground disposal system for wastes from a toilet in an underground mine with the agreement of the joint health and safety committee or the health and safety representative, if any, for the workplace.

O. Reg. 60/94 s. 14

278. (1) Suitable and adequate facilities to wash and shower and to change and dry their clothing shall be provided for workers,

  (a) at an underground mine; and

  (b) at a surface mine, where the workers are subject to dusty, dirty or wet conditions.

(2) At an underground mine, the facilities required by subsection (1) shall be located,

  (a) when above ground, near the principal entrance of the mine;

  (b) unless of noncombustible construction, not nearer than fifteen metres to a shafthouse or portal house; and

  (c) not in a hoistroom or boilerhouse, unless a separate, properly constructed room is provided.

(3) At a surface mine, where the facilities required by subsection (1) are located at a considerable distance from the place of work, adequate transportation to the facilities from the workplace shall be provided to the workers in inclement weather.

854

(4) Where practical, protection from the elements between the shaft entrance and the change rooms shall be provided.

O. Reg. 167/16, s. 1

279. Where the clothing of a worker is likely to be contaminated by a biological or chemical agent that may be a hazard to health suitable facilities shall be provided for,

    (a) laundering work clothing; and

    (b) keeping work clothes separate from street clothes.

280. (1) Cool potable drinking water shall be provided in mining plants,

    (a) from,

        (i) a fountain with an upward jet, or

        (ii) a tap from a piped water supply or a covered vessel, together with a supply of single-use cups in a sanitary container located near the tap;

    (b) on every floor where work is regularly performed; and

    (c) within 100 metres of any area where work is regularly performed.

(2) In underground mines cool potable drinking water shall be provided at locations that,

    (a) are reasonably accessible to a worker; and

    (b) shall be kept in a clean and sanitary condition.

(3) The employer shall ensure that all potable drinking water in a mine or mining plant complies with,

    (a) Ontario Regulation 169/03 (*Ontario Drinking Water Quality Standards*) made under the *Safe Drinking Water Act, 2002*; or

    (b) the regulations governing pre-packaged water made under the *Food and Drugs Act* (Canada).

O. Reg. 291/02 s. 9; 34/14 s. 19

281. (1) Where fifteen or more persons congregate to eat, a lunchroom shall be provided which,

    (a) is of sufficient size to accommodate all the persons therein;

    (b) is heated, lighted and ventilated;

    (c) has hand washing and drying facilities;

    (d) has hot and cold water;

    (e) has facilities for warming of food;

    (f) has suitable seating facilities; and

    (g) has a noncombustible, covered receptacle for waste disposal.

(2) An employer shall ensure that all workers have access to an eating area with,

- (a) hand cleaning facilities;
- (b) potable water;
- (c) suitable seating facilities;
- (d) lighting;
- (e) ventilation;
- (f) facilities to keep food from freezing;
- (g) heating, if working conditions are wet or cold or both; and
- (h) a fire retardant receptacle for waste disposal.

(3) All lunchrooms and eating areas shall be kept sanitary, clean and dry.

O. Reg. 571/92 s. 21; 167/16, s. 1

281.1(1) Every employer shall equip and maintain a first aid room close to the entrance of an underground mine.

(2) A first aid room shall be equipped with at least the items listed in the Schedule.

(3) A first aid room shall be in the charge of a person,

- (a) who is certified in Standard St. John Ambulance First Aid-Mine Rescue or who holds equivalent qualifications;
- (b) who is readily available; and
- (c) who does not perform other work of a nature that is likely to adversely affect the person's availability to administer first aid.

O. Reg. 583/91 s. 6; 167/16, s. 15

281.2(1) Every employer shall ensure that a person trained in extrication and in rescue methods and equipment pertinent to underground mines is readily available.

(2) An employer shall keep at a location near a work area in an underground mine,

- (a) equipment enabling voice communication with the surface;
- (b) a basket stretcher with a spine board and stretcher straps and ropes for lowering and hoisting the basket stretcher;
- (c) two blankets, six triangular bandages and three pressure dressings, all of which are sealed in a container that keeps them clean, dry and serviceable;
- (d) a splint; and
- (e) a cervical collar.

(3) An employer shall consult with the joint health and safety committee or the health and safety representative or, if there is no committee or representative, with the workers to determine what equipment is necessary to rescue injured workers.

(4) An employer shall keep the equipment determined under subsection (3) to be necessary and a list of the equipment at suitable locations at an underground mine.

O. Reg. 583/91 s. 6

281.3(1) An employer shall ensure that all first aid and rescue equipment is inspected at regular intervals as determined by the employer in consultation with the joint health and safety committee or the health and safety representative or, if there is no committee or representative, with the workers.

(2) An employer shall keep a record of all inspections of first aid and rescue equipment.

O. Reg. 583/91 s. 6

282. (1) [Revoked O. Reg. 583/91, s. 7.]

(2) At every mining plant where poisonous or dangerous compounds, solutions or gases are present, there shall be kept or installed in a conspicuous place, as near the compounds, solutions or gases as is practical,

    (a) antidotes and washes;

    (b) eye wash fountains; and

    (c) where necessary, showers for treating injuries received from such compounds, solutions or gases.

(3) Antidotes and washes required under subsection (2) shall be properly labelled and explicit directions for their use shall be affixed to the boxes containing them.

O. Reg. 583/91 s. 7

283. [Repealed O. Reg. 265/15, s. 20.]

284. [Revoked O. Reg. 272/97, s. 52.]

285. Where a box, drum or other container contains a biological or chemical agent which is likely to affect the health or safety of a worker, the box, drum or other container shall be labelled in clear legible print to identify the agent and the label shall state the precautions to be taken in the handling, use, storage and disposal of the agent.

286. (1) If Regulation 833 of the Revised Regulations of Ontario, 1990 (*Control of Exposure to Biological or Chemical Agents*) made under the Act applies and a local exhaust ventilation system recirculates air to the workplace, provision shall be made for a make-up air supply system having sufficient volume to keep any contaminants below the limits prescribed under section 4 of that regulation.

(2) The contaminant level in the recirculated air shall not exceed 20 per cent of the limits described in subsection (1).

O. Reg. 236/99 s. 11; 496/09 s. 5; 265/15 s. 21

287. In sections 288 to 293,

"radon daughters" [Repealed O. Reg. 167/16, s. 16(1).]

"radon progeny" means polonium-218 (RaA), lead-214 (RaB), bismuth-214 (RaC) and polonium-214 (RaC');

"WL" means working level of radon progeny as determined in accordance with subsection 288(1);

"WLM " means working level month of radon progeny as determined in accordance with subsection 288(2).

O. Reg. 583/91, s. 8; 167/16, s. 16

288. (1) One working level of radon progeny is the amount of any combination of radon progeny in one litre of air that will release 1.3×10^5 mega electron volts of alpha particle energy during their radioactive decay to lead-210 (RaD).

(2) One working level month of radon progeny is the amount of a person's exposure to radon progeny resulting from breathing air that contains one WL for a period of 170 hours.

O. Reg. 583/91 s. 8; 167/16, s. 17

289. (1) Samples of air to which workers may be exposed in an underground mine shall be tested for the presence of radon progeny by a competent person.

(2) The air to which workers may be exposed in an underground mine shall be tested,

    (a) before work begins in a mine that is being reopened; and

    (b) within six months after the commencement of excavation of a new mine.

854

(3) The air to which workers may be exposed in an underground mine shall be retested,

> (a) at least monthly, if the concentration of radon progeny in a sample exceeds 0.1 WL; and

> (b) at least quarterly, if the concentration of radon progeny in a sample is greater than 0.06 WL up to and including 0.1 WL.

(4) If the concentration of radon progeny in a sample is less than or equal to 0.06 WL, a competent person shall assess once a year whether to retest the air in the work area in the underground mine and in making the assessment shall consider previous test results and changes in the mine or its operations.

(5) An employer shall keep a record of the results of all tests of samples of air in an underground mine and shall give a copy of all results to the joint health and safety committee or the health and safety representative, if any.

(6) An employer shall post the results of all testing in a place where they are likely to come to the attention of workers as soon as the results become available and shall keep them posted for at least fourteen days.

(7) [Repealed O. Reg. 167/16, s. 18.]

(8) [Repealed O. Reg. 167/16, s. 18.]

O. Reg. 583/91 s. 8; 167/16, ss. 17, 18

290. (1) Every employer shall ensure that the airborne concentration of radon progeny to which workers may be exposed in an underground mine is reduced to the lowest practical level in accordance with good industrial hygiene practice.

(2) An employer shall ensure that no worker who is continuously employed by the employer during a year inhales air which exposes the worker to more than one WLM.

O. Reg. 583/91 s. 8; 167/16, s. 17

291. If the concentration of radon progeny to which a worker may be exposed in an underground mine exceeds 0.33 WL, the employer,

> (a) shall immediately remove all workers from the affected area of the mine;

> (b) shall give written notice of the occurrence to the joint health and safety committee or health and safety representative, if any;

> (c) shall implement the measures and procedures required by sub-section 255(1);

(d) shall provide the written instructions required by subsection 255(3) to all workers assigned to do remedial work; and

(e) shall provide to workers doing remedial work and require the use of respiratory equipment appropriate to prevent or limit the workers' exposure to radon progeny.

O. Reg. 583/91 s. 8; 272/97 s. 53; 167/16, s. 17

292. (1) An employer shall develop and implement in consultation with the joint health and safety committee or the health and safety representative, if any, a written description of work practices for a workplace at which the airborne concentration of radon progeny exceeds 0.1 WL.

(2) The written description of work practices shall include procedures for investigating the cause of and reducing the level of the airborne concentration of radon progeny to the lowest practical level in accordance with good industrial hygiene practice.

(3) An employer shall post the written description of work practices in a place where it is likely to come to the attention of all workers who may be affected by exposure to radon progeny.

(4) [Revoked O. Reg. 272/97, s. 54.]

O. Reg. 583/91 s. 8; 272/97 s. 54; 291/02 s. 10; 167/16, s. 17

293. (1) This section applies with respect to a workplace where a written description of work practices referred to in section 292 has been implemented.

(2) An employer shall train workers in radiation hazards and protection practices.

(3) An employer shall calculate in WLMs the annual cumulative level of exposure of a worker who is exposed to an average concentration of radon progeny greater than 0.1 WL over a period of eight hours.

(4) An employer shall keep a record of the information calculated under subsection (3) and shall give a copy of the record,

(a) to the worker or the next of kin or personal representative of a deceased worker, on receipt of a written request; and

(b) to the joint health and safety committee or the health and safety representative, if any.

(5) An employer shall forward a copy of a record kept under subsection (4) to the National Dose Registry administered by Health Canada's Radiation Protection Bureau.

854

O. Reg. 583/91 s. 8; 291/02 s. 11; 265/15 s. 22;·167/16, s. 17

293.1 [Repealed O. Reg. 383/15, s. 1.]

Part XII
[Heading repealed O. Reg. 99/11, s. 1.]

294 to 313 [Repealed O. Reg. 99/11, s. 1.]

TABLE 1 [Repealed O. Reg. 496/09, s. 7.]

[Repealed O. Reg. 496/09, s. 7.]

SCHEDULE

First Aid Equipment

1. (1) Every first aid room referred to in section 281.1 of this Regulation shall be equipped with,

(a) a current edition of a standard St. John Ambulance First Aid Manual;

(b) medical instruments, including dressing scissors, dressing forceps, safety pins, a graduated medicine glass, tongue depressors and cotton-tipped applicators;

(c) denatured ethyl alcohol; and

(d) dressings, including individually-wrapped adhesive dressings, individually-wrapped sterile gauze pads of various sizes, gauze bandages of various sizes, adhesive plaster, absorbent cotton, triangular bandages, splints of various sizes and splint padding.

(2) Every first aid room shall be furnished with,

(a) hot and cold running water;

(b) three wash basins (preferably stainless steel);

(c) one instrument sterilizer;

(d) one cabinet for surgical dressings;

(e) one enamel foot bath;

(f) one sanitary disposal receptacle with a lid;

(g) one couch in a cubicle separate from or curtained off from the rest of the first aid room;

(h) one stretcher; and

(i) two blankets.

2. (1) Every first aid room shall have one first aid box that contains at least the items listed in this section for use by a medical attendant at the site of an accident.

(2) A first aid box shall contain,

(a) a current edition of a standard St. John Ambulance First Aid Manual; and

(b) dressings, including twenty-four individually-wrapped adhesive dressings, twelve 3′ square gauze pads, four rolls of 2′ gauze bandage, four rolls of 4′ gauze bandage, four individually-wrapped sterile surgical pads suitable for pressure dressing, six triangular bandages and one roll-up splint.

O. Reg. 583/91 s. 9

Form 1

[Repealed O. Reg. 296/11, s. 21.]

854

ONT. REG. 474/07 — NEEDLE SAFETY

made under the *Occupational Health and Safety Act*

O. Reg. 474/07, as am. O. Reg. 317/08; 21/09 (Fr.); 439/09.

1. Definition —

In this Regulation,

"safety-engineered needle" means,

(a) a hollow-bore needle that,

(i) is designed to eliminate or minimize the risk of a skin puncture injury to the worker, and

(ii) is licensed as a medical device by Health Canada, or

(b) a needleless device that,

(i) replaces a hollow-bore needle, and

(ii) is licensed as a medical device by Health Canada.

2. Application —

(1) This Regulation applies in each of the following circumstances:

1. A worker is to do work requiring the use of a hollow-bore needle on a person for a therapeutic, preventative, palliative, diagnostic or cosmetic purpose, in any workplace.

2. A worker is to do any work requiring the use of a hollow-bore needle, in a workplace listed in subsection (2).

(2) The workplaces mentioned in paragraph 2 of subsection (1) are the following:

1. Every hospital as defined in the *Public Hospitals Act*.

2. Every private hospital as defined in the *Private Hospitals Act*.

3. Homewood Health Centre Inc.

4. Every laboratory or specimen collection centre as defined in the *Laboratory and Specimen Collection Centre Licensing Act*.

5. Every psychiatric facility as defined in the *Mental Health Act*.

6. Every long-term care home as defined in the *Long-Term Care Homes Act, 2007*.

7. [Repealed O. Reg. 439/09, s. 1(2).]

8. [Repealed O. Reg. 439/09, s. 1(2).]

O. Reg. 317/08 ss. 1, 2; 439/09 s. 1

3. Provision of safety-engineered needles —

(1) When a worker is to do work requiring the use of a hollow-bore needle, the employer shall provide the worker with a safety-engineered needle that is appropriate for the work.

(2) Subsection (1) does not apply if the employer is unable, despite making efforts that are reasonable in the circumstances, to obtain a safety-engineered needle that is appropriate for the work.

4. Use of safety-engineered needle —

(1) A worker who has been provided with a safety-engineered needle for work described in subsection 3(1) shall use the safety-engineered needle for the work.

(2) Despite subsection (1), the worker may use a hollow-bore needle that is not a safety-engineered needle if he or she believes on reasonable grounds that, in the particular circumstances, the use of a safety-engineered needle would pose a greater risk of harm than the use of the hollow-bore needle.

(3) In subsection (2), "risk of harm" refers to either or both of the following risks:

    1. A risk of harm to the worker or to another worker.

    2. If the work involves the use of a needle on a person, a risk of harm to him or her.

(4) The employer shall develop, establish and provide training for workers to assist them in applying subsection (2).

5. Exceptions, emergencies and risks to health —

(1) Subsection 3(1) does not apply if all of the following conditions are satisfied:

    1. The workplace is located in a part of Ontario in which,

        i. a declaration of emergency made under the *Emergency Management and Civil Protection Act* is in effect, or

        ii. a situation exists that constitutes or may constitute a serious risk to public health.

    2. The employer's supplies of safety-engineered needles appropriate for the work have been exhausted.

3. The risk of harm from postponing the work until a safety-engineered needle appropriate for the work becomes available is greater than the risk of harm from using a hollow-bore needle that is not a safety-engineered needle.

(2) In paragraph 3 of subsection (1), "risk of harm" refers to any or all of the following risks:

1. A risk of harm to the worker or to another worker.

2. If the work involves the use of a needle on a person, a risk of harm to him or her.

3. An immediate or potential risk to the public or to the public interest.

O. Reg. 317/08 s. 3; 439/09 s. 2

6. Commencement —

This Regulation comes into force on September 1, 2008.

ONT. REG. 381/15 — NOISE

made under the *Occupational Health and Safety Act*

Interpretation

1.(1) In this Regulation,

"attenuation" means a reduction in sound pressure level incident upon the ear;

"dBA" means a measure of sound level in decibels using a reference sound pressure of 20 micropascals when measured on the A-weighting network of a sound level meter;

"decibel" means a unit of measurement of sound pressure level that is equal to 20 times the logarithm to the base 10 of the ratio of the pressure of a sound, divided by the reference pressure of 20 micropascals.

(2) An equivalent sound exposure level is the steady sound level in dBA which, if present in a workplace for eight hours in a day, would contain the same total energy as that generated by the actual and varying sound levels to which a worker is exposed in his or her total work day.

(3) The equivalent sound exposure level is determined in accordance with the formula,

$$L_{ex,8} = 10 \, \text{Log}_{10} \left(\frac{\left[\sum_{i=1}^{n} (t_i \times 10^{0.1 \, SPL_i}) \right]}{8} \right)$$

Text alternative: Image of the mathematical equation for determining the equivalent sound exposure level over eight hours that contains the same total energy as that generated by the actual and varying sound levels to which a worker is exposed in his or her total work day. This text alternative is provided for convenience only and does not form part of the official law.

in which,

$L_{ex,8}$ is the equivalent sound exposure level in 8 hours,

Σ is the sum of the values in the enclosed expression for all activities from $i = 1$ to $i = n$,

i is a discrete activity of a worker exposed to a sound level,

t_i is the duration in hours of i,

SPL_i is the sound level of i in dBA,

n is the total number of discrete activities in the worker's total workday.

Duty to protect workers

2.(1) Every employer shall take all measures reasonably necessary in the circumstances to protect workers from exposure to hazardous sound levels.

(2) The protective measures shall include the provision and use of engineering controls, work practices and, subject to subsection (5), hearing protection devices.

(3) Any measurement of sound levels in the workplace that is done in order to determine what protective measures are appropriate shall be done without regard to the use of hearing protection devices.

(4) Without limiting the generality of subsections (1) and (2), every employer shall ensure that no worker is exposed to a sound level greater than an equivalent sound exposure level of 85 dBA, Lex,8.

(5) Except in the circumstances set out in subsection (6), the employer shall protect workers from exposure to a sound level greater than the limit described in subsection (4) without requiring them to use and wear hearing protection devices.

(6) Workers shall wear and use hearing protection devices appropriate in the circumstances to protect them from exposure to a sound level greater than the limit described in subsection (4) if engineering controls are required by subsections (1) and (2) and,

(a) are not in existence or are not obtainable;

(b) are not reasonable or not practical to adopt, install or provide because of the duration or frequency of the exposures or because of the nature of the process, operation or work;

(c) are rendered ineffective because of a temporary breakdown of such controls; or

(d) are ineffective to prevent, control or limit exposure because of an emergency.

(7) Where practicable, a clearly visible warning sign shall be posted at every approach to an area in the workplace where the sound level, measured as described in subsection (3), regularly exceeds 85 dBA.

Training and instruction

3. An employer who provides a worker with a hearing protection device shall also provide adequate training and instruction to the worker in the care and use of the device, including its limitations, proper fitting, inspection and maintenance and, if applicable, the cleaning and disinfection of the device.

Hearing protection devices

4.(1) A hearing protection device shall be selected having regard to,

(a) sound levels to which a worker is exposed;

(b) the attenuation provided by the device; and

(c) the manufacturer's information about the use and limitations of the device.

(2) A hearing protection device shall be used and maintained in accordance with the manufacturer's instructions.

Commencement

5. This Regulation comes into force on the later of July 1, 2016 and the day it is filed.

ONT. REG. 297/13 — OCCUPATIONAL HEALTH AND SAFETY AWARENESS AND TRAINING

made under the *Occupational Health and Safety Act*

O. Reg. 297/13, as am. O. Reg. 253/14

Basic Occupational Health and Safety Awareness Training

1. Basic occupational health and safety awareness training—workers —

(1) An employer shall ensure that a worker who performs work for the employer completes a basic occupational health and safety awareness training program that meets the requirements set out in subsection (3) as soon as practicable.

(2) Subsection (1) does not apply if,

    (a) the worker previously completed a basic occupational health and safety awareness training program and provides the employer with proof of completion of the training; and

    (b) the employer verifies that the previous training meets the requirements set out in subsection (3).

(3) A basic occupational health and safety awareness training program for workers must include instruction on the following:

    1. The duties and rights of workers under the Act.

    2. The duties of employers and supervisors under the Act.

    3. The roles of health and safety representatives and joint health and safety committees under the Act.

    4. The roles of the Ministry, the Workplace Safety and Insurance Board and entities designated under section 22.5 of the Act with respect to occupational health and safety.

    5. Common workplace hazards.

297/13

783

6. The requirements set out in Regulation 860 (*Workplace Hazardous Materials Information System (WHMIS)*) with respect to information and instruction on controlled products.

7. Occupational illness, including latency.

2. Basic occupational health and safety awareness training—supervisors —

(1) An employer shall ensure that a supervisor who performs work for the employer completes a basic occupational health and safety awareness training program that meets the requirements set out in subsection (3) within one week of performing work as a supervisor.

(2) Subsection (1) does not apply if,

(a) the supervisor previously completed a basic occupational health and safety awareness training program and provides the employer with proof of completion of the training; and

(b) the employer verifies that the previous training meets the requirements set out in subsection (3).

(3) A basic occupational health and safety awareness training program for supervisors must include instruction on the following:

1. The duties and rights of workers under the Act.

2. The duties of employers and supervisors under the Act.

3. The roles of health and safety representatives and joint health and safety committees under the Act.

4. The roles of the Ministry, the Workplace Safety and Insurance Board and entities designated under section 22.5 of the Act with respect to occupational health and safety.

5. How to recognize, assess and control workplace hazards, and evaluate those controls.

6. Sources of information on occupational health and safety.

3. Exemptions —

(1) The requirements set out in section 1 do not apply to an employer with respect to a supervisor if,

(a) before this Regulation came into force, the supervisor was performing work as a supervisor for the employer; and

(b) the employer verifies that, before this Regulation came into force, the supervisor completed a basic occupational health and safety awareness training program that meets the requirements set out in subsection 2(3).

(2) The requirements set out in section 1 do not apply to an employer with respect to a worker or supervisor if,

    (a) another employer was exempt with respect to the worker or supervisor under subsection (1); and

    (b) the worker or supervisor provides the employer with proof of the exemption.

4. Record of training —

(1) An employer shall maintain a record of the basic occupational health and safety awareness training required by sections 1 and 2 that is completed by workers and supervisors who perform work for the employer.

(2) An employer shall maintain a record of workers and supervisors who perform work for the employer in respect of whom the employer is exempt under section 3.

(3) If a worker or supervisor completes a training program under subsection 1(1) or 2(1), the employer shall, at the request of the worker or supervisor, provide the worker or supervisor with written proof of completion of the training.

(4) If an employer is exempt with respect to a supervisor under subsection 3 (1), the employer shall, at the request of the supervisor, provide the supervisor with written proof of the exemption.

(5) If, within six months of a worker or supervisor no longer performing work for an employer, the worker or supervisor requests a written proof described in subsection (3) or (4), the employer shall provide the worker or supervisor with the requested written proof.

Certification Training

5. Certification training —

(1) An employer shall carry out the training programs necessary to enable a committee member to become a certified member, and the programs must be selected in accordance with the training and other requirements established by the Chief Prevention Officer under section 7.6 of the Act.

(2) For greater certainty, in subsection (1),

"carry out" includes paying for the training.

297/13

Working at Heights Training — Construction Projects
[Heading amended O. Reg. 253/14, s. 1.]

6. Application — The requirements of section 7 apply to an employer in respect of workers who are required under Ontario Regulation 213/91 (*Construction Projects*) to use any of the following methods of fall protection:

1. A travel restraint system.
2. A fall restricting system.
3. A fall arrest system.
4. A safety net.
5. A work belt.
6. A safety belt.

O. Reg. 253/14 s. 1

7. Working at heights training —

(1) An employer shall ensure the following in respect of a worker who may use a method of fall protection listed in section 6:

1. The worker has successfully completed a working at heights training program that meets the requirements set out in subsection (2).
2. The validity period of the training has not expired.

(2) The following requirements apply to a working at heights training program:

1. It must be approved by the Chief Prevention Officer under subsection 7.1(2) of the Act as meeting the working at heights training program standard that applied at the time of the training.
2. It must be provided by a training provider approved by the Chief Prevention Officer under subsection 7.2(2) of the Act as meeting the working at heights training provider standard that applied at the time of the training.

O. Reg. 253/14 s. 1

8. Training — period of validity —

The working at heights training required under section 7 is valid for three years from the date of successful completion of the training program.

O. Reg. 253/14 s. 1

9. Training requirements under O. Reg. 213/91 —

For greater certainty, the requirements of subsection 26.2(1) of Ontario Regulation 213/91 (*Construction Projects*) apply in addition to the working at heights training requirements of section 7.

O. Reg. 253/14 s. 1

10. Record of training —

(1) An employer shall maintain a record of the working at heights training that is required by section 7.

(2) The training record shall include the following information:
1. The name of the worker.
2. The name of the approved training provider.
3. The date on which the approved training was successfully completed.
4. The name of the approved training program that was successfully completed.

(3) A copy of a worker's proof of successful completion, issued by the Chief Prevention Officer, is a training record for the purposes of subsection (1).

(4) The employer shall make a training record available to an inspector on request.

O. Reg. 253/14 s. 1

11. Transition —

If, before the day Ontario Regulation 253/14 comes into force, a worker has completed training that meets the requirements of section 26.2 of Ontario Regulation 213/91 (Construction Projects), the working at heights training requirements of section 7 do not apply in respect of that worker until two years after that date.

O. Reg. 253/14 s. 1

ONT. REG. 33/12 — OFFICES OF THE WORKER AND EMPLOYER ADVISERS

made under the *Occupational Health and Safety Act*

O. Reg. 33/12

1. Functions of the Offices of the Worker and Employer Advisers —

(1) For the purposes of Part VI (Reprisals by Employer Prohibited) of the Act, the functions of the Office of the Worker Adviser are to educate, advise and represent in proceedings before the Board workers who are not members of a trade union.

(2) For the purposes of Part VI (Reprisals by Employer Prohibited) of the Act, the functions of the Office of the Employer Adviser are to educate, advise and represent in proceedings before the Board employers that have fewer than 50 employees.

2. Commencement —

This Regulation comes into force on the later of the day section 14 of the *Occupational Health and Safety Statute Law Amendment Act, 2011* comes into force and the day this Regulation is filed.

ONT. REG. 855 — OIL AND GAS — OFFSHORE

made under the *Occupational Health and Safety Act*

R.R.O. 1990, Reg. 855, as am. O. Reg. 566/06; 421/10, ss.
1-19, 20 (Fr.); 384/15.

Definitions

1. In this Regulation,

"adequate", when used in relation to a procedure, plan, material, device, object or thing, means that it is,

    (a) sufficient for both its intended and its actual use, and

    (b) sufficient to protect a worker from occupational illness or occupational injury;

"adequately" has a meaning that corresponds to the meaning of **"adequate"**;

"boom" means the projecting part of a backhoe, shovel, crane or similar lifting device from which a load is likely to be supported;

"cathead" means a spool-shaped attachment on a winch around which rope for hoisting and pulling is wound;

"Director" [Repealed O. Reg. 421/10, s. 1.]

"drawworks" means the hoisting mechanism on a rig which raises or lowers the drill stem and bit;

"flammable liquid" means a liquid having a flash point below 37.8° Celsius, and a vapour pressure below 275 kilopascals absolute at 37.8° Celsius;

"kelly" means the heavy steel pipe with four or six sides that is connected to the top of the drill pipe;

"lifting device" means a device that is used to raise or lower any material or object and includes its rails and other supports;

"prime mover" means an initial source of motive power;

"professional engineer" means a person who is licensed as a professional engineer under the *Professional Engineers Act;*

"rig" means any rotary drilling ship, cable tool ship, barge, platform or other rig used for offshore oil or gas exploration, development, production, maintenance, workover, capping, plugging or abandonment operations;

"transmission equipment" means any object or objects by which the motion of a prime mover is transmitted to a machine that is capable of utilizing such motion and includes a shaft, pulley, belt, chain, gear, clutch or other device.

O. Reg. 566/06 s. 1; 421/10 s. 1

Part I — General

2. In applying this Regulation, the composition, design, size and arrangement of any material, object, device or thing may vary from the composition, design, size or arrangement prescribed if the factors of strength, health and safety are equal to or greater than the factors of strength, health and safety in the composition, design, size or arrangement prescribed.

3. This Regulation applies to all work done offshore on or from a rig.

4. The minimum age of a worker is eighteen years of age.

5. Prior to the start of the drilling season, the owner of the licence of occupation under the *Mining Act* shall provide a notice in writing to the Director, setting out,

(a) the contents of the operating manual required under section 14; and

(b) details of an emergency plan to rescue workers in the event of an emergency.

6. An emergency plan shall be prepared in writing and shall include,

(a) a suitable and rapid means of obtaining first aid help and transportation from the rig to a hospital for injured workers; and

(b) the measures and procedures to be used to,

(i) control a major fire,

(ii) react to serious damage to the rig,

(iii) evacuate the rig, and

(iv) notify rescue personnel.

7. The written report required by section 51 of the Act shall include,

    (a) the name and address of the employer;

    (b) the nature and the circumstances of the occurrence and of the bodily injury sustained;

    (c) a description of the machinery or equipment involved;

    (d) the time and place of the occurrence;

    (e) the name and address of the person who was killed or critically injured;

    (f) the names and addresses of all witnesses to the occurrence; and

    (g) the name and address of the physician or surgeon, if any, who is attending or has attended the injury.

O. Reg. 421/10 s. 2

8. For the purposes of section 52 of the Act, notice of,

    (a) an accident, explosion or fire which disables a worker from performing his or her usual work; or

    (b) an occupational illness, shall include,

    (c) the name, address and type of business of the employer;

    (d) the nature and the circumstances of the occurrence and of the bodily injury or illness sustained;

    (e) a description of the machinery or equipment involved;

    (f) the time and place of the occurrence;

    (g) the name and address of the person suffering the injury or illness;

    (h) the names and addresses of all witnesses to the occurrence;

    (i) the name and address of the physician or surgeon, if any, who is attending or has attended the injury or illness; and

    (j) the steps taken to prevent a recurrence or further illness.

O. Reg. 421/10 s. 3

9. A record of an accident, explosion or fire causing injury requiring medical attention but not disabling a worker from performing his or her usual work shall be kept in the permanent records of the employer and include particulars of,

    (a) the nature and circumstances of the occurrence and of the injury sustained;

    (b) the time and place of the occurrence; and

    (c) the name and address of the injured person.

O. Reg. 421/10 s. 4

10. A record kept as prescribed by section 9 for the inspection of an inspector shall be notice to the Director.

11. A record of the qualifications of all workers appointed as competent persons shall be kept in the permanent records of the employer for as long as the worker is employed with the employer.

Part II — Preparation

12. Muster lists shall be posted in two conspicuous locations on the rig and in each cabin.

13. A muster list shall indicate,

    (a) emergency signals or alarms;

    (b) fire stations;

    (c) survival craft stations;

    (d) workers in charge of survival craft; and

    (e) procedures outlined in the emergency plan.

14. An operating manual prescribing the procedures to be followed shall be,

    (a) available for each drilling or related operation; and

    (b) readily accessible to a worker on the drilling site.

15. The employer shall ensure that a rig and its equipment is inspected for compliance with this Regulation,

    (a) in port, by an inspector prior to the drilling season; and

    (b) by a worker who is a competent person at least once every thirty working days while in operation.

16. The employer shall ensure that the derrick or mast is inspected by a competent person,

    (a) before being put into position, raised or lowered; and

    (b) at least once every year while in port.

17. The employer shall ensure that firefighting and life saving equipment is inspected by a competent person at least once every two weeks.

18. The employer shall ensure that a lifting device is examined by a competent person to determine its capability of handling the maximum load as rated,

    (a) before being used for the first time; and

(b) thereafter as often as necessary but not less frequently than recommended by the manufacturer and, in any case, at least once a year.

19. Written reports of inspections required by this Regulation shall be made by a competent person and shall be kept,

(a) on the rig for a period of one year from the date of inspection; and

(b) at the employer's principal office in Ontario for a period of five years from the date of inspection.

20. The employer shall ensure that for each crew of workers on a working rig,

(a) a fire drill is held at least once every two weeks;

(b) an evacuation drill is held at least once every four weeks; and

(c) a man-over-board drill is held at least once every four weeks.

Part III — General Requirements

21. A worker required to wear or use any protective clothing, equipment or device shall be instructed and trained in its care and use before wearing or using the protective clothing, equipment or device.

22. Every worker who is exposed to the hazard of head injury shall wear head protection appropriate in the circumstances.

23. Every worker who is exposed to the hazard of eye injury shall wear eye protection appropriate in the circumstances.

24. Every worker who is exposed to the hazard of foot injury shall wear foot protection appropriate in the circumstances.

25. Long hair shall be suitably confined to prevent entanglement with any rotating shaft, spindle, gear, belt or other source of entanglement.

26. Every worker who is exposed to the hazard of skin injury by contact with,

(a) a noxious gas, liquid, fume or dust;

(b) a sharp or jagged object which may puncture, cut or abrade the worker's skin;

(c) a hot object, hot liquid or molten metal; or

(d) radiant heat, shall be provided with protection by the employer in the form of,

(e) wearing apparel sufficient to protect the worker from injury; or

(f) a shield, screen or similar barrier, appropriate in the circumstances.

27. Where a worker is exposed to the hazard of falling and the surface to which the worker might fall is more than three metres below the position where the worker is situated,

    (a) the employer shall provide and the worker shall wear a fall arrest system consisting of a serviceable safety belt or harness and lifeline that is adequately secured to a fixed support and so arranged that the worker cannot fall freely for a vertical distance of more than 1.5 metres; and

    (b) the fall arrest system described in clause (a) shall,

        (i) have sufficient capacity to absorb twice the energy and twice the load that under the circumstances of its use may be transmitted to it, and

        (ii) be equipped with a shock absorber or other devices to limit the maximum arresting force to 8.0 kilonewtons to the worker.

O. Reg. 421/10 s. 5

28. Every worker who is exposed to the hazard of falling into water shall wear a life jacket.

29. Material, articles or things,

    (a) required to be lifted, carried or moved shall be lifted, carried or moved in such a way and with such precautions and safeguards, including protective clothing, guards or other precautions as will ensure that the lifting, carrying or moving of the material, articles or things does not endanger the safety of any worker;

    (b) shall be transported, placed or stored so that the material, articles or things,

        (i) will not tip, collapse or fall, and

        (ii) can be removed or withdrawn without endangering the safety of any worker; and

    (c) to be removed from a storage area, pile or rack shall be removed in a manner that will not endanger the safety of any worker.

30. Machinery, equipment or material that may tip or fall and endanger any worker shall be secured against tipping or falling.

31. Cylindrical objects stored on their side shall be piled symmetrically with each unit in the bottom row chocked or wedged to prevent motion.

32. Barrels, drums or kegs that are piled on their ends shall have two parallel planks placed on top of each row before another row is added.

33. A storage cylinder for compressed gas shall,

    (a) be secured in position during use;

    (b) have the valve protection cap in position when the cylinder is not in use;

    (c) when containing acetylene, be in an upright position; and

    (d) be protected from physical damage.

34. A silo, bin, hopper, structure, container or thing used for storing or containing bulk material may be entered only where,

    (a) the supply of material thereto is stopped and precautions are taken that will prevent any further supply;

    (b) mechanical equipment that may endanger a worker is,

        (i) disconnected from its power source, and

        (ii) locked out;

    (c) the space is ventilated to provide a safe atmosphere;

    (d) the space is tested for lack of oxygen and presence of combustible gases;

    (e) the worker entering is wearing a safety harness or other similar equipment attached to a rope or lifeline; and

    (f) at least one other worker equipped with a suitable alarm and capable of rendering any necessary assistance is keeping watch nearby.

35. Where the operator of a crane or similar material handling equipment does not have a full view of the intended path of travel of the crane or similar material handling equipment or its load, the crane or similar material handling equipment shall only be operated as directed by a signaler who is a competent person and who is stationed,

    (a) in full view of the operator;

    (b) with a full view of the intended path of travel of the crane or similar material handling equipment and its load; and

    (c) clear of the intended path of travel of the crane or similar material handling equipment and its load.

36. Except for the purpose of a test of the material handling equipment, no material handling equipment shall be loaded in excess of its maximum rated load.

37. A worker who may be exposed to a biological, chemical or physical agent that may endanger the worker's safety or health shall be trained,

(a) in the precautions and procedures to be followed in the handling, use and storage of the agent;

(b) in the proper use and care of required personal protective equipment; and

(c) in the proper use of emergency measures and procedures.

38. No food, drink or tobacco shall be taken into, left or consumed in any room, area or place where any substance that is poisonous by ingestion is exposed.

39. Containers used for handling or storage of corrosive, flammable or hazardous materials shall be,

(a) appropriate for their intended use;

(b) constructed to prevent spillage or leakage;

(c) labelled to identify the contents; and

(d) disposed of in a manner that will not endanger a worker's health or safety and complies with the requirements of the Ministry of the Environment.

40. A rig shall have an easily accessible eyewash station and deluge shower adjacent to the mud mixing facilities.

41. [Repealed O. Reg. 384/15, s. 1.]

42. Where a machine or prime mover or transmission equipment other than a cathead, kelly or rotary table, has an exposed moving part that may endanger the safety of any worker, the machine or prime mover or transmission equipment shall be equipped with and guarded by a guard or other device that prevents access to the moving part.

43. An in-running nip hazard or any part of a machine, device or thing that may endanger the safety of any worker shall be equipped with and guarded by a guard or other device that prevents access to the pinch point.

44. An emergency stop control on a power-driven machine shall,

(a) be conspicuously identified; and

(b) be located within easy reach of the operator.

45. An operating control that acts as a guard for a machine not otherwise guarded shall,

(a) be in a location where the safety of the operator is not endangered by moving machinery;

(b) be arranged so that it cannot be operated accidentally; and

(c) not be made ineffective by a tie-down device or other means.

46. A grinding wheel shall be,

(a) marked with the maximum speed at which it may be used;

(b) checked for defects before mounting;

(c) mounted in accordance with the manufacturer's specifications;

(d) operated at a speed which does not exceed the manufacturer's recommendations;

(e) provided with protective hoods that enclose the wheel as closely as the work will permit;

(f) operated only by workers protected by eye protection; and

(g) stored where it will not be subjected to,

(i) extreme heat or cold, or

(ii) damage from impact.

47. A work rest for a grinding wheel shall,

(a) have a maximum clearance of three millimetres from the grinding wheel;

(b) be in a position above the centre line of the grinding wheel; and

(c) not be adjusted while the grinding wheel is in motion.

48. (1) A lifting device including a crane, pedestal or other mount shall,

(a) be capable of supporting the loads likely to be applied to it;

(b) have the maximum load rating clearly marked near the operating station;

(c) when the hoisting equipment is a crane, have,

(i) a load capacity chart that specifies boom angle and maximum working loads for each block, posted inside the control cab where load rating is more than five tons, and

(ii) boom and block travel-limiting devices;

(d) have hooks equipped with safety catches;

(e) be equipped with suitable ropes, chains, slings and other fittings so as to adequately protect all workers;

(f) have all operating controls clearly identified;

(g) be plainly marked with sufficient information so as to enable the operator of the device to determine the maximum rated load that the device is capable of lifting under any operating condition;

(h) have a cab, screen, canopy guard or other adequate protection for the operator where he or she may be exposed to the hazard of falling material;

(i) when it is a pneumatic or hydraulic hoist, have controls that automatically return to their neutral position when released;

(j) be operated only by,

(i) a competent person, or

(ii) a worker being instructed who is accompanied by a competent person; and

(k) be operated in such a way that,

(i) no part of the load passes over any worker,

(ii) where a worker may be endangered by the rotation or uncontrolled motion of a load, one or more guide ropes is used to prevent rotation or other uncontrolled motion, and

(iii) when its load is in a raised position, the controls are attended by an operator.

(2) Subclause (1)(k)(iii) does not apply to a hydraulic hoist that supports the load from below and is fixed in one location.

421/10 s. 7

49. Hoisting controls operated from other than a cab or cage shall,

(a) be located so that they can be operated at a safe distance from a load being lifted; and

(b) automatically return to their neutral position when released.

50. Where a lifting device is equipped with one or more limit switches,

(a) each limit switch shall automatically cut off the power and apply the brake when the limit is reached; and

(b) no limit switch shall be used as an operating control unless,

(i) the limit switch is designed for such use, and

(ii) the lifting device has a second limit switch in addition to the control limit switch.

O. Reg. 421/10 s. 8

51. A crane, lift truck or similar equipment shall be used to support, raise or lower a worker only when,

(a) the worker is on a platform,

(i) equipped with adequate safety devices that will automatically prevent the platform and load from falling if the platform's normal support fails,

(ii) suspended from a boom, and the person is attached to a separate lifeline suspended from the boom or a fixed support capable of supporting at least four times the weight of the worker, or

(iii) attached to a mast or boom that,

(A) is hydraulically or pneumatically operated, and

(B) is equipped with a safety device that will prevent free fall of the platform in the event of a pressure line failure;

(b) where the equipment is not designed for the specific purpose of hoisting personnel, the load applied to the crane, lift truck or similar equipment is less than one half the maximum rated load;

(c) the platform has a sign indicating the load that may be applied to the crane, lift truck or similar equipment under clause (b);

(d) where controls are provided at more than one location,

(i) each control station is provided with means whereby the operator can shut off power to the equipment, and

(ii) interlocks have been provided so that only one station can be operative at any time; and

(e) except when the controls are operated from the platform, the controls are attended and operated by another worker.

O. Reg. 421/10 s. 9

52. (1) There shall be a guardrail,

(a) at the perimeter of any area where there is a drop of more than one metre;

(b) on a mud tank; and

(c) where there is a hazard of falling into water or other hazardous material.

(2) A guardrail shall consist of,

(a) a top rail not less than 107 centimetres above the surface, floor or platform;

(b) a mid rail located approximately mid way between the top rail and walking surface; and

(c) posts or uprights, supporting the top rail and spaced not more than three metres apart from centre to centre.

(3) A guardrail shall,

(a) be capable of withstanding any load likely to be applied to it; and

(b) where tools or other objects may fall on any worker, have a toe-board extending from the surface, floor or platform to a height of not less than 125 millimetres.

O. Reg. 421/10 s. 10

53. A cover on an opening in a floor, roof or other surface shall be,

(a) secured in place; and

(b) of sufficient strength to support the greater of,

(i) any load likely to be applied to it, or

(ii) 2.4 kilonewtons per square metre.

Part IV — Rigs

54. Where natural lighting is inadequate to ensure the safety of any worker, artificial lighting shall be provided and shadows and glare shall be reduced to a minimum.

55. A rig shall have emergency storage batteries or other system capable of supplying power for twenty-four continuous hours, sufficient to operate,

(a) the marine radio required under the *Ship Station (Radio) Regulations, 1999* under the *Canada Shipping Act, 2001* for transmitting or receiving on the distress frequency;

(b) the navigation and obstruction lights;

(c) the lighting required in communications and navigational control areas of the drill unit.

O. Reg. 421/10 s. 11

56. A rig shall have emergency lighting that,

(a) turns on automatically when the regular lighting fails;

(b) is independent of the regular lighting source;

(c) provides adequate lighting for evacuation of the area; and

(d) is tested at least once every three months, but not less frequently than recommended by the manufacturer to ensure the system will function in an emergency,

in every workplace that is,

(e) a communication centre;

(f) a drill floor;

(g) a well control area;

(h) a stairway;

(i) an exit;

(j) a machinery generator area;

(k) an area where lighting is required for well control;

(l) a passageway;

(m) a navigation control area; or

(n) a survival craft embarkation station.

57. The rig shall be kept clean, tidy and free from accumulation of waste materials, oil and mud in all areas used by a worker.

58. Walkways and the area around the base of a derrick ladder shall be clear of obstruction.

59. Each enclosed workplace at or near which a worker regularly works on a rig shall have at least two exits.

60. An exit shall,

(a) be located as distant from the next required exit as practicable;

(b) be suitably identified with a sign; and

(c) when the opening is covered by a door, have the door hinged to open in the direction of exit travel.

61. A diesel or gas powered engine shall,

(a) be located in an area where combustible gases are not likely to be present;

(b) be located as far as practicable from the centre line of the well bore;

(c) be equipped with an emergency stop control;

(d) be equipped with a fire extinguishing system when in an enclosed area; and

(e) be equipped with one fire extinguisher having a U. L. C. rating of twenty BC or higher in an open area.

62. No person shall smoke during emergencies or in any area except those,

(a) used for recreation;

(b) used for accommodation purposes; or

(c) designated by the employer as a smoking area.

63. Where welding or flame-cutting is planned, the worker shall, prior to starting work,

(a) inspect the working area for fire hazards;

(b) test for the presence of combustible gases;

(c) notify other workers that may be affected by this work; and

(d) ensure that fire fighting equipment is readily available.

64. (1) No person under the influence of, or carrying, an intoxicating alcoholic beverage shall enter, or be on, or knowingly be permitted to enter, or be on, a rig.

(2) Subject to subsection (3), no person under the influence of, or carrying, a drug or narcotic substance shall enter, or be on, or knowingly be permitted to enter, or be on, a rig.

(3) A person required to use a drug for a medical purpose and able to perform work may enter and be on a rig upon establishing medical proof thereof.

65. A rig shall have,

(a) emergency equipment and life-saving devices sufficient in number to provide for the escape of all workers;

(b) a light-weight manoeuverable rescue boat;

(c) a suitable means of launching all survival or life-saving craft;

(d) at least four life buoys, of which at least two shall have self-igniting lights;

(e) life-jackets sufficient in number to provide one for each worker, and in addition, a sufficient number of life-jackets at each survival craft embarkation station to provide one each for 25 per cent of the workers for whom accommodation is available on the survival craft;

(f) personal floatation devices suitable for performing work which are sufficient in number to provide one each for every worker on shift at any one time;

(g) a line throwing apparatus and twelve distress signals;

(h) at least one buoyant personnel transfer basket, except where the drilling unit is not equipped with a crane or where there are fewer than three workers;

(i) first aid appliances and services as prescribed by Regulation 1101 of the Revised Regulations of Ontario, 1990 (*First Aid Requirements*) under the *Workplace Safety and Insurance Act, 1997*; and

(j) at least two workers per shift who possess a standard first aid certificate from St. John Ambulance.

O. Reg. 566/06 s. 3; 421/10 s. 12

66. Life rafts shall be,

(a) sufficient in number so that their combined capacity is capable of accommodating at least two workers more than the maximum number of workers present at any time;

(b) so located that one half of the life rafts are on one side of the rig and the balance on another side; and

(c) equipped with first aid supplies.

67. A life-buoy shall be,

(a) equipped with a line approved by Canadian Coast Guard whose length is at least one and one-half times the distance from the life-buoy station to the water line at shallow drafts;

(b) located so as to be readily available to any worker; and

(c) stored in a location which is clearly identified by a sign or other means.

O. Reg. 421/10 s. 13

68. A rig shall be equipped with,

(a) self-contained breathing apparatus sufficient in number for the working crew, located in areas readily available to the working area;

(b) at least two portable hydrogen sulphide gas detectors;

(c) at least two portable combustible gas detectors; and

(d) at least two portable oxygen gas detectors.

69. A rig shall be equipped with survival suits,

(a) approved by Canadian Coast Guard;

(b) sufficient in number for at least two workers more than the maximum number of workers present at any time; and

(c) located in areas convenient to working, accommodation and survival craft embarkation areas.

O. Reg. 421/10 s. 14

70. A rig shall be equipped with fire protection and detection equipment.

71. A rig shall have a general alarm system consisting of a hailer or public address system that is audible in the workplace.

72. A general alarm shall be sounded to alert workers when there is a danger to,

(a) the safety of the workers;

(b) the security of the drilling unit or the well; or

(c) the health of the workers due to the presence of toxic or combustible gases.

73. A rig shall have a radio communication system that,

(a) includes a very high frequency marine radio telephone;

(b) includes a radio capable of communicating with any support craft used in connection with the drilling operations;

(c) has an emergency back-up system; and

(d) has a competent person who is available to,

(i) maintain a listening watch on the 156.8 MHz frequency, and

(ii) monitor all movements of any support craft operating between the rig and the shore.

O. Reg. 421/10 s. 15

74. A helicopter used in conjunction with an offshore rig shall carry a sufficient number of immersion suits to provide one for each crew member and passenger when surface water temperature is below 18° Celsius.

75. Where a helicopter deck on a rig is used it shall be,

(a) so located as to have an unobstructed approach path on at least a 210° sector;

(b) capable of supporting any type of helicopter that is likely to land on it;

(c) equipped with,

(i) tie-down devices for at least one helicopter,

(ii) internationally recognized markings,

(iii) deck lights suitable for night flying where night flights are made,

(iv) a non-skid deck surface, and

(v) safety nets around the perimeter of the deck;

(d) equal to or larger than the rotor diameter of any single-main rotor helicopter that is likely to land on the deck; and

(e) kept clear of obstructions.

76. Rigs shall not be used for helicopter refuelling.

77. A personnel transfer basket shall,

(a) not be used to transfer cargo except in an emergency;

(b) only be used under conditions of good visibility and weather;

(c) be raised or lowered over water to the greatest extent practicable; and

(d) be operated by a competent person.

78. Living quarters for the drilling crews shall be,

(a) equipped with at least four self-contained breathing apparatus;

(b) clean and sanitary;

(c) capable of being heated to at least 20° Celsius; and

(d) equipped with a smoke detector and alarm in each room.

79. A rig shall have,

(a) its hull, superstructure, bulkheads and decks constructed of material at least as resistant to fire as steel;

(b) a means of embarking all workers so as not to endanger them;

(c) a system of ventilation adequate to ensure that the gas, vapour, dust or fume does not reach a hazardous concentration;

(d) ventilators, ports and other openings in any room so arranged that they can be closed;

(e) its derrick or mast constructed to support any load likely to be applied to it without exceeding the maximum rated load; and

(f) its drilling depth limited to comply with clause (e).

80. Drilling equipment shall be constructed to withstand all loads or pressure applied to it without exceeding the maximum rated load.

81. A cathead shall,

(a) be operated by a competent person;

(b) when a rope is manually operated on it, be,

(i) equipped with a blunt smooth-edged rope divider that has a clearance from the friction surface of the cathead of seven millimetres or less, and

(ii) operated only when the operating area is clear and the portion of the rope not in use is coiled or spooled;

(c) be located so that there is at least 500 millimetres of working area between the outer flanges and a substructure, guardrail or wall;

(d) have its controls attended while in use;

(e) when a rope or line is in use, have all other ropes and lines placed so that they cannot come in contact with,

(i) the cathead, or

(ii) the rope or line in use on the cathead;

(f) when automatic, have a separate control except where,

(i) dual purpose controls are used, and

(ii) a locking device prevents an automatic cathead from being accidentally engaged while the other is in operation;

(g) have a key seat and projecting key covered with a smooth thimble or plate;

(h) when unattended, be kept free of contact with any rope or line; and

(i) have only ropes or lines free from splices come in contact with the friction surface.

O. Reg. 421/10 s. 16

82. A travelling block shall,

(a) be equipped with securely attached sheave guards;

(b) be free of projecting bolts, nuts, pins or parts; and

(c) have any hook to which equipment is attached equipped with,

(i) a safety latch, or

(ii) a wire rope safety line.

83. A counterweight above a derrick floor, when not fully encased or running in permanent guides, shall be held to the frame of the derrick with a wire rope safety line that,

(a) is not less than sixteen millimetres in diameter; and

(b) will prevent the counterweight from coming within 2.4 metres of the floor.

84. A make-up or breakout tool shall have a safety device that prevents its uncontrolled movement.

85. A rotary drilling table shall not be used for final making up or initial breaking out of a pipe connection.

86. Drilling shall occur only if,

(a) all workers and loose materials are clear of the drill;

(b) visual obstructions are removed; and

(c) other measures are taken to protect workers from hazards created by the cathead and tong lines.

87. A hoisting rope, chain, sling or fitting shall,

(a) not be loaded beyond the safe-working load;

(b) not be used to raise or lower a worker, other than an injured worker in case of emergency; and

(c) have the safe-working load established by,

(i) a professional engineer, or

(ii) the manufacturer.

88. A hoisting rope shall be,

(a) securely fastened to the winding drum with at least five full wraps remaining on the drum at any time;

(b) removed from a drum only when the travelling block is,

    (i) lying on the derrick floor, or

    (ii) supported by means of a separate wire rope; and

(c) equipped with a reliable weight indicator that, if hung above the floor, is secured by means of a safety line or chain.

89. Stairways shall be installed,

(a) beside the ramp to a derrick floor and extending from the deck to the derrick floor; and

(b) at the outer end of a walkway which is sixty-one centimetres or more above the deck and extending from the deck to the walkway.

90. Ladder platforms shall be,

(a) in place adjacent to a derrick ladder, other than where the ladder has a climbing device that protects the worker from falling; and

(b) located,

    (i) at the crown of all drill rigs, and

    (ii) approximately equidistant but nine metres or less apart.

91. Where a worker is stationed on an elevated platform on the derrick or mast, an auxiliary means of escape shall,

(a) be in place at the working platform; and

(b) consist of a specially rigged and securely anchored escape line or system.

92. A pipe, kelly hose, cable or rope shall not be used to slide down, other than the escape line in case of emergency.

93. A pipe rack shall,

(a) be capable of supporting the loads to which it is to be subjected;

(b) have a means of preventing pipes and other round material from falling out of the rack; and

(c) be loaded or unloaded in such a way that no worker is,

    (i) on top of the load, or

    (ii) between the load and the pipe rack.

94. Drawworks shall,

(a) have a reliable locking mechanism to hold down the brakes in the engaged position;

(b) be tested for adequate brake function at the beginning of each shift;

(c) except during drilling, be attended at all times while the hoisting drum is in motion;

(d) except if equipped with an automatic feed control, when unattended have the brakes secured in the engaged position; and

(e) be put in motion only when all workers are clear of machinery and lines.

95. (1) The quantities of explosives and detonators stored on a rig shall not exceed 50 kilograms in total.

(2) Explosives shall be stored separately from detonators.

(3) Explosives and detonators shall be stored,

    (a) as far as practicable from,

        (i) work areas,

        (ii) living quarters,

        (iii) sources of ignition, and

        (iv) sources of physical damage;

    (b) in an area protected from lightning and other sources of electricity; and

    (c) in a magazine that,

        (i) is conspicuously marked by "DANGER—EXPLOSIVES" signs,

        (ii) is securely constructed and locked except when required to be opened for the issue or receipt of explosives,

        (iii) provides partitions to separate two or more explosives, and

        (iv) is constructed or lined or covered so as to prevent the exposure of the explosive to any grit, iron, steel or similar substance.

O. Reg. 421/10 s. 17

96. A competent person shall be placed in charge of the explosives magazine to,

    (a) issue and receive explosives;

    (b) inspect the condition and contents of the magazine once a week; and

    (c) issue a report in writing to a supervisor as to the condition and contents of the magazine as identified during the inspection required in clause (b).

97. Electrical equipment shall,

(a) comply with the *Institute of Electrical and Electronics Engineers Recommended Practice for Electrical Installations on Shipboard Standard 45-1983;*

(b) be explosion proof,

    (i) within at least four metres horizontally from the centre line of the well bore,

    (ii) within at least three metres vertically above the drill floor,

    (iii) within at least three metres vertically below the drill floor,

    (iv) within at least three metres vertically and horizontally from a mud ditch, shale shaker, degasser and mud tank, and

    (v) in any enclosed high fire hazard area;

(c) be suitable for its intended use; and

(d) be equipped with two manual shut off switches located distant from each other, which will disconnect the circuit from the power plant to the drilling equipment.

O. Reg. 421/10 s. 18

98. Well stimulation and similar operations shall,

(a) be equipped with a check valve as close as practicable to the well head riser, except where cementing or selective acidizing is being done;

(b) where liquid carbon dioxide is being used, be controlled from a position on the far side of the pumping unit when viewed from the well head riser;

(c) not be carried out until workers are removed a distance of three metres from the well head riser;

(d) be equipped with fire protection positioned to control the increased hazard of fire where flammable fluids are being pumped by two or more pumping units, including blenders;

(e) be equipped with bleed-off valves to release pressure before pipe connections are broken; and

(f) have controls readily operated from the rig floor when oil savers are used.

99. A system used to maintain drilling fluid shall,

(a) be equipped with a pressure relief device adequate to vent excess pressure in a controlled manner;

(b) vent excess pressure to an area which will not endanger workers;

(c) be designed by a professional engineer; and

(d) incorporate a testing and control procedure for hydrogen sulphide where oil, water or gas has been encountered.

100. A blow-out prevention system shall meet the requirements of Ontario Regulation 245/97 (*Exploration, Drilling and Production*) made under the *Oil, Gas and Salt Resources Act*.

O. Reg. 421/10 s. 19

ONT. REG. 856 — ROLL-OVER PROTECTIVE STRUCTURES

made under the *Occupational Health and Safety Act*

R.R.O. 1990, Reg. 856, as am. O. Reg. 357/91 (Fr.).

1. In this Regulation,

"machine" means a self-propelled vehicle, operated by one or more persons who ride on or in it, that is a tractor, bulldozer, scraper, front-end loader, skidder, dumper, grader or compactor other than an asphalt compactor;

"restraining device" means a seat belt with or without an over-the-shoulder strap;

"roll-over protective structure", in relation to a machine, means a structure that protects every operator of the machine who is wearing a restraining device from being crushed if the machine rolls over.

O. Reg. 524/88 s. 1

2. This Regulation does not apply in respect of a machine,

    (a) that is rated by its manufacturer at fifteen kilowatts or less and has a tare mass of 700 kilograms or less;

    (b) that was manufactured before 1980 and is not factory-equipped with adaptors to accept a roll-over protective structure; or

    (c) that is used primarily underground in a mine.

O. Reg. 524/88 s. 2

3. (1) No person shall use or operate a machine unless it is equipped with a roll-over protective structure that meets the requirements of subsection 5(1) and a restraining device that meets the requirements of section 6 for every operator of the machine.

(2) No person shall use or operate a machine that is equipped with a restraining device unless the person is wearing the restraining device.

O. Reg. 524/88 s. 3

4. Despite subsection 3 (1), a restraining device is not required on a skidder that is used in logging.

O. Reg. 524/88 s. 4(2)

5. (1) Every roll-over protective structure,

(a) shall be designed, constructed and maintained so that, when the machine to which it is fastened is travelling at a forward speed of 16 kilometres per hour, engages a thirty degree slope and rolls 360 degrees about its longitudinal axis on a hard clay surface,

(i) the roll-over protective structure will withstand the impact forces,

(ii) upon impact, no part of the roll-over protective structure will enter the space of the machine that is normally occupied by its operator, and

(iii) the roll-over protective structure will support the machine in an upside-down attitude without any part of the roll-over protective structure entering the space of the machine that is normally occupied by its operator;

(b) shall bear a legible label indicating,

(i) the name and address of the manufacturer of the roll-over protective structure or, if it is custom built, the name and address of the professional engineer referred to in subsection (2), and

(ii) the make, model and maximum mass of the machine that the roll-over protective structure is designed to fit;

(c) shall be securely fastened to the frame of the machine; and

(d) shall be capable of withstanding all forces to which it is likely to be subjected.

(2) Every custom built roll-over protective structure, every repair to such a structure and every custom built modification to a roll-over protective structure shall be certified as meeting the requirements of clause (1)(a) by a professional engineer who is registered or licensed as such under the *Professional Engineers Act*.

(3) Every repair to a roll-over protective structure other than a custom built structure shall be approved by the manufacturer of the structure as meeting the requirements of clause (1)(a).

O. Reg. 524/88 s. 5

6. Every restraining device shall be designed, constructed, installed and maintained,

> (a) so that the person using the device is secured in position and within the space protected by the roll-over protective structure if the machine to which it is fastened is travelling at a forward speed of 16 kilometres per hour, engages a thirty degree slope and rolls 360 degrees about its longitudinal axis on a hard clay surface; and
>
> (b) so as to minimize injury to the person using the device, in case of an accident.

O. Reg. 524/88 s. 6

Ont. Reg. 857 — Teachers

made under the *Occupational Health and Safety Act*

R.R.O. 1990, Reg. 857, as am. O. Reg. 352/91 (Fr.).

1. The purpose of this Regulation is to make the Act apply to teachers in a manner that is consistent with the *Education Act*.

O. Reg. 191/84 s. 1

2. Subject to section 3, the Act applies to all persons who are employed as teachers as defined in the *Education Act*.

O. Reg. 191/84 s. 2

3. The following conditions and limitations apply to the application of the Act to teachers:

    1. A principal, vice-principal or teacher appointed by an employer of teachers to direct and supervise a school or an organizational unit of a school is a person who has charge of a school or authority over a teacher and exercises managerial functions.

    2. An employer of teachers that establishes and maintains one joint health and safety committee for all its teachers shall be deemed to have complied with subsection 9(2) of the Act with respect to all its teachers but nothing in this paragraph requires the discontinuance of any joint health and safety committee or committee of a like nature in existence on the 1st day of October, 1979 or prevents the employer from establishing more than one joint health and safety committee for its teachers.

    3. Part V of the Act does not apply to a teacher where the circumstances are such that the life, health or safety of a pupil is in imminent jeopardy.

O. Reg. 191/84 s. 3

ONT. REG. 858 — UNIVERSITY ACADEMICS AND TEACHING ASSISTANTS

made under the *Occupational Health and Safety Act*

R.R.O. 1990, Reg. 858, as am. O. Reg. 353/91 (Fr.).

1. The Act applies to every person who is employed as a member or teaching assistant of the academic staff of a university or a related institution.

O. Reg. 307/84 s. 1.

858

ONT. REG. 859 — WINDOW CLEANING

made under the *Occupational Health and Safety Act*

R.R.O. 1990, Reg. 859, as am. O. Reg. 380/91 (Fr.); 523/92.

Definitions

1. In this Regulation,

"adequate" means adequate to protect a person from the risk of damage to his or her body or health;

"allowable unit stress", in relation to a material, means,

    (a) the allowable unit stress assigned to the material by Regulation 61 of Revised Regulations of Ontario, 1990, or

    (b) where Regulation 61 of Revised Regulations of Ontario, 1990 does not assign an allowable unit stress to the material, the allowable unit stress for the material as determined by a professional engineer in accordance with good engineering practice;

"fall arrest body harness" means a harness worn by a worker that guides and distributes the impact forces of a fall by the worker by means of leg and shoulder strap supports and an upper dorsal suspension assembly;

"fall arrest system" means a fall arrest body harness and the system that supports it, including the lanyard, lifeline and attachment devices;

"professional engineer" means a person who is registered as a professional engineer or a person who is licensed as a professional engineer under the *Professional Educational Act*;

"sill work" means the cleaning of a window by a worker standing on a sill or frame;

"suitable" means suitable for the purpose of protecting a person from the risk of injury to his or her body or health;

"window" includes a skylight, canopy, roof or covering made of glass or any transparent or translucent material;

859

"window cleaning" means the cleaning of the exterior or interior surfaces of a window, the cleaning of trims and claddings which are cleaned in conjunction with a window, and any work necessary or incidental thereto.

O. Reg. 527/88 s. 1.

Application

2. This Regulation applies to employers, including contractors and sub-contractors, who supply window cleaning services, to workers who engage in window cleaning and to owners of buildings where a worker engaging in window cleaning may fall a vertical distance of three metres or more.

O. Reg. 527/88 s. 2.

Alternative Methods and Materials

3. Any procedure or the composition, design, size or arrangement of any material, object, device or thing may vary from the procedure, composition, design, size or arrangement prescribed in this Regulation if the variation affords equal or greater protection to the health and safety of workers.

O. Reg. 527/88 s. 3.

Registration, Reporting and Notice Requirements

4. (1) Every person who carries on the business of window cleaning or of supplying window cleaners shall register with a Director within thirty days of starting business. O. Reg. 527/88, s. 4(1), revised

(2) A registration under subsection (1) shall be made by filing with the Director of the Ministry of Labour a statement setting out,

    (a) in the case of an individual or sole proprietorship,

        (i) the name in full, regular business address and business telephone number of the individual or sole proprietor, and

        (ii) the residence address of the individual or sole proprietor;

    (b) in the case of a partnership or syndicate,

        (i) the name or style of the partnership or syndicate,

        (ii) the business address and telephone number of the partnership or syndicate, and

        (iii) the particulars required by clauses (a) and (c) for the individual or corporate partners, as the case may be;

    (c) in the case of a corporation,

　　　　(i) the name of the corporation,

　　　　(ii) the date of incorporation,

　　　　(iii) the province or jurisdiction in which the corporation was incorporated,

　　　　(iv) the main business address and telephone number of the corporation, and

　　　　(v) the names in full and residence addresses of the principal officers of the corporation and the date when each became a principal officer;

　　(d) the average number of workers employed by the employer to engage in window cleaning;

　　(e) the firm number assigned to the employer by the Workers' Compensation Board; and

　　(f) the rate number assigned to the employer by the Workers' Compensation Board.O. Reg. 527/88, s. 4(2)

(3) The statement referred to in subsection (2) shall be verified by the individual or sole proprietor, a partner in the partnership or syndicate, or an officer of the corporation, as the case may be.

O. Reg. 527/88 s. 4(3).

(4) Every person registered under this section shall notify a Director in writing of any change in the information filed under subsection (2) within thirty days after the change has taken place, setting out the change and date of the change.

O. Reg. 527/88 s. 4(2-4); 523/92 s. 1

5. (1) When a person engaged in window cleaning is killed or critically injured, the written report required by section 51 of the Act shall include,

　　(a) the name and address of the building owner;

　　(b) the name and address of the employer of the injured person;

　　(c) the nature and the circumstances of the occurrence and the bodily injury sustained;

　　(d) a description of the machinery and equipment involved;

　　(e) the time, date and place of the occurrence;

　　(f) the name and address of the person who was killed or critically injured;

　　(g) the names and addresses of all witnesses to the occurrence;

　　(h) the name and address of the physician or surgeon, if any, by whom the person was or is being attended for the injury; and

(i) a description of the measures, if any, taken to prevent a recurrence.

(2) For the purposes of section 52 of the Act, notice of an occurrence which causes injury to a person engaging in window cleaning shall include,

(a) the name and address of the building owner;

(b) the name and address of the employer of the injured person;

(c) the nature and the circumstances of the occurrence and the bodily injury sustained;

(d) a description of the machinery and equipment involved;

(e) the time, date and place of the occurrence;

(f) the name and address of the person suffering the injury;

(g) the names and addresses of all witnesses to the occurrence;

(h) the name and address of the physician or surgeon, if any, by whom the person was or is being attended for the injury; and

(i) a description of the measures, if any, taken to prevent a recurrence.

O. Reg. 527/88 s. 5.

6. When an accident involves the collapse or failure of a temporary or permanent support or structure that was designed by a professional engineer, the employer shall add to the report required by section 51 of the Act or to the notice required by section 52 of the Act a written opinion given by a professional engineer stating the cause of the collapse or failure, to be filed within fourteen days after the report or notice is filed.

O. Reg. 527/88 s. 6.

7. (1) Before any worker begins window cleaning at a building for which a suspended scaffold, boatswain's chair or similar single-point suspension equipment is used, every employer, contractor and sub-contractor who proposes to carry out window cleaning at the building shall give notice of the proposed window cleaning by telephone to an inspector in the office of the Ministry of Labour that is nearest to the building.

(2) The notice mentioned in subsection (1) shall include,

(a) the name, address and telephone number of the employer, contractor or sub-contractor;

(b) a description of the equipment to be used;

(c) the number of workers who will engage in window cleaning;

(d) the anticipated starting date and duration of window cleaning;

(e) the address of the building; and

(f) the name, workplace address and telephone number of the supervisor of the window cleaning.

O. Reg. 527/88 s. 7; 523/92 s. 2

Safety Precautions and Requirements

8. Every person who engages in window cleaning shall be at least eighteen years of age.O. Reg. 527/88, s. 8.

9. (1) Every worker who engages in window cleaning shall wear or use personal protective clothing, equipment or devices that protect the worker from the particular hazard to which the worker may be exposed.

(2) Every worker shall be instructed and trained in the care and use of any protective clothing, equipment or device before the worker wears or uses it.

O. Reg. 527/88 s. 9

10. (1) If a worker who is not working from a ladder is exposed to the hazard of falling more than three metres, the worker shall use a fall arrest system that is adequately secured to a fixed support and arranged so that the worker cannot fall freely for a vertical distance of more than 1.5 metres.

(2) The fixed support mentioned in subsection (1) shall be able to resist all arrest forces when a worker falls.

(3) The fall arrest system mentioned in subsection (1),

(a) shall arrest any fall by the worker without applying a peak force to the worker greater than 8 kilonewtons; and

(b) shall permit the worker to remain suspended safely in it for a period of at least thirty minutes.

(4) Where a suspended scaffold,

(a) has at least two independent means of support or suspension; and

(b) is designed, constructed and maintained so that the failure of one means of support or suspension will not upset the scaffold, the fall arrest body harness or lanyard may be attached to the scaffold.

(5) A lanyard used in a fall arrest system shall have a nominal diameter of at least sixteen millimetres and be made of nylon rope or another durable and adequate material.

(6) A lifeline used in a fall arrest system,

    (a) shall be used by only one worker at a time;

    (b) shall be free from the danger of being chaffed or cut;

    (c) shall be suspended separately and independently from any suspended scaffold, boatswain's chair or similar single-point suspension equipment;

    (d) shall have a nominal diameter of at least sixteen millimetres;

    (e) shall be made of polypropylene or another durable material with equivalent impact strength that provides equal protection to a worker;

    (f) when in a vertical position, shall extend to the ground or the level of egress;

    (g) shall be inspected for wear prior to each day's use by a competent person who shall report any defects or damage to a supervisor; and

    (h) shall not be used when defective or damaged.

(7) No lanyard, lifeline and fall arrest body harness that has arrested a fall by a worker shall be reused.

O. Reg. 527/88 s. 10

11. Every work area, route to and from a work area and a working platform shall be treated with sand or similar material when necessary to ensure a firm footing.

O. Reg. 527/88 s. 11

12. If practicable, signs containing the words "Danger—Work Overhead" in legible letters, shall be posted in prominent locations and in sufficient number to warn pedestrians that window cleaning is being carried out overhead.

O. Reg. 527/88 s. 12

13. Barriers, warning signs or other safeguards for the protection of workers shall be used where vehicular or pedestrian traffic may endanger the safety of any worker or disturb the worker's support lines or lifeline.

O. Reg. 527/88 s. 13

14. (1) Access to and egress from a workplace that is above ground level shall be by stairs, runway, ramp or ladder.

(2) Despite subsection (1), access to and egress from a suspended scaffold, boatswain's chair or similar single-point suspension equipment may be,

(a) directly from a floor or roof where the suspended scaffold, boatswain's chair or similar single-point suspension equipment is adjacent to the floor or roof; or

(b) from ground level where the suspended scaffold, boatswain's chair or single-point suspension equipment is at ground level.

O. Reg. 527/88 s. 14

15. Every container for a combustible, corrosive or toxic substance,

    (a) shall be suitable for the substance that the container holds; and

    (b) shall be clearly labelled to identify,

        (i) the substance it contains,

        (ii) the hazards that are involved in the use of the substance, and

        (iii) the precautions to be taken in handling, using, storing and disposing of the substance.

O. Reg. 527/88 s. 15

16. Materials to be used on, or removed from, a work site shall be stored, moved, lifted and transported in a manner that does not endanger a worker.

O. Reg. 527/88 s. 16

859

Ladders and Related Equipment

17. (1) Every ladder,

    (a) shall have strength, stiffness and stability adequate to support any load likely to be applied to it;

    (b) shall be free from broken or loose members or other faults;

    (c) shall have evenly spaced rungs;

    (d) shall be equipped with slip resistant feet; and

    (e) if it is made of wood, shall not be painted or coated with an opaque material.

(2) The maximum length of a ladder measured along the side rail shall not be more than,

    (a) six metres for a stepladder;

    (b) nine metres for a single ladder; and

    (c) thirteen metres for an extension or sectional ladder.

(3) Every ladder,

    (a) shall be used so as not to endanger any worker;

(b) shall be used only in such a way that the loads applied to it will not cause the materials of which it is constructed to be stressed beyond their allowable unit stresses;

(c) shall be placed on a firm footing and secured against slipping;

(d) if it exceeds nine metres in length, shall be securely fastened or stabilized to prevent it from tipping or falling; and

(e) when it is not securely fastened, shall be inclined so that the horizontal distance from the top support to the foot of the ladder is not less than one-quarter and not more than one third of the length of the ladder.

(4) When a stepladder is being used,

(a) the legs shall be fully spread and the spreader shall be locked; and

(b) the top and the pail shelf of the stepladder shall not be used as a step.

O. Reg. 527/88 s. 17

18. No barrel, box or other loose object,

(a) shall be used by a worker engaged in window cleaning to stand upon while working; or

(b) shall be used to support a ladder, scaffold or working platform.

O. Reg. 527/88 s. 18

19. No platform, bucket, basket, load, hook or sling that is supported by a fork-lift truck, front-end loader or other similar machine shall be used as a workplace for window cleaning.

O. Reg. 527/88 s. 19

20. (1) Every guardrail shall consist of a top rail, intermediate rail and toeboard, and be capable of resisting any load likely to be applied to it.

(2) The top rail of a guardrail shall be located not less than 910 millimetres and not more than 1.07 metres above the surface on which it is installed.

O. Reg. 527/88 s. 20

Scaffolds, Boatswain's Chairs and Related Equipment

21. (1) The erection, alteration or dismantling of a scaffold shall be carried out under the supervision of a competent person.

(2) Work shall not be carried out on or under a scaffold or working platform that is being erected, altered or dismantled unless it is carried out from a part of the scaffold or working platform that complies with the requirements of sections 22 to 31.

O. Reg. 527/88 s. 21

22. (1) Every scaffold,

    (a) shall be capable of supporting at least,

        (i) two times the maximum load to which it is likely to be subjected without exceeding the allowable unit stresses for the materials of which it is constructed, and

        (ii) four times the maximum load to which it is likely to be subjected without overturning;

    (b) shall not be loaded in excess of the maximum load it can reasonably be expected to support and in any event shall not be loaded in excess of the maximum load described in clause (a);

    (c) shall be constructed of suitable structural materials;

    (d) shall have horizontal members that prevent lateral movement and that do not have splices between the points of support;

    (e) shall have footings, sills or supports that are sound, rigid and capable of supporting without unreasonable settlement or deformation at least two times the maximum load to which the scaffold is likely to be subjected;

    (f) if it consists of a structural system of tubular metal frames, shall have connecting devices between components that provide positive engagement in compression and tension;

    (g) shall have all fittings, gears, base plates and wheels installed according to manufacturer's instructions;

    (h) shall have safety catches on all hooks; and

    (i) shall be adequately secured at vertical intervals not exceeding three times the least lateral dimension of the scaffold, measured at the base in order to prevent lateral movement of the scaffold.

(2) Clauses (1)(d) to (i) do not apply in respect of a suspended scaffold.

(3) A scaffold that exceeds fifteen metres in height above its base support, and a scaffold constructed of a tube and clamp system that exceeds ten metres in height above its base support shall be designed by a professional engineer and erected in accordance with the design.

O. Reg. 527/88 s. 22

23. Every scaffold mounted on castors or wheels,

859

(a) shall have a height which does not exceed three times the smallest lateral dimension of the scaffold when it is measured at the base, or measured between the outriggers;

(b) shall be equipped with a suitable braking device on each castor or wheel; and

(c) shall have the brakes engaged when a worker is on the scaffold or the scaffold is unattended.

O. Reg. 527/88 s. 23

24. The working platform of a scaffold,

(a) shall be designed, constructed and maintained to support all loads to which it may be subjected without exceeding the allowable unit stresses for the materials of which it is constructed, and in any event shall support not less than 2.4 kilonewtons per square metre;

(b) shall be at least 460 millimetres wide;

(c) shall be provided with a guardrail at each open side and at the end of the platform;

(d) if the platform consists of sawn lumber planks, shall have planks of Number 1 grade spruce that,

(i) bear a legible grade identification stamp or bear a permanent grade identification mark,

(ii) are at least forty-eight millimetres thick by 250 millimetres wide with a span not exceeding 2.1 metres,

(iii) overhang their supports by not less than 150 millimetres and not more than 300 millimetres, and

(iv) are cleated or otherwise secured against slipping; and

(e) if the platform consists of planks manufactured of laminated wood, metal or a combination of materials, shall consist of planks tested in accordance with good engineering practice to demonstrate their structural equivalence to the sawn lumber planks specified in clause (d).

O. Reg. 527/88 s. 24

25. Sections 26 to 30 apply in respect of every,

(a) suspended scaffold that is permanently installed on a building or structure;

(b) suspended scaffold that is transported in component form and is assembled for use at a work site; and

(c) boatswain's chair or similar single-point suspension equipment intended for the support of one worker.

O. Reg. 527/88 s. 25

26. All mechanically or electrically operated equipment used in connection with equipment described in section 25,

(a) shall be suitable for the purpose for which it is used;

(b) shall have legible operating and maintenance instructions of the manufacturer affixed to the equipment;

(c) shall be operated, inspected and maintained in accordance with the manufacturer's instructions;

(d) shall not be used in a manner which endangers a worker; and

(e) shall not be used when a component which may affect its safe operation is defective or damaged.

O. Reg. 527/88 s. 26

27. (1) Every primary suspension line and lifeline used in connection with equipment described in section 25,

(a) shall be rigged in accordance with generally accepted rigging practice;

(b) shall be rigged so that each line hangs vertically from the roof or access level to the ground or level of egress of a worker using the line;

(c) shall have a breaking strength of at least ten times the static load that the line is intended to support;

(d) shall have each connecting end wrapped around a protective thimble and securely fastened,

    (i) by means of a swagged fitting or eye splice, if applied by the manufacturer of the line, or

    (ii) if the line is a wire rope, by a minimum of three clamps;

(e) shall be inspected before each day's use by a competent person who shall report any defects or damage to a supervisor; and

(f) shall not be used when defective or damaged.

(2) Every primary suspension line for a boatswain's chair or similar single-point suspension equipment that is made of organic or polymer fibres,

(a) shall be doubled from the anchor point or point of suspension of the line to the ground or egress level;

(b) shall be permanently marked with,

    (i) the name of the manufacturer,

    (ii) the date of manufacture of the line, and

    (iii) the length of the line;

(c) shall be protected from abrasion;

859

(d) shall be used only with a descent control or similar device;

(e) shall be tested by a recognized testing laboratory twenty-four months from the date of manufacture of the line and once every twelve months thereafter for compliance with clause (1)(c); and

(f) shall be discarded,

(i) where it is found not to comply with clause (1)(c),

(ii) in accordance with the manufacturer's recommendations, or

(iii) when it is no longer safe for use, whichever occurs first.

(3) Every descent control or similar device referred to in clause (2)(d),

(a) shall be approved by the manufacturer of the device for window cleaning; and

(b) shall be used in accordance with the installation, operating and maintenance instructions of the manufacturer, which instructions shall be kept available for the inspection of an inspector.

O. Reg. 527/88 s. 27

28. Every boatswain's chair,

(a) shall have a seat at least 600 millimetres long and 250 millimetres wide of one piece construction capable of supporting 225 kilograms;

(b) shall be supported by a sling constructed of wire rope of at least nine millimetres that crosses underneath the seat;

(c) shall not be used where the descent exceeds ninety metres;

(d) shall only be used to clean windows within arm's reach of a worker who is freely suspended on the primary support line; and

(e) shall not be used when a worker is using corrosive substances or solutions for window cleaning.

O. Reg. 527/88 s. 28

29. (1) Every static or horizontal line that is rigged between anchor points and to which lifelines or primary support lines are directly attached shall be used as a professional engineer directs, and the professional engineer shall certify the maximum load to be applied to the static or horizontal line.

(2) The support capability of an anchor point shall exceed the total breaking strength of all support lines attached to it.

O. Reg. 527/88 s. 29

30. (1) Every outrigger beam, cornice hook and parapet wall hook that is used to support a primary support line,

(a) shall be capable of supporting at least four times the maximum load to which it may be subjected,

(i) without overturning, and

(ii) without exceeding the allowable unit stress for the materials of which it is constructed;

(b) shall be constructed of steel, aluminum or equivalent material; and

(c) shall be tied back to a fixed support so as to prevent movement of the outrigger beam, cornice hook or parapet wall hook.

(2) Every outrigger beam that is used to support a primary support line,

(a) shall have counterweights that are manufactured for the purpose, marked to indicate their weight and securely attached to the outrigger beam;

(b) shall be accompanied by the supplier's or manufacturer's instructions indicating the number of counterweights necessary for each arrangement of the beam that may be employed for window cleaning and the load that the beam can bear for each arrangement; and

(c) if it is positioned on a rolling undercarriage, shall have the undercarriage fixed to prevent the counterweights from moving while a worker is suspended by the primary support line.

O. Reg. 527/88 s. 30.

31. (1) Every worker on a suspended scaffold, boatswain's chair or similar single-point suspension equipment shall have an effective means of summoning assistance in case of emergency.

(2) Every worker who is on, or is in the process of getting on or off a suspended scaffold or boatswain's chair or similar single-point suspension equipment shall be protected by a fall arrest system.

O. Reg. 527/88 s. 31

Electrical Hazards

32. Electrical equipment, power lines and insulating materials shall be suitable for its or their use and be installed, maintained, modified and operated so as not to present a hazard to a worker.

O. Reg. 527/88 s. 32

33. Tools, ladders, scaffolding and other equipment that are capable of conducting electricity and that may endanger the safety of anyone shall not be used or left in such proximity to any energized electrical installation, equipment or conductor as to make electrical contact with an energized conductor.

O. Reg. 527/88 s. 33

34. (1) No person other than a person authorized by a building owner or the owner's representative shall enter a room or enclosure containing exposed energized electrical parts.

(2) The building owner shall place signs conspicuously at every entrance to a room or other enclosure that contains exposed energized electrical parts warning of the danger of exposed energized electrical parts and stating that only persons authorized by the building owner or the owner's representative may enter the room or enclosure.

O. Reg. 527/88 s. 34

35. (1) No object or piece of equipment shall be brought closer to an energized outdoor overhead electrical conductor with the voltage rating set out in Column 1 of the Table than the distance specified opposite thereto in Column 2.

TABLE

Column 1	Column 2
Voltage Rating of Conductor	**Minimum Distance**
From 750 up to and including 150,000 volts	3 metres
Over 150,000 up to and including 250,000 volts	4.5 metres
Over 250,000 volts	6 metres

(2) Subsection (1) does not apply where,

　　(a) mats, shields or other protective devices adequate to ensure that a person is protected from electrical shock and burns have been installed by the owner of the conductor; and

　　(b) the person who is bringing the object or equipment or is causing the object or equipment to be brought within the minimum distance specified in subsection (1) has been instructed in and is using procedures adequate to ensure the protection of the worker from electrical shock and burns.

O. Reg. 527/88 s. 35

Miscellaneous Equipment

36. Every gear, pulley or belt that is part of a suspended scaffold shall be guarded or fenced unless the gear, pulley or belt is located and constructed so that it will not endanger any worker.

O. Reg. 527/88 s. 36

37. (1) Every rope or cable used by a mechanically powered hoisting device,

    (a) shall be steel wire rope of the type, size, grade and construction that is recommended by the manufacturer for the hoisting device;

    (b) shall be suitable for the sheaves and the drum with which it is used;

    (c) shall not be spliced; and

    (d) shall be suitably lubricated to prevent its corrosion or wear.

(2) Steel wire rope shall not be used by a mechanically powered hoisting device if,

    (a) six randomly distributed wires are broken in one rope lay, or three or more wires are broken in one strand in one rope lay;

    (b) the wear on the rope exceeds one-third of the original diameter of the outside individual wires; or

    (c) there is evidence of kinking, bird-caging, corrosion or any other damage to the rope resulting in distortion of the rope structure that may result in rope failure.

O. Reg. 527/88 s. 37

38. (1) Every hook shall be equipped with a safety catch.

(2) Every load-bearing hook shall have its load rating legibly cast or stamped on it in a location where it can be readily seen.

(3) No hook shall be used that has,

    (a) a crack;

    (b) more than the normal throat opening; or

    (c) any twist from the plane of the unbent hook.

O. Reg. 527/88 s. 38

Duties of the Owner of a Building

39. (1) Every owner of a building where a suspended scaffold, boatswain's chair or similar single-point suspension equipment is to be used for window cleaning shall prepare a sketch or sketches showing all anchor points and related structures on the building that are suitable and adequate for the attachment of the suspended scaffold, boatswain's chair or similar single-point suspension equipment and the lifeline.

(2) The building owner shall provide a copy of the sketch or sketches mentioned in subsection (1) to the person supplying the window cleaning services before the work is begun and no employer may permit a worker to engage in window cleaning using a suspended scaffold, boatswain's chair or similar single-point suspension equipment until the employer has received a copy of the sketch or sketches.

(3) The building owner shall post a copy of the sketch or sketches mentioned in subsection (1) at the building near the entrance to the roof.

O. Reg. 527/88 s. 39

40. (1) Every owner of a building where sill work is done shall prepare a sketch or sketches showing all anchor points and related structures on the building that are suitable and adequate for the attachment of a lifeline for a worker who performs the sill work.

(2) The building owner shall provide a copy of the sketch or sketches mentioned in subsection (1) to the person supplying the window cleaning services before the sill work is begun and no employer may permit a worker to do sill work until the employer has received a copy of the sketch or sketches.

(3) The building owner shall post a copy of the sketch or sketches mentioned in subsection (1) in a conspicuous place where the sketch or sketches are to come to the attention of any worker who does sill work.

O. Reg. 527/88 s. 40

41. (1) The owner of a building mentioned in section 39 or 40 shall cause all anchor points and permanently-installed suspended scaffolds to be inspected by a competent person,

(a) before being used for the first time;

(b) thereafter as often as necessary but not less frequently than recommended by the manufacturer of the anchor points or the suspended scaffolds, as the case may be, and in any case, at least once a year; and

(c) when informed under section 43.

(2) Maintenance and repairs of a permanently-installed suspended scaffold shall be performed in accordance with the manufacturer's instructions.

(3) The competent person making the inspection required by subsection (1) shall immediately upon completion of the inspection report to the building owner any defects or hazardous conditions detected in the anchor points and any permanently-installed suspended scaffold.

(4) A building owner shall ensure that any faulty anchor point is repaired and is suitable for use for window cleaning and sill work before being used.

(5) A building owner shall keep a record of the inspections of any anchor points and any permanently-installed suspended scaffold at a building in a log book to be maintained and retained as long as the anchor points and suspended scaffold are used, showing,

(a) the date on which each inspection is made;

(b) the name and signature of the person making the inspection; and

(c) any modifications or repairs made to an anchor point or a suspended scaffold, including the date they are made and the name and signature of the person making the modifications or repairs.

O. Reg. 527/88 s. 41

Duties of Employers, Supervisors and Workers

42. (1) Every employer who proposes to carry out window cleaning using a suspended scaffold, boatswain's chair or similar single-point suspension equipment or to carry out sill work shall prepare a work plan in writing, signed by the employer, indicating the manner in which any primary support lines and lifelines used are to be attached to the anchor points or related structures shown on any sketch mentioned in subsection 39(1) or 40(1), and setting such other information as may be required for the safety of workers.

(2) The employer shall cause a copy of the work plan referred to in subsection (1) to be provided to each worker who engages in window cleaning or sill work at the building and shall retain a copy for examination by an inspector.

(3) No worker shall begin window cleaning that requires the use of a suspended scaffold, boatswain's chair or similar single-point suspension equipment and no worker may begin doing sill work until the worker has received a copy of the work plan referred to in subsection (1).

O. Reg. 527/88 s. 42

43. If an employer, supervisor or worker believes that any anchor point or related structure that is used to support a suspended scaffold, suspended work platform, boatswain's chair, similar single-point suspension equipment or lifeline is defective or inadequate, the employer, supervisor or worker shall inform the building owner of this fact immediately.

O. Reg. 527/88 s. 43

44. (1) Every employer of a worker who engages in window cleaning using a suspended scaffold, boatswain's chair or similar single-point suspension equipment and every contractor and sub-contractor who proposes to carry out window cleaning in that manner shall appoint a supervisor.

(2) A supervisor appointed under subsection (1) shall visit the location of the window cleaning operation at least once daily.

O. Reg. 527/88 s. 44

45. (1) A safety training program shall be established and maintained by every employer whose workers engage in window cleaning using suspended scaffolds, boatswain's chairs or similar single-point suspension equipment to train the workers in common core skills for the safe use of such scaffolds, boatswain's chairs and similar single-point suspension equipment.

(2) The common core skills referred to in subsection (1) shall include,

　　(a) the proper rigging of support lines;

　　(b) the inspection for wear of primary support lines and lifelines;

　　(c) the safe use of descent control devices;

　　(d) the proper use of fall arrest body harnesses including accepted methods for attaching lifelines to buildings or structures; and

　　(e) the safe use of suspended scaffolds and boatswain's chairs and similar single-point suspension equipment.

(3) No worker who has not successfully completed the training program referred to in subsection (1) shall be permitted to engage in window cleaning using a suspended scaffold, boatswain's chair or similar single-point suspension equipment.

(4) Subsection (3) does not apply to a worker who,

(a) is being instructed in the safe use of window cleaning and fall arrest equipment; and

(b) is accompanied by a person who has successfully completed the training program referred to in subsection (1).

(5) Every employer shall establish and maintain in writing a list of workers who have successfully completed the training program referred to in subsection (1).

O. Reg. 527/88 s. 45

ONT. REG. 860 — WORKPLACE HAZARDOUS MATERIALS INFORMATION SYSTEM (WHMIS)

made under the *Occupational Health and Safety Act*

R.R.O. 1990, Reg. 860, as am. O. Reg. 356/91 (Fr.); 36/93;
168/16, ss. 1 (Fr.), 2, 3, 4(1), (2) (Fr.), (3), 5(1), (2), (3) (Fr.),
(4), (5), 6-15.

1. (1) In this Regulation,

"bulk shipment" means a shipment of a hazardous product that is contained without intermediate containment or intermediate packaging in,

(a) a vessel with a water capacity equal to or greater than 450 litres,

(b) a freight container, road vehicle, railway vehicle or portable tank,

(c) the hold of a ship, or

(d) a pipeline;

"CAS registry number" means the identification number assigned to a chemical by the Chemical Abstracts Service, a division of the American Chemical Society;

"container" includes a bag, barrel, bottle, box, can, cylinder, drum, storage tank or similar package or receptacle;

"controlled product" [Repealed O. Reg. 168/16, s. 3(3).]

"Controlled Products Regulations (Canada)" [Repealed O. Reg. 168/16, s. 3(3).]

"fugitive emission" means a gas, liquid, solid, vapour, fume, mist, fog or dust that meets the following conditions:

1. The gas, liquid, solid, vapour, fume, mist, fog or dust escaped from process equipment, from emission control equipment or from a product.

2. may be readily exposed to the gas, liquid, solid, vapour, fume, mist, fog or dust;

"hazard information" means information on the proper and safe use, storage and handling of a hazardous product and includes information relating to the product's health and physical hazards;

"hazardous product" means any product, mixture, material or substance that is classified in accordance with the *Hazardous Products Regulations* (Canada) in a category or subcategory of a hazard class listed in Schedule 2 to the *Hazardous Products Act* (Canada);

"Hazardous Products Regulations (Canada)" means the *Hazardous Products Regulations*, SOR/2015-17, made under the *Hazardous Products Act* (Canada);

"hazardous waste" means a hazardous product that is acquired or generated for recycling or recovery or is intended for disposal;

"label" means a group of written, printed or graphic information elements that relate to a hazardous product, which is designed to be affixed to, printed on or attached to the hazardous product or the container in which the hazardous product is packaged;

"laboratory sample" means a sample of a hazardous product that is packaged in a container that contains less than 10 kg of hazardous product and that is intended solely to be tested in a laboratory but does not include a sample that is to be used,

> (a) by the laboratory for testing other products, mixtures, materials or substances, or
>
> (b) for educational or demonstration purposes;

"manufactured article" means an article that is formed to a specific shape or design during manufacture, the intended use of which when in that form is dependent in whole or in part on its shape or design, and that, when being installed, if the intended use of the article requires it to be installed, and under normal conditions of use, will not release or otherwise cause an individual to be exposed to a hazardous product;

"material safety data sheet" [Repealed O. Reg. 168/16, s. 3(3).]

"medical professional" means a person who, under the laws of the province in which the person is practising,

> (a) is a legally-qualified medical practitioner, or
>
> (b) is registered as a registered nurse;

"product identifier" means, in respect of a hazardous product, the brand name, chemical name, common name, generic name or trade name;

"research and development" means systematic investigation or search carried out in a field of science or technology by means of experiment or analysis, other than investigation or search in respect of market research, sales promotion, quality control or routine testing of hazardous products, and includes,

(a) applied research, namely, work undertaken for the advancement of scientific knowledge with a specific practical application in view, and

(b) development, namely, use of the results of applied research for the purpose of creating new, or improving existing, processes or hazardous products;

"risk phrase" [Repealed O. Reg. 168/16, s. 3(4).]

"safety data sheet" means,

(a) a supplier safety data sheet, or

(b) a safety data sheet prepared by an employer under subsection 18(1) of this Regulation;

"significant new data" means new data regarding the hazard presented by a hazardous product that change its classification, in accordance with the *Hazardous Products Regulations* (Canada), in a category or subcategory of a hazard class listed in Schedule 2 to the *Hazardous Products Act* (Canada), or results in its classification in another hazard class, or change the ways to protect against the hazard presented by the hazardous product;

"supplier label" means, in respect of a hazardous product, a label provided by a supplier that contains the information required by the *Hazardous Products Regulations* (Canada) for that hazardous product;

"supplier material safety data sheet" [Repealed O. Reg. 168/16, s. 3(4).]

"supplier safety data sheet" means, in respect of a hazardous product, a safety data sheet provided by a supplier that complies with the requirements of the *Hazardous Products Regulations* (Canada) for a safety data sheet;

"workplace label" means, in respect of a hazardous product, a label that discloses,

(a) a product identifier identical to that found on the safety data sheet for the hazardous product,

(b) information for the safe handling of the hazardous product, and

(c) that a safety data sheet, if supplied or produced, is available.

(2) In this Regulation,

"produces" in relation to the production of a hazardous product does not include the production of a fugitive emission or of intermediate products undergoing reaction within a reaction vessel or process vessel.

O. Reg. 644/88, s. 1; 168/16, ss. 2, 3

Designation of Hazardous Materials

2. Every hazardous product is designated as a hazardous material.

O. Reg. 644/88 s. 2; 168/16, s. 2(1)

Assessment of Biological and Chemical Agents

3. (1) An employer shall assess all biological and chemical agents produced in the workplace for use therein to determine if they are hazardous materials.

(2) No employer is required to assess under subsection (1),

    (a) wood or a product made of wood;

    (b) tobacco or a tobacco product within the meaning of section 2 of the *Tobacco Act* (Canada); or

    (c) a manufactured article.

(3) An assessment under subsection (1) shall be performed in accordance with Parts 7 and 8 of the *Hazardous Products Regulations* (Canada).

O. Reg. 644/88,   s. 3; 168/16, ss. 2(2), 4(1), (3)

Application

4. (1) Sections 5 to 25 apply to employers and workers in respect of hazardous products used, stored and handled at a workplace.

(2) Section 8 (supplier labels), section 14 (laboratory samples) and sections 17 and 18 (safety data sheets) do not apply with respect to,

    (a) an explosive within the meaning of section 2 of the *Explosives Act* (Canada);

    (b) a cosmetic, device, drug or food within the meaning of section 2 of the *Food and Drugs Act* (Canada);

(c) a pest control product within the meaning of subsection 2(1) of the *Pest Control Products Act* (Canada);

(d) a nuclear substance that is radioactive and that is within the meaning of a nuclear substance under section 2 of the *Nuclear Safety and Control Act* (Canada); or

(e) a consumer product within the meaning of section 2 of the *Canada Consumer Product Safety Act* (Canada).

(3) Sections 5 to 25 do not apply with respect to a hazardous product that,

(a) is wood or a product made of wood;

(b) is tobacco or a tobacco product within the meaning of section 2 of the *Tobacco Act* (Canada);

(c) is a manufactured article; or

(d) is being transported or handled in accordance with the requirements of the *Dangerous Goods Transportation Act* (Ontario) or the *Transportation of Dangerous Goods Act, 1992* (Canada).

(4) Sections 5 to 25 do not apply with respect to hazardous waste except to the extent that an employer shall ensure the safe storage and handling of hazardous waste through a combination of identification and worker education.

O. Reg. 644/88, s. 4; 168/16, ss. 2(1), (2), 5(1), (2), (4), (5)

Exemptions from Clauses 37(1)(a) and (b) of the Act

5. (1) An employer may store a hazardous product received from a supplier without having a label on it, without obtaining a safety data sheet for it and without conducting a program of worker education about it while the employer is actively seeking a supplier label and a supplier safety data sheet for it.

(2) An employer may store an employer-produced hazardous product without applying a label to it or using other identification for it, without a safety data sheet for it and without conducting a program of worker education about it while the employer is actively seeking the information about it that is required to prepare a workplace label and a safety data sheet.

O. Reg. 644/88 s. 5; 168/16, s. 2(1), (3)

Worker Education

6. (1) An employer shall ensure that a worker who works with or who may be exposed in the course of his or her work to a hazardous product received from a supplier is informed about all hazard information the employer receives from the supplier concerning the hazardous product and all further hazard information of which the employer is or ought to be aware concerning its use, storage and handling.

(2) An employer who produces a hazardous product in a workplace shall ensure that every worker who works with or who may be exposed in the course of his or her work to the hazardous product is informed about all hazard information of which the employer is or ought to be aware concerning the hazardous product and its use, storage and handling.

O. Reg. 644/88,　s. 6; 168/16, ss. 2(1), 6

7. (1) An employer shall ensure that every worker who works with or who may be exposed in the course of his or her work to a hazardous product is instructed in,

(a) the contents required on a supplier label and workplace label, and the purpose and significance of the information contained on the labels,

(b) the contents required on a safety data sheet and the purpose and significance of the information contained on a safety data sheet;

(c) procedures for the safe use, storage, handling and disposal of a hazardous product;

(d) procedures for the safe use, storage, handling and disposal of a hazardous product when it is contained or transferred in,

(i) a pipe,

(ii) a piping system including valves,

(iii) a process vessel,

(iv) a reaction vessel, or

(v) a tank car, a tank truck, an ore car, a conveyor belt or a similar conveyance;

(e) procedures to be followed when fugitive emissions are present; and

(f) procedures to be followed in case of an emergency involving a hazardous product.

(2) An employer shall ensure that the program of worker education required by subsection (1) is developed and implemented for the employer's workplace and is related to any other training, instruction and prevention programs at the workplace.

(3) An employer shall ensure, so far as is reasonably practicable, that the program of worker instruction required by subsection (1) results in the workers being able to use the information to protect their health and safety.

O. Reg. 644/88 s. 7; 169/16, ss. 2(1), (3), 7

Labels

Supplier Labels

8. (1) An employer shall ensure that every hazardous product not in a container, and every container of a hazardous product, received at a workplace from a supplier is labelled with a supplier label.

(2) No employer shall alter a supplier label on a container in which a hazardous product is received from a supplier while any of the hazardous product remains in the container.

(3) If a label applied to a hazardous product or a container of a hazardous product becomes illegible or is removed, an employer shall replace the label with either a supplier label or a workplace label.

(4) Despite subsections (2) and (3), a supplier label may be removed from a container with a capacity of 3 mL or less if the label interferes with the normal use of the hazardous product.

(5) If an employer receives significant new data from a supplier about a hazardous product, the employer shall, as soon as practicable, attach to every relevant supplier label required under this section, new information that reflects the significant new data.

(6) An employer who imports and receives, under the *Hazardous Products Regulations* (Canada), a hazardous product for use in the employer's own workplace, without a supplier label or with a supplier label that does not meet all the labelling requirements of the *Hazardous Products Regulations* (Canada), shall affix to the product a label that meets the *Hazardous Products Regulations* (Canada) labelling requirements for that hazardous product.

(7) An employer who receives at a workplace an unpackaged hazardous product without a supplier label or a hazardous product transported as a bulk shipment without a supplier label, shall affix to the product a label that meets the *Hazardous Products Regulations* (Canada) labelling requirements for that hazardous product.

O. Reg. 644/88, s. 8; 168/16, ss. 2(1), 8

Workplace Labels for Employer-Produced Products

9. (1) An employer who produces a hazardous product in a workplace shall ensure that the hazardous product or the container of the hazardous product has a workplace label.

(2) Subsection (1) does not apply when the hazardous product is in a container that is intended to contain it for sale or disposition and the container is, or is about to be, appropriately labelled.

(3) An employer shall update a workplace label referred to in subsection (1) as soon as practicable after significant new data about the product becomes available to the employer.

O. Reg. 644/88, s. 9, 168/16, ss. 2(1), 9

Workplace Labels for Decanted Products

10. (1) If a hazardous product that an employer receives in a container from a supplier is transferred to another container, the employer shall ensure that the other container has a workplace label.

(2) No supplier label or workplace label is required on a portable container that is filled directly from a container of a hazardous product with a supplier label or workplace label,

    (a) if,

        (i) the hazardous product is under the control of and is used exclusively by the worker who filled the portable container,

        (ii) the hazardous product is used only during the shift in which the portable container was filled, and

        (iii) the contents of the portable container are clearly identified; or

(b) if all of the hazardous product in the portable container is required for immediate use.

O. Reg. 644/88 s. 10; 168/16, s. 2(1)

Identification of a Hazardous Product in Piping Systems and Vessels

[Heading amended O. Reg. 168/16, s. 2(1).]

11. An employer shall ensure the safe use, storage and handling of a hazardous product in a workplace through worker education and the use of colour coding, labels, placards or another mode of identification when the hazardous product is contained or transferred in,

(a) a pipe;

(b) a piping system including valves;

(c) a process vessel;

(d) a reaction vessel; or

(e) a tank car, a tank truck, an ore car, a conveyor belt or a similar conveyance.

O. Reg. 644/88 s. 11; 168/16, s. 2(1)

Placard Identifiers

12. No label is required on a hazardous product,

(a) if the hazardous product,

(i) is not in a container,

(ii) is in a container or in a form intended for export, or

(iii) is in a container that is intended to contain it for sale or distribution and the container is not about to be appropriately labelled as referred to in subsection 9(2) but is to be appropriately labelled within the normal course of the employer's business and without undue delay; and

(b) if the employer posts a placard that discloses the information required on a workplace label for the hazardous product and is of such size and in such a location that the information is conspicuous and clearly legible to workers.

O. Reg. 644/88 s. 12; 168/16, s. 2(1)

[Heading repealed O. Reg. 168/16, s. 10.]

13. [Repealed O. Reg. 168/16, s. 10.]

Laboratory Samples
[Heading added O. Reg. 168/16, s. 10.]

14. (1) No supplier label is required on a laboratory sample of a hazardous product if,

    (a) the laboratory sample is exempt from labelling requirements under subsection 5(5) or (6) of the *Hazardous Products Regulations* (Canada); and

    (b) the supplier provides a label that is affixed to a container of the hazardous product and that discloses the information described in subsection (2).

(2) A label referred to in clause (1)(b) shall disclose the following information about the hazardous product:

    1. The chemical name or generic chemical name, if known to the supplier, of every material or substance in the hazardous product where,

        i. i. individually, the material or substance is classified in accordance with the *Hazardous Products Regulations* (Canada) in a category or subcategory of a hazard class listed in Schedule 2 to the *Hazardous Products Act* (Canada) and is present above the relevant concentration limit, and

        ii. in a mixture, the material or substance is present at a concentration that results in the mixture being classified in a category or subcategory of a hazard class.

    2. The statement "Hazardous Laboratory Sample, for hazard information or in an emergency call/Échantillon pour laboratoire de produit dangereux. Pour obtenir des renseignements sur les dangers ou en cas d'urgence, composez *insert the number described in paragraph 3*.

    3. An emergency telephone number for the purposes of obtaining the information that must be provided on the safety data sheet for the hazardous product.

O. Reg. 644/88, s. 14; 168/16, s. 10

15. (1) If an employer complies with subsection (2), no workplace label is required for a laboratory sample that,

(a) is produced in the workplace or is in a container other than the container in which it was received from a supplier; and

(b) is clearly identified through a combination of identification visible to workers at the workplace and worker education.

(2) For the purpose of subsection (1), the employer shall ensure that the identification and worker education for the laboratory sample enable the workers to readily identify and obtain either the information required on a safety data sheet, if one has been prepared, or the information described in subsection 14(2) on a label.

O. Reg. 644/88, s. 15; 168/16, s. 10

16. (1) If an employer complies with subsection (2), no workplace label is required for a hazardous product that,

(a) is produced in a laboratory;

(b) is intended by the employer solely for evaluation, analysis or testing for research and development;

(c) is not removed from the laboratory; and

(d) is clearly identified through a combination of identification visible to workers at the workplace and worker education.

(2) For the purposes of subsection (1), the employer shall ensure that the identification and worker education for the hazardous product enables workers to readily identify and obtain either the information required on a safety data sheet, if one has been prepared, or such other information as is necessary to ensure the safe use, storage and handling of the hazardous product.

O. Reg. 644/88, s. 16; 168/16, s. 2(1), (3)

Safety Data Sheets

[Heading amended O. Reg. 168/16, s. 2(4).]

17. Supplier safety data sheets — (1) An employer who receives a hazardous product from a supplier for use, storage or handling at a workplace shall obtain a supplier safety data sheet for the hazardous product from the supplier unless the supplier is exempted under the *Hazardous Products Regulations* (Canada) from providing a safety data sheet for the hazardous product.

(2) An employer shall update a supplier safety data sheet obtained under subsection (1) as soon as practicable after significant new data about the product is provided by the supplier or otherwise becomes available to the employer.

(3) An employer may provide a safety data sheet in a different format from that of the supplier safety data sheet for the hazardous product or containing additional hazard information if,

 (a) the safety data sheet provided by the employer, subject to subsection 40(6) of the Act, contains no less content than the supplier safety data sheet; and

 (b) the supplier safety data sheet is available at the workplace and the employer-provided safety data sheet indicates that fact.

(4) [Repealed O. Reg. 168/16, s. 11.]

(5) [Repealed O. Reg. 168/16, s. 11.]

(6) [Repealed O. Reg. 168/16, s. 11.]

         O. Reg. 644/88, s. 17; 168/16, s. 11

Employer Safety Data Sheets
[Heading amended O. Reg. 168/16, s. 2(4).]

18. **(1)** An employer who produces a hazardous product at a workplace shall prepare a safety data sheet for the product that complies with the requirements of the *Hazardous Products Regulations* (Canada) for a safety data sheet.

(2) No safety data sheet is required for a hazardous product that is a laboratory sample produced by the employer at the workplace.

(3) An employer shall update a safety data sheet referred to in subsection (1) as soon as practicable but not later than 90 days after significant new data about the hazardous product becomes available to the employer.

(4) [Repealed O. Reg. 168/16, s. 12.]

         O. Reg. 644/88, s. 18; 168/16, s. 12

Confidential Business Information

19. **(1)** A claim under subsection 40(1) of the Act for exemption from disclosure shall be made only in respect of,

(a) in the case of a material or substance that is a hazardous product,

  (i) the chemical name of the material or substance,

  (ii) the CAS registry number or any other unique identifier of the material or substance, and

  (iii) the chemical name of any impurity, stabilizing solvent or stabilizing additive that is present in the material or substance, that is classified in accordance with the *Hazardous Products Regulations* (Canada) in a category or subcategory of a hazard class listed in Schedule 2 to the *Hazardous Products Act* (Canada) and that contributes to the classification of the material or substance in the hazard class under that Act;

(b) in the case of an ingredient that is in a mixture that is a hazardous product,

  (i) the chemical name of the ingredient,

  (ii) the CAS registry number or any other unique identifier of the ingredient, and

  (iii) the concentration or concentration range of the ingredient;

(c) in the case of a material, substance or mixture that is a hazardous product, the name of any toxicological study that identifies the material or substance or any ingredient in the mixture;

(d) the product identifier of a hazardous product, being its chemical name, common name, generic name, trade name or brand name;

(e) information about a hazardous product, other than the product identifier, that constitutes a means of identification; and

(f) information that could be used to identify a supplier of a hazardous product.

(2) If an employer excludes from a label or safety data sheet information in respect of which an exemption is claimed, the label or safety data sheet must contain all information otherwise required by this Regulation.

O. Reg. 644/88, s. 19; 36/93, s. 1; 168/16, s. 12

20. (1) An employer who files a claim under subsection 40(1) of the Act for exemption from disclosure in respect of a hazardous product shall state on the safety data sheet and, if applicable, on the label for the hazardous product or container in which the hazardous product is packaged, the date that the claim for exemption was filed and the registry number assigned to the claim under the *Hazardous Materials Information Review Act* (Canada).

(2) The information described in subsection (1) shall remain on the safety data sheet or label until,

(a) 30 days after the final disposition of the proceedings in relation to the claim for exemption; or

(b) if an order is issued under the *Hazardous Materials Information Review Act* (Canada) in respect of the claim, the end of the period specified in the order.

O. Reg. 644/88, s. 20; 36/93, s. 2; 168/16, s. 12

21. If an employer files a claim under subsection 40(1) of the Act for an exemption from disclosure in respect of a hazardous product that is produced in the employer's workplace and the employer excludes from the safety data sheet information in respect of which the exemption is claimed, the following rules apply with respect to the safety data sheet:

1. If the claim is being made in respect of information set out in clause 19(1)(a) or subclauses 19(1)(b)(i) or (ii) of this Regulation, the safety data sheet shall include:

i. in the case of a hazardous product that is a material or substance, the generic chemical name of the material or substance, or

ii. in the case of a hazardous product that is a mixture, the generic chemical name of each material or substance in the mixture that,

A. individually, is classified in accordance with the *Hazardous Products Regulations* (Canada) in a category or subcategory of a hazard class listed in Schedule 2 to the *Hazardous Products Act* (Canada), and is present above the relevant concentration limit, or

B. is present at a concentration that results in the mixture being classified in a category or subcategory of a hazard class.

2. If the claim is being made in relation to information set out in clause 19(1)(d) of this Regulation, the safety data sheet shall include the code name or code number of the hazardous product.

O. Reg. 644/88, s. 21, revised; 168/16, s. 12

22. [Repealed O. Reg. 168/16, s. 12.]

23. (1) An employer whose claim or a portion of whose claim under subsection 40(1) of the Act for exemption from disclosure is determined to be valid shall disclose on the safety data sheet and, if applicable, on the label for the hazardous product or container in which the hazardous product is packaged,

(a) a statement that an exemption has been granted;

(b) the date of the decision granting the exemption; and

(c) the registry number assigned to the claim under the *Hazardous Materials Information Review Act* (Canada).

(2) An employer shall disclose the information required under subsection (1) beginning not more than thirty days after the final disposition of the claim and ending on the last day of the exemption period.

O. Reg. 644/88, s. 23; 168/16, s. 13

Disclosure of Information in Medical Emergencies

24. For the purposes of clause 25(2)(b) of the Act, an employer is required to provide information, including confidential business information, to a medical professional.

O. Reg. 644/88 s. 24

Disclosure Of Source Of Toxicological Data

25. Subject to subsection 40(6) of the Act, an employer who produces a hazardous product in a workplace shall disclose as quickly as possible under the circumstances the source of any toxicological data used by the employer to prepare a safety data sheet when the employer is requested to do so by,

(a) an inspector;

(b) a worker at the workplace;

(c) a member of the committee, if any;

(d) the health and safety representative, if any; or

(e) in the absence of a committee or health and safety representative, a representative of the workers at the workplace.

O. Reg. 644/88, s. 25; 168/16, ss. 2(1), (3), 14

Transition

[Heading added O. Reg. 168/16, s. 15.]

25.1 (1) During the first transition period, the following rules apply:

1. An employer may continue to receive and use hazardous products with labels and safety data sheets that comply with the provisions of this Regulation relating to labels and material safety data sheets as they read immediately before July 1, 2016.

2. The worker education provisions of this Regulation as they read immediately before July 1, 2016, relating to the hazardous products described in paragraph 1, continue to apply.

(2) During the second transition period, the following rules apply:

1. An employer may continue to use hazardous products already at the workplace with labels and safety data sheets that comply with the provisions of this Regulation relating to labels and material safety data sheets as they read immediately before July 1, 2016.

2. The worker education provisions of this Regulation as they read immediately before July 1, 2016, relating to the hazardous products described in paragraph 1, continue to apply.

(3) In this section,

"first transition period" means the period beginning on July 1, 2016 and ending on May 31, 2018;

"second transition period" means the period beginning on June 1, 2018 and ending on November 30, 2018.

O. Reg. 168/16, s. 15

Citation

26. This Regulation may be cited as the *Workplace Hazardous Materials Information System (WHMIS) Regulation.*

O. Reg. 644/88 s. 28

ONT. REG. 861 — X-RAY SAFETY

made under the *Occupational Health and Safety Act*

R.R.O. 1990, Reg. 861

1. In this Regulation,

"absorbed dose" means the mean energy per unit mass imparted by ionizing radiation to matter;

"air kerma" means the sum of the initial kinetic energies per unit mass of all the charged particles liberated by uncharged ionizing radiation in air;

"Director" means the Director of the Health and Safety Support Services Branch of the Ministry of Labour;

"dose equivalent" means the product of absorbed dose and a quality factor where the quality factor is a measure of the biological effectiveness of the radiation, and is assigned the value 1.0 for X-rays;

"failsafe design" means a design in which any failure of safety indicators or components that can reasonably be anticipated causes the production or emission of X-rays to cease;

"gray" means,

(a) a unit of absorbed dose, and is realized when one joule of energy has been imparted per kilogram of material, or

(b) a unit of air kerma, and is realized when one joule of energy has been liberated per kilogram of air;

"redundant", when used with reference to a light, means a light with two or more separate and equivalent bulbs so designed that the failure of one bulb will not affect the operation of the other bulb or bulbs;

"shield" or **"shielding"** means radiation absorbing material or materials used to reduce the absorbed dose or absorbed dose rate imparted to an object;

861

"sievert" means a unit of dose equivalent, and for X-rays the dose equivalent measured in sieverts is numerically equal to the absorbed dose measured in grays;

"X-ray machine" means an electrically powered device, the principal purpose of which is the production of X-rays;

"X-ray source" means any device, or that portion of any device, that emits X-rays, whether or not the device is an X-ray machine;

"X-ray worker" means a worker who, as a necessary part of the worker's employment, may be exposed to X-rays and may receive a dose equivalent in excess of the annual limits set forth in Column 4 of the Schedule;

"X-rays" means electrically-generated electromagnetic radiation of maximum photon energy not less than 5,000 electron volts.

O. Reg. 632/86 s. 1

2. Subject to section 3, this Regulation applies to every owner, employer, supervisor and worker at a workplace where,

(a) an X-ray machine is present or used; or

(b) an X-ray source that is not an X-ray machine is present or used, if the X-ray source is capable of producing an air kerma rate greater than 1.0 microgray per hour at any accessible point outside its surface.

O. Reg. 632/86 s. 2

3. (1) This Regulation does not apply to an X-ray source that is licensable under the *Atomic Energy Control Act* (Canada).

(2) Sections 5, 6, 7 and 8 of this Regulation do not apply in respect of an X-ray machine the installation, registration or operation of which is subject to the *Healing Arts Radiation Protection Act*.

O. Reg. 632/86 s. 3

4. Except as permitted under the *Healing Arts Radiation Protection Act*, an X-ray source shall not be operated for the irradiation of a worker.O. Reg. 632/86, s. 4

5. (1) An X-ray source shall not be used at a workplace unless the employer who has possession of the X-ray source is registered with the Director.

(2) An application for registration under this section shall be in Form 1 and shall be filed with the Director.

(3) An employer who was registered under Ontario Regulation 263/84 or Regulation 855 of Revised Regulations of Ontario, 1980 or a predecessor thereof shall be deemed to be registered under this section if the registration was subsisting at the end of the 29th day of October, 1986.

(4) If an employer who is registered under this section ceases to have possession of an X-ray source, the employer shall forthwith give a notice to the Director advising the Director of that fact.

(5) An employer's registration under this section terminates when the employer notifies the Director that the employer no longer has possession of any X-ray sources.

O. Reg. 632/86 s. 5

6. (1) An X-ray source shall not be installed or used in a permanent location and an X-ray source that is designed for portable or mobile use shall not be installed or used regularly in one location unless an application for review, together with plan location drawings, of the installation have been reviewed by and are acceptable to an inspector.

(2) Subsection (1) does not apply to an X-ray source that,

(a) was in use in a permanent location before the 27th day of April, 1984, if it has remained continuously in that location since that time and so long as it remains in that location; or

(b) was installed after the 26th day of April, 1984, if the installation was made in compliance with Ontario Regulation 263/84 and there was compliance with that Regulation until the end of the 29th day of October, 1986.

(3) An application mentioned in subsection (1) shall be in Form 2 and shall be accompanied by the plan location drawings mentioned in that subsection, in duplicate.

(4) Plan location drawings mentioned in subsection (1),

(a) shall bear the name of the applicant and the address of the location;

(b) shall be on a legible scale that is not less than 1:100 and that is suitable for microfilming;

(c) shall indicate the direction north;

(d) shall show the proposed location of the X-ray source and, where applicable, the range of its motion;

861

(e) shall show the proposed location of the X-ray control panel, if the location of the control panel is different from that of the X-ray source;

(f) shall indicate the use of rooms or areas that are adjacent, both horizontally and vertically, to the proposed location;

(g) shall indicate the type and thickness of the shielding installed or to be installed on the boundaries of the proposed location; and

(h) shall indicate the type and location of the safety devices such as warning lights, interlocks and cut-off switches.

(5) An application under this section shall be filed with the Director.

(6) Where an application under this section or a predecessor of this section has been found acceptable by an inspector, the X-ray source to which the application relates shall not be installed except in accordance with the application and the plan location drawings as accepted by the inspector.

(7) An X-ray source to which subsection (1) applies or that is described in subsection (2) shall not be used, if after the installation of the X-ray source there is a change in,

(a) the installation or use of the X-ray source;

(b) the use of rooms or areas adjacent, horizontally or vertically, to the X-ray source;

(c) any shielding of the X-ray source, that may result in an increase in the exposure of a worker to X-rays unless the change has been reviewed by and is acceptable to an inspector.

(8) An employer shall request a review of a change described in subsection (7) by giving the request to the Director. O. Reg. 632/86, s. 6

7. (1) Where an employer comes into possession of an X-ray source that is designed for portable or mobile use and that is so used, notice thereof shall be given to the Director.

(2) The notice required by subsection (1) shall be in writing and shall include,

(a) the name and address of the employer;

(b) the employer's registration number, if any, under section 5;

(c) the location where the X-ray source will normally be stored;

(d) the purpose for which the X-ray source will be used;

(e) the make, model and serial number of the X-ray source; and

(f) the maximum operating voltage and current of the X-ray source.

O. Reg. 632/86 s. 7

8. An employer shall designate a person, for each X-ray source, who is competent because of knowledge, training or experience in the use and operation of X-ray sources and in radiation safety practices, to exercise direction over the safe use and operation of the X-ray source, and shall advise the Director in writing of the name of the person designated.

O. Reg. 632/86 s. 8

9. (1) An employer who employs a person as an X-ray worker shall, at the time that employment begins,

(a) inform the worker in writing that the worker is employed as an X-ray worker;

(b) inform the worker of the limits imposed by subsection 10(1) on the dose equivalent that may be received by the worker; and

(c) if the worker is female, inform her of the dose equivalent limit mentioned in subsection 10(2) applicable to a pregnant X-ray worker.

(2) An employer shall maintain a list of all X-ray workers in the employment of the employer.

O. Reg. 632/86 s. 9

10. (1) The dose equivalent received or that may be received by a worker shall be as low as is reasonably achievable, and in any case,

(a) an X-ray worker shall not receive a dose equivalent in excess of the annual limits set out in Column 3 of the Schedule; and

(b) a worker who is not an X-ray worker shall not receive a dose equivalent in excess of the annual limits set out in Column 4 of the Schedule.

(2) Despite subsection (1), an employer shall take every precaution reasonable in the circumstances to ensure that the mean dose equivalent received by the abdomen of a pregnant X-ray worker does not exceed 5 millisieverts during the pregnancy.

O. Reg. 632/86 s. 10

11. The following measures and procedures shall be carried out in a workplace where an X-ray source is used:

1. X-ray warning signs or warning devices shall be posted or installed in conspicuous locations.

2. Every X-ray source capable of producing an air kerma rate greater than 5 micrograys per hour at any accessible point shall be labelled at its operating controls as a source of X-rays.

3. Where the air kerma in an area may exceed 100 micrograys in any one hour, access to the area shall be controlled by,

    i. locks or interlocks if the X-ray source is one to which subsection 6(1) applies or is described in subsection 6(2), and

    ii. barriers and X-ray warning signs if the X-ray source is portable or mobile and is being so used.

4. To ensure that the dose equivalent limits mentioned in section 10 are not exceeded,

    i. structural or other shielding shall be installed as is necessary, and

    ii. diaphragms, cones and adjustable collimators or other suitable devices shall be provided and used as are necessary to limit the dimensions of the useful X-ray beam.

O. Reg. 632/86 s. 11

12. (1) An employer shall provide to each X-ray worker a suitable personal dosimeter that will provide an accurate measure of the dose equivalent received by the X-ray worker.

(2) An X-ray worker shall use the personal dosimeter as instructed by the employer.

(3) An employer shall ensure that the personal dosimeter provided to an X-ray worker is read accurately to give a measure of the dose equivalent received by the worker and shall furnish to the worker the record of the worker's radiation exposure.

(4) An employer shall verify that the dose equivalent mentioned in subsection (3) is reasonable and appropriate in the circumstances, and shall notify an inspector of any dose equivalent that does not appear reasonable and appropriate.

(5) An employer shall retain an X-ray worker's personal dosimeter records for a period of at least three years.

O. Reg. 632/86 s. 12

13. Where a worker has received a dose equivalent in excess of the annual limits set out in Column 4 of the Schedule in a period of three months, the employer shall forthwith investigate the cause of the exposure and shall provide a report in writing of the findings of the investigation and of the corrective action taken to the Director and to the joint health and safety committee or health and safety representative, if any.

O. Reg. 632/86 s. 13

14. Where an accident, failure of any equipment or other incident occurs that may have resulted in a worker receiving a dose equivalent in excess of the annual limits set out in Column 3 of the Schedule, the employer shall notify immediately by telephone, telegram or other direct means the Director and the joint health and safety committee or health and safety representative, if any, of the accident or failure and the employer shall, within forty-eight hours after the accident or failure, send to the Director a written report of the circumstances of the accident or failure.

O. Reg. 632/86 s. 14

15. (1) This section applies only to X-ray machines used for industrial radiography or industrial fluoroscopy but does not apply to an X-ray machine to which section 17 applies.

(2) No X-ray machine to which this section applies shall be used except by or under the supervision of a competent person.

(3) In addition to any other requirements of this Regulation, the following requirements apply with respect to every X-ray machine to which this section applies:

    1. The control panel of the X-ray machine shall have a plainly visible warning light to indicate when X-rays are being produced in the X-ray tube.

    2. The X-ray machine, if installed in a permanent location or if designed for portable or mobile operation but used regularly in one location, shall be contained in an enclosure.

    3. No person shall be permitted in the enclosure required by paragraph 2 while X-rays are being produced.

    4. The enclosure required by paragraph 2 shall be provided with,

        i. reliable locks or interlocks to prevent any person from entering a radiation enclosure during an exposure and, where an exposure is terminated by an interlock, it shall only be possible to restart the exposure from the control panel, and

        ii. conspicuous warning lights of failsafe or redundant design near each entrance to the enclosure that indicate when X-rays are being produced, and paragraph 3 of section 11 does not apply.

5. If the enclosure required by paragraph 2 is of such a size or is so arranged that the operator cannot readily determine whether it is unoccupied, it shall be provided with,

    i. suitable audible or visible pre-exposure warning signals within the enclosure that shall be actuated for not less than ten or more than thirty seconds immediately before the initiation of an X-ray exposure,

    ii. suitable audible or visible warning signals within the enclosure that shall be actuated during the X-ray exposure, and

    iii. a suitable exit to enable any person to leave the enclosure without delay and without having to pass through the primary X-ray beam or an effective means, within the enclosure, that,

        A. prevents or interrupts an X-ray exposure,

        B. cannot be reset from outside the enclosure, and

        C. can be reached without having to pass through the primary X-ray beam.

6. An X-ray machine shall be operated, and, where an enclosure is required by paragraph 2, the enclosure shall be shielded in such a manner that,

    i. an X-ray worker is not likely to receive an effective dose equivalent in excess of 1 millisievert per week, and

    ii. a worker who is not an X-ray worker is not likely to receive an effective dose equivalent in excess of 100 microsieverts per week.

7. The employer shall ensure that a direct reading dosimeter of a suitable type is provided to each X-ray worker who in the course of his or her work may be exposed to an air kerma rate in excess of 100 micrograys per hour.

8. An X-ray worker provided with a direct reading dosimeter shall use it and shall determine the amount by which its reading has increased during each work day and record that amount at the end of the work day.

9. The employer shall retain the direct reading dosimeter records of each X-ray worker provided with such a dosimeter for a period of at least three years.

10. At least one radiation survey meter of a suitable type shall be provided for each portable or mobile X-ray machine and it shall be

calibrated at least once every twelve months and kept in good working order.

O. Reg. 632/86 s. 15

16. In addition to any other requirement of this Regulation, the following requirements apply to every X-ray machine used for the diagnostic examination of animals:

1. Where practicable, radiographic procedures shall be performed in a room designed for the purpose of performing X-ray examinations of animals.

2. The air kerma due to leakage radiation from the X-ray tube housing or from an attached beam-limiting device shall not exceed 1 milligray in one hour at a distance of 1 metre from the focal spot of the X-ray tube.

3. Exposure duration shall be controlled by a preset timing mechanism and shall be initiated by a switch that requires positive action by the operator to continue the exposure and that allows the operator to remain at least 2 metres from the tube housing.

4. To the extent practicable, the dimensions of the useful beam shall be restricted to not more than those of the film.

5. The film cassette shall not be held by hand during an exposure.

6. The animal being X-rayed shall be restrained or supported by mechanical means where practicable.

7. If an animal is required to be restrained or supported by hand, a protective apron and gloves, providing shielding equivalent to at least 0.5 millimetre of lead, shall be worn by any person providing the restraint or support.

8. A record of radiographic exposures, including the date, kilovoltage, tube current and duration of each exposure, shall be maintained and kept for at least one year.

O. Reg. 632/86 s. 16

17. In addition to any other requirements of this Regulation, where an employer is in possession of an X-ray source in which the X-ray source, the object or the portion of the object being exposed to X-rays and the detection device are enclosed in a cabinet that, independent of existing structures, provides radiation attenuation and prevents access to the X-ray beam, the employer shall comply with the following requirements:

1. A warning device that indicates when X-rays are being produced shall be mounted on or near the cabinet in such a way as to be

861

conspicuous from any position from which the cabinet can be opened.

2. Access doors and sample ports shall be interlocked with the X-ray source or with an adequately shielded shutter of failsafe design and, where operation has been interrupted by an interlock, it shall be possible to resume operation only from the control panel after the interlock has been reset.

3. The cabinet shall be so arranged and shielded as to prevent the air kerma rate from exceeding 5 micrograys per hour at any accessible point 5 centimetres from the external surface, under all possible operating conditions.

4. Cabinet X-ray equipment that is intended to permit the entry of a person shall also be provided with,

  i. suitable audible or visible warning signals within the cabinet that shall be actuated for at least ten seconds immediately prior to the initiation of X-ray production after the closing of any door that is designed to permit human access into the cabinet,

  ii. suitable audible or visible warning signals within the cabinet that shall be actuated during X-ray production, and

  iii. effective means within the enclosure to prevent or interrupt the production of X-rays, that cannot be reset from outside the enclosure and that can be reached without having to pass through the primary X-ray beam.

O. Reg. 632/86 s. 17

18. In addition to any other requirements of this Regulation, where an employer is in possession of an X-ray source that consists of analytic X-ray equipment to which section 17 does not apply and that is primarily used to determine the structure or composition of a sample of a material, the employer shall comply with the following requirements:

1. The control panel shall have an indicator, in close proximity to the X-ray "ON/OFF" switch, that clearly indicates when X-rays are being produced in the X-ray tube.

2. A warning light shall be mounted near each X-ray tube in such a way as to be clearly visible from any direction from which the tube can be approached, that indicates when X-rays are being produced.

3. The condition of each shutter, open or closed, shall be clearly indicated at or near the X-ray tube.

4. Each port shall be designed in such a way that the X-ray beam can emerge only when a camera or other recording device is in its proper position, wherever practicable.

5. At least one of the warning or safety devices mentioned in paragraphs 1 to 4 shall be of failsafe design.

6. A guard or interlock which prevents entry of any part of the body into the primary beam path shall be used, wherever practicable.

7. A shield shall be provided to absorb the primary beam at the nearest practicable position beyond the point of intersection of the beam and the sample that it is intended to irradiate.

8. All unused ports shall be secured in such a way as to prevent inadvertent opening.

O. Reg. 632/86 s. 18

19. In applying this Regulation, a procedure or device may vary from the procedure or device prescribed in this Regulation if the protection afforded thereby is equal to or greater than the protection afforded by the procedure or device prescribed.

O. Reg. 632/86 s. 19

SCHEDULE

	EXPOSURE		
PART OF BODY IRRADIATED	**CONDITIONS AND COMMENTS**	**DOSE EQUIVALENT ANNUAL**	
		LIMIT (MILLISIE-VERTS)	
		X-Ray Workers	Other Workers
COLUMN 1	**COLUMN 2**	**COLUMN 3**	**COLUMN 4**
Whole body or trunk of body	Uniform irradia-tion	50	5
Partial or non-uniform irradia-	The limit applies to the effective	50	5

861

tion of body	dose equivalent defined in Note (a)		
Lens of eye	Irradiated either alone or with other organs or tissues	150	50
Skin	The limit applies to the mean dose equivalent to the basal cell layer of the epidermis for any area of skin of 1 square centimetre or more	500	50
Individual organs or tissues other than lens of eye or skin	The limit on effective dose equivalent applies, with an overriding limit on the dose equivalent to the individual organ or tissue	500	50

Notes to the Schedule:
(a) The Effective Dose Equivalent, H_E, is determined by the following formula: $H_E = \Sigma_T W_T H_T$ where:

      (i) T is an index for tissue type;

      (ii) H_T is the annual dose equivalent in tissue T;

      (iii) W_T is a weighting factor which has the following values:

            0.25 for the gonads,

            0.15 for the breast,

            0.12 for the red bone marrow,

            0.12 for the lungs,

0.03 for the bone surfaces,

0.03 for the thyroid,

0.06 for each of the five other organs or tissues receiving the highest dose equivalents, but excluding the skin, extremities and eye lenses. The exposure of all other remaining tissues can be neglected. When the gastro-intestinal tract is irradiated, the stomach, small intestine, upper large intestine and lower large intestine shall be considered as four separate organs; and

(iv) $\Sigma_T W_T H_T$ is the sum of the $W_T H_T$ values for all irradiated tissues which receive more than 1 millisievert in a given year.

(b) The annual limits do not include any dose equivalent received by a worker from background sources or received as a patient undergoing medical diagnostic or therapeutic procedures.

(c) The annual limits include any dose equivalent received by a worker, as a consequence of his or her occupation, from all sources of ionizing radiation.

Form 1 — Occupational Health and Safety Act

Application for Registration

Ontario Ministry of Labour

Radiation Protection Service

Registration No. ....

Note: Insert "X" in all applicable boxes.

The undersigned, as employer □ or as agent for the employer □ applies for registration with the Radiation Protection Service of the Ministry of Labour.

A. The employer is: ....

     Name ....

     Telephone No. ....

     Business Address ....

     City ....

     Postal Code ....

    B. The person to whom correspondence should be addressed is as at "A" □, or is:

     Name ....

Telephone No. ....
Position or Title ....
Address ....
City ....
Postal Code ....

C. The general nature of the employer's business is (check one category only):

☐ Industrial and Commercial
☐ Veterinarian
☐ Research and Development
☐ Education and Training
☐ Other (Please specify) ....

D. As of the date of this registration, the employer is in possession of the following X-ray sources at the locations indicated (for portable or mobile units indicate where normally stored):

LOCATION (Room,

MAKE	MODEL	Building, Street, City)	DATE INSTALLED

Dated at, ... this .... day of .... 19..........
Signature of Applicant .... Name (please type or print) ....

Form 2 — Occupational Health and Safety Act

Application for Review of Permanent X-Ray Location

Ontario Ministry of Labour
Radiation Protection Service
Registration No. ....
Note: Insert "X" in all applicable boxes.

Part A — General

The undersigned, as
☐ employer ☐ owner ☐ contractor ☐ architect ☐ engineer ☐ agent

applies for review of a permanent X-ray location. The application covers a total of .... X-ray sources in .... rooms. It is accompanied by related floor plans in duplicate and by one completed Part B for each X-ray source for which review is sought.

1.

The name of the X-ray facility for which review is sought is ....

2.

The employer is:

Name ....
Telephone No. ....
Number, Street ....
City ....
Postal Code ....

3. The employer's registration number is: ....
OR the employer is not registered ☐

4. This application is submitted for the following reason:

☐ Opening of a new facility
☐ Relocation of sources
☐ Replacement of old sources in existing facilities
☐ Additional sources
☐ Acquisition of existing facility from: Previous owner's name .... Registration No. ....
☐ Change of shielding provisions, structure of safety devices
☐ Compliance with Inspector's direction Operation is expected to commence on the following date: ....
    19..........

5. The X-ray source(s) will be (or are at present) located as at 2 ☐, or at:

Number, Street ....
City ....
Postal Code ....

6. The person who exercises (or will exercise) direction over the safe use and operation of the X-ray source at the above location is the employer ☐, or is:

Name ....
Telephone No. ....
Position ....
Relevant Qualifications ....

861

7. The drawings and specifications were prepared by:
☐ employer ☐ architect ☐ other (specify)

....

Name ....
Telephone No. ....
Number, Street ....
City ....
Postal Code ....

8. The information set out in this application and in each Part B accompanying this application is accurate to the best of my knowledge.

Dated at, ..., this .... day of .... 19..........

Signature of Applicant .... Name (please type or print)

....

Part B — Specific

Please note: one copy of Part B is required for each X-ray source for which review is sought.

1. This sheet refers to X-ray source number .... of .... X-ray sources located in the room designated as .... and so marked on the accompanying drawings.

2. This X-ray source is used for .... It is identified by:

Make/Model .... Serial No. .... and has the following operating characteristics:

(a) the maximum rated tube voltage .... is kilovolts;

(b) the maximum rated tube current .... is milliamperes;

(c) the anticipated maximum workload .... is milliampere-minutes per week.

3.

The composition of the boundaries of the room, including windows and doors, are (give material types and thicknesses):

Floor ....
Ceiling ....
Walls:
North ....
East ....
South ....
West ....

| Direction | Occupancy (See Note 1) | | Usage Factor (See Note 2) Per cent |
	Type	Per cent	
Down	....	....	....
Up	....	....	....
North	....	....	....
East	....	....	....
South	....	....	....
West	....	....	....

Notes:

Note 1: Occupancy type is the nature of use of the area in the indicated direction relative to the X-ray source (e.g. office, waiting room, parking lot, etc.). Occupancy per cent is the fraction, expressed as a percentage, of the time the area will be occupied while the source is on (omit if unknown).

Note 2: The use factor is the fraction of the time the beam will be pointed in the direction indicated, as a percentage of the total time the source is on. For uncollimated, panoramic or multiple beams, the sum may exceed 100 per cent. The information given in this Part must correspond with that given on the accompanying floor plans.

861

ONT. REG. 1101 — FIRST AID REQUIREMENTS

made under the *Workplace Safety and Insurance Act, 1997*

R.R.O. 1990, Reg. 1101

1. (1) A first aid station shall contain,

    (a) a first aid box containing the items required by Regulation; and

    (b) a notice board displaying,

        (i) the Board's poster known as Form 82,

        (ii) the valid first aid certificates of qualification of the trained workers on duty, and

        (iii) an inspection card with spaces for recording the date of the most recent inspection of the first aid box and the signature of the person making the inspection.

(2) A first aid station shall be in the charge of a worker who works in the immediate vicinity of the first aid station and who is qualified in first aid to the standards required by this Regulation.

(3) First aid stations shall be located as to be easily accessible for the prompt treatment of any worker at all times when work is in progress.

2. (1) A first aid box shall contain as a minimum the first aid items required by this Regulation and all items in the box shall be maintained in good condition at all times.

(2) The box shall be large enough so that each item is in plain view and easily accessible.

3. Every employer shall at all times keep posted in other conspicuous places in the place of employment the Board's poster known as Form 82 respecting the necessity of reporting all accidents and receiving first aid treatment.

4. The expense of furnishing and maintaining first aid appliances and services shall be borne by the employer.

5. Every employer shall keep a record of all circumstances respecting an accident as described by the injured worker, the date and time of its occurrence, the names of witnesses, the nature and exact location of the injuries to the worker and the date, time and nature of each first aid treatment given.

6. Employers shall inspect first aid boxes and their contents at not less than quarter-yearly intervals and shall mark the inspection card for each box with the date of the most recent inspection and the signature of the person making the inspection.

7. The Board or its appointees may make inspections of first aid stations, appliances, services and records.

First Aid Requirements

8. (1) Every employer employing not more than five workers in any one shift at a place of employment shall provide and maintain at the place of employment a first aid station with a first aid box containing as a minimum,

    (a) a current edition of a standard St. John Ambulance First Aid Manual;

    (b) 1 card of safety pins; and

    (c) dressings consisting of,

        (i) 12 adhesive dressings individually wrapped,

        (ii) 4 sterile gauze pads, 3 inches square,

        (iii) 2 rolls of gauze bandage, 2 inches wide,

        (iv) 2 field dressings, 4 inches square or 2 four-inch sterile bandage compresses, and

        (v) 1 triangular bandage.

(2) The employer shall ensure that the first aid station is at all times in the charge of a worker who,

    (a) is the holder of a valid St. John Ambulance Emergency First Aid Certificate or its equivalent; and

    (b) works in the immediate vicinity of the station.

9. (1) Every employer employing more than five workers and not more than fifteen workers in any one shift at a place of employment shall provide and maintain a first aid station with a first aid box containing as a minimum,

    (a) a current edition of a standard St. John Ambulance First Aid Manual;

    (b) 1 card of safety pins; and

(c) dressings consisting of,

    (i) 24 adhesive dressings individually wrapped,

    (ii) 12 sterile gauze pads, 3 inches square,

    (iii) 4 rolls of 2-inch gauze bandage,

    (iv) 4 rolls of 4-inch gauze bandage,

    (v) 4 sterile surgical pads suitable for pressure dressing individually wrapped,

    (vi) 6 triangular bandages,

    (vii) 2 rolls of splint padding, and

    (viii) 1 roll-up splint.

(2) The employer shall ensure that the first aid station is at all times in the charge of a worker who,

    (a) is the holder of a valid St. John Ambulance Standard First Aid Certificate or its equivalent; and

    (b) works in the immediate vicinity of the box.

10. (1) Every employer employing more than fifteen and less than 200 workers in any one shift at a place of employment shall provide and maintain at the place of employment one stretcher, two blankets and a first aid station with a first aid box containing as a minimum,

    (a) a current edition of a standard St. John Ambulance First Aid Manual;

    (b) 24 safety pins;

    (c) 1 basin, preferably stainless steel; and

    (d) dressings consisting of,

        (i) 48 adhesive dressings, individually wrapped,

        (ii) 2 rolls of adhesive tape, 1 inch wide,

        (iii) 12 rolls of 1-inch gauze bandage,

        (iv) 48 sterile gauze pads, 3 inches square,

        (v) 8 rolls of 2-inch gauze bandage,

        (vi) 8 rolls of 4-inch gauze bandage,

        (vii) 6 sterile surgical pads suitable for pressure dressings, individually wrapped,

        (viii) 12 triangular bandages,

        (ix) splints of assorted sizes, and

        (x) 2 rolls of splint padding.

(2) The employer shall ensure that the first aid station is at all times in the charge of a worker who,

1101

(a) is the holder of a valid St. John Ambulance Standard First Aid Certificate or its equivalent; and

(b) works in the immediate vicinity of the box.

First Aid Room

11. (1) Every employer employing 200 or more workers in any one shift at a place of employment shall provide and maintain a first aid room equipped with,

(a) a current edition of a standard St. John Ambulance First Aid Manual;

(b) instruments consisting of,

(i) dressing scissors,

(ii) dressing forceps,

(iii) safety pins,

(iv) graduated medicine glass,

(v) tongue depressors, and

(vi) applicators, cotton tipped;

(c) denatured ethyl alcohol;

(d) dressings consisting of,

(i) adhesive dressings, individually wrapped,

(ii) sterile gauze pads of assorted sizes, individually wrapped,

(iii) gauze bandages of assorted sizes,

(iv) adhesive plaster,

(v) absorbent cotton,

(vi) triangular bandages,

(vii) splints of assorted sizes, and

(viii) splint padding; and

(e) furnishings consisting of,

(i) hot and cold running water,

(ii) 3 washbasins, preferably stainless steel,

(iii) 1 instrument sterilizer,

(iv) 1 cabinet for surgical dressings,

(v) 1 enamel foot bath,

(vi) 1 sanitary disposal receptacle with lid,

(vii) 1 first aid box containing as a minimum the items required by subsection 9(1), for use by the attendant at the scene of an accident before the patient is moved to the first aid room or general hospital,

(viii) 1 couch curtained off or in a separate cubicle,

(ix) 1 stretcher, and

(x) 2 blankets.

(2) The employer shall ensure that the first aid room is in the charge of,

(a) a registered nurse; or

(b) a worker who,

(i) is the holder of a valid St. John Ambulance Standard First Aid Certificate or its equivalent,

(ii) works in the immediate vicinity of the first aid room, and

(iii) does not perform other work of a nature that is likely to affect adversely his ability to administer first aid.

(3) The certificate referred to in subclause 2(b)(i) shall be prominently displayed in the first aid room.

12. Where the first aid station referred to in section 9 or 10 or the first aid room referred to in section 11 is not easily accessible in order to provide prompt treatment of any worker, an additional first aid station or stations shall be established to comply with subsection 1(3).

Transportation, Construction, Farm and Bush Sites

13. For the purposes of sections 8, 9, 10 and 11,

(a) a railway train, vessel or bus on a route, other than an urban or suburban route, on which a worker is employed;

(b) the central point from which bush workers are dispatched daily to work sites;

(c) a vehicle being used by an employer to transport workers; or

(d) the site of the construction, repair or demolition of a building,

shall be deemed to be a place of employment.

14. (1) Where the place of employment is the site of construction, repair or demolition of a building, a first aid station shall be maintained in the time office for the project.

(2) Where there is no time office for the project, a first aid station shall be maintained in a vehicle or building at the site and the provisions of section 1 shall apply.

15. Where the construction, repair or demolition of a building is in the charge of a general contractor, the general contractor shall provide and maintain the first aid station or stations required by this Regulation in

1101

respect of the workers in the same manner as if he were the employer of the workers.

16. (1) Every employer of bush workers or farm workers, or both, shall provide at a central location a first aid box containing,

   (a) a current edition of a standard St. John Ambulance First Aid Manual;

   (b) 1 card of safety pins;

   (c) dressings consisting of,

      (i) 16 adhesive dressings, individually wrapped,

      (ii) 6 sterile gauze pads, 3 inches square,

      (iii) 4 rolls of 3-inch gauze bandage,

      (iv) 2 sterile surgical pads suitable for pressure dressings, individually wrapped, and

      (v) 4 triangular bandages.

(2) Every employer using a vehicle to transport workers shall equip the vehicle with a first aid box containing,

   (a) a current edition of a standard St. John Ambulance First Aid Manual;

   (b) 1 card of safety pins;

   (c) dressings consisting of,

      (i) 16 adhesive dressings, individually wrapped,

      (ii) 6 sterile gauze pads, 3 inches square,

      (iii) 4 rolls of 3-inch gauze bandage,

      (iv) 2 sterile surgical pads suitable for pressure dressings, individually wrapped, and

      (v) 4 triangular bandages.

(3) The employer of workers engaged in transporting goods outside an urban area in a vehicle shall equip the vehicle with a first aid kit containing,

   (a) a current edition of a standard St. John Ambulance First Aid Manual;

   (b) dressings consisting of,

      (i) 12 adhesive dressings, individually wrapped,

      (ii) 1 four-inch bandage compress,

      (iii) 2 two-inch bandage compresses, and

      (iv) 1 triangular bandage.

(4) Where a worker is operating heavy construction and maintenance equipment in a place where a first aid station is not readily available to him in the event of an accident, his employer shall equip the machinery with a first aid kit containing the items required in subsection (3).

(5) A bus operated on a route other than an urban route shall be equipped with a first aid kit containing the items required in subsection (3).

(6) Motive power units of all railways other than units used in yard service shall be equipped with a first aid box equipped with the items required in subsection (2).

Occupational Health & Safety Addresses and Resources

Ministry of Labour—Occupational Health and Safety Branch

Main Office(s)

Occupational Health & Safety Branch
505 University Ave., 19th Floor
Toronto ON M7A 1T7
Toll free: 1-877-202-0008 (province-wide)
TTY: 1-855-653-9260
Fax: (905) 577-1316
Web: www.labour.gov.on.ca

Material Testing Laboratory
Willet Green Miller Centre
Building C
933 Ramsey Lake Road
Sudbury P3E 6B5
(705) 670-5695
Fax: (705) 670-5698

Legal Services Branch
400 University Ave., 11th Floor
Toronto M7A 1T7
(416) 326-7950
Fax: (416) 326-7985

Dispute Resolution Services
400 University Ave., 8th Floor
Toronto M7A 1T7
(416) 326-7575
Fax: (416) 314-8755

Resources

Employment Practices Branch
400 University Avenue, 9th Floor
Toronto ON M7A 1T7
Call Centre
(416) 326-7160 (Greater Toronto Area)
1-800-531-5551 (Canada-wide)
Fax: (416) 326-7061
Publications
Publications Ontario
416-326-5300
1-800-668-9938
Toll-free: 1-800-268-7095
Web: www.publications.serviceontario.ca

Field Offices

Central Region East

5001 Yonge Street
Suite 1600
North York ON M7A 0A3
Tel: (647) 777-5005
Fax: (647) 777-5010
2275 Midland Avenue, Unit #1
Scarborough ON M1P 3E7
Tel: (416) 314-5300
Fax: (416) 314-5410 or (416) 314-5405

Central Region West

17345 Leslie Street, Units 101 and 102
Newmarket ON L3Y 0A4
Tel: (905) 715-7061 or 1-888-299-3138
Fax: (905) 715-7140
1290 Central Parkway West, 4th Floor
Mississauga ON L5C 4R3
Tel: (905) 273-7800 or 1-800-268-2988
Fax: (905) 615-7098 or (905) 615-7078

Eastern Region

Kingston

Beechgrove Complex
51 Heakes Lane
Kingston K7M 9B1
(613) 545-0989
Toll free: 1-800-267-0915
Fax: (613) 545-9831

Ottawa

347 Preston Street,
Tower III, 4th Floor
Ottawa K1S 3J4
(613) 228-8050
Toll free: 1-800-267-1916
Fax: (613) 727-2900

Peterborough

300 Water Street North
3rd Floor, South Tower
Peterborough K9J 8M5
(705) 755-4700
Toll free: 1-800-461-1425
Fax: (705) 755-4724

Northern Region

North Bay

200 First Avenue West,
Unit 204
North Bay P1B 3B9
(705) 497-5234
Toll free: 1-877-717-0778
Fax: 705-497-6850

Sault Ste. Marie

70 Foster Dr., Ste. 480
Sault Ste. Marie P6A 6V4

Resources

(705) 945-6600
Toll free: 1-800-461-7268
Fax: (705) 949-9796

Sudbury

159 Cedar St., Ste. 301
Sudbury P3E 6A5
(705) 564-7400
Toll free: 1-800-461-6325
Fax: (705) 564-7437

Thunder Bay

435 James St. S., Ste. 222
Thunder Bay P7E 6S7
(807) 475-1691
Toll free: 1-800-465-5016
Fax: (807) 475-1646

Timmins

Ontario Government Complex
D Wing
5520 Highway 101 East.
South Porcupine P0N 1H0
(705) 235-1900
Toll free: 1-800-461-9847
Fax: (705) 235-1925

Western Region

Hamilton/Halton/Brant

Ellen Fairclough Building
119 King Street West
Hamilton ON L8P 4Y7
(905) 577-6221
Toll free: 1-800-263-6906
Fax: (905) 577-1200

Kitchener-Waterloo

155 Frobisher Dr., Unit G213
Waterloo N2V 2E1

(519) 885-3378
Toll free: 1-800-265-2468
Fax: (519) 883-5694

London/Sarnia

217 York St., 5th Fl.
London N6A 5P9
(519) 439-2210
Toll free: 1-800-265-1676
Fax: (519) 672-0268

Niagara

301 St. Paul St., 8th Fl.
St. Catharines L2R 7R4
(905) 704-3994
Toll free: 1-800-263-7260
Fax: (905) 704-3011

Windsor

4510 Rhodes Dr., Ste. 610
Windsor N8W 5K5
(519) 256-8277
Toll free: 1-800-265-5140
Fax: (519) 258-1321

Health and Safety Ontario

www.healthandsafetyontario.ca

Infrastructure Health & Safety Association

(serves aggregates, construction, electrical, natural gas, ready-mix concrete, transportation, and utilities industries)

Centre for Health and Safety Innovation
5110 Creekbank Road, Suite 400
Mississauga ON L4W 0A1
(905) 625-0100
Toll Free: 1-800-263-5024
Fax: (905) 625-8998
Email: info@ihsa.ca
Web: www.ihsa.ca

Skills Development Centre (SDC)
5345 Creekbank Road
Mississauga ON
L4W 5L5

Voyager Training Centre
21 Voyager Court South
Etobicoke ON M9W 5M7
Fax: (416) 674-8866
Email: info@ihsa.ca

Public Services Health & Safety Association

(serves Ontario's public service sector, including universities, colleges and school boards, municipalities, health and community care organizations, emergency services and First Nations)

Main Office

4950 Yonge Street, Suite 902
Toronto ON M2N 6K1
(416) 250-2131
Toll Free: 1-877-250-7444
Fax: (416) 250-7484
Web: www.pshsa.ca

Workplace Safety North

(serves all northern Ontario firms and provides province-wide services for forestry, mining, smelters, refineries, pulp & paper, and printing industries)

Main Office

690 McKeown Avenue
P.O. Box 2050, Station Main
North Bay ON P1B 9P1
(705)-474-7233
Toll Free: 1-888-730-7821 (Province of Ontario only)
Fax: (705) 472-5800
Web: www.workplacesafetynorth.ca

Workplace Safety & Prevention Services
(serves agricultural, manufacturing and service sectors)
    (905) 614 1400
    Toll free: 1-877-494 WSPS (9777)
    Fax: (905) 614 105
    customercare@wsps.ca
    www.wsps.ca

Main Office
    5110 Creekbank Road
    Mississauga ON L4W 0A1

Guelph Office
    Ontario Agricentre
    100 Stone Road West, Suite 101
    Guelph ON N1G 5L3

Ottawa Office
    Carleton Technology & Training Centre
    Suite 3100, Carleton University
    1125 Colonel By Drive
    Ottawa ON K1S 5R1

Medical Clinics and Training Centre
    Occupational Clinics for Ontario Workers Inc.
    1090 Don Mills Rd., Suite 606
    Toronto ON
    M3C 3R6
    (416) 510-8713
    Toll free: 1- 877-817-0336
    Fax: (416) 443-9132
    www.ohcow.on.ca

    Workers Health and Safety Centre
    802 15 Gervais Drive
    Toronto ON
    M3C 1Y8
    (416) 441-1939
    Toll free: 1-888-869-7950

Resources

www.whsc.on.ca

Workplace Safety and Insurance Board (WSIB)—Prevention Division

Workplace Safety and Insurance Board (WSIB)
200 Front St. West, 11th Floor
Toronto M5V 3J1
General Inquiries (416) 344-1000
Toll free: 1-800-387-0750
Fax: (416) 344-4684 or 1-888-313-7373
TYY: 1-800-387-0050
E-mail: ExperienceRating@wsib.on.ca
Web: www.wsib.on.ca

WSIB Collections Branch
P.O. Box 2099 Stn. LCD1
120 King Street West
Hamilton ON L8N 4C5
Toll Free: 1-800-268-0929
Fax: (905) 521-4203

Fraud and Non-Compliance
Toll free: 1-888-SI-Leads (1-888-745-3237)
E-mail: sileads@wsib.on.ca

Offices

Guelph
(deals with Agricultural sector only. For all other small business services in the area, see Kitchener.)
100 Stone Road West
2nd floor
Guelph N1G 5L3
(416) 344-1000
Toll free: 1-800-387-0750
Fax: (416) 344-4684 or 1-888-313-7373

Hamilton
120 King Street West

Hamilton L8N 4C5
(416) 344-1000
Toll free: 1-800-387-0750
Fax: (416) 344-4684 or 1-888-313-7373

Kingston

234 Concession Street
Suite 304
Kingston K7K 6W6
(416) 344-1000
Toll free: 1-800-387-0750
Fax: (416) 344-4684 or 1-888-313-7373

Kitchener

55 King Street West
3rd Floor
Kitchener N2G 4W1
(416) 344-1000
Toll free: 1-800-387-0750
Fax: (416) 344-4684 or 1-888-313-7373

London

148 Fullarton Street
7th Floor
London N6A 5P3
(416) 344-1000
Toll free: 1-800-387-0750
Fax: (416) 344-4684 or 1-888-313-7373

North Bay

128 McIntyre Street West
North Bay P1B 2Y6
(416) 344-1000
Toll free: 1-800-387-0750
Fax: (416) 344-4684 or 1-888-313-7373

Ottawa

180 Kent Street
Tower 4, Suite 400

Resources

Ottawa K1P 0B6
(416) 344-1000
Toll free: 1-800-387-0750
Fax: (416) 344-4684 or 1-888-313-7373

Sault Ste. Marie

153 Great Northern Road
Sault Ste. Marie ON P6B 4Y9
(416) 344-1000
Toll free: 1-800-387-0750
Fax: (416) 344-4684 or 1-888-313-7373

St. Catharines

301 St. Paul Street
8th Floor
St. Catharines L2R 7R4
(416) 344-1000
Toll free: 1-800-387-0750
Fax: (416) 344-4684 or 1-888-313-7373

Sudbury

30 Cedar Street
Sudbury P3E 1A4
(416) 344-1000
Toll free: 1-800-387-0750
Fax: (416) 344-4684 or 1-888-313-7373

Thunder Bay

1113 Jade Court
Suite 200
Thunder Bay P7B 6V3
(416) 344-1000
Toll free: 1-800-387-0750
Fax: (416) 344-4684 or 1-888-313-7373

Timmins

5520 Highway 101 East,
Ontario Government Complex
PO Bag 4020

South Porcupine P0N 1H0
(416) 344-1000
Toll free: 1-800-387-0750
Fax: (416) 344-4684 or 1-888-313-7373

Toronto

200 Front Street West
Toronto M5V 3J1
(416) 344-1000
Toll free: 1-800-387-0750
Fax: (416) 344-4684

Windsor

2485 Ouellette Avenue
Windsor N8X 1L5
(416) 344-1000
Toll free: 1-800-387-0750
Fax: (416) 344-4684 or 1-888-313-7373

Other Safety Resources

Canadian Centre for Occupational Health and Safety (CCOHS)
135 Hunter St. East
Hamilton L8N 1M5
General Tel: (905) 572-2981
Toll Free: 1-800-668-4284 (Canada & US)
Fax: (905) 572-4500
Web: www.ccohs.ca

Canadian Standards Association (CSA)
Head Office
178 Rexdale Blvd.
Toronto M9W 1R3
(416) 747-4000
Toll Free: 1-800-463-6727
Web: www.csagroup.org
Online Store: www.shopcsa.ca/

Occupational Hygiene Association of Ontario
6700 Century Ave., Suite 100

Mississauga L5N 6A4
(905) 567-7196
Fax: (905) 567-7191
Web: www.ohao.org

Office of the Fire Marshal
Ministry of Community Safety and Correctional Services
25 Morton Shulman Ave.
Toronto M3M 0B1
(647) 329-1100
Toll free: 1-800-565-1842
Fax: (647) 329-1218
Web: www.ofm.gov.on.ca

Electrical Safety Authority
155 Matheson Blvd. W.
Mississauga L5R 3L5
Toll free: 1-877-372-7233
Web: www.esasafe.com

Safe Communities Canada
Parachute
150 Eglinton Avenue E., Suite 300
Toronto M4P 1E8
(647) 776-5100
Toll Free: 1-888-537-777
Web: www.safecommunities.ca

Young Worker Awareness Program
Toll free: 1-800-663-6639
E-mail: info@ywap.ca
Web: www.ywap.ca

Other OH&S Resources

Human Rights Legal Support Centre
(416) 597-4900
Toll free: 1-866-625-5179
TTY: (416) 597-4903

TTY Toll Free: 1-866 612-8627
Web: www.hrlsc.on.ca

Ontario Labour Relations Board (OLRB)
505 University Avenue, 2nd Floor
Toronto M5G 2P1
(416) 326-7500
Toll free: 1-877-339-3335
TTY: (416) 212-7036
Fax (416) 326-7531
Web: www.olrb.gov.on.ca

Ryerson University Library
350 Victoria St.
Toronto M5B 2K3
(416) 979-5055
Fax: (416) 979-5215
Web: www.library.ryerson.ca
(Maintains former Ministry of Labour library.)

National Institute of Disability Management and Research
(NIDMAR)
4755 Cherry Creek Rd.
Port Alberni BC V9Y 0A7
(778) 421-0821
Fax: (778) 421-0823
E-mail: nidmar@nidmar.ca
Web: www.nidmar.ca

Canada-Ontario Business Service Centre (COSCC)
151 Yonge St.
4th Floor
Toronto M5C 2W7
Toll free: 1-888-576-4444
TTY: 1-800-457-8466
Fax: (519) 685-1104

Resources

895

Web: www.cbo-eco.ca (information on starting or expanding a business)

Threads of Life (Workplace Tragedy Family Support)
P.O. Box 9066, 1795 Ernest Ave.
London N6E 2V0
(519) 685-4276
Toll free: 1-888-567-9490
Fax: (519) 685-1104

Occupational Health Clinics for Ontario Workers Inc. (OHCOW)
1090 Don Mills Road, Suite 606
Toronto, Ontario M3C 3R6
(416) 510-8713
Fax: (416) 443-9132
Web: http://ohcow.bluelemonmedia.com
Email: ask@ohcow.on.ca

Workers Health and Safety Centre
675 Cochrane Drive, Suite 710, East Tower
Markham, Ontario L3R 0B8
(416) 441-1939
Toll-Free: 1-888-869-7950
Web: www.whsc.on.ca
Email: contactus@whsc.on.ca

Health and Safety Publications and Resources

Thomson Reuters, 2075 Kennedy Road, Toronto, M1T 3V4, 1-800-387-5164, www.carswell.com

In addition to this book, Thomson Reuters publishes a wide variety of unique, practical health and safety resources, such as:

- ABC's of OH&S in Ontario—0-459-56241-X
- Accessibility for Ontarians with Disabilities Act Implementation Guide: Standards for Customer Service—978-0-7798-3469-3; Integrated Standards 978-0-7798-5205-5
- Canadian Labour Reporter Special Report: Accident/Incident Investigation in the Workplace, Second Edition—978-0-7798-7053-0

- Best Practices: Health and Safety—978-0-7798-0011-7
- Bill 168 Implementation Guide—978-0-7798-2711-4
- Canada Labour Code: Quick Reference, 2017 ed.—978-0-7798-7148-3
- Canadian Health and Safety Compliance Issues, 3rd ed. (CLV Special Report Series)—0-978-7798-5563-6
- Canadian Health and Safety Law: A Comprehensive Guide to the Statutes, Policies and Case Law—L88804-248
- The Careful Workplace: Seeking Psychological Safety at Work in the Era of Canada's National Standard—978-0-7798-7238-1
- Canadian Safety Reporter—A20208
- Corporate and Organizational Liability for Safety Under Bill C-45 (CLV Special Report Series)—0-459-28335-9
- Emerging and Critical Issues in OH&S (CLV Special Reports Series)—978-0-7798-1764-1
- Employer Liability for Contractors Under the Ontario Occupational Health and Safety Act, 2nd ed. (CLV Special Reports Series)—978-0-459-28276-9
- Employer's Guide to Ontario Workplace Safety & Insurance—0-459-56361-0
- Employer's Health and Safety Manual—Ontario Edition, 2nd ed.—0-459-56278-9
- Handi-Guide to Alberta's OH&S Act, Regulation and Code—2014 ed. 978-0-7798-6066-1
- Handi-Guide to Atlantic Canada's Workplace Health and Safety Legislation, 2016—978-0-7798-7312-8
- Handi-Guide to British Columbia's OH&S Regulation—2015 ed. 978-0-7798-6684-7
- Handi-Guide to Federal Health and Safety Legislation—2015 ed. 978-0-7798-7323-4
- Handi-Guide to Manitoba's Workplace Safety and Health Act and Regulations—2014 ed. 978-0-7798-6384-6
- Handi-Guide to Saskatchewan's OH&S Act and Regulations—2013 ed. 978-0-7798-5476-9
- Hazard Assessment Toolkit—L895065-34
- HR Manager's Guide to Health and Safety (Ontario), 5th ed.—978-0-7798-7838-3
- HR Manager's Guide to Managing Disability in the Workplace, 2nd ed.—978-0-7798-7255-8

Resources

- Human Resources Guide to Preventing Workplace Violence, 2nd ed.—L88804-490
- Human Resources Guide and Toolkit: The Duty to Accommodate and Disability Management—978-0-88804-613-0
- Investigating Harassment in the Workplace, 2nd ed. (CLV Special Report Series)—978-0-7798-4938-3
- Human Resources Guide to Workplace Investigations—L888804-443
- Joint Health and Safety Committees—The Road to Excellence (CLV Special Report Series)—978-0-7798-2170-9
- Loi et règlements sur la santé et la sécurité au travail en Ontario 2017 — édition consolidée (Pocket Ontario OH&S Act and Regulations 2017—(French version)—978-0-7798-7845-1
- OH&S Across Canada (Canada Labour Reporter Special Report Series)—978-0-7798-6398-3
- OH&S Due Diligence: A Practical Guide, 2nd ed. (CLV Special Reports Series)—0-459-28275-1
- OH&S Due Diligence Handbook, 2nd Ed.—0-978-7798-2730-5
- Ontario Health and Safety Law: A Complete Guide to the Law and Procedures, with Digest of Cases—L88804-075
- Ontario Occupational Health and Safety Act Quick Reference, 2017—978-0-7798-7153-7
- Ontario Health & Safety Compliance Toolkit—0-459-56363-7
- Ontario OH&S Act, Regulations and Related Legislation CD—L97200
- Ontario OH&S Act and Regulations Training Program 2016—Reading, Referencing and Learning About OHS Legal Provisions—Participant's Workbook (Use with Pocket Ontario OH&S)—978-0-7798-7240-4
- Ontario's OH&S Act and Regulations Training Program 2016—Reading, Referencing and Learning About OHS Legal Provisions—Instructor's Lesson Plan + CD (use with Pocket Ontario OH&S) —978-0-7798-7241-1
- Ontario's OH&S Act and Regulations Training Program 2016—Reading, Referencing and Learning About OHS Legal Provisions—Participant's Workbook (use with Ontario OH&S—Consolidated Edition) —978-0-7798-7242-8
- Ontario's OH&S Act and Regulations Training Program 2016—Reading, Referencing and Learning About OHS Legal Provisions -

Instructor's Lesson Plan + CD (use with Ontario OH&S—Consolidated Edition)—978-0-7798-7243-5
- Ontario OH&S Act and Regulations 2016—Consolidated ed. 978-0-7798-7846-8
- Ontario Workplace Insurance: Claims Management and Return to Work—0-459-56341-6
- Organizational Safety Management: Strategies and Implementation—978-0-7798-6707-3
- Pocket Ontario OH&S Act, 2016—978-0-7798-7844-4
- Pocket Ontario OH&S Guide to Violence and Harassment—978-0-7798-7306-7
- Pocket Ontario OH&S Guide to OHS Program Elements—978-0-7798-6697-7
- Pocket Ontario OH&S Guide to Hazard Management—978-0-7798-6668-7
- Pocket Ontario OH&S Guide to Duties and Rights—978-0-7798-6667-0
- Practical Guide to Occupational Health and Safety and Workers' Compensation Compliance in Alberta—L88804-450
- Practical Guide to Occupational Health and Safety in Ontario, 4th ed.—978-0-88804-713-7
- Preventing Workplace Meltdown: An Employer's Guide to Maintaining a Psychologically Safe Workplace—978-0-7798-3640-6
- Psychological Illness in the Workplace (CLV Special Report Series)—978-0-7798-4897-3
- Return to Work Compliance Toolkit—0-459-27704-9
- Study Guide to Alberta's OH&S Act, Regulation and Code, 2014 ed.—978-0-7798-6071-5
- Study Guide to British Columbia's OH&S Regulation, 2nd ed.—978-0-7798-5545-2
- TDG Compliance Manual: Clear Language Edition—0-459-27727-8
- Understanding, Preventing and Controlling Back and Neck Pain (CLV Special Report Series)—978-0-7798-2880-7
- Violence in the Workplace, 4th ed. (Canada Labour Reporter Special Report Series)—978-0-7798-6427-0
- WHMIS Compliance Manual—0-459-33081-0
- WHMIS Pocket Guide, 4th Edition—0-459-28294-8

Resources

Index

Consolidated Edition—Act & Regulations

GUIDE TO USING: This Index contains listings for all of the legislation in this book. The first number in the listing refers to the regulation number; the second indicates the section(s) of that regulation; and the third lists the page number where that section begins. For example 213/91, s. 240, **p. 251** refers to Ontario Regulation 213/91, section 240, on page 251.

911

Index

Designated substances — *Continued*
- • measuring airborne concentrations 490/09, s. 24, Schedule 1, **p. 385**
- • posting of monitoring results 490/09, s. 25, **p. 385**
- • worker's duty re control program 490/09, s. 26, **p. 386**
- definitions 490/09, s. 1, **pp. 373, 374**
- employer duties
- • re other isocyanates 490/09, s. 17, **p. 379**
- • to limit airborne exposure 490/09, s. 16, **p. 378**
- • to third party workers 490/09, s. 15, **p. 378**
- • where respiratory equipment permitted 490/09, s. 18, **p. 379**
- exposure limits 490/09, Table 1, **pp. 390-393**
- medical examinations and clinical tests
- • medical examination after exposure to arsenic or ethylene oxide 490/09, s. 28, **p. 386**
- • physician to receive records 490/09, s. 27, **p. 386**
- • results of examinations and tests 490/09, s. 29, **p. 387**
- • retention
- • • personal exposure records 490/09, s. 30, **p. 388**
- • • records of medical examinations 490/09, s. 31, **p. 388**
- substances, designated

- • acrylonitrile 490/09, s. 2, **p. 374**
- • arsenic 490/09, s. 2, **p. 374**
- • asbestos 490/09, s. 2, **p. 375**
- • benzene 490/09, s. 2, **p. 375**
- • coke oven emissions 490/09, s. 2, **p. 375**
- • ethylene oxide 490/09, s. 2, **p. 375**
- • isocyanates 490/09, s. 2, **p. 375**
- • lead 490/09, s. 2, **p. 375**
- • mercury 490/09, s. 2, **p. 375**
- • silica 490/09, s. 2, **p. 375**
- • vinyl chloride 490/09, s. 2, **p. 375**
- variance from a code 490/09, s. 32, **p. 389**

Designations
- designation of a construction project 213/91, s. 4, **p. 112**

Detonators
- offshore oil and gas rigs 855, ss. 95, 96, **p. 810**

Diesel or gas powered engine
- safety regulations 855, s. 61, **p. 803**

Director *See also* Inspector
- acting as inspector Act, s. 6(2), **p. 9**
- appointment Act, s. 6(1), **pp. 8-9**
- constructor's notice of project Act, s. 23(2), **p. 33**
- defined Act, s. 1(1), **p. 2**
- designation of construction project 213/91, s. 4, **p. 112**
- hazardous materials *See* Hazardous materials
- notice of accident, explosives, etc. Act, s. 53, **p. 65**

Index

Index

Index

Index

Index

Index

Index

957

Index

Index

Index

Index

Index

Index

Index

Index

Index

Index

Index

Index

Index

Index

Index